# planet earth

Harper's Geoscience Series
Carey Croneis, Editor

# planet earth:
# its physical systems
# through geologic time

## arthur n. strahler

**harper & row, publishers**
new york   evanston   san francisco   london

PLANET EARTH:
ITS PHYSICAL SYSTEMS THROUGH GEOLOGIC TIME

Copyright © 1972 by Arthur N. Strahler

Printed in the United States of America. All rights
reserved. No part of this book may be used or reproduced in any manner whatsoever without written permission except in the case of brief quotations embodied
in critical articles and reviews. For information address
Harper & Row, Publishers, Inc., 49 East 33rd Street,
New York, N.Y. 10016.

Standard Book Number: 06–046459–3

Library of Congress Catalog Card Number: 77–174526

# contents

# preface

This book is written to meet changing academic viewpoints as well as to induce further changes in response to demands by students, faculties, and the informed public for a new set of priorities in science education and research. Two key words focus attention on these new standards of priority: *unification* and *relevance*. Both words suggest a need to reverse the long-term drift of natural science to a position and function no longer entirely acceptable to society.

First, the proliferation of scientific information, as specialties have been exploited by more and more research workers, has served to make science textbooks larger and larger. In desperation, authors (the writer included) have added summaries of new data in each textbook revision, while retaining all that was already there. This substantive-descriptive approach has built into it a basic defect—that of fragmentation and compartmentation of knowledge. Clearly, a unification and simplification of

natural science concepts is in order but requires a common principle that has heretofore been absent or at best weakly developed. The concept of open dynamic systems and steady states provides the common principle capable of unifying a wide range of natural phenomena. This concept also provides the criterion for sloughing off what is irrelevant, trivial, and static in the storehouse of scientific data.

Second, our new generation of students has led a powerful movement to alter the emphasis of scientific research from science-for-science's sake, until now a sacrosanct tradition, to science as a servant of mankind. Until such time as the human race can alleviate its environmental problems and chart a stable course, first priority must be given to integrative research bearing on those complex problems of interaction between Man and his environment. If we accept this premise and are prepared to make our contribution effective, there must follow a major restructuring of the courses of study in natural sciences generally and in the earth sciences particularly.

A unified and relevant science produces some strange bedfellows because the approach is problem-oriented. For example, one aspect of the problem of climatic change relates to the increase in concentration of dusts in suspension in the upper atmosphere. To what extent is this increase to be attributed to burning of hydrocarbon fuels? To what extent is the dust a product of volcanic eruptions? The science of vulcanology is thus linked to the science of physical climatology under pressure for evaluation of a question of environmental change.

The structure and content of this book represent my attempt to supply unification and relevance in the study of the earth sciences. The main body of the book treats the basic principles of these sciences from the systems point of view. The Prologue sketches in broad strokes the principles of natural open systems and their steady states. These generalizations will acquire substance only after the 15 text chapters have been studied, so that the Prologue is equally appropriate as a summary in retrospect. There follows an Epilogue, in which we look into Man's role in changing the balance of natural systems. Here the approach is through environmental problems and the consequences of Man's consumption of the earth's natural resources. In using the book, one might well begin with the Epilogue and state the problems at the outset. In that case, the main body of the text will serve as the source of basic information needed to explore and understand the problems.

Because large sections of text and many illustrations in this book are taken from my larger work, *The Earth Sciences,* Second Edition (Harper & Row, Publishers, 1971), acknowledgment is due many of the same reviewers whose suggestions and corrections improved the parent text in both of its editions. The principal reviewers were the following: Professor William D. Sellers, Institute of Atmospheric Physics, University of Arizona

(Chapter 1); Professor John E. Nafe, Department of Geology and Lamont-Doherty Geological Observatory, Columbia University (Chapter 2); Professor Theodore G. Mehlin, Department of Astronomy, Williams College (Chapters 3, 12, and 15); Professor Elmar R. Reiter, Department of Atmospheric Science, Colorado State University at Fort Collins (Chapters 4 and 5); Dr. Martin Prinz, Institute of Meteoritics, University of New Mexico at Albuquerque (Chapter 7); Professor Earle F. McBride, Department of Geology, University of Texas at Austin (Chapter 8); Professor Stanley A. Schumm, Department of Geology, Colorado State University at Fort Collins (Chapter 9); Professor Charles L. Drake, Department of Earth Sciences, Dartmouth College (Chapter 10); Dr. John A. Wood, Smithsonian Institution Astrophysical Observatory, Cambridge, Massachusetts (Chapter 11); Professor A. G. W. Cameron, Belfer Graduate School of Science, Yeshiva University (Chapter 12); Professor Preston Cloud, Department of Geology, University of California at Santa Barbara (Chapter 12); Professor A. Lee McAlester, Department of Geology and Geophysics, Yale University (Chapters 13 and 14); Professor Helmut E. Landsberg, Institute for Fluid Dynamics and Applied Mathematics, University of Maryland (Epilogue, Part I); Professor Alan H. Strahler, Department of Environmental Sciences, University of Virginia (Epilogue); Dr. William R. Thurston, Office of the Director, U.S. Geological Survey (Epilogue, Part II).

There are many more individuals to whom thanks are due for suggesting corrections and changes in portions of the text published previously as parts of *The Earth Sciences.* Regrettably, for lack of space the names of these contributors cannot be included, but their total input has been highly significant and is deeply appreciated.

ARTHUR N. STRAHLER

# planet earth

# prologue
# physical systems
# of planet earth

Taking the widest view, the *earth sciences* include a study of all physical phenomena of the solid-earth realm of mineral matter (*lithosphere*), the free-water realm of the earth (*hydrosphere*), and the gaseous envelope of the earth (*atmosphere*). Because activities within the realm of plant and animal life (*biosphere*) interact with and make changes in the physical environment, life forms cannot be entirely neglected. Because planet Earth receives essential energy from the sun, we must investigate this star, which is the hub of our solar system. To understand our own planet better, it is also necessary to investigate the other planets and our own close satellite, the moon.

To learn about all of these vast realms of matter and energy and derive some meaning from them in a single course of study seems at first like a hopeless undertaking. Scientists collect new knowledge faster than any single person could possibly assimilate it. Then, too, many thinking persons are saying that first priority in both research and education must be given to the study of our environment and that scientists should put aside investigations offering no immediate promise of providing the means of solving society's most crucial problems.

What goals should we set for ourselves in entering a study of the earth sciences? First, we can rise to an intellectual challenge to master and interrelate the outstanding concepts governing the ceaseless planetary fluxes of matter and energy. Second, there is an impelling necessity to put these concepts to work for the alleviation of Man's environmental problems. But understanding of concepts can never be gained merely through talk about abstractions. Science has been built upon a solid foundation of facts. The main problem is to cull from the enormous bin of facts those essentials needed to explain realistically how processes operate.

## A SYSTEMS APPROACH

The solution adopted here to meet the dilemma of theory and relevance is that of a *systems approach,* by means of which a single conceptual framework can encompass properties of all naturally occurring states of matter within the whole range of the earth sciences.

First, what is a *system* in the sense that we will use the term? A system is a particular concentration of matter and energy having a recognizable or arbitrary boundary and characterized by the flow of matter or energy into and out of the boundaries, as well as within the system itself. In the earth sciences, systems occur naturally or spontaneously. They are generally far more complex and usually much larger than the systems of chemistry and physics. Here we see the distinction between *pure science* and *natural science.* Physics and chemistry are commonly designated as pure sciences, perhaps because matter is reduced to its most elementary units, and these are studied in isolation. Thus a physicist, using a particle accelerator, focuses his attention upon recognition of a single type of elementary particle. A chemist, using a spotlessly clean aggregation of glassware, and the purest possible ingredients, examines a single change in state of matter, which may be synthesis of a compound from its component elements, or some exchange reaction. The earth sciences which, along with the biological sciences, are described as natural sciences, deal with the condition of things as Nature presents them. This scientist is only an observer, not an organizer or controller.

## CHARACTERISTICS OF OPEN SYSTEMS

The word *system* is so broad in scope and can cover so many phenomena of the real world that its use requires very careful consideration. Specifically, the concept used here is that of the *open system,* which requires that the following elements be included: (1) a given concentration of matter in space with discrete *boundaries,* or subject to being defined by arbitrary boundaries; (2) an *import* of energy or matter, or both, through the system boundaries; (3) an *export* of energy or matter through the system boundaries. An open system is characterized by the ability to reach a *steady state,* in which rates of import and export of energy and matter are balanced and the internal configuration and energy level of the system do not change with time. These state-ments represent an extreme in abstraction; a simple illustration is called for.

Imagine that a black metal sphere is placed where it is exposed to the sun's rays on a clear, calm day. The sphere is in itself a simple open system, for it has a discrete boundary surface and a set of physical properties. Energy in the form of solar radiation falls upon the sphere and is absorbed by its surface, raising the temperature within the sphere. But the sphere also radiates energy outward. The temperature of the sphere will rise to a given level and then remain constant, representing the balance of import and export of energy through the system boundaries. Even this simple example, which involves only flux of energy and not of matter, requires some knowledge of basic laws of energy radiation to be fully understood.

As a preview of Chapter 1, consider the sun-earth-space radiation system. Two bodies, with intervening and surrounding space, constitute the matter of the system, its boundaries being arbitrarily defined as an encompassing envelope (see Figure 1.1). Thermal energy is produced in the sun by a process of conversion of matter to energy. This thermal energy is sent outward in all directions from the sun's surface by radiation and travels with the speed of light. Some extremely tiny fraction of this energy is intercepted by the earth, which sends a fraction directly back into space by reflection, while absorbing the remainder. Thus our earth is the receiving member of the energy system and will tend to accumulate solar energy. But the earth, like the black sphere, is also a natural radiator of energy and emits energy into space. By a self-balancing mechanism, the emission of energy by the earth rises in intensity to balance the increasing energy it absorbs. Hence a steady state in the earth's store of heat energy is quickly achieved and is manifested in a long-term average constancy of temperature.

It is important to make a distinction between open systems and closed systems. The latter have enclosing boundaries through which no matter or energy enters or leaves. It is typical of a closed system that it quickly "runs down," reaching an unchanging equilibrium. (It can be said that the closed system achieves a state of maximum entropy.) A simple example of a closed system is that of a sealed container, such as a bell jar, occupied by water and air. When the jar and its contents are maintained at constant temperature, the quantity of water held as vapor in the air space remains constant. Thus the conditions of a closed system are met. Nature presents us with few, if any, examples of a closed system.

The open system not only has a flux of matter or energy, or of both, through its boundaries, but it depends upon such flux for its very operation. If the supply of energy or matter upon which the system depends is cut off, the system itself disintegrates or disappears.

From consideration of the sun-earth-space radiation system it can be seen that the open system also has characteristic *paths of flow* of energy, i.e., a straight-line path from sun to earth and a spherical-radial system of energy flow from earth into outer space. Note also that the energy flow in this case is *one way* only, from the center of production to the region of irretrievable loss in space. This system as a whole appears to be consuming its own substance, and we may reason that such a process cannot go on indefinitely. Nevertheless, during a particular short period of time in which we observe an open system, the following law, known as *Von Bertalanffy's law,* can be stated:

*Time rate of change of energy within the system equals the sum of the rate of production of energy within the system plus the rate of export of energy through the system boundaries. Furthermore, when the two terms of the above equation are themselves equal to zero, the system is said to be in steady state.* *

## A PREVIEW OF OTHER OPEN SYSTEMS

Another system deserving of study is the earth-moon-sun tidal system, discussed in Chapter 3. Neglecting for the moment the involvement of the sun in producing tides on earth, we see that the moon and earth are linked together by mutual gravitational attraction while at the same time the earth turns on its axis. In a manner explained in Chapter 3, this combination of masses and their motions subjects the earth to unequal stresses. The substances of the earth yield to these stresses. In

* From Ludwig Von Bertalanffy (1950), *Science,* vol. 111, pp. 23–24. The law is formally stated as follows: $\partial Q_i / \partial t = T_i + P_i$, where $Q_i$ is concentration of energy in the $i^{th}$ element of a system, $T_i$ = velocity of transport of $Q_i$ element, $P_i$ = rate of production or destruction of energy of the $Q_i$ element. In steady state: $\partial Q_i / \partial t = 0$, or $T_i + P_i = 0$.

particular, the waters of the oceans yield easily and engage in rhythmic flow, which we see in the tidal rise and fall of ocean level and in the ebb and flood currents of water near the coasts.

In analyzing the tidal system, note first that energy is not being generated from matter in either earth or moon. Instead it exists as kinetic energy of revolution and rotation of these enormous masses. This kinetic energy is inherited from the time of formation of the solar system. Notice also that there is no flow of energy from moon to earth or back, either by radiation or by any flow of particles of matter. Inherited kinetic energy of motion (mechanical) energy performs work in moving masses of water against resistance. Mechanical energy is thus transformed to heat and eventually lost by radiation into outer space, never to be returned. Again, we can predict that the source of energy will eventually become exhausted. But for any given short period of time, such as the lifetime of a human being or of civilization, the law of Von Bertalanffy will apply. We simply eliminate from his law the term involving rate of production of energy.

A third example of a natural system is the river—or better, a branching system of streams together with their water-contributing surfaces of sloping lands, explained in Chapter 6. Taking the ground surface as one system boundary, matter enters the system from the atmosphere as rain or snow. By reason of its elevated position above sea level, this water possesses potential energy. Similarly, the particles of mineral matter that constitute the soil and rock possess potential energy. As the water flows to lower levels, entraining solid particles with it, the potential energy of position is transformed into kinetic energy of motion. Resistance is encountered in the flow of the fluid. As resistance is overcome, kinetic energy of the masses in motion is transformed to energy of heat. This heat in turn is lost by conduction or radiation. The mouth of the stream at sea level is the exit-boundary for the water and mineral matter. This stream system represents a simple gravity-flow mechanism. As long as rain falls, the system will be supplied with matter and potential energy. Such supply may be quite constant as averaged over long periods of time. But what of the supply of soil and rock particles? Erosion and transportation processes diminish the substance of the system itself. The land is lowered. Its store of potential energy is gradually reduced. Rain entering the system boundary enters at progressively lower elevations. The stream system is therefore self-consuming and must in the long run be brought to a state of virtual exhaustion.

## MATTER, SIZE, AND TIME IN NATURAL SYSTEMS

We have seen that the flow of energy in an open system may be accompanied by a change in the form of the energy. For example, mechanical energy may be converted to heat energy; potential energy into kinetic energy. Energy is also transformed in changes of state: i.e., gaseous state to liquid or solid state, or the reverse.

The following are the various forms that the flow of matter can take in natural open systems:

**a.** *Motion of discrete solid particles.* Examples: Planets and their satellites in orbital motions and in rotation; pebbles moving in a stream bed; hailstones falling and rising in a thunderstorm cloud; volcanic bombs impelled from the throat of a volcano; atmospheric dust in suspension in turbulent air.

**b.** *Fluid motion in liquids.* Examples: Ocean currents, streams, ground water, magma (molten rock), convection currents in the earth's core and mantle, and flow in capillary water films in soil.

**c.** *Fluid motion in gases.* Examples: Atmospheric winds (in troposphere), including local winds (land and sea breezes), cyclonic storms, and the jet stream.

**d.** *Motion of atomic and subatomic particles.* Examples: Ion clouds and solar wind (protons and electrons) from sun; electron flow in ionospheric currents.

Natural systems come in all sizes. Consider the range in scale of various systems. The largest systems (disregarding galactic systems and the universe as a whole) are those involving the sun and planets in the solar system. Intermediate in size are terrestrial systems, such as the system of circulation of water in a single ocean, or the subcrustal motions involved in the making of mountain chains.

A smaller order of magnitude is seen in such phenomena as a single thunderstorm cloud, a stretch of beach, a single sand dune, or a square yard of soil surface. Still smaller systems involving individual colloidal particles, molecules, or atoms can be thought of as being in the realm of physics and chemistry.

Natural systems in the earth sciences span a vast range of time, as well as of spatial dimension. Time span here refers to the time required for a system to run down completely from some initial point of maximum intensity, or for a system to complete one cycle of a series of repeating changes. The following is a classification of time scales with which we are dealing:

**a.** *Cosmologic time.* Life of our sun as a star emitting energy by fusion of hydrogen: 10 billion years (b.y.).

**b.** *Geologic time.* Cycle of deposition of sediment and its subsequent deformation into a mountain chain: 100 to 300 million years (m.y.). Cycle of erosion in which a mountain chain is reduced to sea level: 5 to 50 m.y.

**c.** *Secular time.* Period required for one oceanic circulation: 100 to 1000 yr. Growth and decay of a cyclonic storm: 10 to 20 days. Tidal cycle of ebb and flood: 12½ or 25 hr.

## A CLASSIFICATION OF SYSTEMS

All of the natural open systems of the earth sciences can be analyzed and categorized as to whether they represent (a) a decay, or running-down, system; (b) a cyclic, or rhythmic, system; or (c) a random fluctuation system.

A *decay system* uses or consumes its own substance, whether that substance is a supply of matter or energy, or of both. The rate at which the system decays is said to be *exponential* and is *negative* in sign. In exponential decay, the rate of running down is itself diminishing. Moreover, the rate at which the diminution takes place is proportional to the remaining quantity.

An outstanding example of such a system is found in the radioactive decay of certain minerals within the crust of the earth, explained in Chapter 7. One form of uranium, in particular, can be used to illustrate. This uranium isotope is *uranium-238,* which spontaneously decays, giving off heat, and eventually becomes a stable isotope, *lead-206.* The rate of decay per unit of mass is absolutely constant despite all outside influences. Consequently, if a given quantity of uranium-238 is enclosed in a mineral grain, it will produce lead-206 at such a rate that in each period of 4.5 b.y. the quantity of uranium-238 is halved and the quantity of new lead-206 is doubled. The curve of diminishing uranium is described as a *negative-exponential decay curve* (see Figure 7.2). The period 4.5 b.y. is referred to as the *half-life.*

Another exponential-decay system is seen in the life history of erosion of a mass of land brought above sea level by elevation of the earth's crust. This is discussed in Chapter 9. The rate at which erosion lowers the mass toward sea level is carried out on a negative-exponential decay curve.

Activity in a cyclic, or rhythmic, system follows the pattern of *simple harmonic motion*. Examples of simple harmonic wave motion abound in such fields of physics as optics, radio, and sound. The variable quantity plotted against time forms a sine curve, or cosine curve, in which the acceleration is directly proportional to the displacement (see Figure 3.22). A single wavelength, involving one cycle of reversal and return to the starting value, is accomplished in one period.

Examples from the earth sciences of natural open systems which follow the cyclic pattern are those governed by astronomical controls. One control is the period of earth rotation, giving the daily rhythm. The heating and cooling of the lower atmosphere and of the surfaces of the land and of water bodies represent daily cycles. A second control is latitude. Because of the inclination of the earth's axis with respect to the plane of the earth's orbit, an annual cycle of incoming and outgoing solar radiation is imposed on the earth and gives seasonal cycles. These cycles are explained in Chapter 1.

Another annual cycle is that of flooding in rivers, many of which experience rather regular annual alternations of flood flow and low flow. Even more rigorous is the cycle of lunar tides. Here several ingredients of simple harmonic motion, each with a different period and amplitude, combine to dictate the system of rise and fall of water level for a given place and time. Still another cycle of apparently consistent period is the 11-year sunspot cycle.

Systems of random and irregular fluctuation represent the third basic type. Many natural processes are characterized by instability of action. Changes occur in seemingly unpredictable amounts and at unpredictable times. Instability that produces irregular fluctuations is particularly a characteristic of the flow of fluids—both liquid and gaseous. Fluids readily develop *turbulence,* a disturbed eddying in which vortices of flow continually form and dissolve. At any particular point in the fluid, turbulence results in pulses and surges of flow

in a variety of directions. An example may be seen in the origin and development of cyclonic storms in the lower atmosphere (Chapter 5). Cold air and warm air cannot flow smoothly past one another for any length of time without developing a vortex. This vortex grows and intensifies, constituting a storm. Ultimately the storm weakens and dissolves. Although the approximate time and place of occurrence of such a storm can be guessed at, the precise schedule of events appears to be unpredictable.

Instability manifests itself in nature in various ways. A river develops sinuous bends, known as meanders, because the flow of water in a straight channel is easily deflected by the most trivial irregularities in the bed and banks of the channel. Meander development is explained in Chapter 9. Once a bend begins to form the tendency is for the bend to grow (see Figure 9.9). In other words, the effects of instability tend to be self-aggravating. Only when a river bend grows so large that the channel meets with itself and forms a cutoff is the stream restored to a straight course. Examples of such cutoffs, or *wave occlusions,* are seen not only in streams, but also in ocean currents, cyclonic storms in the lower atmosphere, and the jet stream at high altitude.

Various geologic events, too, show seemingly unpredictable times and places of occurrence. The precise timing and location of a fault movement that generates an earthquake follows such a pattern. Similarly, the time of a volcanic eruption cannot be predicted on the basis of any cycle of known period. The occurrences of sunspots or of solar flares on the sun's surface likewise are not predictable in detail. Systems which perform their activities on a random or unpredictable schedule of timing and location are perhaps the most difficult to explain.

Most large natural open systems are complex. One common type of complexity is seen in subcycle systems, or cycle-within-cycle. For example, the great sun-earth-space radiation system includes many systems of lower order on the earth. One such secondary system is the world-wide atmospheric circulation by means of which heat is transferred from equatorial regions to polar regions (see Figure 4.1). Another is the ocean-wide system of water currents by means of which heat is exchanged between high and low latitudes. Yet another is the cycle of movement of water from atmosphere to lands and return to the sea—a system commonly designated as the *hydrologic cycle* (see Figure 6.1).

Another form of complexity exists where several forms of time variation are superimposed. The erosion system represented by a stream and its branches is basically an exponential decay system, but in shorter periods of time the system is subjected to annual rhythms of floods and low waters. In addition, the stream is subjected to random and irregular fluctuations, such as the building of sand bars or the development of meander bends.

Finally, a third form of complexity is that induced by the purely accidental encounter of one system with another. Geologic process provides such incongruous encounters. Deep within the earth there operates the system of generation of heat by radioactivity, resulting in occasional events of mountain-making and volcanic activity. As the earth's crust responds, there arises a mountain chain, cutting irregularly across the neatly ordered global zones of atmospheric winds, air pressure, and storms. The disruptive effect of the mountain range is manifested in a unique patchwork of climatic types.

The concept of open systems developed here for the earth sciences provides the foundation for an understanding of almost every conceivable event or form that may come to our attention. If our premise is correct that all natural phenomena are organized into open systems governed by a common set of general laws, we have at our disposal the necessary keys to comprehending our earth as we see it today with all its varied forms and processes. Order can then be seen in all ranges of time and spatial dimension, and we need not be overwhelmed by the vast aggregation of individual and specific facts and observations known to science.

## MAN: HIS ENVIRONMENT AND NATURAL RESOURCES

Early in this Prologue the need to put concepts of science to work to alleviate Man's environmental problems was set forth as a worthy aim of the study of the earth sciences. Man's impact upon planet Earth is the subject of the Epilogue of this book. Analysis of environmental problems and problems of the consumption of natural resources requires that we draw upon a wide range of background concepts and facts within the earth sciences. Such problems become exceptionally complex because they must also mesh with concepts and facts from the biological and social sciences. Fortunately, there is a systems theory for every science, and there are many close analogies between systems of any two disciplines. These basic similarities permit scientists of differing specialties to understand each other and to communicate during research. By the same token, analogies between systems will enable you, as a student, to acquire the breadth of outlook and comprehension needed to define those courses of action society must take to preserve and maintain itself on planet Earth.

# chapter 1
# sun-earth-space
# energy system:
# the planetary
# radiation balance

As a planet, earth is an interceptor of radiant energy from the sun. But our earth is also an emitter of radiant energy. Treating the earth as a whole planet, the rates of interception and emission of energy must be balanced on the average over a long period of time. Such a balance within an open system is described as a *steady state*.

The system sun-earth-space is shown schematically in Figure 1.1. If, on the one hand, the earth were to intercept more radiant energy than it emits to outer space, the planetary temperature would rise indefinitely and our planet would melt and finally vaporize. If, on the other hand, the earth were to lose more energy from radiation into space than it gains by interception of solar energy, the planetary temperature would fall and earth would become a solidly frozen mass close to absolute zero. Geological evidence that our earth's surface temperature has remained in a middle range, not much different from its present

value, throughout at least 0.5 billion years (b.y.), leads us to be confident that the flux of energy within this system has indeed maintained an average steady state.

This chapter examines components of the sun-earth-space radiation system, tracing the radiation of energy from the sun's surface to the earth's outer atmosphere, through that atmosphere with modifications and losses, to the earth's solid or liquid surface. Return radiation through the atmosphere and into outer space completes the energy flow. Because radiation falls upon the earth unequally according to latitude and season, there must be heat exchanges from one part of the earth's surface to another to balance radiation deficits and surpluses. Such exchanges of energy take place through motions of the atmosphere and oceans and are treated in later chapters as subsystems contributing to maintaining the earth's heat balance.

A good place to start an investigation of this

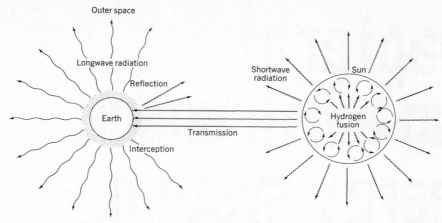

Figure 1.1. Schematic diagram of the sun-earth-space radiation system. (From A. N. Strahler, "The Life Layer," *Jour. of Geography,* vol. 69, no. 2, p. 72, Figure 1. © 1970 by The Journal of Geography; reproduced by permission.)

great system is with the energy source itself—our sun, a star of about medium size and temperature in terms of the overall range of stars.

## OUR SUN AS A RADIATOR

The sun is a huge sphere of incandescent gas more than 100 times the diameter of the earth, with a mass more than 330,000 times that of earth and a volume 1,300,000 times that of earth. The sun's surface gravity is 34 times as great as that of the earth.

The visible surface layer of the sun is the *photosphere.* The outer limit of the photosphere constitutes the edge of the sun's disk as seen in white light. Gases in the photosphere are at a density less than that of earth's atmosphere at sea level. Temperature at the base of the photosphere is about 11,000° F (6000° K)* but decreases to about 4300° K at the outer photosphere boundary. Light production is about 300,000 candlepower/in.$^2$ of surface. Beneath the photosphere, temperatures and pressures increase to enormously high values in the interior, or *nucleus,* where temperatures are between 13 and 18 million (13 to 18 × 10$^6$) °K.

Although almost all the known elements can be detected by spectroscopic analysis of the sun's rays, hydrogen is the predominant constituent of the sun, with helium also abundant. It is estimated that hydrogen constitutes at least 90% of the sun, and hydrogen and helium

* The *Kelvin scale* has the same degree units as the centigrade scale, but the zero point is at −273° C, a value known as *absolute zero,* or 0° K.

together total about 98%. (Composition of the sun's atmosphere is given in Table 12.1.)

The source of the sun's energy is the conversion of hydrogen into helium within the sun's interior, a nuclear reaction producing its vast total radiant energy output of about 5 × 10$^{23}$ horsepower (hp) (3.86 × 10$^{33}$ ergs/sec).

The process of production of energy within the sun is that of *nuclear fusion,* in which hydrogen is transformed into helium. In the fusion process, mass is converted into energy. At temperatures over 4 million (4 × 10$^6$) °K within the interior of a star, there occur several forms of reactions—involving the elements lithium, beryllium, and boron—in which helium is produced. At internal temperatures exceeding 15 million (1.5 × 10$^7$) °K yet another series of complex reactions occurs. In these, isotopes of carbon, nitrogen, and oxygen play an essential part in the process of transformation of hydrogen into helium. The mass lost in the fusion process is extremely small (about 0.7%), so that the total mass of the star is scarcely diminished over vast spans of time.*

Prior to a knowledge of nuclear reactions,

* Relationship of energy to mass in a nuclear reaction is given by the Einstein equation $e = mc^2$, where $e$ is energy in ergs, $m$ is mass of matter in grams, and $c$ the velocity of light in centimeters per second. Because $c$ has a value of 3 × 10$^{10}$ cm/sec, the quantity of energy produced by conversion of one gram of matter into energy is truly enormous: 9 × 10$^{20}$ ergs. At its present rate of energy production (about 4 × 10$^{33}$ ergs/sec, or 5 × 10$^{23}$ hp) the mass of the sun will diminish by only one-millionth part of its mass in 15 million (15 × 10$^6$) years (m.y.).

the sun's energy was attributed entirely to the mechanical process of contraction under its own gravitation. The process, known as *Helmholtz contraction* (also *Kelvin contraction*), depends on the principle that a gas forced to occupy a smaller volume undergoes a rise of temperature. Calculations made over 100 years ago by the physicist Hermann von Helmholtz (1821–1894) demonstrated that the amount of energy produced by the sun in one year could be derived through a reduction of about 280 ft (85 m) in its diameter.

Assuming that the sun was formed from a highly dispersed body of gases, gravitational contraction to its present diameter was calculated to require 50 million years (m.y.). As will be explained in Chapters 10 and 12, radiometric dating of the age of material in the solar system points to a vastly longer span of time in which the solar system has endured in essentially the complete form we find it today. While the Helmholtz contraction process does not account for the sun's present production of energy, it remains a valid principle when applied to the early stages of contraction of dispersed matter to produce a star.

Heat produced in the sun's innermost core region moves outward by a process of radiation through the extremely dense gas of the interior. In a zone nearer the sun's exterior a process of convection (mixing) is postulated to transport the heat to the surface.

## SOLAR RADIATION

A star, heated to incandescence at temperatures of many thousands of degrees, radiates energy which travels through space until it falls upon some gaseous, liquid, or solid material which transmits or absorbs the radiation or turns it away by reflection. Described as *electromagnetic radiation,* this radiant energy may be thought of as being in large part a wavelike motion, something like the waves which travel over the surface of a quiet pond from the point where a stone is dropped. Using this illustration for the moment, we can describe the waves in two ways: (1) by the distance separating successive wave crests, or *wavelength,* and (2) by the number of wave crests moving past a fixed point each second of time, or *frequency.* Figure 1.2 illustrates the point that *long waves* have *low frequency* while *short waves* have *high frequency,* provided, of course, that all waves have the same speed of travel. Electromagnetic radiation travels at the

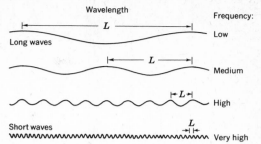

Figure 1.2. Frequency and wavelength of long and short waves.

constant rate of 186,000 mi/sec (299,800 km/sec), the "speed of light." Solar radiation thus takes about 8⅓ min to reach the earth.

Figure 1.3 illustrates the component parts of the entire electromagnetic spectrum. The horizontal scale is a logarithmic scale (constant ratio scale) such that each division has a value 10 times as great as that next to it on the left. The upper scale gives wavelength in centimeters. English units are not shown, as these are not used in scientific discussions of the electromagnetic spectrum. In treating the visible-light range of wavelengths, a commonly used unit is the *Angstrom* (symbol A). One Angstrom unit is equivalent to 0.000,000,01 cm ($10^{-7}$ cm). The expanded scale of colors within the visible-light wavelength band is labeled in Angstrom units.

At the very short wavelength (very high frequency) end of the spectrum are *gamma rays* and *X rays.* These are high-energy rays capable of deep penetration into opaque substances. Next comes the *ultraviolet* band, followed by the *visible-light* band. Composed of still longer wavelengths is the *infrared* band, overlapping the even longer wavelength band of *radio waves,* which continue to lengths of many kilometers.

All parts of the electromagnetic spectrum are radiated into space by the sun and other stars. Practically all information about the composition and structure of stars is derived from analysis of their spectra.

Electromagnetic radiation is a flow of energy outward into space in all directions from the spherical surface of the sun. The total energy of radiation is not, however, equally distributed among the various wavelengths. The energy curve of the sun's radiation is shown in Figure 1.4. Notice that the curve rises from close to zero in the ultraviolet region to a peak value in the blue region of the visible-light band, then

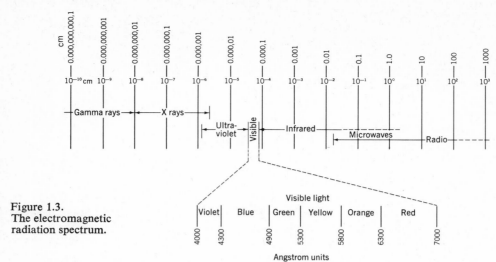

Figure 1.3.
The electromagnetic
radiation spectrum.

declines to very low values in the infrared region. Units of radiation represent the energy emitted per unit of time for a unit of surface area of the sun's photosphere.

A basic law of physics, *Planck's law,* relates the intensity of energy radiation at each wavelength to the temperature of the emitting surface. Ideally, this law relates to a surface described as a "perfect radiator" or, more rigorously, a *black body.* A black body not only will absorb all radiation falling upon it, but also will emit radiation in a manner solely dependent upon its temperature. The energy curve of black-body radiation can be calculated for any given temperature. The total energy radiated by each unit of surface per unit of time varies as the fourth power of the absolute temperature (°K). This law is referred to as the *Stefan-Boltzmann law.*

Figure 1.4 shows a number of curves of ideal black-body radiation for various temperatures. Notice that for higher temperatures the peak of the curve rises higher and the total area (total energy) under the curve is also greater. Also, for a higher temperature the peak represents a shorter wavelength and, correspondingly, a higher frequency. The ideal black-body curve that best fits the observed frequency curve of the sun is that for a temperature of about 6000° K. Obviously, a star whose temperature is higher than that of the sun not only will emit a greater total quantity of radiant energy per unit area of its surface, but also will have its peak at a shorter wavelength.

Energy in the sun's radiation spectrum is apportioned about as follows: ultraviolet wavelength, 9%; visible light wavelengths, 41%; infrared and longer, 50%.

## SOLAR AND TERRESTRIAL RADIATION COMPARED

Figure 1.5 shows the electromagnetic emission spectra of the sun and the earth. The wavelength scale on the horizontal axis of Figure 1.5 (as in Figure 1.3) is a constant-ratio (logarithmic) scale but spans only the range from ultraviolet through infrared wavelengths. In this discussion the *micron* is used; it is equal to 0.001 cm. The smoothly arched curve at the left is the radiation curve of a black body at 6000° K, representing the idealized sun. The smooth symmetrical curve at the right is the radiation curve of a black body at 300° K (27° C; 80° F), representing the idealized earth.

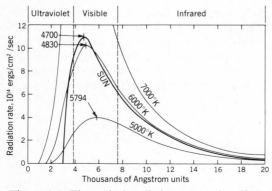

Figure 1.4. Theoretical radiation curves for 5000, 6000, and 7000 °K compared with the observed radiation curve of the sun. [From T. G. Mehlin (1959), *Astronomy,* New York, John Wiley & Sons, p. 93, Figure 4–8.]

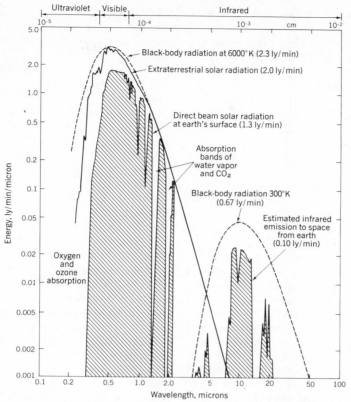

Figure 1.5. Spectrum of incoming and outgoing radiation from sun and earth. Logarithmic scales are used for both energy and wavelength. (From W. D. Sellers, *Physical Climatology,* Chicago, Univ. of Chicago Press, p. 20, Figure 6. © 1965 by the University of Chicago.)

The standard unit of radiation is the *langley,* equal to 1 gm cal of heat* received (or emitted) by 1 cm² of surface (about ¹⁄₁₆ in.²). Units used on the vertical scale of Figure 1.5 are langleys per minute for each subdivision of the spectrum having a width of 1 micron (0.0001 cm). The idealized sun at 6000° K radiates about 100,000 langleys per minute (ly/min). Less than 0.0025% of this quantity (or 2.3 ly/min) would be intercepted by the earth. Actually, the solar radiation at the outer limit of the atmosphere, on a surface held perpendicular to the sun's rays, is approximately 2.0 ly/min, a value known as the *solar constant.* The actual solar radiation curve is shown as a highly irregular line below the smooth curve.

* The gram calorie, the standard unit for expressing amount of heat, is that quantity of heat needed to raise the temperature of 1 gram of water through 1 C° at 15° C. It takes 252 cal to equal 1 British thermal unit (BTU).

For many years, scientists of the Smithsonian Institution of Washington have evaluated the solar constant from measurements made at the earth's surface. Since the advent of orbiting satellites, carrying instruments to measure solar radiation continuously over long periods of time, the solar constant has been more precisely determined—the value of 1.95 ly/min at a height of 53 mi (85 km) was announced in 1968. From surface observations it was known that the solar constant fluctuates slightly, being increased or decreased by as much as 1.5% because of variations in the ultraviolet output of the sun.

Notice in Figure 1.5 that the smooth curve at the right, representing the radiation of a black body at 300° K, differs from the solar radiation curve in two respects. First, the emission is entirely within the infrared portion of the spectrum and is not visible. The peak occurs at about 10 microns (0.001 cm). Second, the black-body radiation at 300° K is only 0.67 ly/min, or about one-third the value of the solar constant. The actual curve of outgoing terrestrial radiation lost to space shows sharp peaks and conspicuous gaps. It lies below the smoothly arched curve and totals only 0.1 ly/min. This quantity is only one-twentieth as large as the solar constant.

The question immediately arises: How can a radiation balance be achieved if incoming radiation per unit area of surface is so much greater than outgoing radiation? Consider, first, that infrared radiation leaves the earth continuously from its entire spherical surface, whereas the incoming solar radiation is received at any given instant over only one hemisphere. This hemisphere presents to the sun a right angle receiving surface equivalent to only the earth's cross section. The ratio of area of a circle to surface area of a sphere of the same radius is 1 to 4, so that geometry alone must account for part of the discrepancy in radiation rates. Consider, second, that some part of the incoming solar radiation is directly reflected into space without contributing to heating of the earth. Third, some part of the incoming solar energy is absorbed by the atmosphere and is radiated back into space without heating the earth's surface. These mechanisms will be examined in paragraphs to follow.

## SOLAR RADIATION OVER A SPHERICAL EARTH

Because the earth is a sphere (disregarding its slight oblateness), only one point on earth presents a surface at right angles to the sun's rays. This *subsolar point* coincides with the occurrence of solar noon at that latitude where the sun reaches the zenith position for an observer (Figure 1.6). In all directions away from the subsolar point the earth's curvature causes the receiving surface to be turned away from the sun at an increasing angle with respect to the rays, until, at the *circle of illumination,* a horizontal surface parallels the rays. The hemisphere lying beyond this great circle is, of course, in darkness.

Assuming for the moment that the earth possesses a geometrically perfect spherical surface but has no atmosphere, the total quantity of solar energy received by 1 cm$^2$ of horizontal surface in one day will depend upon two factors: (a) the angle at which the sun's rays strike the earth and (b) the length of time of exposure to rays. These factors are varied by latitude and by the seasonal changes in the path of the sun in the sky.

It is important to understand that the earth's axis of rotation is not oriented at a right angle to (perpendicular to) the plane of the earth's orbit (also called the *plane of the ecliptic*). Instead, as shown in a perspective drawing in Figure 1.10, the earth's axis is inclined at an angle of 23½° away from the perpendicular and constantly maintains this angle while always aimed at the same point in space. As a result, there are two points in the orbit at which the axis is inclined neither toward nor away from the sun: These are the *equinoxes.* There are also two other points in the orbit in which the full value of axial inclination is directed toward the sun: These are the *solstices.* Names and dates of equinoxes and solstices are given in Figure 1.7.

If the earth's axis were perpendicular to the plane of the ecliptic (that is, if there were no axial tilt), the conditions of equinox would prevail throughout the entire year. Equinox conditions at noon are shown in Figure 1.8. Radiation at the equator is 100%, with a value of 2.0 ly/min. At 30° N and S the percentage is reduced to 86.6%, or 1.73 ly/min; at 60° N and S values are zero.* These facts lead to the general statement that the earth will receive its greatest total solar radiation at the equator and the least at the poles.

For an entire day at equinox, the input of solar radiation will need to be totaled for each minute that the sun is above the horizon. The changing angle, from zero at sunrise to a maximum value at noon, then back to zero at sunset, will need to be determined for each

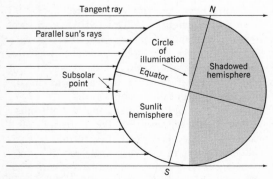

Figure 1.6. Relation of the sun's rays to latitude at a date intermediate between equinox and solstice.

---

* The equation is $Q = 2.0 \cos \phi$, where $Q$ is radiation in ly/min and $\phi$ is latitude in degrees.

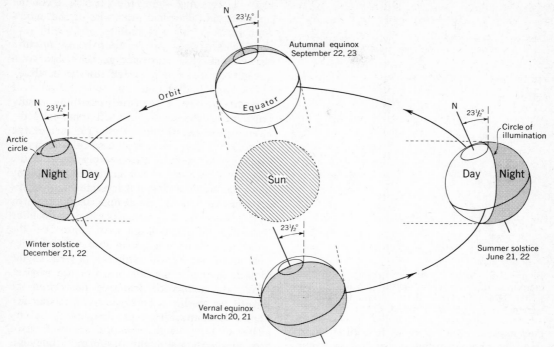

Figure 1.7. Orientation of the earth's axis remains fixed in space as the earth revolves about the sun, producing the seasons.

minute of the 24-hr day. When this calculation is made, the daily radiation totals are roughly as follows:

| Latitude | ly/day |
|----------|--------|
| 0 | 890 |
| 10 | 880 |
| 20 | 840 |
| 30 | 770 |
| 40 | 680 |
| 50 | 570 |
| 60 | 445 |
| 70 | 305 |
| 80 | 155 |
| 90 | 0 |

Because of the earth's annual cycle of change of axial tilt relative to sun's rays from solstice to solstice, the incoming radiation at a given parallel of latitude will change through an annual cycle. The resulting curves are shown for various north latitudes in Figure 1.9. Notice that the equator has a cycle with two maxima and two minima, because the sun passes overhead twice each year; nevertheless, radiation is very strong throughout the entire year. At 20° N latitude the double maxima persist, but with only a slight dip at summer

solstice. At all latitudes between 23½° and 66½° the radiation curve shows one maximum and one minimum, the amplitude increasing with higher latitude. Poleward of 66½° a part of the year has no incoming radiation. At the poles, this period of zero value is six months long and spans the entire period between equinoxes. The seasonal cycle does not make the yearly total of incoming radiation for the entire globe different from an ideal situation in which the earth's axis would not be inclined, but it

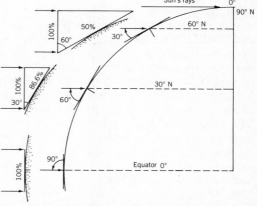

Figure 1.8. Radiation intensity and latitude.

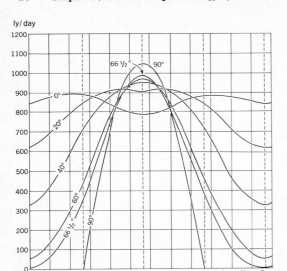

Figure 1.9. Annual cycle of variation in daily quantities of solar radiation at selected latitudes in the Northern Hemisphere. (Data from Smithsonian Institution, Washington, D.C.)

does cause a great difference in both latitudinal and seasonal distribution of the incoming radiation. The environmental consequences are of very great importance to life on earth.

Consider, first, that if the earth's axis were perpendicular to the orbital plane the poles would not receive any radiation, regardless of time of year, whereas the equator would receive an unvarying maximum. In other words, equinox conditions would apply every day of the year. The earth's inclination, by exposing the poles alternately to the sun, redistributes the yearly total radiation toward higher latitudes but deducts somewhat from the equatorial zone.

Second, the earth's axial inclination produces seasonal differences in radiation at any given latitude, and these differences increase toward the poles, where the ultimate in opposites (six months of day; six of night) is reached. Along with the variation in angle of sun's rays operates another factor, the duration of daylight. At the season when the sun's path is highest in the sky, the length of time it is above the horizon is correspondingly greater. The two factors thus work hand in hand to intensify the contrast between amounts of incoming radiation at opposite solstices.

## THE EARTH'S ATMOSPHERE

In order to understand how solar radiation is modified as it penetrates the earth's atmosphere, one must know a good deal about the physical and chemical properties of that atmosphere, as well as its structure.

The earth's atmosphere consists of a mixture of various gases surrounding the earth to a height of many miles. Held to the earth by gravitational attraction, this spherical shell of gases is densest at sea level and thins rapidly upward. Although 97% of the mass of the atmosphere lies within 18 mi (29 km) of the earth's surface, the upper limit of the atmosphere cannot be drawn sharply because the density of gas molecules grades imperceptibly into the near-emptiness of interplanetary space. A working figure of 6000 mi (10,000 km) for the thickness of the atmospheric shell can be useful. Note that this thickness approaches the diameter of the solid earth itself. The science of *meteorology* deals with the physics of the lower 60 mi (100 km) of the atmosphere, while the science of *aeronomy* deals with the overlying portion. From the earth's surface upward to an altitude of about 60 to 75 mi (100 to 120 km) the chemical composition of the atmosphere is highly uniform throughout, in terms of the proportions of its component gases. The name *homosphere* has been applied to this lower uniform layer, in contrast to the overlying *heterosphere,* which is nonuniform in an arrangement of spherical shells.

The homosphere consists of (1) a mixture of gases referred to collectively as the *pure dry air,* (2) water vapor, and (3) dust particles. The first two components are true gases composed of discrete molecules, whereas dust consists of solid particles much larger than molecules, but still so tiny as to mix freely with the gases and to stay aloft almost indefinitely. Clouds and fog, which are composed of tiny water droplets or ice crystals, are also present much of the time in the lower atmosphere the world over.

Consider, first, the individual gases of pure dry air. One group, making up almost the entire volume, is unvarying in proportions over the entire globe and from the ground surface to a height of 50 mi (80 km). In Figure 1.10 these gases are listed and their proportions given. The largest part by far is *nitrogen,* about 78%, or more than three-fourths, of the pure dry air by volume. Nitrogen can be thought of as an inactive gas, or space filler, for the most part, although it is extracted from the air by certain bacteria which form nitrogen compounds vital to plant life. *Oxygen,* the second

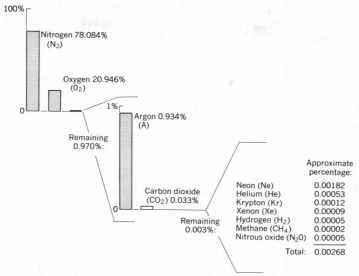

Figure 1.10. The nonvarying components of the earth's lower atmosphere. [Data from E. Glueckauf (1951), *Compendium of Meteorology,* Boston, Amer. Meteorological Soc., p. 6, Table V.]

largest component, makes up about 21%, or one-fifth, of the air by volume. Oxygen is chemically very active, combining readily with rock-forming minerals in rock decay, with metals in rusting, with fuels in burning, and with food to provide heat and energy in animals. Despite its chemical activity the quantity of oxygen in the air remains constant from year to year because the amount used is exactly balanced by oxygen given back to the atmosphere by plants. Both nitrogen and oxygen exist in the *molecular state,* in which each molecule consists of two atoms and is neutral in charge.

Because nitrogen and oxygen together make up about 99% of the air, the nine other gases listed in Figure 1.10 are measured in very small parts. Of the remaining 1% the gas *argon* takes more than 9/10 of 1%. Argon and its less abundant relatives *neon, helium, krypton,* and *xenon* are known as *inert gases,* meaning that they do not naturally combine chemically with other elements of the atmosphere, oceans, or earth. These gases exist in the *atomic state,* i.e., as single atoms of an element.

*Carbon dioxide,* although forming only 33/1000 of 1% of the air, is an extremely important chemical compound, both in climate control and in sustaining life on earth. Climatically, carbon dioxide is important as an absorber of infrared radiation and as an insulating blanket, helping to regulate air temperatures near the earth's surface. Biologically,

carbon dioxide is essential for the growth of plant life.

Since Man has begun to burn prodigious quantities of wood, coal, and oil, much more carbon dioxide is being released into the atmosphere now than was released half a century ago. Since 1900 the amount of carbon dioxide has increased more than 10% and is believed to be rising steadily. Although commonly listed as one of the unvarying constituents, carbon dioxide actually varies in concentration in the horizontal direction over the earth, in some places being added to, in other places being taken from, the atmosphere. For example, over the water of the Arctic Ocean the carbon dioxide content is only about one-half the average value because of absorption by the cold ocean water.

To complete the list of nonvariable gases, minute quantities of *hydrogen, methane,* and *nitrous oxide* have been measured. Besides these unvarying constituents there are several gases whose proportion differs greatly from place to place. Most important in the science of the atmosphere is *ozone,* an uncommon molecular form of oxygen found not only in traces in the lower air but in higher concentrations in the upper atmosphere. Then there are important amounts of *sulfur dioxide, nitrogen dioxide,* and *ammonia* introduced into the lower air layers over large cities by fuel combustion and industrial processes.

The second major component of the homosphere is *water vapor,* the gaseous state of water in which individual water molecules ($H_2O$) have the same freedom of movement as molecules of nitrogen or oxygen gas; therefore the water molecules diffuse, or mix completely with the air. Water vapor is not visible to the eye and should not be confused with fog and clouds, which are composed of liquid or solid particles.

The amount of water vapor present in the air, or *humidity,* varies greatly from time to time and place to place throughout the earth's atmosphere. In very warm humid air of equatorial regions the weight of water vapor in a given volume of space can be one twenty-fifth as great as the weight of the air with which it is mixed, whereas in very cold and dry arctic regions the proportion is sometimes as little as 1 part water vapor to 10,000 parts air. Water vapor supplies the water for all clouds and rain, and during condensation it releases latent heat which supplies the energy for storms. More will be said of this essential atmospheric ingredient in the discussion of moisture and precipitation (Chapter 5).

Dust in the lower atmosphere consists of particles so tiny that, for example, 250,000 of them placed side by side would be needed to make a line 1 in. long. Most atmospheric dust comes from the earth's surface. Smoke from grass and forest fires is an important source. Winds blowing over dry land surfaces of deserts raise mineral particles thousands of feet into the air. Volcanoes in eruption contribute dust clouds whose travel in world-wide atmospheric circulation can be easily followed. Especially important in the formation of clouds and precipitation are tiny salt crystals left by the evaporation of spray droplets swept up in turbulent winds blowing over crests of breaking waves. Dust is also added by meteoroids that vaporize upon entering the upper atmosphere, creating countless solid particles.

Whereas the gases of pure dry air are of uniform proportions throughout the homosphere, despite its rapidly decreasing density upward, the additional components (water vapor and suspended solid and liquid particles) are by no means uniformly distributed either horizontally or vertically. Because both water vapor and atmospheric solids originate mainly from the earth's surface and depend upon air motions to be lifted vertically, these components tend to be most heavily concentrated in the lowermost air layers and to diminish to nearly zero values at the top of the homosphere.

## THE HETEROSPHERE

The heterosphere, encountered about 55 mi (90 km) above the earth's surface, consists of four gaseous layers, each of distinctive composition (Figure 1.11). Lowermost is the *molecular nitrogen layer,* consisting dominantly of molecules of nitrogen ($N_2$) and extending upward to about 125 mi (200 km). Above this height lies the *atomic oxygen layer,* consisting dominantly of oxygen atoms (O). Between about 700 and 2200 mi (1100 and 3500 km) lies the *helium layer,* composed dominantly of helium atoms (He). Above this region lies the *atomic hydrogen layer,* consisting of hydrogen atoms (H). No definite outer limit can be set to the hydrogen layer. A height of 6000 mi (10,000 km) may perhaps be taken as an arbitrary limit, for here the density of the hydrogen atoms is approximately the same as that found throughout interplanetary space. However, hydrogen atoms rotating about the earth, and hence belonging to the earth's atmosphere, may exist as far out as 22,000 mi (35,000 km).

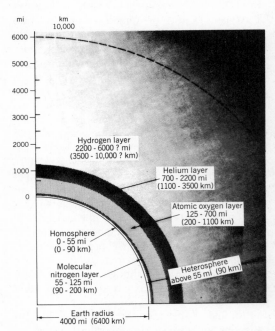

Figure 1.11. Homosphere and heterosphere. (Based on data of R. Jastrow, NASA, and M. Nicolet.)

It should be noted that the four layers described above have transitional boundary zones, rather than sharply defined surfaces of separation. The arrangement of predominant gases is in order of their weights: Molecular nitrogen, the heaviest, is lowest; atomic hydrogen, the lightest, is outermost. It should further be kept in mind that at the extremely high altitudes of the heterosphere the density of the gas molecules and atoms is extremely low. For example, at 60 mi (96 km), close to the base of the heterosphere, the atmosphere has a density of only about one-millionth that at sea level.

## SUBDIVISIONS OF THE HOMOSPHERE

The atmosphere has been subdivided into layers according to temperatures and zones of temperature change. Three temperature zones lie within the homosphere; a fourth is assigned to the lower heterosphere. Figure 1.12 shows how temperature is related to altitude. Starting at the earth's surface, temperature falls steadily with increasing altitude at the fairly uniform average rate of 3.5 F° per 1000 ft (6.4 C° per kilometer). This rate of temperature drop is known as the *normal temperature lapse rate.* Departures from this rate will be observed, depending upon geographical location and season of year. The layer in which the normal lapse rate applies is known as the *troposphere,* the

properties of which are discussed in detail below.

The normal lapse rate gives way rather abruptly at a height of 6 to 8 mi (10 to 13 km) to a layer, known as the *stratosphere,* in which temperature holds essentially constant with increasing height (see Figure 1.15). The level at which the troposphere gives way to the stratosphere is termed the *tropopause.* Figure 1.13 shows that the altitude of the tropopause is least at the poles, 5 to 6 mi (8 to 10 km), whereas at the equator the tropopause is encountered at 10 mi (17 km). If the troposphere is thought of as a complete surface in three dimensions, it resembles an oblate ellipsoid with a polar flattening and an equatorial bulge.

Seasonal changes in the altitude of the tropopause are marked in middle and high latitudes. For example, at 45° latitude the average altitude in January is 8 mi (12.5 km) but rises to 9 mi (15 km) in July. Temperatures at the tropopause are markedly lower at the equator than at the poles, as shown in Figure 1.13. At first glance, this relationship may seem strange, accustomed as we are to considering the equatorial region to be hot and the poles cold. However, with a constant temperature lapse rate assumed, the higher the tropopause, the colder will be the air.

Upward through the stratosphere, tempera-

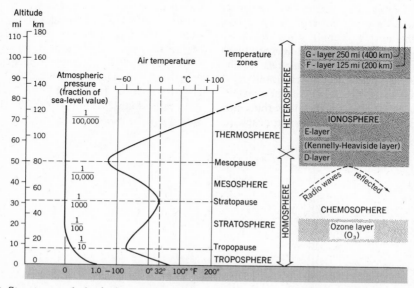

Figure 1.12. Structure and physical properties of the atmosphere. (© 1970, John Wiley & Sons, New York.)

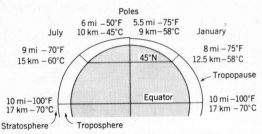

Figure 1.13. Average elevation and temperature of the tropopause shown schematically for July (*left*) and January (*right*). [Data from *Handbook of Geophysics* (1960), New York, Macmillan.]

tures rise gradually up to a level of about 30 mi (50 km), where the *stratopause* is encountered, marked by a temperature maximum of about 32° F (0° C) but with a range of 36 F° (20 C°) more or less than that value. (Cause of heating at this level is explained in a later paragraph.)

Above the stratopause lies a zone of diminishing temperature, the *mesosphere,* shown in Figure 1.12. At the *mesopause,* about 52 mi (85 km), temperatures reach a minimum value, averaging about −129° F (−83° C). However, the minimum value can be as much as 45° F (25° C) greater or less than the average value.

Above the mesopause lies the *thermosphere,* a zone of rapid temperature increase to extremely high values of over 1300° F (700° C) at an altitude of 125 mi (200 km). Above this altitude the rate of temperature increase falls off, and there is only a slight increase of temperature in the next 100 mi (160 km). This region of approximately constant temperature is designated the *isothermal region.* Although thermosphere temperatures reach 2000 to 3000° F (1100 to 1650° C), such figures have little meaning when we consider that the density of the air is so slight as to approach a

vacuum. Very little heat can be held or conducted by air of such low density.

## RADIATION LOSSES IN THE ATMOSPHERE

As the sun's electromagnetic radiation penetrates the earth's atmosphere a series of selective depletions and diversions of energy take place. At an altitude of 95 mi (150 km) the radiation spectrum possesses almost 100% of its original energy, but in penetration to an altitude of 55 mi (88 km) absorption of X rays is almost complete and some of the ultraviolet radiation has been absorbed as well.

Of particular interest in the development of radio communication on a global scale is a layer known as the *ionosphere,* located in the altitude range of 50 to 250 mi (80 to 400 km). This position coincides with the bottom of the heterosphere, in which the molecular nitrogen layer and the atomic oxygen layer are found (Figure 1.12). Furthermore, the ionosphere is essentially identical in position with the lower thermosphere. The ionosphere consists of a number of layers in which the process of *ionization* takes place. Here highly energetic gamma rays and X rays from the solar-radiation spectrum are absorbed by molecules and atoms of nitrogen and oxygen. In the absorption process, each molecule or atom gives up an electron, becoming a positively charged *ion.* The electrons thus released form an electric current which flows freely on a global scale within the ionosphere. Of particular interest in the field of radio communication is the ability of the layers of ions to reflect radio waves and thus to turn them back toward the earth. Most of the important reflection of longwave radio waves takes place in the lower part of the ionosphere, which bears the name of *Kennelly-Heaviside layer* (Figure 1.14). Without such reflection, long-distance radio communication would not be possible. Because the process of

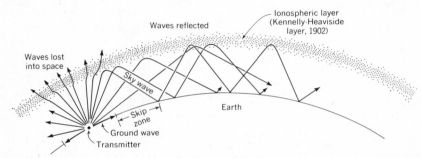

Figure 1.14. Reflection of radio waves from the ionosphere. (After J. C. Johnson, *Physical Meteorology,* p. 321, Figure 10.1. © 1954 by the Massachusetts Institute of Technology.)

ionization requires direct solar radiation, the ionospheric layers, of which there are five, are developed on the sunlight side of the earth (Figure 1.15). On the dark side, under nighttime conditions, the layers tend to weaken and disappear.

Yet another phenomenon, one of vital concern to Man and all other life forms on earth, is the presence of an *ozone layer,* largely occurring in the region from 12 to 21 mi (20 to 35 km) elevation but also extending upward to an elevation of 30 to 35 mi (50 to 55 km) (Figure 1.12). The ozone layer is a region of concentration of the form of oxygen molecule known as *ozone* ($O_3$), in which three oxygen atoms are combined instead of the usual two atoms ($O_2$). Ozone is produced by the action of ultraviolet rays upon ordinary oxygen atoms. The ozone layer thus serves as a shield, protecting the troposphere and earth's surface from most of the ultraviolet radiation found in the sun's radiation spectrum. If these ultraviolet rays were to reach the earth's surface in full intensity, all exposed bacteria would be destroyed and animal tissues severely burned. Thus the presence of the ozone layer is an essential element in Man's environment. It is also interesting to note that warming at the stratopause is produced by the absorption of the ultraviolet rays in the upper part of the ozone layer. The level of greatest ozone concentration is at its highest altitude in low latitudes (28 mi; 48 km) but descends to the lowest altitude in arctic latitudes (22 mi; 35

km). There are also marked seasonal variations in altitude in middle latitudes.

## ENERGY LOSSES IN THE LOWER ATMOSPHERE

As solar radiation penetrates into deeper and denser atmospheric layers gas molecules cause the visible light rays to be turned aside in all possible directions, a process known as *Rayleigh scattering* (Figure 1.16). Where dust particles are encountered in the troposphere further scattering occurs. The total process may be described as *diffuse reflection.* That the clear sky is blue in color is explained by Rayleigh scattering of the shorter visible wavelengths. These predominantly blue light waves reach our eyes indirectly from all parts of the sky. The red wavelengths and infrared rays are less subject to scatter and largely continue in a straight-line path toward earth. The setting sun appears red because a part of the red rays escape deflection from the direct line of sight. Total diffuse reflection amounts to about 5% of incoming radiation (Table 1.1).

As a result of all forms of shortwave scattering, some solar energy is returned to space and forever lost, while at the same time some scattered shortwave energy also is directed

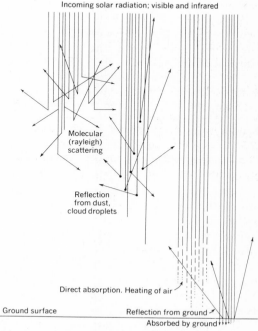

Figure 1.16. Schematic diagram of scattering, reflection, and absorption of solar radiation entering the atmosphere.

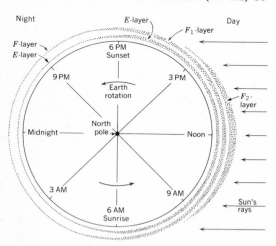

Figure 1.15. A schematic representation of the ionospheric layers under the sun's rays and in hours of darkness. [After B. F. Howell, Jr. (1959), *Introduction to Geophysics,* New York, McGraw-Hill, p. 351.]

Table 1.1. THE GLOBAL RADIATION BUDGET

| Incoming Solar Radiation (shortwave) | | Percentage |
|---|---|---|
| Total at top of atmosphere | | 100 |
| Diffuse reflection to space (Rayleigh scatter, dust) | 5 | |
| Reflection from clouds to space | 21 | |
| Direct reflection from earth's surface | 6 | |
| Total reflection loss to space by earth-atmosphere system (Earth's albedo) | | 32 |
| Absorbed by molecules, dust, water vapor, $CO_2$, clouds | 18 | |
| Absorbed by earth's surface | 50 | |
| Total absorbed by earth-atmosphere system | | 68 |
| Sum of absorption and reflection | | 100 |

| Outgoing Radiation (longwave) | | |
|---|---|---|
| Infrared radiation from earth's surface | 98 | |
| Lost to space | 8 | |
| Absorbed by atmosphere | 90 | |
| Infrared radiation emitted by atmosphere | 137 | |
| Lost to space | 60 | |
| Absorbed by earth's surface as counter-radiation | 77 | |
| Effective (net) outgoing radiation from earth's surface | | 21 |
| Effective (net) outgoing radiation from atmosphere | | 47 |
| Effective (net) outgoing radiation from earth-atmosphere system | | 68 |

Source: Data from W. D. Sellers (1965), *Physical Climatology,* Chicago and London, Univ. of Chicago Press, Tables 6 and 9.
Note: 100% represents a value of 263 kly/yr.

earthward. The latter is referred to as *diffuse sky radiation,* or *down scatter.*

Absorption is another form of energy loss that takes place as the sun's rays penetrate the atmosphere. Both carbon dioxide and water vapor are capable of directly absorbing infrared radiation. Absorption results in a rise of sensible temperature of the air. Thus some direct heating of the lower atmosphere takes place during incoming solar radiation. Although carbon dioxide is a constant quantity in the air (0.033% by volume) the water-vapor content varies greatly from place to place, from as low as 0.02% under desert conditions to as high as 1.8% in humid equatorial regions. Absorption correspondingly varies from one global environment to another. An additional but minor cause of energy loss is that which occurs in the ozone layer.

All forms of direct absorption listed above—namely, X ray, gamma ray, and ultraviolet absorption in the ionosphere and ozone layer, combined with direct longwave absorption by carbon dioxide, water vapor, and other gas molecules and dust particles, as well as by clouds—are estimated to be as low as 10% for conditions of clear, dry air and as high as 30%

when a cloud cover exists. A world average figure is about 18% (Table 1.1).

Figure 1.17 shows in a highly diagrammatic way the range of values of the various forms of reflection and absorption that may occur. When skies are clear, reflection and absorption combined may total about 20%, leaving as much as 80% to reach the ground.

Yet another form of energy loss must be brought into the picture. The upper surfaces of clouds are extremely good reflectors of shortwave radiation. Air travelers are well aware of how painfully brilliant the sunlit upper surface of a cloud deck can be when seen from above. Cloud reflection can account for a direct turning back into space of from 30% to 60% of total incoming radiation (Figure 1.17). So we see that under conditions of a heavy cloud layer, the combined reflection and absorption from clouds alone can account for a loss of from 35% to 90% of the incoming radiation and allow from 45% to 0% to reach the ground. A world average value of 21% for cloud reflection is a reasonable figure (Table 1.1).

The surfaces of the land and ocean reflect some shortwave radiation directly back into the

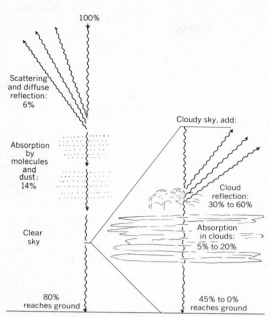

Figure 1.17. Schematic diagram of losses of incoming radiation on clear and cloudy days.

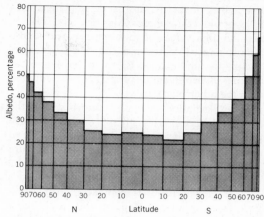

Figure 1.18. Meridional profile of earth's mean albedo based on satellite data. Latitude is scaled proportionate to sine of latitude, and graph areas are in true proportion to earth's surface areas between successive 10° parallels of latitude. [Data from T. H. Vonder Haar and V. E. Suomi (1969), *Science*, vol. 163, p. 667, Figure 1.]

atmosphere. This quantity, which is very small, averages about 6% on a global basis. It may be combined with cloud reflection and diffuse reflection to give total reflective losses of about 32% for the globe as a whole (Table 1.1).

The percentage of radiant energy reflected back by a surface is termed the *albedo*. This is an important property of the earth's surface because it determines the relative rate of heating of the surface when exposed to radiation. Albedo of a water surface is very low (2%) for nearly vertical rays, but high for low-angle rays. For oceans generally, albedos range from 6% to 10%. Albedo is extremely high for snow or ice (45% to 95%). For fields, forests, and bare ground the albedos are of intermediate value, ranging from as low as 5% to as high as 30%. Albedo of cloud layers is high, up to 90%.

In calculating the earth's radiation balance, it is extremely important to determine albedos over large regions and ultimately to estimate the earth's total average albedo year in and year out.

Consider the albedo of the earth as measured from beyond the outer limits of the atmosphere. Meteorological satellites, continually orbiting the earth and providing long-term data, have made a major contribution to the global assessment of the radiation budget. Figure 1.18 shows the average albedo profile from pole to pole as measured from outer space by orbiting satellites of the *Tiros* type. It is interesting to notice that albedos range from high values (50% to 60%) near the poles to low values (20% to 30%) in tropical and equatorial latitudes. The hemispheres are quite similar in this respect, despite the great preponderance of land areas in the Northern Hemisphere. Similarity of hemispheres suggests that albedo depends more upon cloud cover than upon the albedos of the land and sea surfaces.

Recently published estimates of the earth's albedo, based on satellite measurements, give values between 29% and 34%. These are average annual values for the earth as a planet. Table 1.1 uses the value of 32%, which falls within the range obtained by satellite observation. Consider other planetary albedos for comparison:

|  | Percentage |
| --- | --- |
| Mercury | 6 |
| Venus | 76 |
| Earth | 29–34 |
| (Moon) | (7) |
| Mars | 16 |
| Jupiter | 73 |
| Saturn | 76 |
| Uranus | 93 |
| Neptune | 94 |
| Pluto | 14 |

The earth's albedo is intermediate between the low values of the moon and inner planets with little or no atmosphere (Mercury and Mars), and the high values of those planets with dense atmospheres (Venus and the great planets). Again, we find planet Earth to have another unique environmental property as compared with the other planets.

Solar radiation actually absorbed by the earth's surface varies greatly not only from pole to pole, but also from land areas to ocean areas within the same latitude zone. Figure 1.19 is a profile from pole to pole, showing the mean annual radiation absorbed by the earth's surface (lower line) as compared with radiation entering at the top of the atmosphere (upper line). The shaded area between the curves represents the total loss of energy by the various forms of reflection and absorption discussed in earlier paragraphs, including reflection from the surface.

## LONGWAVE RADIATION

The surfaces of the continents and oceans, possessing heat derived originally from absorption of the sun's rays, continually radiate this energy back into the atmosphere, a process known as *ground radiation,* or *terrestrial radiation.* This infrared radiation occurs at wavelengths longer than 3 or 4 microns and is referred to here as *longwave* radiation (Figure 1.5). The atmosphere also radiates longwave

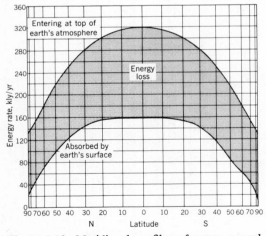

Figure 1.19. Meridional profiles of mean annual values of entering solar radiation at top of atmosphere and radiation absorbed by earth's surface. Area between the two curves represents energy loss in atmosphere. [Data from W. D. Sellers (1965), *Physical Climatology,* Chicago, Univ. of Chicago Press, p. 22, Figure 7.]

energy both toward the earth and outward into space, where it is lost. It is essential to understand that longwave radiation is quite different from reflection, in which the rays are turned back directly without being absorbed. Longwave radiation from both ground and atmosphere continues during the night, when no solar radiation is being received.

Energy radiated from the ground is easily absorbed by the atmosphere because it consists largely of very long wavelengths (4 to 50 microns), in contrast to the visible light rays (0.4 to 0.7 microns) and shorter infrared rays (0.7 to 3.0 microns) which make up almost all of the entering solar radiation (Figure 1.5). Absorption of longwave radiation by water vapor and carbon dioxide takes place largely in wavelengths from 5 to 8 microns and 12 to 20 microns. However, radiation in the range of wavelengths between 8 and 11 microns passes freely through the earth's atmosphere and into outer space. About 8% of the longwave radiation directed outward leaves the atmosphere in this manner (Table 1.1).

Thus the atmosphere receives much of its heat by an indirect process in which the incoming energy in shortwave form is permitted to pass through, but that in longwave form is not readily permitted to escape. For this reason the lower atmosphere with its water vapor and carbon dioxide acts as a warm blanket which returns heat to the earth and helps to keep surface temperatures from dropping excessively during the night or in winter at middle and high latitudes. Somewhat the same principle is employed in greenhouses and in homes using the solar-heating method. Here the glass permits entry of shortwave energy. Accumulated heat cannot escape by mixing with cooler air outside. The expression *greenhouse effect* has been used by meteorologists to describe this atmospheric heating principle.

## TERRESTRIAL RADIATION AND THE RADIATION BUDGET

Let us return to consideration of the earth's total radiation budget. It is a requirement of a radiation balance that just as much energy, on the average over long periods of time, is sent out from the entire planet Earth into space as is received from the sun. It can also be inferred that the earth's total surface (including both land and water surfaces) on the yearly average must return to the atmosphere exactly as much energy as it receives, otherwise the surface temperature would rise or sink.

The lower part of Table 1.1 gives a summary of outgoing radiation. Certain of the large radiation quantities listed here may prove confusing. Notice that infrared radiation from the earth's surface is given as 98% of total incoming radiation, whereas the total absorption of solar radiation by the earth's surface (upper part of table) is only 50%. The explanation lies in the exchange of energy between atmosphere and the earth's surface. Radiation returned to earth is designated *counter-radiation*. To obtain the effective (or net) value of the outgoing radiation from the surface (21%), we must subtract the amount absorbed by the earth's surface as counter-radiation (77%) from the total infrared radiation from the earth's surface (98%). The summed values of effective outgoing radiation from earth's surface and atmosphere total 68%, which equals the total absorbed by the earth-atmosphere system. It should be kept in mind that the figures in Table 1.1 are estimates and are subject to revision as more data are obtained.

Two lines of figures in Table 1.1, when compared, appear to constitute a discrepancy in the radiation budget. Notice that whereas the earth's surface absorbs 50% annually, the effective outgoing radiation from this same surface is given as only 21% annually. Subtracting the outgoing radiation value from the incoming value leaves a difference of 29% that must be otherwise transferred to the atmosphere. Accepting the data as valid, we must look for an explanation, which lies in the fact that the earth's surface gives back heat energy to the atmosphere not only by longwave ground radiation, but also by two other heat-transfer mechanisms. The first of these is by *latent heat* associated with evaporation and subsequent condensation of water. As water evaporates from free-water surfaces and moist soil, heat energy is absorbed and enters into a latent (stored) form in water vapor. This water vapor diffuses and mixes with the lower atmosphere, carrying the latent heat with it. Condensation in clouds and precipitation in the form of rain and snow releases the latent heat into sensible heat form, raising the temperature of the atmosphere. (This process is treated in further detail in Chapter 5.)

The second additional mechanism for transfer of heat energy from ground to atmosphere is by direct conduction. Heat is transferred directly from land or sea surfaces to the air in contact with it. Turbulent air motions accompanying winds mix the heated air with higher layers. Of course, when the ground is colder than the air above it, conduction acts in reverse and the ground receives heat from the air.

Orbiting earth satellites have provided global information on the average outgoing longwave radiation from the earth as a planet. Sensing instruments, directed earthward, can measure the longwave radiation emanating from the earth-track below the satellite. The albedo of the earth below is measured at the same time through other instruments, also directed downward, but sensitive to reflected shortwave radiation.

Figure 1.20 is a profile of average outgoing infrared radiation from pole to pole. Whereas the incoming radiation at the top of the atmosphere amounts to 263 kly/yr, the average value of the profile is about 179 kly/yr. Notice the double maxima in the profile, about over latitudes 15° to 20° N and S, and a small dip over equatorial latitudes. The two maxima are situated over the tropical desert belts where skies are clear much of the time.

## NET ALL-WAVE RADIATION

When all forms of radiation, both incoming and outgoing, are summed the *net all-wave radiation* can be calculated. This quantity represents the net exchange of energy by radiation between the earth's surface and the atmosphere. Incoming radiation includes both direct and indirect shortwave radiation and downward longwave radiation, while outgoing radia-

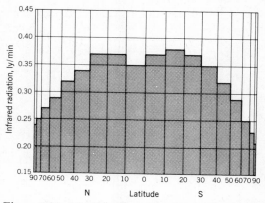

Figure 1.20. Meridional profile of mean longwave radiation from the earth, as determined from satellite data. [Data from T. H. Vonder Haar and V. E. Suomi (1969), *Science*, vol. 163, p. 667, Figure 1.]

tion consists of longwave radiation from the ground and reflected shortwave radiation.

Net all-wave radiation $(R)$, also referred to as the *radiation balance,* is rigorously defined as follows:

$$R = (Q + q)(1 - a) + I_d - I_u$$

where $Q$ is direct incoming solar radiation,
  $q$ is indirect incoming solar radiation,
  $a$ is the albedo of the receiving surface,
  $I_d$ is downward counter-radiation,
and $I_u$ is outgoing longwave radiation from the surface.

In the above equation the term $(1 - a)$ gives the percentage of incoming radiation that is actually absorbed by the surface.

Figure 1.21 is a profile from pole to pole giving net all-wave radiation of the earth's surface (upper curve), of the atmosphere (lower curve), and of the combined earth-atmosphere system (middle curve). Where the curves lie above the zero line a surplus exists, and where they lie below the zero line a deficit exists. It is obvious that a huge global-radiation surplus exists for the earth's surface, while a correspondingly large global deficit exists for the atmosphere alone. But when the two systems are combined into a single earth-atmosphere system, the net radiation is zero, a condition

that must exist if the earth is not to be getting steadily warmer or colder.

The above relationships can be summarized in the following table. Units are kilolangleys per year; figures in parentheses are percentages (see Table 1.1).

|  | Radiation Absorbed | Radiation Lost | Net Radiation |
|---|---|---|---|
| Earth's surface | 131 (50) | 55 (21) | +76 |
| Earth's atmosphere | 48 (18) | 124 (47) | −76 |
| Entire earth-atmosphere system | 179 (68) | 179 (68) | 0 |

In Figure 1.21 there are shaded areas labeled "surplus" and "deficit" between the middle curve and the zero line. The surplus area on the graph is equal to the combined areas of deficit. Thus the net radiation for the whole system is zero.

The radiation surplus of the earth's surface and the equal deficit of the atmosphere require that large quantities of heat shall flow from the earth's surface to the atmosphere. This vertical heat flux takes place in two ways, as already noted. First, heat is conducted from the surface to the adjacent air, then carried upward and mixed through the lower atmosphere by turbulent air motions. Second, the evaporation of water from land and ocean surfaces causes

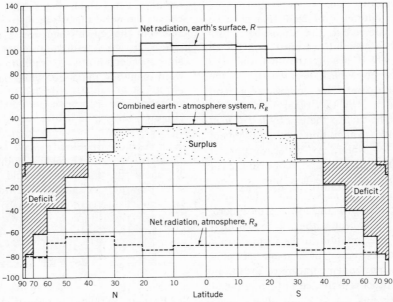

Figure 1.21. Meridional profiles of mean net radiation at earth's surface, from atmosphere, and from combined earth-atmosphere system. [Data from W. D. Sellers (1965), *Physical Climatology,* Chicago, Univ. of Chicago Press, p. 66, Figure 19.]

heat to pass into the atmosphere in the latent form.

As Figure 1.21 shows, there exists a great radiation surplus between about 40° N and 40° S latitudes and a corresponding deficit between 40° N and 40° S latitudes and the poles. Unless heat is exported from the surplus zone to the deficit zone, the earth's low-latitude zone will become hotter and the polar zones will become colder. The necessity of poleward transport of heat is obvious, if average conditions are not to change. This poleward or *meridional* heat transfer must be at a maximum value in the latitude belts of about 30° to 50° N and S but will be essentially zero at the equator and at both poles. The following figures are estimates of the yearly poleward heat transfer, or heat flux. The unit of heat is the kilocalorie (1000 cal), multiplied by 10 raised to the 19th power.*

| Latitude (°N) | Heat Flux (kcal/yr × 10^19) |
|---|---|
| 90 | 0.00 |
| 80 | 0.35 |
| 70 | 1.25 |
| 60 | 2.40 |
| 50 | 3.40 |
| 40 | 3.91 |
| 30 | 3.56 |
| 20 | 2.54 |
| 10 | 1.21 |
| 0 | −0.26 |

This meridional heat flow is accomplished by circulation of the atmosphere and oceans. Heat is carried both as sensible heat of the air and water, and as latent heat in water vapor contained in the air. When condensation of water vapor takes place, this latent heat is released and passes into the sensible form. These processes are explained in Chapters 4 and 5.

## PLANETARY TEMPERATURES

The effective temperature of the earth, its *planetary temperature,* is that single value which is required of a spherical body, with a given albedo and a given ability to emit longwave radiation, in order for it to return to pace exactly the amount of solar energy intercepted. For the earth, this temperature is estimated to be about 245° K (−28° C; −18° F).

* Data from W. D. Sellers (1965), *Physical Climatology,* Chicago and London, Univ. of Chicago Press, Table 12.

Effective planetary temperatures, in °K, are as follows:*

| | °K |
|---|---|
| Mercury | 616 |
| Venus | 235 |
| Earth | 245 |
| Mars | 209 |
| Jupiter | 105 |
| Saturn | 78 |
| Uranus | 55 |
| Neptune | 43 |
| Pluto | 42 |

It is obvious that in general the closer a planet is to the sun, the higher its effective temperature; otherwise it could not radiate energy into space at a rate equal to the rate at which it is received. Differences in atmospheres and surface properties modify the effect of distance from the sun.

## SEASONAL RADIATION CYCLES

The discussion of radiant-energy flow, or *energy flux,* both incoming and outgoing, at the earth's surface has thus far dealt with annual averages only. Such annual figures would apply well to individual months only in equatorial regions where the sun is constantly at a high elevation and the days are about of equal length throughout the year. In middle latitudes strong seasonal effects are felt; these increase poleward, where great extremes exist. We have already considered how season affects the cycle of incoming shortwave radiation at the top of the atmosphere (Figure 1.9).

An example of the seasonal rhythm of incoming solar radiation is seen in the record of an entire year at a desert station in California (Figure 1.22). The actual record shows sharp dips, particularly in winter months, because of the presence of cloudy days. A smoothly drawn curve over the highest points of the record shows the curve as it would look if clear skies persisted constantly. The upper curve is that of radiation at the top of the atmosphere.

The seasonal cycle of incoming solar radiation also imposes a seasonal cycle upon the net all-wave radiation as measured at ground level. Examples for a wide range of global latitudes are shown in Figure 1.23. Notice that in a general way these curves follow the form of

* Data from S. I. Rasool (1967), *Encyclopedia of Atmospheric Sciences,* R. W. Fairbridge, ed., New York, Reinhold, p. 734, Table 1.

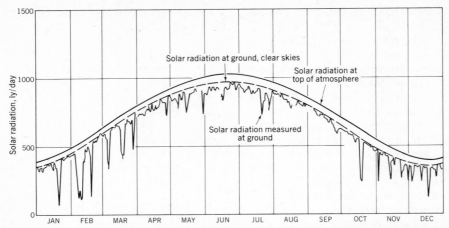

Figure 1.22. A 1-yr record of incoming solar radiation at Inyokern, California. (From W. D. Sellers, *Physical Climatology,* Chicago, Univ. of Chicago Press, p. 28, Figure 11. © 1965 by the University of Chicago. Based on data of ESSA, Weather Bureau, Climatological Data, National Summary, vol. 13, 1962.)

curves of solar radiation shown in Figure 1.9 for approximately corresponding latitudes. The two lower latitude stations show no deficit and have large annual totals. The two higher latitude stations have three and six months of radiation deficit but nevertheless have substantial annual surpluses.

## DAILY CYCLE OF RADIATION

The cycle of incoming direct and diffuse solar radiation begins at sunrise. A maximum intensity is reached at noon by local apparent solar time, followed by a symmetrical decline and a cessation at sunset. Incoming-radiation curves are illustrated in Figure 1.24 for the months of June and December at Hamburg, Germany, at 53½° N latitude. Notice the enormous difference in total quantity of radia-

tion received at summer solstice (June) as compared with winter solstice (December). The peak value at noon in June is more than four times greater than at noon in December. Notice also that radiation commences about 5

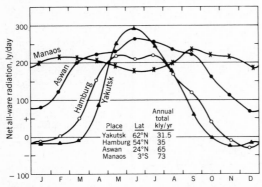

Figure 1.23. Net all-wave radiation throughout the year at four representative stations. (Data by courtesy of David H. Miller.)

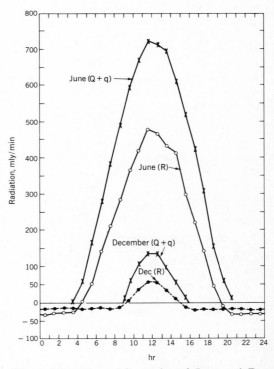

Figure 1.24. Mean daily cycles of June and December incoming and outgoing radiation at Hamburg, Germany. (Data by courtesy of Ernst Frankenberger.)

hr earlier and ceases about 5 hr later in June than in December. Equinox curves, not shown, would fall between the June and December curves, beginning with sunrise at about 6 AM and ending with sunset at about 6 PM.

Figure 1.24 also shows curves of net all-wave radiation for June and December at Hamburg. Radiation is given in units of thousandths of langleys per minute (mly/min). During hours of darkness energy loss from the ground continues by longwave radiation, and a small deficit exists more or less uniformly throughout the night. Net radiation becomes positive shortly after sunrise, rises sharply in the morning hours, and peaks at noon. Heat now flows from ground to atmosphere, and a large surplus of radiation is accumulated during the day. Following a rapid decline in the late afternoon, net radiation becomes negative about an hour before sunset and thereafter heat flows from the air to the ground. In June, net radiation at noon is about 65% of the incoming radiation, whereas in December the proportion is only about 43%.

Radiation surplus for the entire day can be compared with deficit for the entire day by comparing the area lying above the zero line with that lying below the zero line. When this is done it will be seen that a very large net daily surplus is obtained in June, whereas for December there is a small net daily deficit. These observations are in agreement with the annual cycle of net all-wave radiation at Hamburg (Figure 1.23), which shows a June surplus of 210 ly/day and a December deficit of 30 ly/day.

## THE EARTH'S HEAT BALANCE

The base of the atmosphere forms a continuous interface with the continental and interspersed ocean surfaces. The earth's energy budget involves not only the flow of energy in the form of electromagnetic radiation, but also the flow and storage of energy in the form of sensible heat in the atmosphere, the continental surfaces, and the oceans.

*Sensible heat,* measured in terms of the temperature of a substance as indicated by a thermometer, constitutes an environmental factor of prime importance in the surface layer of planet Earth. We are all aware that our planet possesses extremes of thermal environment— from permanent frost of the great icecaps to permanent warmth of the equatorial belt. We are also aware that certain parts of the globe

have a strong seasonal rhythm of severe winter cold alternating with summer heat. There is also a familiar daily rhythm of rising and falling temperatures. Obviously, these seasonal and daily thermal cycles are locked into the corresponding cycles of incoming and outgoing radiation.

Sensible heat can be gained by direct absorption of radiation falling upon an opaque ground surface or penetrating the partially transparent gas of the atmosphere and liquid of water bodies. Correspondingly, these same substances can lose sensible heat by radiating energy outward in the longwave lengths.

Heat can also be gained or lost by the process of *conduction,* in which sensible heat flows through the substance. For heat conduction to occur a *temperature gradient,* or *thermal gradient,* must exist; flow of heat is then from regions of higher temperature to regions of lower temperature. Heat flow increases as the thermal gradient increases.

In addition to heat exchanges by radiation and conduction, there occurs within fluids a transport of sensible heat through the movement of the fluid itself. This form of heat transport is sometimes referred to as *turbulent exchange.* To combine all of the above mechanisms of gain or loss of heat, the term *sensible-heat flux* is used.

An important process by which liquid or moist surfaces lose sensible heat is evaporation. This heat loss may be called the *latent-heat flux,* to distinguish it from the sensible-heat flux. Note also that condensation of water vapor within the atmosphere liberates heat energy, a process that tends to raise the sensible temperature of the surrounding air. The condensation process will be treated in detail in Chapter 5. Latent heat flux is a highly important component of the heat budget over ocean and lake surfaces. It also operates in varying degrees from land surfaces, depending upon the moisture content of the exposed soil or rock. A related evaporative process, which can be included within the latent-heat flux, is *transpiration* of water from plant foliage. In this process water drawn upward from the soil is evaporated through pores in the leaves. The combined evaporation from soil and transpiration from plants is termed *evapotranspiration.*

Let us put together some of the principles of heat flow into a simple equation expressing the heat balance as it applies to a column of water or soil extending from the free upper surface

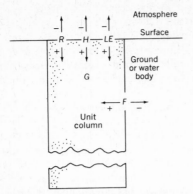

Figure 1.25. Schematic diagram of the heat-balance equation.

downward to a depth where temperature changes are practically zero. This depth will generally be very much greater in water than in soil or rock. Figure 1.25 is a schematic diagram of the unit column and the various forms of heat flux that are involved in the equation.

The equation seeks to evaluate the rate at which the heat content of the unit column changes, stated, for example, as the number of calories of heat gained or lost per minute of time. This quantity is given the symbol $G$ in the equation

$$G = R - H - LE - F$$

where $R$ is net all-wave radiation at the surface,

$H$ is transfer of sensible heat through the upper surface by conduction and turbulent exchange (positive when air is warmer than the surface, negative when air is cooler than the surface),

$LE$ is latent-heat transfer by evaporation ($L$ is latent heat of vaporization, about 590 cal/gm of water; $E$ is the quantity of water evaporated),

and $F$ is horizontal transfer of heat out of the column.

Because we are interested in evaluating $R$, rather than $G$, these terms are transposed to give the following basic heat-balance equation:

$$R = H + LE + G + F$$

The term $R$ is now a measure of the radiative energy available to warm the air or the column of soil or water and to evaporate water.

The term $F$ is a measure of the net horizontal flow of heat out of the column of water

or soil below the surface. In the case of soil or rock, the value of $F$ is negligible, since there is no movement of matter and adjacent columns are subject to the same rates of gain or loss of heat through the upper surface. In the case of water bodies, however, currents readily transport heat out of or into the column, and the quantity $F$ is then important.

The heat-balance equation can apply for any small unit of time, such as 1 sec or 1 min, or it may be applied to longer spans of time, such as a day, a month, a year, or a century. The equation may also be applied to the earth's surface as a whole, in which case the horizontal transport, $F$, is canceled out through circulation of the oceans, leaving only the following terms:

$$R = H + LE + G$$

The global heat balance will be evaluated in Chapter 4, after the atmospheric and oceanic circulation patterns are described.

We will next examine the basic heat-balance equation in daily and annual cycles of change.

## THE ANNUAL HEAT-BALANCE CYCLE

In middle and high latitudes, where there is a strongly developed annual cycle of incoming solar radiation (see Figure 1.9), the heat balance runs through a corresponding cycle of change involving each of the four component terms. Figure 1.26 shows data for Madison, Wisconsin. A maximum value of net all-wave radiation, $R$, occurs near summer solstice and a minimum value near winter solstice. Negative values are experienced in the winter. Latent-heat flux, $LE$, is large in summer months.

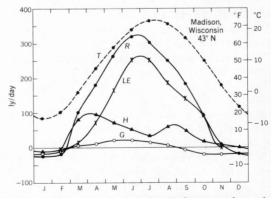

Figure 1.26. The annual heat-balance cycle and mean air-temperature cycle at a humid middle-latitude station (Madison, Wisconsin). [Data from W. D. Sellers (1965), *Physical Climatology*, Chicago, Univ. of Chicago Press, p. 106, Figure 30.]

Sensible-heat flux, *H*, on the other hand, is of small importance at Madison except in early spring before foliage appears. The flow of heat into and out of the soil, *G*, follows a simple annual rhythm in both examples.

The mean daily air temperature, measured in a thermometer shelter about 4 ft (1.2 m) above the ground surface, follows a strong annual cycle (Figure 1.26, dashed line), but the maximum value lags by a month or more after the peak of net radiation. So long as the soil is gaining heat, its temperature continues to rise and to supply increased heat radiation to the lower air layer.

With decreasing latitude, the range of variation in both net radiation and air temperature is generally diminished, so that near the equator the ingredients of the heat-balance equation run almost uniformly throughout the year.

## THE DAILY HEAT-BALANCE CYCLE

When the hourly values of the components of the heat-balance equation are plotted, a daily cycle is revealed. Figure 1.27 shows an example of the heat balance throughout a summer day at middle latitudes. The example is typical of a humid climate with a dense vegetative cover.

The curve of net all-wave radiation, *R*, is symmetrical about the noon-hour peak and is essentially flat during hours of darkness, when the value of *R* is negative. The latent-heat flux, *LE*, is the most important quantity throughout most of the day, because of evaporation and transpiration from plant foliage and moist soil.

Sensible-heat flux, *H*, is moderately great, but less than latent-heat flux. Rate of heat gain by the soil through downward flow, *G*, is relatively small, but will cause a rise in soil temperature during the day. In hours of darkness, all components of the equation are small and of zero or negative value. Thus during the night the soil will become cooler. During the predawn hours the latent heat flux becomes negative, indicating the liberation of heat by condensation of dew.

The air-temperature curve in Figure 1.28 shows a minimum close to sunrise, followed by a rapid rise in the morning hours. The peak occurs in mid-afternoon, since heat continues to be gained from the ground well past the peak of net radiation. The decline in air temperature continues through the hours of darkness as heat is radiated from air to the ground below and to the atmosphere above.

## LAND AND WATER CONTRASTS IN THE TEMPERATURE CYCLES

Air-temperature cycles in the layer close to the earth's surface show quite different daily and seasonal characteristics, depending on whether the surface beneath is that of the ocean or of a continent. For a number of reasons the surface of any extensive deep body of water heats more slowly and cools more slowly than the surface of a large body of land, when both are subject to the same intensity of incoming radiation.

The slower rise of water-surface temperature can be attributed to (1) direct penetration of radiation, distributing the absorbed heat

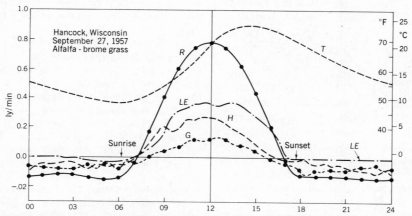

Figure 1.27. The daily heat-balance cycle at a representative middle-latitude station (Hancock, Wisconsin) in a humid climate. [Data from W. D. Sellers (1965), *Physical Climatology*, Chicago, Univ. of Chicago Press, p. 112, Figure 33.]

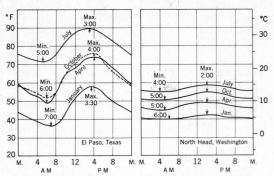

Figure 1.28. Average values of temperature throughout the day at El Paso, Texas, a desert station of the continental interior, and at North Head, Washington, a coastal station. (© 1960, John Wiley & Sons, New York. Data from U.S. Dept. of Agriculture.)

throughout a substantial water layer; (2) the higher specific heat of water; (3) mixing through eddy motions, which carry the heat to lower depths; and (4) cooling by evaporation from the water surface. In contrast, the more rapid rise of land-surface temperature can be attributed to (1) opaqueness of the soil or rock, concentrating the heat in a shallow layer; (2) lower specific heat of mineral matter; (3) poor conductivity of the soil, if it is dry; and (4) absence of mixing. As the capacity of a deep-water body to hold heat is greater than that of a shallow layer of soil or rock, surface temperatures fall more gradually at the water surface than at the ground surface.

The effect of land and water contrasts is seen in the daily air-temperature curves as recorded in the standard thermometer shelter (Figure 1.28), comparing stations of different situations. El Paso, Texas, exemplifies the thermal regime of an interior desert in middle latitudes. Soil-moisture content is low, vegetation sparse, and cloud cover generally light. Responding to intense heating and cooling of the ground surface, air temperatures show an average daily range of 20 to 25 F° (11 to 14 C°). North Head, Washington, is a coastal station strongly influenced by air brought from the adjacent Pacific Ocean by prevailing westerly winds; thus it exemplifies a maritime thermal environment. The average daily range at North Head is a mere 5 F° (3 C°) or less. Persistent fogs and cloud cover also contribute to the small daily range.

Seasonal contrasts in continental and oceanic air temperatures are also seen in Figure 1.28. For El Paso, temperature difference

between July and January curves runs about 30 F° (17 C°); that for North Head is only about 15 F° (8 C°). These seasonal differences constitute the *annual range* of temperature. Greatest annual ranges occur in northern Siberia (110 F°; 62 C°); smallest ranges are over equatorial oceans (less than 5 F°; 3 C°). Obviously there exists a great diversity in surface thermal environments over the globe.

## A SYSTEM IN REVIEW

The great radiation system—sun to earth to space—is clearly the primary determinant of the surface environment of our planet. This enormous flux of energy not only establishes the thermal properties of the earth's surface, but it also drives secondary systems of atmospheric and oceanic circulation which distribute heat over the globe.

Perhaps the most remarkable property of the radiation system is its persistent uniformity within rather narrow limits over vast spans of geologic time. The existence of advanced forms of plant and animal life in abundance the world over since the dawn of the eon of abundant life, some 600 m.y. ago, attests to the remarkably uniform thermal environments that have prevailed over large areas of our planet. True, there have been climatic fluctuations of such severity to bring on the spread of great ice sheets, and these cold episodes have probably had important effects upon organic evolution. But when we consider that some planets— Mercury and Venus particularly—have surfaces much too hot to permit life to endure, while others—Jupiter and the other great planets—have surfaces far too cold to harbor life, an equability of thermal environment is a truly outstanding characteristic of planet Earth.

**References for further study**
Mehlin, T. G. (1959), *Astronomy,* New York, Wiley, 392 pp., chap. 4.
Bates, D. R. (1964), *The Planet Earth,* 2nd ed., Oxford, Pergamon, 370 pp., chaps. 7, 12.
Riehl, H. (1965), *Introduction to the Atmosphere,* New York, McGraw-Hill, 365 pp., chaps. 1, 2.
Sellers, W. D. (1965), *Physical Climatology,* Chicago, Univ. of Chicago Press, 272 pp., chaps. 3–6, 8.
NASA (1966), *Significant Achievements in Satellite Meteorology 1958–1964* (NASA SP–96), Washington, D.C., U.S. Govt. Printing Office, 139 pp.
Lowry, W. P. (1969), *Weather and Life: An In-*

*troduction to Biometeorology,* New York and London, Academic, 305 pp., chaps. 2–4, 7, 8.

Strahler, A. N. (1971), *The Earth Sciences,* 2nd ed., New York, Harper & Row, 826 pp., chaps. 4, 12–14.

## Review questions

1. Describe the sun's photosphere and give approximate temperatures. What are the most important constituent elements in the sun, and in what proportions are they present?

2. What is the source of the sun's energy? Describe the physical processes acting within the sun's interior. What temperatures exist there? Can contraction account for the sun's energy? Explain.

3. Describe the electromagnetic radiation spectrum in terms of the component parts or bands and proportion of energy in each. At what speed does this radiation travel? Explain black-body radiation in terms of Planck's law and the Stefan-Boltzmann law.

4. How does the earth's radiation spectrum compare with that of the sun in terms of wavelength and black-body temperature? Define the *solar constant.* Is it in fact a constant quantity? Explain the discrepancy between incoming and outgoing radiation rates at the earth's surface.

5. What variable factors control the amount of solar radiation received at any given location on the globe throughout a single day? Describe the effects of both latitude and season upon radiation received daily upon a horizontal unit area at the earth's surface, assuming no atmosphere to exist.

6. How thick is the earth's atmosphere? What sciences deal with the atmosphere? List the important gases of constant proportion in the homosphere, giving approximate percentages. Comment upon the chemical properties and importance of each gas. What is the role of water vapor in the homosphere? of dust particles?

7. Describe the layers of the heterosphere, naming the principal gas found in each. Explain the order in which these gases are arranged. Do the outermost atoms rotate with the earth?

8. Where is the troposphere located? At what rate does air temperature fall with increasing elevation in this layer? How does the altitude of the tropopause vary with latitude and season? Name the temperature zones and describe the temperature-altitude curve from the tropopause upward into the top of the atmosphere.

9. What parts of the electromagnetic spectrum are absorbed in the upper atmosphere? Describe and explain the ionosphere. What processes take place in the ionosphere, and how is radio communication affected?

10. What is the ozone layer, and how is it formed? At what altitude does it lie? Of what importance is this layer to life on earth?

11. Describe the various forms of losses of incoming solar energy in a cloudless atmosphere. Approximately what percentages of total solar energy are lost in each form? How does the presence of clouds influence the amount of energy reaching the ground?

12. What happens to incoming shortwave radiation when it reaches the earth's surface? Define the term *albedo* and use it in your explanation. What is the earth's albedo as a planet, and how is it measured? Compare this value in a general way with that of the other planets.

13. Describe and explain longwave radiation from the earth's surface. What happens to this radiation when it enters the atmosphere? What role is played by water vapor and carbon dioxide in this process of energy exchange?

14. Describe the radiation budget of the earth as a whole. What part does counter-radiation play in the energy budget? In what other ways besides longwave radiation does the earth's surface give back energy to the atmosphere?

15. Define the term *net all-wave radiation.* In the equation of radiation balance, what are the variable quantities that determine the net all-wave radiation? Describe the profile of average pole-to-pole net all-wave radiation for the entire earth-atmosphere system, explaining the regions of surplus and deficit. What is the value of net radiation for the entire globe?

16. How is the earth's heat balance maintained? What forms of heat transport are involved? What is the direction of this transport? At what latitudes is it most rapid? Explain the concept of planetary temperature.

17. Describe seasonal cycles of incoming solar radiation and net all-wave radiation in middle latitudes. Describe typical daily cycles of incoming radiation and net all-wave radiation. How will these daily cycles change with season of year in middle latitudes?

18. Discuss the earth's heat balance in terms

of processes of heat transfer and heat storage. State the general heat-balance equation and define each term used.

19. Describe the annual and daily cycles of the four component terms of the heat-balance equation. How is air temperature related to these cycles?

20. Explain how the physical properties of land and water surfaces affect the daily and annual cycles of air temperature. On a global basis, where will the greatest and least annual ranges of air temperature be found? Explain.

21. Describe in broad terms the sun-earth-space radiation system and its environmental significance. How has this system functioned throughout geologic time? Compare earth with other planets in terms of thermal environments.

# chapter 2
# particle flux system, sun-earth-space: solar wind and the earth's magnetic field

Different in both physical nature and energy level from the sun-earth-space radiation system described in Chapter 1 is a system of flux of matter and energy from sun to earth that has come into major importance in the earth and space sciences only in recent decades. The sun emits particles into space. These particles are protons and electrons derived from the ionization of solar hydrogen. Sent outward at various levels of intensity, this stream of particles travels at speeds considerably slower than the speed of light. The earth intercepts these particles, entrapping them in its planetary magnetic field. Particles can also escape into intergalactic space from the magnetic field, completing the flow path of the open system. However, both the timing and intensity of the particle input into the earth's magnetic field lack the cyclic rhythms—daily and seasonal—that characterize the input of solar electromagnetic radiation into the earth's atmosphere. Instead, we are dealing with events whose tim-

ing and intensity levels are partly random, and hence not subject to prediction as specific events.

## THE SUN'S ATMOSPHERE

To go further you will need to learn more about the sun's surface and atmosphere. Recall from Chapter 1 that the visible surface layer of the sun is the photosphere, with a basal temperature of about 6000° K. It is from the photosphere that the principal electromagnetic radiation emanates.

Above the photosphere lies a low solar atmosphere, the *chromosphere*, a region which includes rosy, spikelike clouds of hydrogen gas termed *solar prominences* (Figure 2.1). Still farther above the sun's surface is the *corona*, a region of pearly-gray streamers of light which constitute the sun's outer atmosphere (Figure 2.2). At times the solar prominences reach far out into the corona as luminous archlike bodies (Figure 2.3), rising to heights of over 1 million

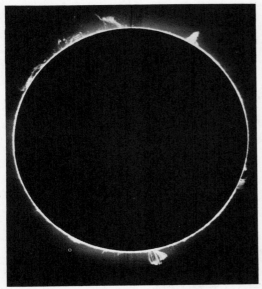

Figure 2.1. This photograph of the entire edge of the sun shows several prominences. (The Hale Observatories.)

mi (1.6 × 10⁶ km) and extending as far as 500,000 mi (8 × 10⁵ km) along the sun's surface. Temperatures increase outward through the chromosphere, rapidly reaching 20,000° K. Temperature increases sharply outward in the corona until values as high as 2 million (2 × 10⁶)°K are reached. Thus, surprisingly, the photosphere, or the sun's surface, is its coolest

Figure 2.2. Photograph of the sun's outer corona taken during a total eclipse. The moon's disk completely covers the sun, permitting this pearly-white tenuous outer layer of gases to be seen. (The Hale Observatories.)

Figure 2.3. This great solar prominence rose to a height of 140,000 mi (225,000 km). (The Hale Observatories.)

layer. The intense heating of the corona is an important problem of science.

Density of the ionized gas constituting the corona is extremely low and approaches that of interplanetary space at a distance of 1 million or so miles out from the sun's surface. From the corona there emanates a steady flow of electrons and protons that radiates outward into planetary space. To this flow is given the name *solar wind*. Velocities are in the range of 60 to 600 mi/sec (100 to 1000 km/sec). The ionized solar gas is described by physicists as *plasma*, a substance capable of transporting a magnetic field outward from the sun to the outer limits of the solar system. In the sense that the solar wind envelopes the earth and other planets, we can think of solar system as lying within the sun's outer atmosphere.

Dark spots, of irregular shape and distribution, develop from time to time upon the sun's photosphere. These are *sunspots* (Figure 2.4). They were first seen by Galileo with his simple telescope and can be observed by anyone. Take warning: Never attempt to observe the sun directly with the unaided eye, binoculars, or a telescope. Although telescopes can be fitted with dense filters that make direct viewing safe, it is best to observe the sun indirectly. A white card can be held a few inches from the tele-

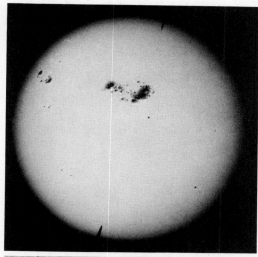

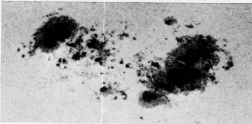

Figure 2.4. (*Above*) The whole disk of the sun shows a large sunspot group. (*Below*) An enlargement of the group of spots shows the umbra and penumbra regions. (The Hale Observatories.)

scope eyepiece. The sun's image on the card will show sunspots and eclipses very nicely.

Sunspots are from 500 to 50,000 mi (800 to 80,000 km) wide. Each spot has a dark central region, the *umbra,* which is surrounded by a border of lighter color, the *penumbra* (Figure 2.4). Sunspot groups appear and dissolve within time spans of from several days to several weeks. They move slowly eastward

across the face of the sun's disk, traveling with the sun's rotation. Sunspots represent features of intense disturbance. Possibly a sunspot is a type of vortex into which surface gases are being drawn. Temperatures within the spot are somewhat cooler than the average for the photosphere. Magnetic fields of high intensity are associated with the spot and suggest rapid rotation of ionized gases in vortices within the spot.

### SUNSPOT CYCLES

Sunspot activity can be assessed in terms of the number of spots counted within the year. On this basis, there is a strongly defined 11-yr cycle consisting of a maximum frequency and a minimum frequency. During the peak of the sunspot cycle, from 50 to 120 spot groups occur within a year's time. During the low point of the cycle the number is on the order of 10 spot groups or less per year (Figure 2.5). The International Geophysical Year (IGY), a program of intensive world-wide observation of solar and upper atmospheric phenomena, was undertaken in 1957 and 1958 to coincide with maximum sunspot activity of the 11-yr cycle. In contrast, the International Years of the Quiet Sun (IYQS) in 1964 and 1965 were chosen as a period for observations with minimum sunspot activity.

### SOLAR FLARES AND ION CLOUDS

Of particular importance in influencing phenomena on earth are *solar flares* related to sunspot activity. A solar flare is an emission of ionized hydrogen gas from the vicinity of a sunspot. The flare emits a burst of X-ray radiation, which travels outward with the speed of light. The stream of hydrogen ions (electrons and protons) then follows and reaches the earth from half a day to a full day later.

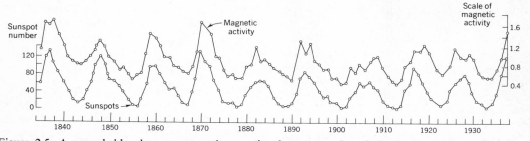

Figure 2.5. A remarkably close correspondence exists between cycles of change in number of sunspots and in the intensity of magnetic disturbances. [After S. Chapman and J. Bartels (1951), *Geomagnetism,* London, Oxford Univ. Press.]

Solar flares occur in much greater numbers than sunspots. As many as 2000 to 4000 flares occur per year during times of maximum sunspot activity. Flares are thus about 20 times more frequent events than sunspots, but their duration is correspondingly much shorter. A single sunspot group in the course of its duration will produce as many as 40 flares. So we see that, in addition to the steady solar wind, the earth intercepts intense bursts of X rays and ionized particles at irregular intervals.

## THE INTERPLANETARY MEDIUM

The sun rotates upon an axis oriented perpendicular to the plane of its orbit and thus essentially parallel with the earth's axis. However, while the earth as a solid body rotates as a unit, the sun, being in the gaseous state, rotates at a rate greater in one part than another. If the motion of a number of sunspots is traced day after day, it will be found that spots closest to the sun's equator rotate most rapidly. At increasing latitude away from the equator, the rotation is progressively less rapid. Note that both liquids and gases are fluids. A fluid is a substance that readily engages in shearing motions, which is to say that adjacent particles or layers of the fluid move at different speeds. Such flow is termed *rotational flow*. From observations of sunspot motions, it is obvious that gases of the photosphere engage in rotational flow. At the sun's equator, the period of surface rotation is about 24½ days. At a latitude of about 60° the period is about 32 days. The average value is 27.4 days.

Rotation of the sun affects the outward paths of flow of the solar plasma and the lines of magnetic force that the flow generates. Imagine that you are watering a lawn with a garden hose. Suppose that you stand in one spot on the lawn, turning at a uniform rate toward your left (anticlockwise). The water drops of the spray will appear to follow curved paths as they travel outward. These paths take the mathematical form of the Archimedes spiral. (Actually, a particular drop follows a straight radial path, but drops preceding and following it occupy different radii.) Similarly, the solar plasma seems to emanate from the sun in spiral paths. Lines of force of the magnetic field also take this form (Figure 2.6). At the earth's orbit, the force lines intersect the orbit at an angle different from a radial line to the sun. This angle, which is about 45°, has been appropriately dubbed the *garden-hose*

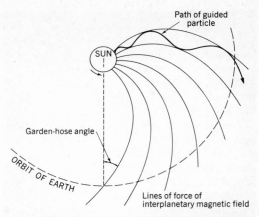

Figure 2.6 Magnetic field of the sun, showing the garden-hose effect caused by the sun's rotation. [Based on a drawing by K. G. McCracken (1967), in *Encyclopedia of Atmospheric Sciences and Astrogeology*, R. W. Fairbridge, ed., New York, Reinhold, p. 489, Figure 1.]

*angle* by space physicists. The strength of the interplanetary magnetic field at the earth's orbit is about $5 \times 10^{-5}$ oersted.* The plasma here has a density of about 5 protons/cm³.

Some cosmic rays are generated in solar flares. These highly energetic, charged particles are believed to be channeled in paths between the spiral lines of force of the sun's magnetic field, as shown in Figure 2.6.

The outward flow of solar wind continues far beyond the earth's orbit. It has been estimated that outward flow continues to a distance of about 50 astronomical units from the sun. (Note: One astronomical unit is the distance between earth and sun, or about 93 million mi.) At this distance, the *intergalactic magnetic field* with an intensity of about $5 \times 10^{-6}$ oersted is encountered.

We have now examined the first stage of the sun-earth-space system, in which particles are emitted from the sun and sent on their way toward earth. We turn next to the second stage of the system, which is the interception of the solar particles by the earth's magnetic field.

## THE EARTH AS A MAGNET

Awareness that the earth acts as a great magnet may have been reached during the eleventh century A.D., when mariners' compasses using lodestone were put into use by Arabs and Persians. Lodestone, a naturally magnetic form of the iron mineral *magnetite* (see Figure 8.15), could be floated upon a

* The oersted is defined on p. 38.

piece of wood or a cork to serve as a magnetic compass (Figure 2.7). Similarly, an iron needle could be magnetized by contact with lodestone and floated on water. That lodestone possessed the property of attracting iron was known to Greeks as early as the seventh century B.C., for this fact is stated in the writings of Thales (640–546 B.C.).

Use of the magnetic compass in Europe is first mentioned in a Latin treatise written about A.D. 1187 by Alexander Neckham, an English monk. He refers to the magnetization of a needle by contact with lodestone. In the middle of the thirteenth century Petrus Peregrinus, a Frenchman, experimentally investigated the properties of lodestone. He can be credited with discovering that when a piece of lodestone is broken into many smaller fragments, each piece becomes a magnet. Using a small magnetized needle, he was able to demonstrate the magnetic axis within a spherical piece of lodestone, finding that the needle was oriented perpendicular to the surface of the lodestone over the polar position.

Peregrinus improved the magnetic compass by replacing the floating lodestone with a magnetized needle pivoting on two bearings and referred to a graduated rim. Points projecting from the needle permitted direct sighting of distant objects (Figure 2.8).

It is to Sir William Gilbert, physician to Queen Elizabeth, that credit is due for important advances in scientific study of terrestrial magnetism. In his treatise *De Magnete,* published in 1600, Gilbert described his experiments with a 5-in. sphere of lodestone, known as a *terella.* Using a tiny pivoted compass needle the size of a "barleycorn," he was able to describe the external magnetic field. Gilbert proposed the hypothesis that the earth acts as a great lodestone and, in fact, is formed of an interior sphere of lodestone surrounded by a nonmagnetic shell. Working from the assump-

Figure 2.7. A medieval floating compass. Stars mark the poles of the piece of lodestone. (From Athanasius Kircher, 1643.)

tion that the magnetic axis of the sphere coincides with the earth's pole of rotation, he was able to predict the inclination (dip) of the compass needle at any latitude (Figure 2.9).

The science of *geomagnetism,* or *terrestrial magnetism,* has developed rapidly since Gilbert's time, largely through the necessity of accurate mapping of the earth's surface magnetic field for use in marine navigation. In the past two decades, the exploration of space by orbiting satellites and space probes has brought into prominence a new branch of the science dealing with the external magnetic field and its relationship to the flow of plasma from the sun.

## THE EARTH'S MAGNETIC FIELD

In its most simple aspect, the earth's magnetic field resembles that of a bar magnet located at the earth's center (Figure 2.10). The axis of the imaginary bar magnet is situated approximately coincident with the earth's geographic axis. At points where the projected line of the magnetic axis emerges from the earth's surface are the *north magnetic pole* and *south magnetic pole.* Note that the earth's magnetic axis (*geomagnetic axis*) forms an angle of about 20° with respect to the geographic axis, hence that the magnetic poles do not coincide with the geographic poles. The north magnetic pole lies approximately at latitude 73° N, longitude 100° W, which is a point near Prince of Wales Island in the arctic region of Canada. The south magnetic pole lies about at latitude 68° S, longitude 143° E, a point near the coast of Antarctica. It is obvious from these figures of latitude and longitude that the two magnetic poles do not occupy antipodal positions on the globe and that the geomagnetic axis does not pass through the earth's center. The geomagnetic axis passes closest to the earth's center at a point directly beneath the middle of the Pacific Ocean. (This relationship is shown in Figure 2.11 but has been omitted for simplification from Figure 2.10.)

Figure 2.11 shows lines of force of the earth's magnetic field as passing through a common point close to the earth's center. The geomagnetic axis is oriented vertically in this diagram. There exists a *magnetic equator,* lying in a plane at right angles to the geomagnetic axis and encircling the earth's surface approximately in the region of the geographic equator. However, because of the angle between geographic and geomagnetic axes, the geomagnetic

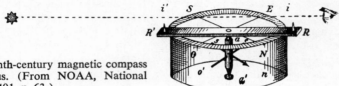

Figure 2.8. A thirteenth-century magnetic compass devised by Perigrinus. (From NOAA, National Ocean Survey, Publ. 401, p. 63.)

equator approximates a great circle departing as much as 20° of latitude from the geographical equator.

Because unlike poles of two magnets attract each other, whereas like poles repel each other, that point of the needle of a magnetic compass which points toward magnetic north is of opposite polarity to the geomagnetic pole. Assuming that the geomagnetic pole which lies in the arctic region is to be designated as the "north" magnetic pole, it follows that the needle end pointing toward that pole is actually the "south" pole of the smaller magnet. In referring to the end of the compass needle that indicates north, we should take care to refer to it as the *north-seeking pole* of the compass.

Visualized in three dimensions, the lines of force of the earth's magnetic field form a succession of doughnutlike rings, suggested in Figure 2.11. The *magnetic core* is the common point to which the rings converge.

In describing the earth's magnetic field, two properties are of importance: (1) the directions taken by the force lines and (2) the magnitudes of the forces at various points in the field. Figure 2.11 shows that the lines of force cut through the earth's surface with a variety of inclinations, ranging from perpendicular to the surface at the magnetic poles to progressively lower angles as the magnetic

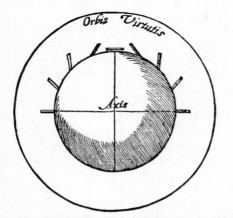

Figure 2.9. Gilbert's diagram of his terella with small magnets showing inclination. [From W. Gilbert (1600), *De Magnete*.]

equator is approached. At the magnetic equator the force lines exactly parallel the earth's surface.

The angle of intersection of a line of force with the earth's surface at a given point is termed the *magnetic inclination,* or *dip*. This angle can be measured with a simple instrument known as a *dip needle* (Figure 2.12). The needle of this instrument is first brought into perfect balance horizontally on a jeweled bearing while in a nonmagnetized state. The needle is then magnetized and will subsequently assume a position at rest oriented in the direction of the lines of force. (The needle housing must be turned so as to lie in the vertical plane of the force lines.)

After large numbers of determinations of magnetic inclination have been made over the earth's surface, a map can be constructed. On such a map, lines of equal inclination (*isoclinic lines*) are drawn through all points of the same angle of inclination. Figure 2.13 consists of isoclinic maps of the two polar regions. As one would expect, dip reaches a maximum value of 90° at each magnetic pole. For this reason, these poles are often designated as *dip poles*. Inclination will, of course, be zero on the magnetic equator.

Intensity of the magnetic field can be given in units of the oersted.* For the earth's surface, lines of equal intensity, designated *isodynamic lines,* can be shown on a world map (Figure 2.14). The highest values of intensity occur close to the north and south magnetic poles where values reach from 0.6 to over 0.7 oersted. This represents an extremely weak field compared to that of even a small bar magnet (100 to 200 oersteds). Magnetic intensity decreases toward the magnetic equator, where the minimum is under 0.25 oersted.

## MAGNETIC DECLINATION

It is obvious that, because the geomagnetic axis and equator do not coincide with the geographic axis and equator, the north-seeking

* In the field of 1 oersted, a unit magnetic pole is subjected to a force of 1 dyne. In turn, a unit magnetic pole is defined as a pole that repels a like pole with a force of 1 dyne at a distance of 1 cm.

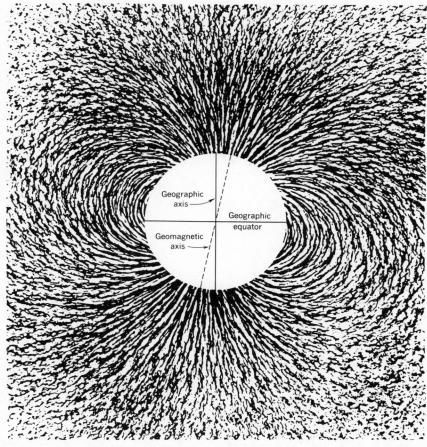

Figure 2.10. The magnetic field about the earth is illustrated here by the pattern of iron filings around a simple bar magnet. [From J. A. Fleming (1939), *Physics of the Earth,* vol. 8, Washington, D.C., Nat. Acad. Sci., p. 4, Figure 1. Reproduced by permission of the National Academy of Sciences and the McGraw-Hill Book Co.]

needle of the compass will generally not point to geographic north. The relationship is shown schematically in Figure 2.15, in which a compass is imagined to be placed at various points in the Northern Hemisphere. There exists a meridian which passes through both geographic and magnetic poles. At any point on this meridian the compass needle will lie along the geographic north-south line. Note, however, that along that part of the meridian between poles, the north-seeking end of the needle will point due south.

Along most meridians, the compass will point in a direction at some angle to the true north direction. To the horizontal angle between the geographic meridian and the compass needle is given the term *magnetic declination* (also *magnetic variation*). Declination is designated as *east* or *west,* depending upon the relationship between magnetic and true north,

as indicated in Figure 2.15. Lines of equal declination, referred to as *isogonic lines,* can be drawn on a world map (Figure 2.16). Note that the angle of declination can range from zero (*agonic line*) to a maximum of 180° in the polar regions. It is obvious that in marine and air navigation by means of the magnetic compass, the amount of declination is of utmost importance. True north can only be ascertained by adding or subtracting the declination from the magnetic compass reading. Consequently, isogonic lines are carried on all navigation charts and the amount of declination is printed on all detailed maps of land areas.

## VARIATIONS IN THE EARTH'S MAGNETIC FIELD

Judging from the three magnetic maps (isodynamic, isoclinic, and isogonic), the earth's

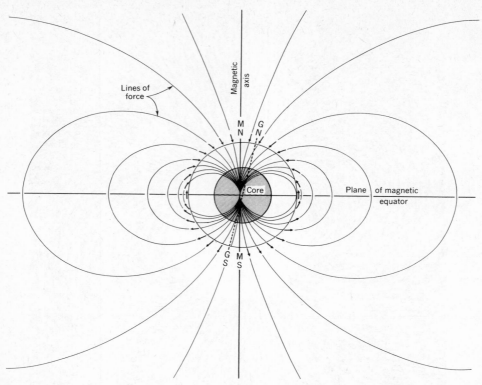

Figure 2.11. Lines of force in the earth's magnetic field shown in cross section passing through the magnetic axis. Letter *M* designates *magnetic,* and *G, geographic.* Arrows at the surface of the earth show the orientation of a dip needle.

magnetic field is far from being that of a simple bar magnet within a homogeneous sphere. Instead, the lines show many forms of irregularities, which can be attributed to nonuniform production of the magnetic force field, as well as to nonuniform physical properties of the earth's crust and interior. Our analysis of the magnetic field has assumed a simple, idealized force field as a basis for explaining fundamental concepts.

A further complication in terrestrial magnetism lies in the fact that the field undergoes gradual changes with time. Such changes in intensity, dip, and declination are referred to as *secular changes,* measurable over periods of years. Although small in terms of the annual amount of change, the accumulated result over decades and centuries is very large. Consequently, geomagnetic maps require occasional revision.

Figure 2.17 shows the changes in magnetic declination at several widely separated stations. The longest record is that of London, dating from 1540. Here the declination has ranged from more than 10° E to almost 25° W, a total range of about 35°. Dip has also undergone marked changes in the same period, changing at London by more than 8° between 1700 and 1900.

Secular changes in the magnetic field are assumed to be tied in with changes within the earth's interior, where the magnetic field is

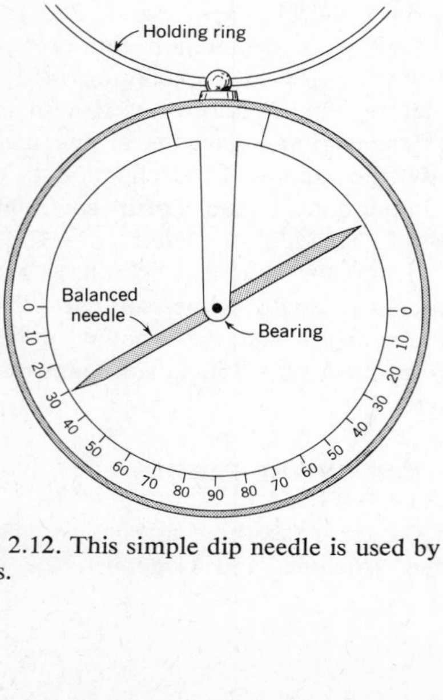

Figure 2.12. This simple dip needle is used by prospectors.

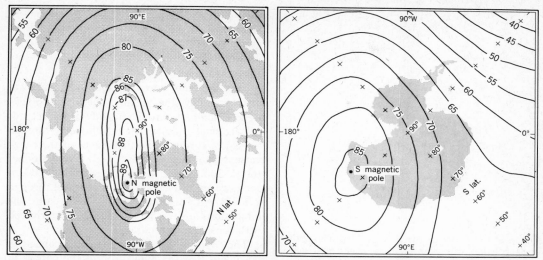

Figure 2.13. Inclination (dip) of the earth's magnetic field in arctic and antarctic regions for 1955, shown by isoclinic lines in degrees. (Data from U.S. Navy Oceanographic Office.)

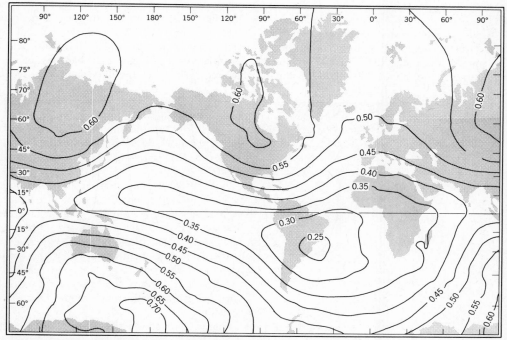

Figure 2.14. World map of total magnetic intensity for 1955. Values are given in oersteds. (Data from U.S. Navy Oceanographic Office.)

believed to be generated. The cause of the earth's magnetic field therefore must be considered.

## EARTH'S CORE AND MAGNETISM

In structure and composition, the earth consists of two large fundamental divisions: *core* and *mantle* (Figure 2.18). The core, with a radius of 2160 mi (3475 km), occupies the earth's center. Surrounding the core is the mantle, 1800 mi (2895 km) thick. Thus the core is encountered at approximately one-half of the radial distance to the earth's center. A third division of the solid earth, the crust, is

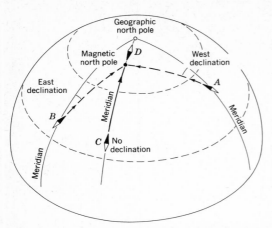

Figure 2.15. Compass declination depends upon one's position with respect to magnetic and geographic north poles.

only 10 to 25 mi (16 to 40 km) thick and can be regarded, for purposes of this discussion, as being only a very thin skin.

Whereas the mantle consists of rock in a solid state (either crystalline or glassy), the core is largely composed of iron and is in a liquid state in the outer 1380 mi (2220 km). The innermost core, about 780 mi (1255 km)

in radius, is thought to be in the solid state. Density of the outer core is on the order of 10 gm/cm³; temperatures are 2700° to 2800° K; pressures are from 1½ to 3 millions of atmospheres (Figure 2.18).

That the outer core is in the liquid state was discovered by the distinguished seismologist Beno Gutenberg through a study of the records of earthquake waves that travel deeply through the earth. It was found that waves of the transverse type (shear waves, or S-waves) do not travel through the core. The nature of transverse waves is that they will not travel through a liquid. After a study of many wave paths, the dimensions of the core could be determined with considerable accuracy.

The *dynamo theory* of earth magnetism postulates that the liquid iron of the core is in slow rotary motion with respect to the solid mantle that surrounds it. It can be shown that such motion will cause the core to act as a great dynamo, generating electrical currents, and at the same time setting up a magnetic field (Figure 2.19). A single, symmetrical current system can thus explain the main field as essentially resembling a single bar magnet.

Irregularities in the field and the secular

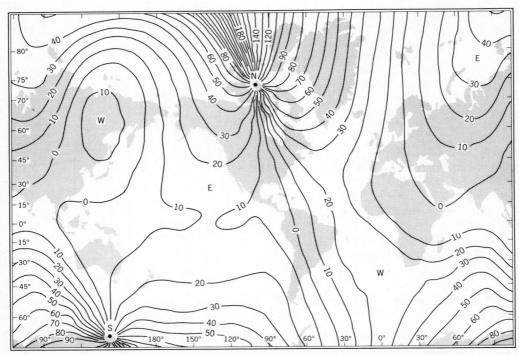

Figure 2.16. World isogonic map. Declination of the compass for 1955 is shown by isogonic lines for every 10°. (Data from U.S. Navy Oceanographic Office.)

ing of *transient variations,* i.e., they come and go. All transient variations of the magnetic

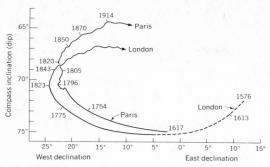

Figure 2.17. Secular changes in compass declination and dip are shown here for Paris and London for more than three centuries of records. [Data from Gaibar-Puertas. After J. A. Jacobs, R. D. Russell, and J. T. Wilson (1959), *Physics and Geology,* New York, McGraw-Hill, p. 122, Figure 6-4.]

changes in the field are explained as resulting from the development of eddies of fluid motion within the core. As these eddies form, move, and dissolve, they cause changes in the declination, intensity, and dip of the magnetic field as it is observed at the earth's surface. The general pattern of magnetic irregularities appears to be drifting in a westward direction around the earth. This drift can be explained by postulating that the core is rotating eastward at a speed slightly less than that of the surrounding mantle. Therefore, in relation to the mantle, the core shows a very slow westward drift. The entire magnetic field, which reflects conditions in the core, is therefore apparently shifting slowly westward.

## TRANSIENT VARIATIONS IN THE MAGNETIC FIELD

At magnetic observatories, a continual record is made of the minor changes in magnetic intensity and direction by means of extremely sensitive instruments. A number of forms of variation can be measured. These are relatively rapid fluctuations, compared with the slow secular changes, and take place in time spans of minutes, days, or weeks. Altogether, these fluctuations are grouped under the head-

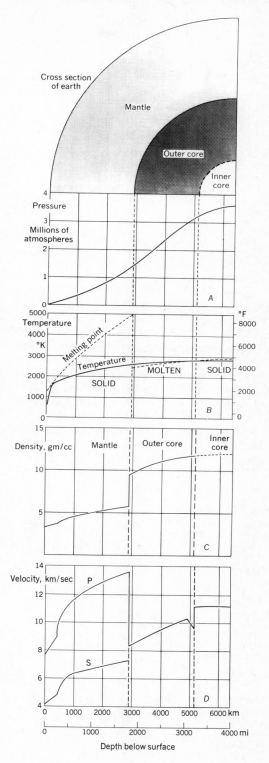

Figure 2.18. (*A*) Increase in pressure with depth in the earth. (*B*) Increase in temperature with depth. (*C*) Increase in density with depth. (*D*) Velocity of P and S waves. [Data from J. Verhoogen (1960), *American Scientist,* vol. 48; and K. E. Bullen (1963), *An Introduction to the Theory of Seismology,* 3rd ed., Cambridge, Cambridge Univ. Press.]

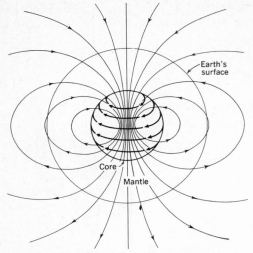

Figure 2.19. Schematic representation of electric currents in the earth's core believed capable of producing the earth's dipole magnetic field. [After S. K. Runcorn (1955), *Scientific American,* vol. 193, no. 3, p. 158.]

field are related in one way or another to influences above the earth's solid surface and are classed as *external* in cause.

Of particular interest in the theme of this chapter, which is to relate solar phenomena to the earth's magnetic field, is a daily rhythm of fluctuation in the magnetic field. Highly sensitive magnets, which act as precision compass needles, will show a daily cycle of change in the declination at a magnetic observatory (Figure 2.20). The total daily change may be as much as 10 minutes of arc. The compass

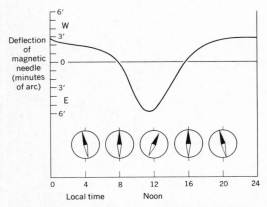

Figure 2.20. The daily cycle of change in magnetic declination for a typical middle-latitude station reflects changes in direction and strength of the dynamo current passing overhead. Compare with Figure 2.21.

needle turns first toward a west declination, then reverses the trend and turns toward an eastward declination. Furthermore, if average curves are plotted for summer solstice, equinox, and winter solstice, it can be clearly seen that the range of daily fluctuation is greatest in summer and least in winter.

The daily and annual cycle of change in magnetic declination immediately suggests that the sun's path in the sky influences the magnetic field. In this case, it is the change in intensity of electromagnetic radiation that is responsible. How can changes in intensity of sunlight cause magnetic fluctuations? To answer this question, recall from Chapter 1 that the ionosphere exists at levels of about 50 to 250 mi (80 to 400 km). Here gamma rays, X rays, and ultraviolet rays of the sun's spectrum cause ionization of nitrogen and oxygen. Electrons thus released move horizontally through the ionosphere in electric-current systems measured in thousands of amperes. Figure 2.21 shows the electric-current patterns. Note that currents are strong on the hemisphere under the sun's rays but weak on the side of the earth that is in darkness. The electric currents of the ionosphere set up a magnetic field, which is superimposed upon the earth's internal magnetic field. As a result, the sensitive compass needle at the observing station is deflected first west, then east as the current system passes overhead. The deflection is greater in summer, when the sun's radiation is more intense. An annual rhythm is therefore produced. Corresponding daily and annual changes can also be seen in magnetic field intensity and dip, as well as in declination.

We can view the daily and annual changes in the magnetic field as fluctuating subsystems which result in no net changes or trend over long periods of time. In this respect, the rhythmic magnetic fluctuations of external origin bear a resemblance to the daily and seasonal rhythms of solar radiation and of atmospheric heating and cooling, and to the systems of ocean tides. While the causative forces in all such systems are imposed according to the model of simple harmonic motion, the effects depart from the ideal sine curve of that motion. (See Figure 3.22.) For example, the daily and annual rise and fall of solar radiation at a given point outside the atmosphere follows the sine curve of simple harmonic motion (see Chapter 1). However, when we look at the resulting curves of air temperature near the ground, or

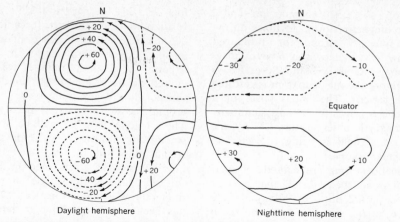

Figure 2.21. Schematic representation of dynamo electric currents in the ionosphere during equinox conditions. Figures give electric current in thousands of amperes. [After S. Chapman and J. Bartels (1951), *Geomagnetism*, London, Oxford Univ. Press.]

the changes in magnetic declination, dip, or intensity, we see that the daily curve is no longer a pure sine curve, although there is a wave form with one maximum and one minimum value in the cycle.

## MAGNETIC DISTURBANCES AND STORMS

From rhythmic subsystems of fluctuations of external origins, we turn to the highly irregular external disturbances that affect the earth's magnetic field. In all magnetic observatories, a continuous record is kept of the intensity of the magnetic field. Intensity, which is measured as either the horizontal or vertical component of the total intensity, is conventionally scaled in

units of *gammas*. (One gamma is equivalent to 0.00001 oersted.) Figure 2.22 shows a typical record of horizontal intensity, known as a *magnetogram,* for a normal day described as magnetically *quiet*. The observatory is at Tucson, Arizona. Here the horizontal intensity averages about 26,000 gammas. On a quiet day there are minor irregular fluctuations on the order of 5 to 50 gammas in periods of minutes or hours.

Wide fluctuations of magnetic intensity, abruptly terminating the quiet record, mark the onset of a *magnetic storm,* or period of *magnetic disturbance*. A sudden commencement of disturbance is shown in Figure 2.22. Rapid

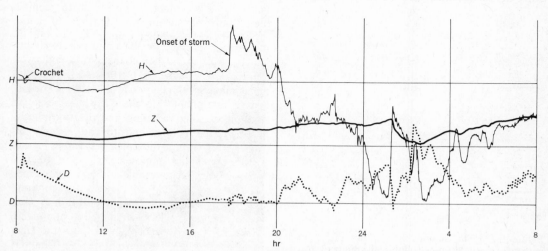

Figure 2.22. Magnetogram for a magnetically disturbed day, September 12, 1957, recorded at Tucson, Arizona. *H* represents horizontal intensity, *Z* vertical intensity, and *D* declination. [From NOAA, National Ocean Survey (1962), *Magnetism of the Earth,* Publ. 40-1, p. 26, Figure 14.]

fluctuations of 100 to 500 gammas are typical of an intense magnetic storm. At times during the storm, intensity drops for prolonged periods to low values, known as *bays*. A magnetic storm may last many hours. Several days may elapse before the magnetogram is restored to the quiet pattern. The initial phase of a major magnetic storm is felt almost simultaneously at all magnetic observatories. Clearly, the external magnetic field is being subjected to forces of planetary scope.

That magnetic storms are caused by solar flares is well established. Recall that a solar flare emits an initial burst of X rays. These travel to earth at the speed of light and reach the earth in about nine minutes. The ultraviolet rays cause a sudden increase in the electric currents of the ionosphere, which in turn causes a fluctuation in the magnetic intensity. On the magnetogram, this initial fluctuation is termed the *crochet* and is observed simultaneously at all stations. The onset of the storm does not take place until some 12 to 24 hr after the crochet is recorded. During this time, the burst of highly ionized gas of the solar flare is traveling from sun to earth, moving at speeds of 1000 to 2000 mi/sec. As the electrons and protons of the cloud enter the earth's magnetic field, they become entrapped in the lines of force. As the electrons reach the ionosphere, they alter the electric ring currents, causing major changes in the magnetic intensity.

Figure 2.23 shows how particles from the solar ion cloud are trapped by the force lines of the external geomagnetic field. Traveling at high velocity, the particle is reflected back and forth, remaining within the force field.

Solar flares that produce magnetic storms emanate largely from sunspots that rotate with a period of about 27 days. If we imagine the curved stream of ionized gas emitted by such a sunspot, it will appear to be a jet that sweeps around the sun at a steady pace (Figure 2.6). The earth in its orbit will be struck by this stream about once every 27 days, just as the stream from the turning nozzle of a garden hose will strike a given place on the lawn once for each turn of the nozzle. A recurrence of moderate magnetic storms in a 27-day interval has been observed, although the major magnetic storms do not seem to show such regularity of occurrence. Frequency of magnetic storms is closely related to sunspot activity, following the 11-yr cycle, as Figure 2.5 clearly shows.

## EFFECTS OF MAGNETIC STORMS

Magnetic storms are attended by interesting optical and electrical effects. Well known as one of nature's most dramatic displays is the *aurora*, an illumination of the nighttime sky seen at high latitudes (*aurora borealis* in the Northern Hemisphere, *aurora australis* in the Southern Hemisphere). The aurora is a shifting series of bands, rays, or draperies of light originating in the ionospheric zone at altitudes of from 50 to 175 mi (80 to 280 km) (Figure 2.24). From long scientific observation of auroras, it is well established that the phenomenon is concentrated in two zones. An arctic zone is centered upon the north geomagnetic pole at an angular distance of about 22½° of arc from that center. A correspond-

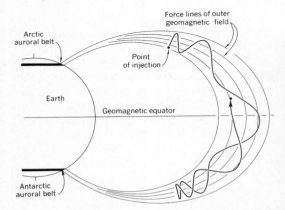

Figure 2.23. The sinuous line shows the typical path of a particle tapped within the lines of force of the earth's outer magnetic field. [After R. Jastrow (1959), *Jour. Geophys. Research,* vol. 64, p. 1794, Figure 4.]

Figure 2.24. The aurora borealis photographed during the winter night in Alaska. (Courtesy of The American Museum—Hayden Planetarium.)

ing antarctic zone surrounds the geomagnetic south pole.*

Light of the aurora is similar to the pale light emitted by fluorescent substances under ultraviolet light ("black light"). The auroral light is, however, produced by the action of electrons and protons trapped within the external magnetic field, as shown in Figure 2.23. These energetic particles excite atoms and molecules of oxygen and nitrogen within the ionosphere, causing light to be emitted. The two high-latitude bands of auroral intensification represent zones in the force field in which the entrapment of energetic particles is most dense. Auroras occur where the force lines reach close to the earth. Here the charged particles are able to contact the gases of the ionosphere. Auroras are most frequent and spectacular during magnetic storms. This correlation is to be expected since the magnetic storm is caused by a heavy influx of solar electrons and protons.

Magnetic storms also create serious disturbances to radio communication. The effect is particularly marked in the higher frequencies used for long-distance radio communication. Because radio transmission depends upon reflection from the layers of the ionosphere, the disruption of those layers by electrons injected from solar sources can make communication difficult or impossible. Disruption is most severe in high latitudes, where the electrons entrapped by the magnetic force lines can reach down most easily to the ionospheric layers.

Also related to magnetic storms are *earth currents*. These are electric currents induced in the surface layer of earth by ionospheric currents. Such earth currents can at times reach intensities sufficient to cause serious voltage fluctuations in power transmission systems and in transoceanic cables.

## THE MAGNETOSPHERE

For purposes of simplicity, the earth's external magnetic field has thus far been described as a symmetrical system of force lines such as that surrounding a bar magnet (see Figure 2.11). If we assume, for purposes of comparison, that the earth's atmosphere extends outward from the earth to a distance equal to

---

* The geomagnetic poles referred to here are not the same as the dip poles described in earlier paragraphs. The geomagnetic poles refer to an ideal, symmetrical dipole field.

twice its own radius, or 8000 mi (13,000 km), it becomes evident that the magnetic field extends far beyond the farthest limits of the atmosphere. Recall that we define the earth's atmosphere as including all gas molecules and atoms of neutral charge that rotate with the earth's rotation. In Chapter 1, the outer limit of the hydrogen layer was given as 6000 mi (10,000 km). The effective limit of the external magnetic field lies perhaps 40,000 to 80,000 mi (64,000 to 130,000 km) from the earth. All of the region within this limit is referred to as the *magnetosphere*.

The simplest geometrical model for the shape of the magnetosphere would be a doughnut-shaped ring surrounding the earth. The plane of the ring would lie in the plane of the magnetic equator, while the earth would occupy the opening in the center of the doughnut.

From information sent to earth by orbiting satellites and space probes it gradually became apparent that the symmetrical shape of the magnetosphere does not exist. Under the pressure of the solar wind, the lines of force are strongly distorted. Between the plasma of the solar wind, with its magnetic force lines radiating spirally from the sun, and the earth's magnetic field there exists a sharply defined boundary, known as the *magnetopause*. Under pressure of the solar wind the magnetopause is pressed close to the earth at the subsolar point (Figure 2.25). Here the distance to the magnetopause is on the order of 10 earth radii (about 40,000 mi, or 64,000 km). Lines of force in this region are crowded together and the magnetic field is intensified. On the opposite side of the earth, in a line pointing away from the sun, the magnetopause is drawn far out from the earth and the force lines are greatly attenuated. The extent of this magnetic "tail" is not known, but the entire shape of the magnetosphere has been described as resembling a comet. Length of the magnetic tail has been estimated to be at least 4 million mi (6 million km) and is possibly vastly longer.

In advance of the magnetopause, on the side close to the sun, there is developed a curved *shock front*. Here the smooth flow of the solar plasma is disrupted and the flow lines become irregular as they diverge and pass around the magnetosphere.

It is interesting to consider whether other planets of the solar system have magnetic fields resembling the earth's. Thus far, instruments

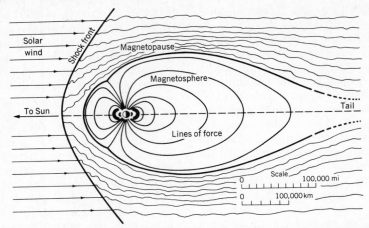

Figure 2.25. Cross section of magnetosphere, showing magnetopause and shock front. [Based on data of C. O. Hines, *Science* (1963), and B. J. O'Brien, *Science* (1965); © 1969, John Wiley & Sons, New York.]

on the *Mariner* space vehicles have detected no magnetic field or indication of a magnetosphere on Mars. Similar space probe data show that a magnetosphere seems to be missing from Venus as well. Both planets have atmospheres that show ionization, i.e., they have ionospheres. There is some suggestion that the ionosphere surrounding Venus acts to deflect the solar wind, causing it to diverge around the planet. The boundary between the ionosphere of Venus and the solar wind has been named the *ionopause*. The period of rotation of Venus is very long (243 days) compared with that of Earth (24 hr) and Mars (24½ hr). If a planetary magnetic field results from dynamo action between a liquid iron core and a surrounding solid rock mantle, the slow speed of rotation of Venus could explain the lack of a magnetic field. The same argument cannot be applied to Mars. However, Mars is a much smaller planet than either Earth or Venus, and we might propose the hypothesis that a liquid iron core does not exist in Mars. Mercury, a still smaller planet and possessed of a slow rotation, would seem to be even less likely to have a magnetic field and a magnetosphere.

Study of radio waves emanating from Jupiter has revealed that this giant planet has a magnetosphere very much larger than that of Earth. As in the case of Earth, the Jovian magnetic polar axis is inclined about 10° with respect to the axis of rotation. However, the magnetic dipole center lies about seven-tenths of the radial distance south of the planetary center (Figure 2.26).

It is now generally thought that the bulk of the interior of Jupiter consists of hydrogen in a very dense liquid or metallic state. There may exist a mantle region of liquid hydrogen comparable to the Earth's rocky mantle and a core region of hydrogen in the metallic state (see Chapter 12). If so, a dynamo mechanism may result from convection within the liquid hydrogen mantle, explaining the off-center location of the dipole.

Lacking an atmosphere, the moon's surface is subject to direct impact of gas ions of the solar wind, as well as to the intensified particle flux from solar flares. To measure this effect astronauts of the *Apollo 10* mission in 1969 placed a sheet of aluminum foil in an orientation such as to receive the impact of the solar wind for a period of 77 min. Analysis made

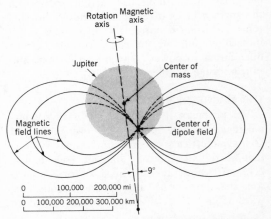

Figure 2.26. Magnetosphere of the planet Jupiter. [After NASA (1967), *Handbook of the Physical Properties of the Planet Jupiter*, Washington, D.C., p. 48, Figure 8-1.]

later showed that the foil had trapped ions of helium-4 at the rate of about 5 to 7 million atoms/cm²/sec. Thus a calculation of the solar-wind flux could be made without the disrupting presence of a magnetosphere. (The moon has no appreciable external magnetic field.)

Analysis of lunar dust collected on the *Apollo 11* mission showed a great enrichment with the noble gases (helium, neon, argon, krypton, and xenon), most of which are thought to have been derived from the solar wind. Analysis of lunar-rock materials has led to the conclusion that the average flux of protons from solar flares has not changed significantly in the past 10 million years (m.y.).

## RADIATION BELTS

In 1958, satellites *Explorer I* and *III*, carrying geiger counters, sent to earth information concerning the existence of a region of intense radioactivity within the magnetosphere. It was soon discovered that two ring-shaped belts of radiation existed, one lying within the other (Figure 2.27). These rings were named the *Van Allen radiation belts,* after the physicist who first described them. An inner belt was found to lie about 2300 mi (2600 km) from the earth's surface; an outer and much more intense belt was found to lie at about 8000 mi to 12,000 mi (13,000 to 19,000 km) distance.

The Van Allen radiation belts represent concentrations of charged particles (protons and electrons) trapped within lines of force of the magnetosphere. These highly energetic particles are injected into the magnetic field from solar ion clouds emitted by solar flares. Intensity of trapped radiation fluctuates over a wide range, being high at times of magnetic storms. Because the Van Allen belts lie relatively close to the earth, as judged in terms of the dimensions of the magnetosphere, they are not appreciably distorted by the force of the solar wind. The belts are shown to scale in relation to the magnetosphere in Figure 2.25. Following intensification as a result of solar-flare injection, the Van Allen belts gradually decrease in intensity as particles escape from the field. Jupiter's magnetosphere also contains belts of trapped energetic particles resembling the Van Allen radiation belts.

The particle flux system sun-earth-space is completed by the escape of trapped electrons and protons from the magnetosphere. The particles make their way toward the tail of the magnetosphere and eventually join the solar wind to travel farther out into the interplanetary medium. Ultimately they reach the intergalactic magnetic field.

## SYSTEMS IN REVIEW

In reviewing the characteristics of the system examined in this chapter, we note that the system is an open one and that flux of matter and energy is a one-way movement from sun, through the earth's magnetosphere, and eventually to outer space. In this respect the system resembles the electromagnetic radiation system. The striking difference between the two lies both in the difference in the physical phenomena themselves (electromagnetic radiation spectrum versus plasma or ion clouds) and in the regularity of the flow. Whereas the solar electromagnetic radiation is characterized by its constancy (witness the solar constant), the emanation of charged particles from the sun take place in irregular bursts of matter from sunspot flares superimposed upon steady flow of plasma from the sun's corona.

Terrestrial cycles of rise and fall of solar radiation follow uniform and symmetrical daily and seasonal cycles resembling simple harmonic motion. The receipts of solar plasma follow an essentially unpredictable timetable, despite the presence of the 11-yr and longer cycles of greater and lesser overall activity.

An interconnection between the two systems is seen in the way in which daily and seasonal cycles of solar radiation cause corresponding

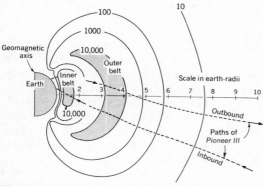

Figure 2.27. A schematic cross section of the Van Allen radiation belts, as deduced from geiger-counter data supplied by satellites *Explorer IV* and *Pioneer III.* Each contour line of equal radiation intensity has a value 10 times that of the next lower line. [After J. A. Van Allen (1959), *Jour. Geophys. Research,* vol. 64, p. 1684.]

cycles of fluctuation in the magnetic field. Except for this link, the two systems can be regarded as entirely independent in action.

We are not yet finished with the earth's magnetic field as a phenomenon of the earth sciences. One of the great scientific discoveries of the past decade or so has been that the earth's magnetic field was subjected to sudden reversals of polarity throughout geologic time. The record of these reversals is firmly held in magnetized mineral particles of rocks and can be read today with instruments much like those used to observe the external magnetic field. The role of magnetic polarity reversals in establishing the time scale of geological events of the past 3 m.y. will be a subject for analysis in Chapter 10.

The earth's magnetic field and its variations comprise an important part of the terrestrial environment, although we as animals are not able to perceive magnetic phenomena directly with our senses. Changes in the magnetic field are thought possibly to be tied in with processes of organic evolution (Chapter 12), and much remains to be learned about the influence of radiation phenomena upon genetic materials. So we see that compared with Venus and Mars, the only planets besides ours thought capable of harboring any life forms, planet Earth has yet another unique environmental quality—that of a dense atmosphere combined with a strongly developed magnetosphere.

### References for further study

Howell, B. F., Jr. (1959), *Introduction to Geophysics,* New York, McGraw-Hill, 399 pp., chap. 22.

Mehlin, T. G. (1959), *Astronomy,* New York, Wiley, 392 pp., chap. 4.

Nelson, J. H., L. Hurwitz, and D. G. Knapp (1962), *Magnetism of the Earth,* NOAA Coast and Geodetic Survey, Publ. 40-1, Washington, D.C., U.S. Govt. Printing Office, 79 pp.

Jacobs, J. A. (1963), *The Earth's Core and Geomagnetism,* Oxford, Pergamon, New York, Macmillan, 137 pp.

Bates, D. R. (1964), *The Planet Earth,* 2nd ed., Oxford, Pergamon, 370 pp., chaps. 6, 14, 17.

### Review questions

1. Describe the sun's chromosphere and corona. What is a solar prominence? What range of temperatures is encountered throughout the corona? What is the solar wind? Of what is it composed, and how fast does it travel?

2. What are sunspots? How may they be observed? Describe the form and dimensions of a typical large sunspot. How long do sunspots last, and how do they appear to move? What kind of activity do sunspots represent? Describe the sunspot cycle in terms of period and numbers of spots.

3. What is a solar flare? Compare the occurrence of solar flares with that of sunspots. How are the two phenomena related?

4. Describe the outward flow paths of solar plasma in space. How does the sun's rotation influence the form of the paths? How far out into space does the solar wind travel?

5. Give a brief historical review of the progress of early studies of the earth's magnetism. What was the motivation behind much of this investigation?

6. Describe the earth's magnetic field. Define the magnetic poles and equator. Relate the geomagnetic axis to the earth's axis of rotation. How does the magnetic needle of a compass behave with respect to the magnetic poles?

7. Define the magnetic elements of inclination, declination, and intensity. How is a dip needle constructed and used? Of what importance are maps showing compass declination? In what units is magnetic intensity stated?

8. What is meant by *secular change* in the magnetic elements? Describe observed changes in declination and dip. Suggest a possible cause for such secular changes.

9. Describe the earth's core and mantle, giving approximate dimensions. Of what substances are the core and mantle composed, and what is their physical state? What theory has been proposed to explain the earth's magnetism? How can this theory also explain secular changes in magnetic elements?

10. What are transient variations in the external magnetic field? Describe and explain the daily variations in compass declination. Is an annual cycle also observed? Describe the systems of electric currents in the ionosphere.

11. What is the nature of magnetic disturbances and storms? Describe a typical magnetogram for a severe magnetic storm. How long do such storms last? Relate magnetic disturbances to solar flares.

12. Describe the aurora and relate its occurrence to solar flares. In what geographical regions is the aurora most intense? Why? What other side effects are related to magnetic storms?

13. Describe the arrangement of lines of force of the external magnetic field in space. What is the magnetosphere? How large is it,

and how is its shape related to the solar wind? What is the magnetopause? the shock front? the tail? Do Venus, Mars, and Jupiter show evidence of having magnetic fields? Explain the observed phenomena (or lack of any) in terms of size and internal structure of these planets.

14. Does the moon have a magnetic field? Why is the moon's surface a good place on which to study the solar wind and related phenomena? What is the scientific importance of such observations?

15. In what way were the Van Allen radiation belts discovered? Describe these belts. Of what kind of matter are these belts composed, and what is its source?

16. Describe in broad terms the system of particle flux from sun to earth to space. Compare it with the electromagnetic radiation system described in Chapter 1. In what ways is the earth's external magnetic field a factor in the environment of Man and other life forms on the earth's surface?

# chapter 3
# kinetic energy system of masses in motion: planets and satellites

In this chapter we view Earth* as a planet in the setting of the solar system. Members of the solar system, taken as discrete masses in motion in space, represent a system of inherited kinetic energy. We shall first examine this system in its present-day condition, with emphasis upon the various solid bodies involved, their distribution in space, and their motions.

Final consideration of the geological nature and origin of the solar system is deferred to Chapters 11 and 12. History of the Earth and Moon involves a process that has almost ceased to act: the infall of particles under gravitational attraction to build the members of the solar system to their present dimensions. The energy of gravitational collapse of matter and impacts by infall of discrete objects constitutes another system, which can be viewed as a transient phase in the life history of a star with

its planets. That phase of growth is essentially over for our Sun.

We see now only an apparently unchanging arrangement of solid bodies in orbital motions about the Sun and about one another. Within the span of human history, these motions continue with no appreciable change. Nothing within the experience of Man is so completely reliable, so exact in its schedule, and so beyond the power of Man to alter, as the apparent motions of the Sun, Moon, planets, and stars. Of all natural phenomena, the mechanical system of large objects in motion in the solar system comes closest to representing an exact equilibrium state without change. Yet it is a postulate of systems theory that states must change with time. The most convincing sign which we, as casual observers of nature, can read to tell us that the system of celestial motions must be running down is in the ocean tides. Any person can observe the unceasing rhythm of rise and fall of enormous masses of water, as well as their horizontal motions in

---

* In this chapter Earth, Moon, and Sun are capitalized to be consistent with the names of the other planets.

tidal currents. Such motions involve friction, both within the moving water and at its contact with the solid bottom over which the water moves. Friction transforms kinetic energy into heat, which in turn moves out of the system by conduction and longwave radiation; the heat is eventually lost to outer space. It can be generalized that the motion of celestial bodies, while under mutual gravitational attraction, inevitably sets up the tidal flexing, which dissipates energy. Assuming that the masses remain constant, their velocities of motion must gradually diminish. Orbits must therefore change with time. One might be led to reason that, unless other events intervene (such as internal changes within the Sun), the ultimate demise of the kinetic energy system of masses in orbital motion must be the infall of all members of the solar system into the Sun.

## SOLAR-SYSTEM MEMBERS

Members of the solar system fall into two classes. First there are the *planets* and related planetary objects, all of which revolve in orbits about the Sun, i.e., their orbits are *heliocentric* (Greek *helios,* for Sun). These objects include the nine major planets. In addition there are the asteroids (often referred to as *minor planets*), comets, and meteoroid swarms, discussed in Chapter 11. The second class of objects consists of the *satellites,* which revolve in orbits about the planets. Satellites can also be referred to simply as *moons.*

An observation of fundamental importance in understanding the solar system is that the orbits of the planetary bodies and satellites lie approximately in the same plane, which is essentially the same as the plane of the Sun's equator. Rotation upon an axis is also a characteristic motion observed in the planets and Earth's Moon. With one outstanding exception (Uranus), the direction of rotation of the planets is the same for all, and their axes of rotation are more or less perpendicular to the orbital plane. This overall uniformity in revolution and rotation throughout the solar system could scarcely be the result of pure chance.

## THE MAJOR PLANETS

The nine major planets are commonly divided into two groups. The *inner,* or *terrestrial,* planets, of which there are four, lie closest to the Sun. In order of distance outward from the Sun, they are *Mercury, Venus, Earth,* and *Mars* (Table 3.1). These four planets are of the same general order of diameter and

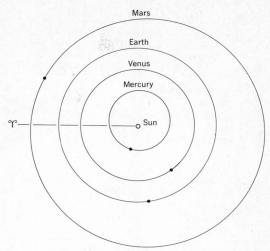

Figure 3.1. Orbits of the four planets near the Sun. The black dots represent perihelion points. [After E. A. Fath (1934), *Elements of Astronomy,* New York, McGraw-Hill.]

density. Their orbits appear highly circular as plotted to scale in Figure 3.1. As a group, they lie relatively close to the Sun and are subject to rather high surface temperatures from direct solar radiation.

The outer planets, five in number, are *Jupiter, Saturn, Uranus, Neptune,* and *Pluto.* Orbits of these planets are shown in Figure 3.2. The orbits of the outer planets are nearly circular, except for that of Pluto. The eccentricity of Pluto's orbit is such that it passes

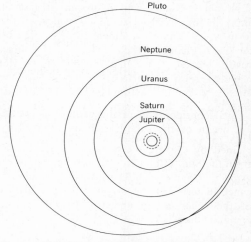

Figure 3.2. Orbits of the outer planets. The innermost circle represents Mars' orbit, and the dashed circle represents the zone of asteroid orbits. Pluto will not collide with Neptune because Pluto's orbit is inclined more the 17° with respect to the ecliptic.

Table 3.1. THE PRINCIPAL PLANETS

| Name | Distance from Sun (mi × 10⁶) | (km × 10⁶) | Astronomical Units | Eccentricity of Orbit | Inclination to Ecliptic | Period of Revolution Sidereal | Diameter (mi × 10³) | (km × 10³) |
|------|------|------|------|------|------|------|------|------|
| *The terrestrial planets* **Inner planets** | | | | | | Days | | |
| Mercury | 36 | 58 | 0.387 | 0.206 | 7°00′ | 88 | 3 | 4.9 |
| Venus | 67 | 108 | 0.723 | 0.007 | 3°24′ | 225 | 7.6 | 12.2 |
| Earth | 93 | 150 | 1.000 | 0.017 | 0°00′ | 365¼ | 7.9 | 12.7 |
| Mars | 142 | 228 | 1.524 | 0.093 | 1°51′ | 687 | 4.2 | 6.7 |
| *The great planets* **Outer planets** | | | | | | Years | | |
| Jupiter | 484 | 779 | 5.20 | 0.048 | 1°18′ | 12 | 89 | 142 |
| Saturn | 886 | 1430 | 9.55 | 0.056 | 2°30′ | 29½ | 72 | 115 |
| Uranus | 1780 | 2870 | 19.2 | 0.047 | 0°46′ | 84 | 29 | 47.4 |
| Neptune | 2790 | 4500 | 30.1 | 0.008 | 1°47′ | 165 | 28 | 44.6 |
| Pluto | 3670 | 5900 | 39.4 | 0.250 | 17°17′ | 248 | 3.5(?) | 5.6(?) |

within the orbit of Neptune. On the basis of its small size, Pluto is quite unlike the other four, which can be usefully grouped into a class designated the *Great Planets.*

Drawn to scale against a part of the Sun's disk, the nine planets show strikingly their grouping into the terrestrial four, the great four, and Pluto in a class by itself (Figure 3.3). Little is known of the diameter, mass, or density of Pluto, so that its group affiliation is uncertain.

Densities of the four Great Planets are strikingly low in comparison with those of the terrestrial planets. Whereas the latter are composed almost entirely of silicate rock and metal, the Great Planets are believed to have liquid hydrogen cores and large volumes of ammonia, methane, and hydrogen in gaseous atmospheres, as well as much water in the form of ice. The gravitational force exerted by the Great Planets at their surface is, of course, vastly greater than that of the terrestrial planets. Prevailing surface temperatures of the Great Planets are extremely low, in contrast with those of the terrestrial planets, and range from −216° F (−138° C) on Jupiter to −330° F (−201° C) on Neptune. Coldness is explained by the great distance of these bodies from the Sun. (Refer to planetary temperatures given in Chapter 1.) These facts have significance in terms of the origin and early history of the solar system and will be referred to again in Chapter 12.

## LAWS OF PLANETARY MOTION

The orbit of each planetary object is an *ellipse,* within which the Sun occupies one

*focus* (Figure 3.4). The ellipse contains a *major axis,* its longest diameter, and a *minor axis,* its shortest diameter. These axes are, of course, at right angles and bisect one another. To any point on the ellipse there can be drawn a line from each focus. Each of these lines is a *radius vector.* A geometrical property of the ellipse is that the sum of the two radius vectors is a constant. This fact can be put to use in drawing an ellipse. If a loop of thread is passed around two pins, one representing each focus, and a pencil point is held so as to keep the thread taut, the point will describe an ellipse as it is moved around the pins (Figure 3.5).

The degree of flattening of an ellipse (i.e., the degree to which it departs from a circle) depends upon the relative separation of the foci. In the true circle, the foci become a single point at the center of the circle. In terms of planetary orbits, the degree to which the elliptical orbit departs from a circle is known as the *eccentricity.* If the distance from one focus to the center of the ellipse is designated *c,* and one-half the length of the semimajor axis by the letter *a,* the eccentricity *e* of the ellipse is shown below and also in Figure 3.6.

$$e = \frac{c}{a}$$

Table 3.1 gives the values of orbital eccentricities for the nine planets. Orbits of Venus and Neptune are nearly circular. Orbits of Mercury and Pluto are most highly eccentric. Notice that the inclinations of the orbital planes of Mercury and Pluto also have the greatest values.

Three laws of planetary motion bear the

Table 3.1.   *(Continued)*

| Mass, Relative to Earth | Mean Density (gm/cm³) | Period of Rotation | Number of Moons |
|---|---|---|---|
| 0.06 | 5.0 | 58ᵈ17ʰ | 0 |
| 0.81 | 5.1 | 243ᵈ | 0 |
| 1.00 | 5.5 | 23ʰ56ᵐ | 1 |
| 0.11 | 3.9 | 24ʰ37ᵐ | 2 |
| 318 | 1.3 | 9ʰ50ᵐ | 12 |
| 95 | 0.7 | 10ʰ14ᵐ | 10 |
| 15 | 1.7 | 10ʰ42ᵐ | 5 |
| 17 | 1.6 | 15ʰ48ᵐ | 2 |
| 0.9 | ? | 6ᵈ | 0 |

name of Johannes Kepler (1571–1630), the great German astronomer, whose calculations of the planetary orbits were based upon many accurate measurements made at an observatory near Prague, Bohemia, by Kepler's predecessor, Tycho Brahe. Almost a century earlier, Copernicus had proposed a model of the solar system in which the planetary orbits were shown as circles. Copernicus' values for the radii of these orbits (Mercury through Saturn only) were remarkably close to the true values for mean radius of each orbit. It remained for Kepler to discover that the orbits are elliptical.

Kepler's first law states that the orbit of each planet is an ellipse and that the Sun is located at one focus of the ellipse. His second law states that a planet moves with varying speed in its orbit, such that the radius vector sweeps over equal areas in equal intervals of time. The geometrical significance of the second law is illustrated in Figure 3.7. Here the area of an elliptical orbit has been divided into sectors of equal area by 12 radius vectors. For Earth, each sector represents a month of the year, assuming all months to be of exactly equal length. The planet in its orbit must cover the distance $MN$ in the same time period as it covers the distance $PQ$, since areas $A$ and $B$ are equal. Obviously, the orbital speed is faster from $M$ to $N$ than from $P$ to $Q$.

Points at which the major axis cuts the ellipse mark the points at which the planet is closest to the Sun and farthest from the Sun. These positions are known as *perihelion* and *aphelion*, respectively (Figure 3.7). The speed of the planet is greatest at perihelion and least at aphelion. The difference in maximum and

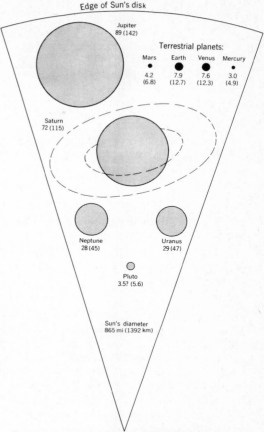

Figure 3.3. Relative diameters of the Sun and planets. Figures give diameters in thousands of miles, with thousands of kilometers in parentheses. [After C. C. Wylie (1942), *Astronomy, Maps, and Weather,* New York, Harper & Row.]

minimum speeds is greater as the eccentricity of the orbit is larger.

Kepler's third law, which he formulated nine years after the first two, is sometimes designated as the *harmonic law*. It states that for any two planets the squares of the periods of revolution are proportional to the cubes of their mean distances from the Sun. In the following equation, the subscripts $a$ and $b$ denote any two planets, $P$ is the period of revolution, and $R$ the distance:

$$\frac{P_a{}^2}{P_b{}^2} = \frac{R_a{}^3}{R_b{}^3}$$

In testing the law, calculations can be greatly simplified by using Earth as one planet, with its period of revolution taken as unity (one Earth year) and its distance from Sun as unity (one

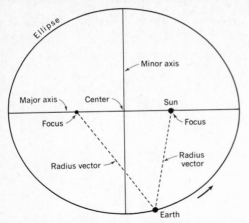

Figure 3.4. The orbit of every planet is an ellipse in which the sun occupies one focus.

astronomical unit). The equation then simplifies to:

$$P = \sqrt{R^3}$$

where $P$ is the period of the planet in Earth years and $R$ is the planet's distance from Sun in astronomical units. (One astronomical unit is about 93 million mi, or 150 million km.)

Referring to Table 3.1, and using the data for Neptune, we find that distance $R$ is 30.1 astronomical units. Substituting in the simplified formula above,

$$P = \sqrt{(30.1)^3} = \sqrt{27,270.9} = 165 \text{ approx.}$$

The calculated period agrees closely with the observed value given in Table 3.1.

Strictly, Kepler's laws are correct only for the case of a single planet in relation to the Sun. Actually, the gravitational influence of other planets deflects a given planet slightly from its ideal elliptical orbit.

As a practical consequence of the third law, we see that the periods of revolution of the planets range from 88 days for Mercury, which lies closest to the Sun, to 248 yr for Pluto, the most distant.

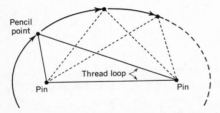

Figure 3.5. An ellipse is easily constructed using a loop of thread.

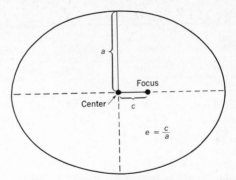

Figure 3.6. Definition of eccentricity of an ellipse.

## GRAVITATION AND CENTRIPETAL FORCE

Kepler based his three laws solely upon observations of planetary motion. A valid physical explanation for elliptical orbits and varying speed was yet to come. Galileo (1564–1642), a contemporary of Kepler, was investigating the principles of the pendulum and the inertia and acceleration of falling bodies. Upon the foundations which Galileo had laid, Sir Isaac Newton developed his laws of gravitation and motion, published in 1687 under the title of *Philosophiae naturalis principia mathematica* (Mathematical Principles of Natural Philosophy).

The key to planetary motion lies in the *law of gravitation*, which states that any two bodies attract each other with a force that is proportional to the product of their masses and inversely proportional to the square of the distance between them. Where $M_1$ and $M_2$ represent the two masses, $R$ the separating distance, and $F$ the force of gravity:

$$F = \frac{GM_1 M_2}{R^2}$$

The term $G$ in the above equation is the universal constant of gravitation. Although $G$ has

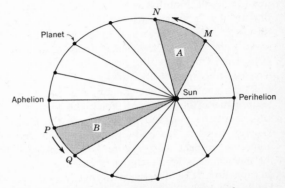

Figure 3.7. An ellipse divided into 12 equal areas.

been precisely determined, its numerical value is of no interest in our discussion.

Take the case of a small object whirled in a horizontal circle while attached by a cord to a fixed central point. (The same principle applies to any small element of mass of a rotating wheel or sphere.) Newton's first law of motion states that every body continues in a state of rest or of uniform motion in a straight line unless forced to change that direction by some external force. Accordingly, the weight tends to follow a tangent, straight-line path at every instant. Such a tangential path is shown in Figure 3.8 for points $P_1$ and $P_2$. However, tangential flight is prevented by a *centripetal force* acting as tension in the radial cord.

In the case of a planet, the force of gravitational attraction replaces the centripetal force in the example cited above. The gravitational force constantly deflects the planet from its straight tangential path.

Let us attempt to follow through the verification of Kepler's third law in terms of Newton's law of gravitation. Centripetal force, $F_c$, is defined as the product of the mass times the square of the velocity, divided by the radius, expressed as follows:

$$(1) \qquad F_c = \frac{M_1 V^2}{R}$$

where $M_1$ is the mass of the planet. Because the gravitational force plays the role of an equal centripetal force in holding the planet in its circular orbit, we can set the equation for centripetal force equal to that for gravitational force, as follows:

$$(2) \qquad \frac{M_1 V^2}{R} = \frac{GM_1 M_2}{R^2}$$

where $M_2$ is the mass of the Sun.

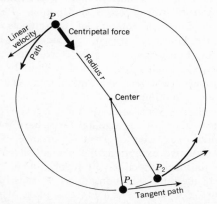

Figure 3.8. Centripetal force acts upon an object in a circular path of motion.

To proceed further, we will need to make some substitutions of equivalent terms. Recall that Kepler's law refers to the "periods of revolution" of the planets. Let $T$ stand for period of revolution. When an object moves in a circle, its period, $T$, is equal to the circumference of the circle, $2\pi R$, divided by its linear velocity, $V$. Therefore we write:

$$(3) \qquad T = \frac{2\pi R}{V}$$

Solving for $V$ in the above equation we obtain:

$$(4) \qquad V = \frac{2\pi R}{T} \text{ and } V^2 = \frac{4\pi^2 R^2}{T^2}$$

We are now ready to substitute the equivalent term for $V^2$ into the left-hand side of the equation (2), giving the following:

$$(5) \qquad \frac{M_1 4\pi^2 R^2}{T^2 R} = \frac{GM_1 M_2}{R^2}$$

Collecting "$R$'s" and canceling "$M_1$'s" on both sides, this simplifies to:

$$(6) \qquad 4\pi R^3 = GM_2 T^2$$

For a given planet only $R$ and $T$ are simultaneously variable quantities.

So we see that the cube of the radius is proportional to the square of the period, as stated in Kepler's third law. To obtain this agreement with Kepler's work we have assumed, as he did, that a planet revolves around the center of the Sun, rather than around the common center of gravity of both planet and Sun. (The revolution of two bodies about a common center of gravity is discussed in later paragraphs.)

## ANGULAR MOMENTUM AND ELLIPTICAL ORBITS

Any mass in circular motion possesses a property known as *angular momentum*. We can think of the word *momentum* as describing the "quantity of motion." For a body moving in a straight line, momentum is defined as the product of the mass and the velocity ($M \cdot V$). Angular momentum, $L$, which applies to a body traveling in a curved path, is equal to the product of its linear momentum and the radius of the arc in which it is moving:

$$L = M \cdot V \cdot R$$

If the two bodies are moving under their mutual gravitational attraction, they will both orbit around their common center of gravity, or *barycenter*, which is located on a line joining their individual centers of gravity at a distance from each of them which is inversely proportional to their respective masses. If no energy is added to, or taken away from, the system, the angular momentum of the system must remain constant, a principle known as the *law of conservation of angular momentum.* Since the Sun is more than a thousand times as massive as the heaviest of the planets (Jupiter), a very close approximation to the actual situation is achieved if we consider the Sun to be stationary and attribute all the motion to the planet. Thus the angular momentum of any planet must remain constant while it orbits the Sun. However, there can be continual changes in both the velocity and radius, provided that one change exactly compensates for the other. Let us apply this principle to the elliptical orbits of the planets.

When a planet approaches perihelion, the radius of curvature of its path is diminishing. In compensation, the linear velocity of the planet is increasing. When the planet approaches aphelion, the radius is lengthening, while the velocity is decreasing. Angular momentum thus is kept constant at all times. Here we have the explanation of Earth's greater orbital speed near perihelion and its lower speed near aphelion.

## ANGULAR MOMENTUM OF THE SOLAR SYSTEM

A planet possesses angular momentum both because of its revolution about the Sun (heliocentric motion) and its rotation upon an axis. The satellites also possess angular momentum because of corresponding circular motions of revolution and rotation. The Sun, although fixed at the center of the solar system, has angular momentum because of its rotation, a phenomenon discussed in Chapter 2.

The mass and angular momentum of the Sun and of each of the first eight planets are given in Table 3.2 in terms of percentage of the total.* At once we see that the Sun has almost all of the mass, but only a very small proportion of the total angular momentum. The angular momentum lies largely with the great planets by virtue of their large orbital radii and great linear velocities, combined with their

* Inclusion of Pluto would not change this picture greatly. The data of Table 3.2 represent the known facts at a time when they were used to refute the nebular hypothesis of solar-system origin, discussed in Chapter 12.

Table 3.2.  MASS AND ANGULAR MOMENTUM OF SUN AND PLANETS

|  | Mass (percentage of total) | Angular Momentum (percentage of total) |
| --- | --- | --- |
| Sun | 99.86590 | 2.7423 |
| Mercury | 0.00001 | 0.0017 |
| Venus | 0.00025 | 0.0576 |
| Earth | 0.00030 | 0.0827 |
| Mars | 0.00003 | 0.0112 |
| Jupiter | 0.09558 | 59.9273 |
| Saturn | 0.02852 | 24.1924 |
| Uranus | 0.00430 | 5.2845 |
| Neptune | 0.00511 | 7.7003 |
| Totals | 100.00000 | 100.0000 |

relatively large masses and rapid rotation. Jupiter alone has almost 60% of the momentum of the whole system. Even if the planet Pluto, the asteroids, and other minor objects are taken into account, the Sun has 98.85% of the total mass, but only about 2% of the angular momentum. In Chapter 12 it will be noted that the distribution of angular momentum within the solar system must be explained by any acceptable hypothesis of origin of the solar system.

## PLANETARY ROTATION

The periods of rotation of six planets (all but Venus, Mercury, and Pluto) are surprisingly similar, considering the vast differences in diameter and mass (Table 3.1). The rotational periods of Earth and Mars differ by less than an hour; those of the four great planets fall between 9 and 16 hr. The period of rotation of Mercury is much longer (59 days); that of Venus is very much longer (243 days). Pluto's rotational period has been established as 6.4 days, but the direction cannot be determined. Except for Uranus, Venus, and possibly Pluto, the directions of rotation of the planets are uniform, i.e., they turn counterclockwise when viewed from a point in space above the north polar axis. Such motion is referred to by astronomers as *direct* motion; the reverse is *retrograde* motion.

From the standpoint of the origin of the solar system, the foregoing facts have been considered as being of great importance. Note that with two exceptions the planets all rotate in a uniform direction, all revolve about the Sun in the same direction, all have orbits lying within a few degrees of a common plane. These facts strongly suggest that the members of the solar system had a common mechanism of origin, by which all received the same directions of rotational impulse. Were this not so, we might expect to find the planets revolving in a variety of orbital planes and at least some of them revolving and rotating in opposite directions from others.

Effects of rate of planetary rotation are of great importance in surface environments. Centrifugal force (the opposite and equal force to centripetal force) increases as rotation rate increases. One effect of centrifugal force is to cause the surface gravity of the planet to be slightly reduced, an effect that decreases with distance from the equator. On Earth, for example, gravity at the equator is reduced by rotation to an amount about 1/289 less than gravity at the poles. Another effect of rotation is to deform the planet into an *oblate ellipsoid of revolution,* making the equatorial diameter larger and the polar axis shorter, than for a sphere of equivalent volume (Figure 3.9).

Yet another product of rotation, is the *Coriolis effect,* which causes objects in motion to be deflected toward the right hand in the direction of motion in the Northern Hemisphere. (See p. 78.) The results in terms of atmospheric and oceanic circulation are most profound on planet Earth. Coriolis effect must also operate on other rotating planets, and because it is directly proportional to the angular velocity, which is measured by rotation rate, it will be highly important in atmospheric motions on the great planets, whose angular velocities are greater than the Earth's. Venus, with its very slow rotation, will have an extremely weak Coriolis effect affecting its thick, dense atmosphere.

## THE INNER PLANETS

A brief description of the characteristics (mostly astronomical) of each planet helps us to develop an appreciation of the uniqueness of environment which we enjoy on planet Earth. Study of the geological character and origin of the planets will be deferred until a foundation of geological principles is built.

Mercury, fourth brightest of the planets, is the closest planet to the Sun, with an orbital radius only two-fifths that of Earth. In looking over the facts about Mercury in Table 3.1 note that this planet is unusual in having a high orbital inclination from the ecliptic (7°) and a high degree of eccentricity (0.206).

Mercury probably has no appreciable atmosphere because its surface gravity is only about three-tenths that of Earth, and the escape velocity is thus only 2.7 mi/sec (4.3 km/sec). Mercury's rate of rotation is very slow, and a day there lasts for 59 Earth days. Consequently, on the side of Mercury which happens to be facing the Sun, where intense and prolonged heating prevails, gases would be activated to high velocities of molecular travel and would readily escape into space. It is estimated that, in perihelion, surface temperatures on Mercury rise to perhaps 790° F (420° C), a value exceeding the melting points of tin and lead. In contrast, temperatures on the shadowed side of Mercury may fall nearly to absolute zero. No other planet has so vast a temperature range on its surface. Although little can be discerned of the surface features of Mercury, it is reasonable to suppose that it resembles our Moon in having an extremely rough terrain of dark color, possibly with numerous craters, and with no evidences of erosion processes. Mercury can be assumed to be completely devoid of any forms of life. The average density of Mercury (5.0) is only a little less than that of Earth, suggesting that, like Earth, Mercury has a core of iron.

Venus, the most brilliant object in the sky except for the Sun and Moon, approaches closer to Earth than any other planet; a distance of some 26 million mi (42 × 10⁶ km) separates the two bodies at the minimum separation. The maximum distance is about 160 million mi (260 × 10⁶ km). As a result of this sixfold difference in separating distances, Venus seems to change greatly in apparent

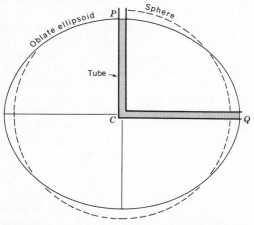

Figure 3.9. Fluid in radial tubes, connected to one another at the earth's center, would stand at different heights because of rotation.

diameter throughout its orbit (Figures 3.10 and 3.11). Moreover, the changing positions of Venus relative to Earth and Sun result in a series of phases of illumination ranging from a full disk to a thin crescent (Figures 3.10 and 3.11). Observation of these phases showed Galileo that Venus must revolve about the Sun. Consequently, his discovery gave strong support to the Copernican theory of solar-system motions.

From the standpoint of diameter, mass, density, and length of year, Venus more closely resembles Earth than any other planet does. Moreover, Venus has a dense atmosphere, held by a gravitational force almost as strong as that of Earth. Atmospheric pressure at the surface of Venus is about 100 times as great as that on Earth. One proof of the presence of an atmosphere on Venus is that at crescent phase a band of light extends entirely around the full circle, showing that sunlight is refracted around the sphere by a thick layer of gases (Figure 3.10).

Data secured in 1967 by space vehicle *Venera 4* showed that carbon dioxide constitutes 90% to 95% of the atmosphere of Venus. Oxygen has been found in substantial quantities, whereas the presence of water vapor is at most barely detectable. Nitrogen has not been detected. Water was probably present on Venus at an early stage in the planet's history, but

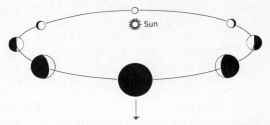

Figure 3.11. The orbit of Venus is shown here in perspective, as if viewed from a point above the north pole of Earth. See Figure 3.10 for corresponding photographs. (Used by permission of the publishers from F. L. Whipple, *Earth, Moon, and Planets,* 3rd ed., Cambridge, Mass., Harvard University Press. Copyright 1941, 1963, 1968 by the President and Fellows of Harvard College.)

hydrogen atoms could not be held to the planet and most escaped into space.

Because of the presence of some kind of fine, suspended particles in its atmosphere—possibly clouds of dust particles or ice crystals—Venus reflects sunlight brilliantly, and little can be seen of its surface. Viewed in ultraviolet light, Venus shows slowly moving dark patches that may be cloud masses. Although water in all forms is believed to be absent from the planet's solid surface, it has been postulated that the patches are clouds of water droplets.

Temperatures on the surface of Venus have been obtained from temperature analysis of radio waves. An average value of 500° C (950° F) was announced in 1968. Despite the almost complete absence of water, a deficiency that would exclude the possibility of life forms such as those found on Earth, Venus has an environment in which human beings, if located on the dark side and suitably protected from high atmospheric pressure, otherwise might be able to survive for limited periods.

Until radar was developed, it was practically impossible to determine the rotation period of Venus. Recent studies of reflected radar signals have yielded a period of 243 days, which is somewhat longer than the planet's period of revolution of 225 days. Furthermore, the rotation of Venus is slowly clockwise, or retrograde, in contrast to the counterclockwise, or direct, rotation of the other planets. The cause of this unusual rotation is taken up in later paragraphs.

Passing over planet Earth, we come to Mars, the first of the planets to be found in an orbit larger than that of Earth. Little more than half as large in diameter as Earth, the mass of Mars

Figure 3.10. The planet Venus photographed at five different phases, showing its true relative sizes at various distances from Earth. Compare with Figure 3.11 to determine position in orbit. Note that in the largest view the atmospheric ring is complete. (Lowell Observatory photograph.)

is only one-tenth that of Earth and the surface gravity only about one-third (Table 3.1).

Reddish in hue, Mars has definite surface features, which were recognized and speculated about as early as the mid-seventeenth century (Figure 3.12). Study of these features has enabled astronomers to measure with precision the period of axial rotation of Mars, which is about 24½ hr, only a little longer than that of Earth. Also, the plane of Mars' equator is inclined about 25° with respect to its orbital plane, a value very close to Earth's inclination of 23½°.

As seen from Earth, markings on the surface of Mars consist of dark areas (termed *seas*) and light areas (termed *deserts*) in a permanent pattern. Much speculation arose over the significance of recurrent dark markings, which seemed to form an intersecting network of narrow bands. These were early interpreted as canals, their apparent straightness suggesting that they were artificially produced by Martians, possibly to serve as irrigation canals.

Our knowledge of the surface of Mars has been enormously enhanced by data obtained by *Mariner 6* and *7* spacecraft, which passed close to that planet in 1969 and sent back many detailed photographs of the Martian surface. (See Figure 11.25). Extensive cratered areas, resembling the lunar surface, were photographed. No evidence was obtained to suggest the presence of the supposed canals, or of any forms of life.

Of great interest in the earth sciences is the seasonal growth and disappearance of white *polar caps* on Mars. *Mariner 7* spacecraft photographs provided new and detailed information on this remarkable phenomenon. Like Earth, Mars has a winter season in one hemisphere while it is summer in the opposite hemisphere. The polar cap grows during the autumn season of that hemisphere, spreading equatorward to a maximum in mid-winter, then receding with the approach of spring. (Note that the Martian year lasts 687 Earth days, or nearly twice as long as an Earth year.) Until recently it was assumed that the polar caps were a form of snow or frost, possibly similar to the ice crystals in snow or hoarfrost on Earth, but carbon dioxide in solid form (dry ice) is now regarded as the most probable substance of the polar caps.

The colors and color changes on Mars are remarkable. The dark areas are of green, blue-green, or gray color, which show a seasonal browning to earth-red colors (brick-red to ocher) and may represent barren areas of weathered rock or soil rich in hydroxides of iron. Note that the average density of Mars is 3.9, a value well below that of Earth. This fact suggests that Mars may have a proportionally smaller core of iron and proportionally greater volume of rock.

The atmosphere of Mars is very thin. Atmospheric pressure at the surface is about one-hundredth that at the Earth's surface. Carbon dioxide is the principal component of the Martian atmosphere. Nitrogen has not been de-

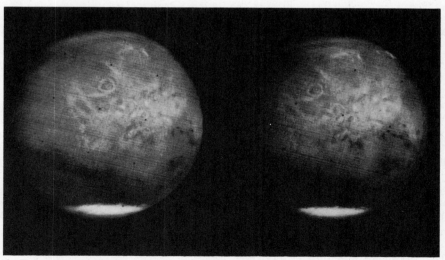

Figure 3.12. Far-encounter photographs of Mars taken from *Mariner 7* spacecraft at distances between 267,000 and 280,000 mi (430,000 and 450,000 km). The dark spot at upper left is *Nix Olympia*. This photo pair can be viewed stereoscopically for three-dimensional effect. (NASA photograph.)

tected, and the amount of free oxygen is very small. Water vapor has been measured in extremely small quantity. Perhaps there was originally much more oxygen, some or most of which may have been taken up by chemical rock weathering. Although there now is little water in any form on Mars, there was probably once much more. Some of the original water may have combined with minerals to be held there permanently. Escape of hydrogen would have been favored by the small gravity of Mars (only one-third that of Earth); the escape velocity is only 3.1 mi/sec (5.1 km/sec).

Surface air temperatures on Mars average much lower than on Earth because of greater distance from the Sun. Data from *Mariner 4* spacecraft gave surface-temperature readings at middle latitudes of −171° F (−113° C) for a winter day, −36° F (−38° C) for a summer night. However, in equatorial latitudes under direct rays of the Sun, surface temperatures may rise over 85° F (30° C). Temperature measurements based on the infrared radiation of Mars substantiate these observations and suggest a total daily temperature range of 200 F° (112 C°) in Mars' equatorial region.

Of all the planets Mars would seem to offer the greatest possibility of harboring life, but the life would have to be adapted to a scanty supply of oxygen and water and to the low density of atmosphere and small gravitational attraction. As far as interplanetary travel is concerned, Mars would perhaps be the most favorable of the planets for human survival, but a visitor from Earth would have to provide his own life-support system.

Between the orbits of Mars and Jupiter lies the belt of *asteroids,* mostly small objects numbering in the tens of thousands. The asteroids are described in Chapter 11 in their geological context.

### THE GREAT PLANETS

Strikingly unlike the terrestrial planets are the four great planets: Jupiter, Saturn, Uranus, and Neptune. Even the smallest of these, Neptune, has almost 4 times the diameter and 15 times the mass of Earth; whereas the giant of the group, Jupiter, has 11 times the diameter and 300 times the mass of Earth. Apart from their size, a second striking difference in these two groups of planets is that of density (Table 3.1). The least dense is Saturn (0.7), about one-eighth the density of Earth and less than three-fourths that of liquid water. The other

three have densities of 1.3 to 1.7, values only one-fourth to one-third that of Earth.

A third striking difference in the two groups of planets is the extremely low prevailing temperature on the surfaces of the great planets, ranging from −216° F (−138° C) on Jupiter to −330° F (−201° C) on Neptune. A fourth striking difference is in composition, discussed further in Chapter 12. Whereas the four terrestrial planets are probably all composed of a rock mantle surrounding an iron core and have either no atmosphere or atmospheres of almost insignificant mass, the four great planets have massive atmospheres of methane, ammonia, hydrogen, and water. These volatile substances make up most of the mass of each planet.

Jupiter appears through the telescope as a somewhat flattened disk with dark and light bands extending across the surface in rough parallelism with the planet's equator (Figure 3.13). The bands are made irregular by cloud-like patches that, if observed over a period of days or weeks, show changing patterns. Apparently the bands are produced by systems of flow in Jupiter's atmosphere analogous to Earth's planetary wind systems. Relatively rapid rotation of Jupiter causes the planet to be appreciably oblate.

Spectroscopic analysis of the light from Jupiter shows that the atmosphere is composed largely of ammonia ($NH_3$) and methane

Figure 3.13. The planet Jupiter, photographed in blue light with the 200-in. (500-cm) Palomar telescope, shows a large red spot. To the upper right is seen the satellite Ganymede, its shadow visible as a black spot near the planet's upper edge. (The Hale Observatories.)

(CH$_4$). The abundance of hydrogen in these gases suggests that the planet as a whole has hydrogen as the predominant constituent. Jupiter may have a core of hydrogen in an extremely dense state. It has been inferred that free hydrogen gas comprises most of the atmosphere beneath the outer gaseous layer of ammonia and methane. All the planet's original oxygen may have been combined with hydrogen to produce water, possibly forming an ice layer beneath the free hydrogen.

Saturn is well known to all through its distinctive *rings,* which are seen as concentric bands of light and dark color lying in a very thin zone in the plane of the planet's equator (Figure 3.14). The rings consist largely of individual fragments of ice, each revolving about the planet in an orbit as if each were an independent satellite of the planet. The particles may be on the order of the size of gravel, or coarse silt; altogether they constitute not more than one-millionth of Saturn's mass.

Although believed to be generally similar to Jupiter in composition and structure, Saturn's proportion of hydrogen must be larger to yield the low average density of only 0.7.

Uranus and Neptune are nearly twins so far as diameter and mass are concerned. Because of their great distances from Earth these planets are rather difficult to observe and show little or no surface marking. Under spectroscopic analysis both planets show methane to be the dominant atmospheric constituent, whereas ammonia appears only in a trace. The dominance of methane over ammonia is perhaps explained by the ammonia being frozen out of the atmosphere as a result of the very low sur-

face temperature of these planets—under −300° F (−185° C). Lower temperature is a result of their great distances from the Sun. The general composition and structure of these planets are thought to resemble those of Saturn and Jupiter, but the proportion of free hydrogen is much less in Uranus and Neptune.

## PLUTO

As already noted, Pluto is in a class by itself, being on the same order of size as the terrestrial planets but located in a highly eccentric orbit beyond the great planets. Although its existence was suspected because of irregularities in the orbits of Uranus and Neptune, Pluto was discovered only in 1930 as a very faint object found to have changed position among the stars on successive photographs taken six days apart. The mass of Pluto has been calculated, from its distortion of Neptune's orbit, to be 93% of Earth's mass, but the planet is too small to permit its diameter to be measured. Consequently, Pluto's density cannot be ascertained. Its surface temperature is judged to be not far above absolute zero.

## SATELLITES OF THE PLANETS

Altogether 32 satellites, or moons, have been identified in orbits around the 9 planets, but the distribution is highly varied in terms of numbers per planet (Table 3.1). The 2 innermost planets, Mercury and Venus, have no moons. Mars has 2: *Deimos* and *Phobos.* Both are smaller than Earth's single moon and both orbit much closer to the parent body.

Jupiter's 12 moons consist of 4 large ones and 8 small ones. Galileo, using the first astronomical telescope, discovered the 4 large moons in 1610, and they have since been designated the *Galilean satellites.* Their names are *Io, Europa, Ganymede,* and *Callisto,* stated in order outward. Inside the orbit of Io is another very small satellite. The remaining 7 lie far beyond the orbit of Callisto and are very small objects.

The Galilean satellites are easily seen through a low-powered telescope or good pair of binoculars (Figure 3.15). The apparent positions of these moons change greatly from night to night, but all revolve in about the same plane and in the same direction. Galileo's observation of these satellites was a powerful point in favor of the Copernican theory of the solar system, because it provided a small-scale model of planets orbiting a Sun. Io, Europa,

Figure 3.14. The planet Saturn and its rings, photographed with the 100-in. (250-cm) Hooker telescope on Mount Wilson. (The Hale Observatories.)

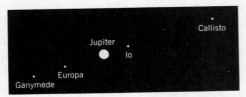

Figure 3.15. The four Galilean satellites of Jupiter as they might appear through binoculars or a small telescope. Distances from Jupiter are shown to correct scale, as if all four satellites were in a line at right angles to the observer. Diameters are not to scale.

and Ganymede have densities that suggest they are of rock composition, whereas Callisto has a very low density and may consist of frozen water or ammonia. Three of Jupiter's moons (numbers 8, 9, and 11) have retrograde orbits. Saturn has 10 known moons. The 10th moon, *Janus,* was discovered only in 1966. The farthest distant moon is *Phoebe,* traveling in a retrograde orbit of 8 million mi (13 million km) with a period of over 100 days.

Little is known of the 5 moons of Uranus and the 2 of Neptune, but their motion deserves comment. The axis of rotation of Uranus is inclined 98° to the plane of planet's orbit. Note that this is an angle greater than 90° (Figure 3.16). When so regarded, the north polar axis of Uranus points at an angle of 8° below its orbital plane. In this sense, its direction of rotation is direct, i.e., eastward rotation similar to that of Earth. If, on the other hand, the axis of Uranus is considered to be inclined 82° from the perpendicular, its rotation and that of its moons must be designated as retrograde. In either case, the moons revolve in orbits that are

almost perpendicular in plane to the planet's orbital plane. Finally, we note that one of Neptune's two moons is in retrograde orbit.

Recall that the planet Pluto has a highly eccentric orbit inclined at a 17° angle to the plane of the ecliptic (Figure 3.2). These facts have given rise to the possibility that Pluto was formerly a satellite of Neptune but escaped from that planet's gravitational field and went into heliocentric orbit.

### THE EARTH'S MOON

Of all the satellites, the Earth's Moon is unique in that it is a very large body in ratio with the planet which it orbits. With a diameter of 2160 mi (3476 km), compared with an Earth diameter of about 8000 mi (13,000 km), the ratio of diameters is about 1 to 4. Our Moon has a mass of about one eighty-first that of Earth. Because of the Moon's relatively large size, astronomers have commented that the Earth-Moon system can be regarded as comprising a "binary planet."

Figure 3.17 gives details of the Moon's orbit and distances from Earth. The Moon's orbit is quite strongly eccentric. When closest to Earth, the Moon is said to be in *perigee;* when most distant, in *apogee.* These terms apply to corresponding positions of any satellite, including the man-made orbiting satellites. Notice that the Moon revolves about the Earth in a direction that can be described as counterclockwise (direct motion), when we imagine ourselves to be viewing the system from a point above the Earth's north pole. Rotation of both Earth and Moon are also direct in this sense.

The period of the Moon's revolution, calculated in terms of 360° of angle with reference

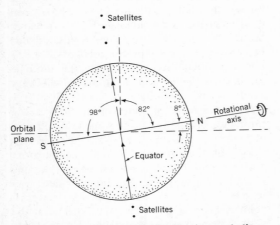

Figure 3.16. Angle of axial inclination and direction of rotation of Uranus.

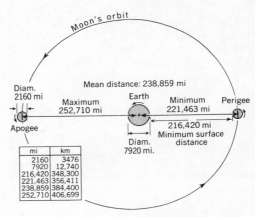

Figure 3.17. Dimensions of the Moon's orbit.

to the fixed stars, is 27.32 days and is designated the *sidereal month*. However, when measured in terms of reference of the Sun's position in the sky, and hence from one new moon to the next, the period averages 29½ days and is termed the *synodic month*. We shall see that a monthly rhythm of the tides follows the synodic month.

Of great interest in history of both Earth and Moon is the fact that the Moon always shows the same face to observers on Earth. Until orbited by manned *Apollo* spacecraft, no human being had directly viewed the opposite side of the Moon, although photographs returned by unmanned satellites had previously revealed many details of that surface. The fact that we can see only one side of the Moon requires that the Moon's period of rotation upon its axis be exactly the same as its period of revolution with respect to the stars. Hence, the Moon rotates once in 27.32 days. Such a coincidence could scarcely be ascribed to mere chance. Instead, as we shall see, the identity of the two periods has a mechanical explanation in terms of the tides.

## THE EARTH-MOON PAIR

While viewing the Moon's revolution about the Earth, we are likely to give no thought to the fact that the gravitational attraction of these two large bodies is a mutual phenomenon. Actually, both Earth and Moon revolve about a common center of gravity, the barycenter, which lies within the Earth at a point about 2900 mi (4700 km) out from the Earth's center (Figure 3.18). The Moon's average distance from this same barycenter is about 236,000 mi (380,000 km). Now, the turning moment of each body, which is equal to the product of the mass and distance from barycenter, must be the same for Earth as for Moon. The ratio of distances from barycenter, which is about one eighty-first, is therefore the same as the inverse ratio of masses of the two bodies. When we speak of the "Earth's orbit" as conforming with Kepler's laws, we should instead be more precise and say that the barycenter of the Earth-Moon pair follows an orbit in conformance with those laws.

## TIDE-RAISING FORCES

As the Earth-Moon pair revolves about the common center of gravity, or barycenter, the centrifugal forces of circular motion exactly balance the attractive forces of gravitation for

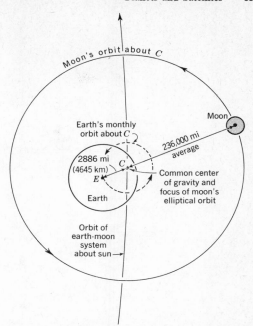

Figure 3.18. Earth and Moon revolve about a common center of gravity.

the system as a whole. If this were not so, the two bodies would either move closer together or farther apart. But the statement applies only if the opposed forces are considered to act only at the centers of mass of the two bodies (Figure 3.19). At the point *C,* the Earth's center, the Moon's gravitational attraction upon a mass that would weigh 1 kg at the Earth's surface is a force of 3.38 mg. The centrifugal force on the same mass is also 3.38 mg. However, at a point on the Earth's surface directly in line with the Moon on the closer side of Earth (point *T* in Figure 3.19) the gravitational force is increased to 3.49 mg, whereas centrifugal force remains constant at 3.38 mg. Thus, there exists a force difference of 0.11 mg, directed in a line toward the Moon.

Correspondingly, at point *A,* the force of gravitational attraction on a mass of 1 kg is 3.27 mg, which is 0.11 mg less than at the center, point *C.* As a consequence, there is a force of 0.11 mg directed away from the Moon. So we find that at both *A* and *T,* the 1-kg masses are acted upon by small forces that tend to move the masses away from the Earth's center along the line connecting Earth and Moon. The smallness of these forces is evident when we compare the ratio between 1 kg (1 million mg), which represents the Earth's grav-

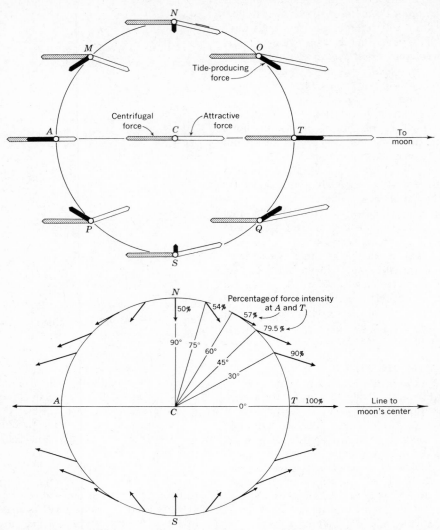

Figure 3.19. (*Above*) The tide-producing force is produced by combined action of centrifugal force and the moon's gravitational attraction. (*Below*) Direction and intensity of the tide-producing force varies with position on the globe. [After G. H. Darwin (1898), *The Tides*, Boston, Houghton Mifflin; and A. Defant (1961), *Physical Oceanography*, vol. II, New York, Pergamon.]

itational attraction for the mass, with 0.11 mg, the tide-producing force. The ratio is about 1 to 9 million. In other words, the weight of any object at point $A$ or $T$ is reduced by one ninemillionth because of the tide-producing force.

The upper part of Figure 3.19 shows the force vectors at various points on a spherical Earth. Notice that the centrifugal force is the same at all places and maintains a parallelism of direction. Gravitational forces are directed at the Moon's center and decrease in magnitude from right to left. The vector sum at each point is represented by a black arrow. In the

lower diagram of Figure 3.19 these force vectors are shown as arrows, proportionately scaled in length to the force magnitude. We see that at the points $N$ and $S$ the force is half that at $A$ and $T$ and is directed toward the Earth's center. This statement holds for all points on a great circle around the entire Earth and perpendicular to the line $AT$. Viewing the entire pattern of force arrows, it is obvious that the spherical body, if free to adjust its shape in response to the force system, will be deformed into a *prolate ellipsoid*, i.e., into a form resembling an American football. In this shape the Earth's circumference is decreased in the plane of *NS* while its diameter is lengthened on the line *AT*.

## EARTH TIDES

Let us now add to the tide-producing force system described above the provision that the Earth rotates upon its polar axis (imagined for simplicity to pass through points *N* and *S* in Figure 3.19). With respect to the Moon, the rotation period is 24$^h$ 50$^m$ (24.84 hr). A given point on the Earth's equator will pass under point *T* every 24$^h$ 50$^m$. The same point will move from *T* to *A* in 12$^h$ 25$^m$ (12.42$^h$), which is designated the *semidaily interval*. As a result, at intervals of 12$^h$ 25$^m$ the moving point on the equator experiences the maximum tidal force away from Earth's center. At the half-point of the semidaily interval the moving point will be subjected to a force acting exactly toward the Earth's center.

The flexings of the solid Earth in response to the changing tide-producing forces are known as *earth tides*. Although the range of up-and-down motion of the crust in each semidiurnal interval is very small, on the order of a few inches to 1 ft (30 cm), the motion can be measured with extremely sensitive instruments.

Response of the solid Earth to the tide-producing forces enables the rigidity of the Earth to be measured. The rigidity proves to be about the same as for steel. Consequently, the flexings by Earth tides are about what would occur in a steel ball the size of Earth.

## OCEAN TIDES

Waters of the oceans are set in motion by the tide-producing forces. However, since the water motion is horizontal, the response is to the horizontal component of the tide-raising force. We designate this component, which acts along the Earth's surface, as the *tractive force*. The relationship between tide-producing forces and tractive forces is shown in Figure 3.20. Seen in three dimensions over the surface of the Earth in Figure 3.21, the tractive forces converge upon the two points *T* and *A*. The ocean water therefore tends to move toward these two centers, where the water level is raised. The water tends to move away from the great circle through points *N* and *S,* with the result that the water level is lowered. Consequently, a point on the Earth's equator tends to experience one rise and one fall of water level in each semidiurnal interval of 12$^h$ 25$^m$.

The rise and fall of ocean level would be ideally a *sine curve* with respect to time, as shown in Figure 3.22. In this diagram the semidiurnal interval is considered for simplicity to consist of exactly 12 *lunar hours*. Height of the water surface is shown for each lunar hour. This type of curve represents the case of *simple harmonic motion* and is observed in many phenomena of science, including the swing of a pendulum, the vibration of a tuning fork, and the up-and-down flexing of a coil spring to which a weight is attached.

The semidaily *tide curve* as it is actually measured in a harbor shows the sine curve of

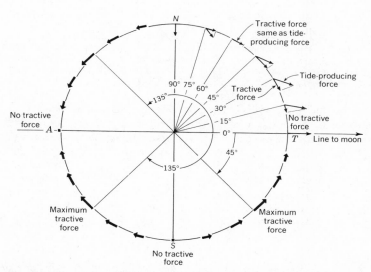

Figure 3.20. Tide-producing force can be resolved into tractive force, acting parallel to the earth's surface.

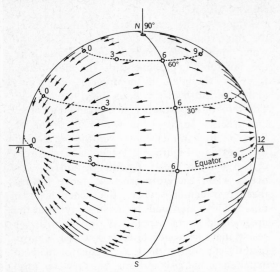

Figure 3.21. Tractive forces at a fixed point on earth change in direction and intensity as the earth rotates on its axis. Figures give lunar hours. [After G. H. Darwin (1898), *The Tides,* Boston, Houghton Mifflin.]

harmonic motion rather well (Figure 3.23), but there are many other complicating factors that cause actual tide curves to depart from the ideal form.

One complicating factor is the ellipticity of the Moon's orbit. When in perigee, the Moon's tide-producing force is about 15% to 20% greater than average; when in apogee, the force is about 20% less than average. Tide range is thus increased toward a maximum once each month, as well as reduced toward a minimum once each month.

The tide-raising force of the Sun is a second complicating factor. Every body in the solar system attracts every other body, in conformity with the law of gravitation. Therefore the Earth will be subject to a tide-raising force from the Sun and the other planets; however, for practical purposes only the Sun's influence need be considered. Although the Sun's mass is enormously greater than the Moon's mass, the Sun's vastly greater distance more than compensates. Consequently, the Sun's tide-raising force is about five-elevenths that of the Moon's. The Sun's attraction will tend to produce two high waters and two low waters for each rotation of earth with respect to Sun, an average period which is 24 hr of mean solar time. Although the Moon's influence governs the timing of high and low waters, the effect of the Sun is to increase or decrease the tide range. Thus, when Sun and Moon are in a single line, whether on opposite sides of Earth, or both located on one side, the tide range is greater than normal by about 20%, a condition known as *spring tides*. These tides coincide with new moon and full moon (Figure 3.23). When Sun and Moon are at right angles with respect to Earth, at first- and third-quarter phases of the Moon, the tide range is reduced

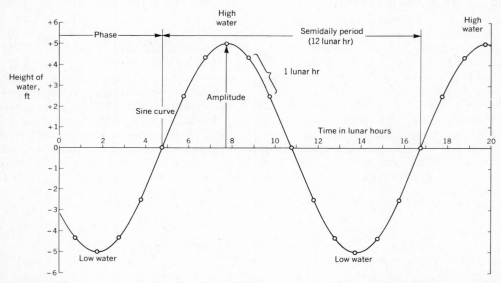

Figure 3.22. This graph of simple harmonic oscillation illustrates the features of an idealized semidaily tidal cycle.

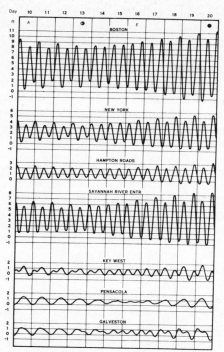

Figure 3.23. Typical tide curves for ports of the United States Atlantic and Gulf coasts. The letter *A* indicates date on which moon had its greatest declination, and the letter *E* the date on which moon's declination was zero. [From *Tide Tables* (1961), NOAA, National Ocean Survey.]

by about 20%, a condition known as *neap tides*. On occasions when perigee coincides with spring tides, the range is abnormally high; when apogee coincides with neap tides, the range is abnormally low.

The various rhythmic astronomical variables that influence the tide-raising force are known as *tidal constituents*. These are accurately known, and their combined influence can be closely calculated in prediction of the tide curve for a given port. Lord Kelvin was a leading contributor to the harmonic analysis of tides and in 1872 invented a tide-predicting instrument. Modern tide-predicting machines handle as many as 60 tidal constituents simultaneously and can predict tidal information for a single port for an entire year in two days' time. Of course, the electronic computer has now replaced the mechanical devices.

## OSCILLATION THEORY OF TIDES

If one compares the time of occurrence of high water at a given time and place with the time at which the Moon is at its highest point

in the sky, or in a position directly opposite on the globe, it will usually be found that the two events do not coincide in time. There may be a delay of several hours from the time that the Moon makes its meridian passage to the time that high water arrives. In fact, then, the two tidal centers of convergence of tractive forces (*A* and *T* in Figure 3.21) exist in theory, but the actual high waters follow along in different geographical locations. Newton, who first developed tidal theory, was aware of this discrepancy between tidal forces and occurrence of high and low waters, but he did not explain it. Further progress was made by Laplace, whose *dynamical theory* of tides suggested that the tide-producing forces would set up wavelike motions within the ocean basins but that the properties of these waves would be determined by the form and dimensions of the ocean basins themselves, by frictional resistance, and by the Coriolis effect.

Present-day tidal theory, based upon Laplace's principles, may be described as the *oscillation theory* of tides. In brief, this theory states that each ocean body has its own natural period of oscillation, or rhythmic up-and-down motion of water. The case is much the same as that of a stretched piano string or a tuning fork, which has a given period of vibration. The string will develop sympathetic vibrations in response to a sound wave train of the same frequency. Similarly, bodies of water of differing sizes and forms respond in different degrees to the tide-raising forces.

## TIDES AND THE EARTH'S ROTATION

We have seen that the solid earth is continually flexed by tidal forces and that the oceans respond by ceaseless rise and fall of water level. Tidal rise and fall is also accompanied by horizontal water motions, designated *tidal currents*. These currents are particularly conspicuous along the shorelines of the continents and reach powerful proportions in inlets, bays, and harbors. From the standpoint of the thesis of this chapter (namely, that we are analyzing a system of astronomical bodies in motion), the important point is that responses of planetary bodies to tides involve frictional resistance and that such resistance dissipates energy. The continuous work done by tides upon the whole Earth is estimated to be on the order of 2 billion hp. The action is that of a brake upon the Earth's rotation.

Astronomical events such as eclipses and occultations of stars and planets can be predicted with extreme precision based upon past observations. Slowing of the Earth's rotation will result in such events taking place slightly ahead of the predicted times. Based upon the schedule of solar eclipses going back into ancient times, decrease in rate of earth rotation has in fact been demonstrated. The rate of slowing of rotation is such that the day is lengthened by 0.0016 sec per century. This change is much too small to be measured for short periods of time, but shows up distinctly over long periods of time, since the error accumulates. In 2000 yr the accumulated time loss totals about 3 hr. However, there are also changes of rate of Earth rotation that occur over periods of time on the order of magnitude of a century. These fluctuations, which are probably related to changes of mass distribution within the Earth's core, are superimposed upon a slowing of rotation due to tidal friction. Consequently, the latter quantity is difficult to measure accurately as a trend by itself.

Tidal attraction by the Earth also sets up a tide-raising force upon the Moon. Whatever may have been the Moon's rate of rotation in the past, the braking effect of tidal flexing has been to gradually reduce the rate of the Moon's rotation until, as noted in an earlier paragraph, the period of rotation exactly matches the period of revolution.

Somewhat the same result has been achieved by the action of solar tide-raising forces upon the planet Mercury, which lies closest of all planets to the Sun. Mercury's rotational period of about 58.7 days has been measured to a high degree of accuracy by radar astronomy. At this rate, Mercury completes three turns on its axis for each two revolutions around the Sun, showing that the planet's rotation has become locked into the gravity field of the Sun.

The explanation of the slow, clockwise rotation of Venus may lie in the effect of tidal forces exerted by Earth. Venus has no known satellites which might affect its rotation. Its clockwise rotation in a period of 243.1 days with respect to the stars is at such a rate that the same side of Venus faces Earth, on the average, every 145.9 days. The *synodic period* of Venus (the interval between its closest approaches to the Earth) is 583.9 days which, well within the uncertainties of measurement, is exactly four times the synodic period of

rotation of 145.9 days. It thus appears that although Venus is rotating slowly with respect to Earth, each time it passes closest to our planet it presents exactly the same side to us.

The case of Venus seems to be unique. We may postulate that while the tidal forces of the Sun were slowing the clockwise rotation of Venus in its early stage, an extraordinary concentration of mass developed on one side of the planet near its equatorial belt. Eventually the rotation reached a stage at which the mass concentration made exactly four clockwise rotations between two successive nearest approaches of Venus to Earth, at which point Earth's tidal effect on Venus "locked on" to the rotation of Venus and stabilized it at the presently observed value and direction. Artificial satellites sent to orbit around Venus may do much to clarify this picture within the next few years.

Slowing of the Earth's rotation by tidal friction has the effect of changing the angular momentum of the Moon. Recall that the total angular momentum of the Earth-Moon system must remain constant. Therefore, the slowing of Earth rotation must be accompanied by an increase in angular momentum of the Moon. This increase takes the form of an increase in Moon's linear velocity. It is estimated that with each revolution about Earth, distance to the Moon is increased by about $\frac{1}{3}$ in. (0.8 cm).

Sir George Darwin, son of Sir Charles Darwin and an authority on tides, was intrigued by the implications of the change in the Moon's angular momentum and distance. Looking back into farthest reaches of geologic time—4 to 5 billion years (b.y.) or so—Darwin reasoned that the Moon must have been very close to the Earth, and both objects may have been at that time a single body. He therefore proposed a theory of origin of the Moon in which a large chunk of the Earth was torn out to become the Moon. Darwin reasoned if the rate of rotation at this early time in Earth history was as rapid as once in three hours, the centrifugal forces acting upon the Earth would exceed the gravitational forces that hold it together and that a violent rupture would occur, much as when a flywheel reaches the limit of its cohesive strength and ruptures. Pieces of the earth would have been hurled far from the Earth's surface and would have later become consolidated into a single object, the Moon. This hypothesis is examined in Chapter 11.

Looking far into the future, George Gamow, a physicist-astronomer of great distinction, has written the following:

A few more words may be said about the future of the Moon as it can be calculated on the basis of celestial mechanics. As a result of gradual recession, the Moon eventually will get so far from the Earth that it will become rather useless as a substitute for lanterns at night. In the meantime solar tides gradually will slow down the rotation of the Earth (provided the oceans do not freeze up), and there will come the time when the *length of a day will be greater than the length of a month*. The friction of lunar tides will then tend to accelerate the rotation of the Earth, and, by the law of conservation of angular momentum, the Moon will begin to return to the Earth until at last it will come as close to the Earth as it was at birth. At this point, the Earth's gravity forces will probably tear up the Moon into a billion pieces, forming a ring similar to that of Saturn. But the dates of these events, as given by celestial mechanics, are so far off that the Sun probably will have run out of its nuclear fuel and the entire planetary system will be submerged in darkness.*

## A SYSTEM IN REVIEW

In this chapter we have analyzed a planetary system of kinetic energy of bodies in orbital motion. It has been necessary to review Kepler's laws of planetary motion and the laws of motion and gravitation formulated by Newton, partly upon foundations laid by Galileo. The motions of planets, their satellites, and other objects of the solar system follow common laws, among them the law of conservation of angular momentum. A high degree of uniformity in motions of these celestial objects, including directions of revolution and rotation, point to a single uniform direction of motion in the primitive matter from which the solar system evolved.

Tide-raising forces, existing with respect to any celestial bodies, lead to dissipation of the kinetic energy of rotation, and this energy eventually is lost through radiation into space. Tidal friction has been important in the history of planets and particularly in the history of planet Earth with its disproportionately large Moon. The Earth's enormous oceans are in

*From *Gravity* by George Gamow. Copyright © 1962 Educational Services Incorporated. Reprinted by permission of Doubleday & Company, Inc.

constant motion from tide-raising forces, and a slowing of rotation has been documented. The Moon has responded by increasing its angular momentum and moving farther away from the Earth. The possibility that the Moon was once close to Earth, where it raised enormous tides, is something to be reckoned with in the interpretation of geologic history.

Energy losses within the system of inherited motions of planets and satellites are extremely small, and it seems probable that these motions will, by and large, continue essentially as at present fully as long as the Sun continues to maintain its radiant-energy output through fusion processes. There will, however, continue to be from time to time radical changes in the status of individual bodies in the solar system as collisions occur or tidal disruptions take place through the proximity of one body to another. These events will form the subject of Chapter 11, and their consideration will lead to further speculation upon the origin of the Earth, Moon, and other members of the solar system in Chapter 12.

## References for further study

Darwin, G. H. (1898), *The Tides and Kindred Phenomena in the Solar System*, Boston and New York, Houghton Mifflin, 278 pp. Reprinted (1962), San Francisco and London, Freeman.

Defant, A. (1958), *Ebb and Flow*, Ann Arbor, Univ. of Michigan Press, 121 pp.

Mehlin, T. G. (1959), *Astronomy*, New York, Wiley, 392 pp., chaps. 9–11, 13.

Macmillan, D. H. (1966), *Tides*, New York, American Elsevier, 240 pp.

Clancy, E. P. (1968), *The Tides, Pulse of the Earth*, Garden City, N.Y., Doubleday, 228 pp.

Whipple, F. L. (1968), *Earth, Moon, and Planets*, 3rd ed., Cambridge, Mass., Harvard Univ. Press, 297 pp.

Strahler, A. N. (1971), *The Earth Sciences*, 2nd ed., New York, Harper & Row, 826 pp., chaps. 1–3, 5, 8, 9.

## Review questions

1. What kinds of objects constitute the solar system? To what extent are the paths and directions of motion of these objects uniform? What is the significance of such uniformity?

2. Name the major planets in order outward from the Sun. Group the planets into two classes. In what respects are planets similar within each group? What are the major differences between the two groups?

3. Describe the orbit of a planet in terms of the properties of an ellipse. What is eccentricity, and how is it stated? How can an ellipse be constructed?

4. State Kepler's first and second laws of planetary motion. How does the second law explain the difference in speeds of revolution at aphelion and perihelion?

5. State Kepler's third law of planetary motion. How can the astronomical unit be used to simplify statement of the law? Does a planet exert any influence upon the motions of other planets?

6. State Newton's law of gravitation. When and in what volume was it first published? How does the law of gravitation apply to planetary motion? Explain centripetal force of a mass moving in a curved path. In the case of a planet moving around the sun, what is the relationship between gravitational force and centripetal force?

7. What is angular momentum? What variables determine angular momentum of a body moving in a straight-line path? in a curved path? What is the law of conservation of angular momentum? How does it apply to the case of two bodies in space moving about a common center of gravity?

8. What planetary and solar motions contribute to the total angular momentum of the solar system? Which planets contribute the most? Explain. How does the Sun's contribution compare with the total? Has the pattern of momentum distribution any bearing upon the origin of the solar system? Explain.

9. Compare periods of planetary rotation in broad terms, giving approximate values. Which planets have direct motion? Which have retrograde motion? Is direction of rotation significant? Explain. List three effects of planetary rotation upon surface environment.

10. Give a brief résumé of each of the inner planets (excluding Earth), including such items as relative size, gravity, escape velocity, presence or absence of atmosphere, atmospheric composition, surface temperatures, and distinctive surface features. Then compare or contrast the surface environment of each planet with that of Earth. Which of the three is the most likely to sustain life forms?

11. Describe Jupiter in some detail and then compare it with Saturn, Uranus, and Neptune in more general terms. What may be the internal structure and composition of these great planets? How do their surface temperatures compare with one another and with those of the inner planets? What is known about Pluto?

12. What is the total number of satellites identified for the nine planets? Which planets have none? Which planet has the most? How does our Moon compare with other planetary satellites? What are the Galilean satellites? What influence did their discovery by Galileo have upon conflicting views of his time concerning solar-system motions?

13. Compare the Moon with Earth in terms of diameter, mass, and surface gravity. Describe the Moon's orbit with regard to eccentricity. What are perigee and apogee? What is the Moon's period of revolution with respect to the stars? with respect to the Sun? How does the Moon's period of rotation compare with its period of revolution?

14. Describe the revolution of the Earth and Moon about a common center of gravity. Where does the barycenter lie? What relationship exists between distances from barycenter and masses of the two bodies?

15. Give an analysis of the tide-raising forces exerted upon the Earth by the Moon. How does the tide-raising force compare in magnitude with the Earth's gravitational attraction? What geometrical figure tends to be produced from a sphere by action of the tide-raising force?

16. How will a fixed point on the Earth be affected by the tide-raising force as the Earth rotates on its axis? What is the semidaily interval? In what way do Earth tides show a response to the changing force?

17. Explain how the tide-raising force is resolved into a tractive force on the Earth's surface. How will tractive forces tend to act to cause surface motion of ocean waters over the globe as the Earth rotates? How will a rise and fall of ocean level result from such water motion?

18. Analyze the semidaily (semidiurnal) tide curve in terms of an ideal sine curve of harmonic motion. How does ellipticity of the Moon's orbit impose a variation upon the simple sine curve? How does changing geometrical relationship among positions of Moon, Sun, and Earth cause a variation in the tide curve throughout the synodic month? What names are given to tides of maximum and minimum range in this monthly cycle?

19. In what way does the actual schedule of high and low water fail to conform with the ideal schedule set by the tide-raising force?

What are the essential concepts of the dynamical theory and oscillation theory of tides?

20. What influence has the flexing of the Earth by tides had upon Earth rotation? How has such a change been demonstrated, and what is its magnitude? How has the Moon's rotation been affected by tides? Are the rotation rates of Mercury and Venus controlled by tidal forces? Explain. What effect does slowing of Earth rotation have upon the Moon's linear velocity and distance from Earth? Explain.

21. Describe the solar system as a system of kinetic energy of masses in motion. Where did this energy originate? How can it be dissipated? How long will the system continue to operate?

# chapter 4 transport systems: i. atmospheric-oceanic circulation and the earth's heat balance

Two great global circulation systems exist on planet Earth. In these systems air and water—both of which are fluids—move in closed circuits, transporting heat and distributing it more uniformly over the planetary surface.

Recall from Chapter 1 that the sun-earth-space radiation system supplies the globe with radiant energy in shortwave and longwave forms. Energy is received largely in the shortwave form but returned to the atmosphere and ultimately dissipated into outer space in the longwave form. A planetary temperature is maintained as a long-term balance, or steady state, within this system. If there were no mechanisms of heat transport within the radiation system, the equatorial region of the earth would be hotter and the polar regions colder than they actually are. The gaseous atmosphere and fluid oceans flow across the parallels of latitude, taking heat from equatorial regions of surplus to polar regions of deficit (Figure 4.1). This heat transfer greatly reduces the thermal

differences that would otherwise exist over the globe and is of major importance in determining the thermal environment of terrestrial life.

Both atmospheric and oceanic circulation systems can be thought of as *subsystems* within the sun-earth-space radiation system. The word *subsystem* denotes the secondary position of these systems with respect to the larger solar-radiation system within which they operate. The concept here is that the flow of the atmosphere and oceans is set in motion and sustained by energy from the larger system. However, atmospheric motion comes first, since it is powered directly by unequal heating of large masses of air. Movement of the air in turn sets surface water layers in motion. We can say that the oceanic circulation is largely *wind-driven*. But water also moves in response to inequalities in its density from place to place, and these inequalities can be traced back largely to differences in water temperature or to unequal evaporation rates, both of which

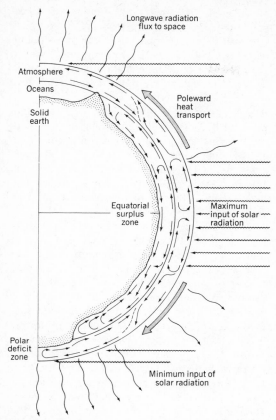

Figure 4.1. Schematic diagram of the global system of meridional heat transport. (From A. N. Strahler, "The Life Layer," *Jour. of Geography,* vol. 69, no. 2, p. 73, Figure 2. © 1970 by The Journal of Geography; reproduced by permission.)

factors are controlled by contact with the overlying atmosphere or by direct absorption of solar radiation.

In this chapter a most important *interface, or surface of discontinuity,* is to be studied. This interface is the contact of the atmosphere with the ocean water beneath it. Both matter and energy are exchanged across this interface. Energy can be transferred either mechanically, as a kinetic energy transfer, or indirectly through the changes of state: liquid state to gaseous state, and vice versa. Radiative-heat transfer as well as direct conduction of heat also occur, as in the relationships between atmosphere and ground studied in Chapter 1.

Air in motion constitutes *wind,* a phenomenon so well known to all that definition is hardly necessary. A wind is described in terms of its speed and direction. Speed, given in miles per hour, meters per second, or knots, is mea-

sured by the *anemometer.* Direction, which is stated as that compass point from which the air comes, can be given in terms of the cardinal points, or as an azimuth ranging from 0° to 360° clockwise from geographic north. Most winds with which we are concerned are dominantly horizontal motions. There are also vertical motions of the atmosphere—updrafts and downdrafts—as well as gradual rising or subsiding motions. Large-scale horizontal air motions are described by the term *advection;* vertical motions in thin columns by the term *convection.* The adjectives *advective* and *convective* will be encountered frequently in the discussion of atmospheric circulation.

## BAROMETRIC PRESSURE AND WINDS

The curve of *atmospheric pressure,* or *barometric pressure,* resembles the atmospheric density curve when measured from the ground to increasing altitudes. As Figure 4.2 shows, pressure is at the maximum at sea level, where the mean value is 1013.2 millibars (mb). A *millibar* is one-thousandth of a bar, while the *bar* is a force of 1 million dynes/cm². Stated in terms of the length of a column of mercury that sea-level pressure will counterbalance, the

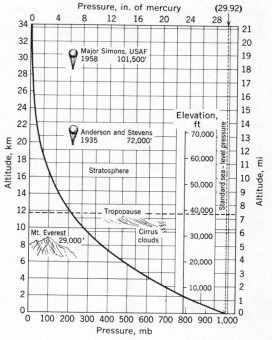

Figure 4.2. A smooth curve represents the decrease of atmospheric pressure with increasing elevation. No perceptible break occurs at the tropopause. (© 1960, John Wiley & Sons, New York.)

equivalent to 1013.2 mb is 29.92 in., or 760 mm.

The decrease of barometric pressure with altitude follows a smooth curve of decline (an exponential decrease), such that for each 950 ft of increase in elevation, the pressure decreases by one-thirtieth of its value. Figure 4.2 shows the curve of pressure versus altitude for troposphere and stratosphere. If the earth's atmosphere were in complete equilibrium at rest, this relationship would apply at all times and places. However, at any given location and instant, the decrease in pressure may show marked departures from the ideal curve.

Air is set in motion on a large scale within the atmosphere in response to differences in barometric pressure existing in a horizontal direction, i.e., along surfaces of uniform elevation above the earth's surface. Where such pressure differences are present there exists a *pressure-gradient force,* tending to cause the air to move in the direction from higher to lower pressure. The direction of the pressure gradient is measured along the line of most rapid change of pressure from one point to another in the reference surface. Figure 4.3 shows a particular configuration of pressure gradient as it is drawn both in plan view (seen from above) and in cross section (seen from the side). Notice that two kinds of surfaces are recognized: (1) surfaces of equal elevation (*horizontal surfaces*) and (2) surfaces of equal pressure (*isobaric surfaces*). In the example shown, the isobaric surfaces are sloping with respect to the horizontal and cut across a given surface of equal elevation. Consequently, as we follow along the 5000-ft level from left to right, we encounter isobaric surfaces of decreasing value, e.g., 800 mb, 825 mb, 850 mb, and 875 mb. Where the isobaric surface is at low elevation, a low-pressure condition exists; where the isobaric surface is at high elevation, a high-pressure condition exists. In Figure 4.3 the pressure gradient is from right to left (high pressure to low pressure) and at right angles to the isobars.

The pressure-gradient force exists because of the change in average kinetic energy of the gas molecules in a horizontal direction. In the region of higher barometric pressure a greater density of gas molecules exists, hence their collisions are more frequent and they exert a greater total pressure against a confining surface than where pressure and density are lower. Molecules traveling by chance in the direction toward lower pressure will tend to have longer average paths than when traveling toward higher pressure. Hence, the gas molecules, as a swarm, tend to drift toward the lower pressure. It is this tendency to drift that is given the designation of a "force." Obviously, the more rapid the change of pressure, the stronger is the force. The flow of air that ensues will be more rapid where the pressure gradient is steeper. In general, the strength of winds can be inferred directly by examining the spacing of the isobars as shown on a weather map. Where these are closely crowded, we can expect strong winds.

## SIMPLE CONVECTIVE CIRCULATION

A simple wind system, comprising a complete circulation pattern in closed loops, can be studied through an idealized model, shown in Figure 4.4. In diagram *A,* isobaric surfaces are horizontal and parallel. No pressure gradient exists. Such an initial condition would apply to an atmosphere of uniform temperature at any given level. There is no air motion. In diagram *B,* we have postulated that the atmosphere is heated in the central region of the diagram (*Y*) but not heated in the regions on either side. Such heating might result from longwave radiation from the ground in the region of *Y,* because of solar radiation. Whatever the source of the heat, the heated air expands. Each

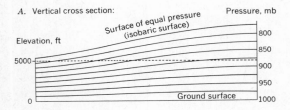

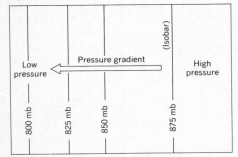

Figure 4.3. (*A*) Isobaric surfaces seen in vertical cross section. (*B*) An isobaric map corresponding with the profile above.

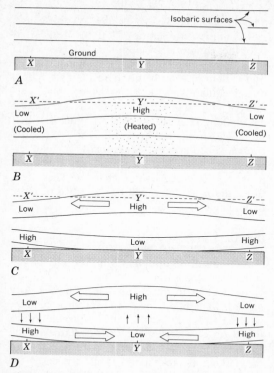

Figure 4.4. A simple convective system of winds produced by unequal warming and cooling of the atmospheric layer.

isobaric surface is raised somewhat. In the area of Y′ the isobaric surface has been lifted and is higher than at X′ and Z′ at equivalent elevations. Therefore, high pressure exists at Y′, while relatively low pressure exists at X′ and Z′. As a result of the pressure gradient from Y′ toward X′ and Z′, air begins to move from higher to lower pressure, as shown by arrows in diagram C. As soon as such flow occurs, additional masses of air will be introduced at X′ and Z′, loading the atmospheric columns at those places. At ground level at X and Z, barometric pressure will be increased and will become high relative to pressure at Y, which now has relatively lower pressure near the

ground. The flow of air at low level now commences in the direction of the pressure gradient, as shown by arrows in diagram D. Now winds move in opposite directions at high and low levels. Mass transport is completed by sinking and rising motions as indicated by the small arrows in diagram D. Two complete flow circuits have been established. As long as excess heat continues to be fed into the air column at Y-Y′, this flow will continue. Presumably, the heat is lost at an equal rate by outward radiation in the regions of X-X′ and Z-Z′.

The model described above is known as *simple convective* circulation. A real, but small-scaled, example in nature is found in the *sea breeze* and *land breeze,* illustrated in Figure 4.5. Diagram A shows conditions of calm, with isobaric surfaces horizontal. In diagram B, heating of the ground surface has caused the lower air layer to be expanded, giving low pressure at the surface and high pressure at higher levels. A pressure gradient now exists from water to land, with the result that a sea breeze is produced. At night, as shown in diagram C, the air over the land is excessively cooled by rapid longwave radiation from the ground. At this time high pressure develops near the ground, lower pressure at higher levels. With the pressure gradient now directed seaward, a land breeze sets in.

## SIMPLE CONVECTIVE CIRCULATION ON A NONROTATING EARTH

As a first step in understanding the atmospheric circulation patterns of our earth, we can consider another hypothetical and simple model, shown in Figure 4.6. In diagram A, the atmosphere is imagined to be a layer of uniform thickness and to have exactly uniform conditions of density, pressure, and temperature at equal elevations above the spherical surface. For reasons explained in a later paragraph, it is necessary to postulate that the earth does not rotate. We imagine, instead, that there

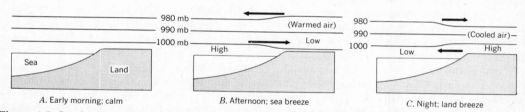

Figure 4.5. Sea breeze and land breeze. [After S. Petterssen (1958), *Introduction to Meteorology,* New York, McGraw-Hill, p. 165, Figure 116.]

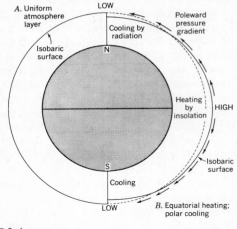

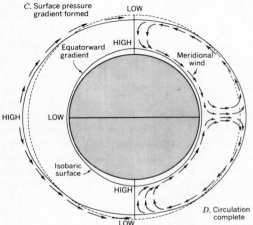

Figure 4.6. Simple wind system on an imagined nonrotating earth.

is a source of heat applied simultaneously and uniformly to the atmosphere around the equatorial belt, whereas heat radiates away from the two polar regions. Results of such unequal application of heat are shown in diagram *B*. High pressure at high levels over the equatorial region in contrast to low pressure at high levels over the poles causes a pressure gradient from low to high latitudes and a consequent flow of air poleward along the meridians. Piling up of air over the poles increases the barometric pressure at low levels, producing high-pressure centers, as shown in diagram *C*. In contrast, pressure at low levels is low in the equatorial belt. As a result, air moves from poles to equator in a surface wind blowing along the meridians. We may call these *meridional winds.* The two convection circuits are completed by a rise of air over the equatorial belt

and a sinking of air over the poles, as shown in diagram *D*. The system is now complete and will continue to operate as long as heat is fed into the equatorial region and lost from the polar regions. The imagined meridional circulation system in each hemisphere is single-celled, or unicellular. This model serves to explain certain of the observed features of the earth's circulation. There is, in fact, an equatorial belt of low barometric pressure, the *equatorial trough.* Furthermore, there exist at high atmospheric levels two great, strongly developed lows, one centered over each pole. These features, the *polar lows,* will be described in more detail later.

## CORIOLIS EFFECT AND THE GEOSTROPHIC WIND

As we all know, there is no meridional system of winds on earth. The reason is obvious: Our earth rotates upon a polar axis. Any masses in motion over the earth's surface, whether solid objects or the molecules of a liquid or gas, tend to be deflected toward the right in the Northern Hemisphere and toward the left in the Southern. This tendency for deflection is named the Coriolis effect (discussed earlier on p. 59) after a French mathematician, G. G. Coriolis, who presented the first analysis of the phenomenon in 1835.

We shall not enter into a physical analysis of the Coriolis effect, but instead try to obtain an appreciation of the basic cause of the phenomenon by examining the path of an orbiting earth satellite. Consider the hypothetical case of a satellite launched at the earth's north pole along a course aimed due south, along the Greenwich meridian (0° longitude) (Figure 4.7). Once the satellite is in orbit at a height of, say, 300 mi (500 km) the effect of frictional drag by the earth's atmosphere is so slight as to be neglected. If the earth did not rotate, the satellite would take a great-circle path southward over the Greenwich meridian, over the south pole, and then north along the 180th meridian back to the north pole. This path would be maintained indefinitely. However, the earth turns eastward at a rate of 15° per hour of sidereal time. The satellite must, because of gravitational attraction, follow a circular path around the earth's center of gravity. But the satellite must also conform with Newton's laws of motion and will maintain the plane of its circular path in a fixed position with reference to coordinates of reference in

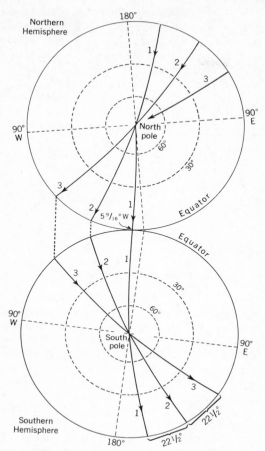

Figure 4.7. The earth trace of an artificial satellite in polar orbit curves to the right in the Northern Hemisphere and to the left in the Southern Hemisphere. This map combines two polar stereographic projections.

space, i.e., with respect to the stars. Consequently, the satellite circular path remains fixed in space while the earth turns within that circle at a constant angular rate.

The earth-trace, or path of satellite over the earth's surface directly beneath it, is shown in Figure 4.7. Successive orbits are labeled 1, 2, and 3. The satellite has a speed of 18,000 mph (29,000 km/hr). By the time the satellite reaches the equator, 22½ min after it left the pole, the earth has turned through 5%₁₆°. The earth-trace will be curved toward the right of the direction of motion, which is southward. In the Southern Hemisphere, the earth-trace will curve to the left, as shown in the figure. Since the satellite completes its orbit in 90 min, the earth turns 22½° during the same period. Therefore, in successive orbits the earth-trace

crosses the equator at points 22½° of longitude farther westward.

Consider the case of an orbiting earth satellite that is launched at an angle with respect to the meridians (Figure 4.8). Note that the path curves toward the right throughout the Northern Hemisphere and to the left throughout the Southern Hemisphere. In this example, the period of the orbit was 99 min and the earth-trace crossed the equator 24¾° of longitude farther west with each orbit.

Objects in motion on the earth's surface are constrained physically by forces of friction and are not generally free to respond perfectly to the Coriolis effect, as in the case of the earth satellite. Nevertheless, the response of moving fluids (water and air) to the Coriolis effect is highly pronounced and has far-reaching effects upon the flow paths of currents of water and air. It is an environmental factor of major importance.

For purposes of convenience, the Coriolis effect can be thought of as a force that always acts at exactly right angles to the path of motion. This principle is illustrated in Figure 4.9. Moreover, the magnitude of the force depends upon latitude, being of zero value at the equator and increasing as the sine of the latitude to reach a maximum value at either pole. In order to apply the Coriolis principle, we must add that the force is directly proportional to the speed of motion. A third term in the Coriolis force is angular velocity of rotation of the earth. However, as this term is a constant, it does not enter into application of the principle in interpreting current patterns.*

In applying the Coriolis effect to winds, consider the motion of a small parcel of air starting at rest from point *A* of Figure 4.10. Isobars show the pressure gradient to be uniformly lower toward the left. The pressure-gradient force, which acts toward the left with constant value at all times, tends to set the air parcel in motion in that direction. However, as soon as motion has commenced, the Coriolis force acts at right angles to the path of motion, as shown by very small arrows. The air parcel responds by turning toward the right. As speed of motion increases, the Coriolis force also increases. Ultimately, motion is turned to the extent that it is in a direction at right angles to

* The equation for the Coriolis effect, defined as an *acceleration* in units of cm/sec² is: $V\ 2\ \Omega \sin \phi$, where $V$ is linear velocity in cm/sec, $\Omega$ is angular velocity of rotation in radians/sec, and $\phi$ is latitude in degrees.

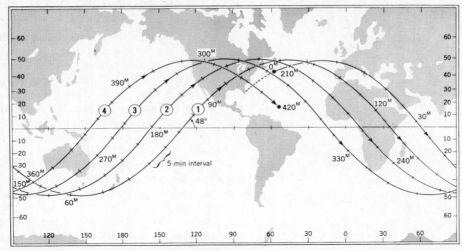

Figure 4.8. Earth trace of the first four orbits of satellite *Tiros I* (1960 Beta 2) plotted on the Mercator projection. Marks show the satellite's position at 5-min intervals; figures show elapsed time at 30-min intervals. (After *I. G. Y. Bulletin,* no. 35, 1960.)

the pressure gradient but parallel with the isobars (point *B* of Figure 4.10). Here the Coriolis force exactly balances the pressure-gradient force and no further turning ensues. In the case of straight, parallel isobars, the flow of air at point *B* is termed the *geostrophic wind*.

Where air moves in curved paths, centrifugal force enters into the picture, either to add to or subtract from the pressure-gradient and

Coriolis forces, depending upon direction of the curved path with respect to the pressure gradient and upon which hemisphere is in-

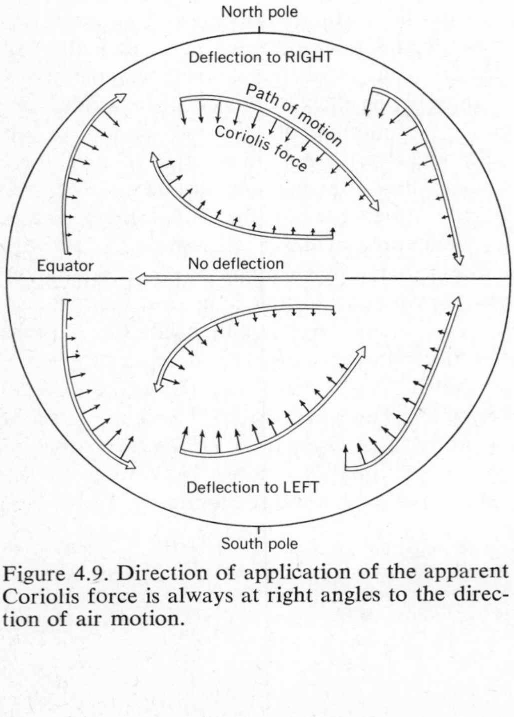

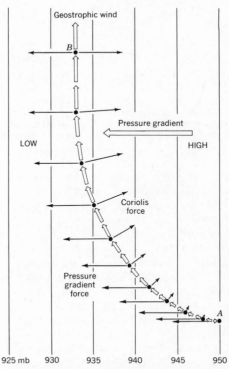

Figure 4.10. A parcel of air starting from a position of rest at *A* is deflected until it is moving parallel with the isobars at *B*. [After S. Petterssen (1958), *Introduction to Meteorology,* New York, McGraw-Hill, p. 152, Figure 105.]

Figure 4.9. Direction of application of the apparent Coriolis force is always at right angles to the direction of air motion.

volved. Without going into a detailed explanation of the action of these three forces, it can simply be noted that at high elevations wind direction parallels the isobars even when they are curved lines.

Close to the ground, the force of friction also enters into the picture. Here the frictional effect is to cause the wind to cross the isobars at an angle, which ranges from 25° to 45° The air flow is thus partly in the direction of the pressure gradient, and the mass of air thus travels from an area of higher pressure to one of lower pressure. Above about 3000 ft (1000 m) the frictional effect is absent and the air travels in close parallelism with the isobars. Where a center of low pressure exists, the air travels in a counterclockwise motion about the

center; such a case is referred to as a *cyclone* (Figure 4.11). In the case of a center of high pressure, known as an *anticyclone,* the wind follows a clockwise motion about the center.

Figure 4.11 compares the flow paths of air in both upper-air and surface cyclones and anticyclones in both hemispheres. Obviously, the inspiraling air motions in a cyclone at low levels constitutes a *convergence* of air, which must therefore rise to higher levels. The outspiraling motions in an anticyclone, by contrast, constitutes a *divergence* of air and must be accompanied by subsidence of the overlying air column.

With a practical knowledge of the existing relationships between winds and isobars, we can return to the analysis of the global patterns of air motion.

### THE PLANETARY CIRCULATION

The next step in developing our simple model of atmospheric circulation is to introduce the Coriolis force, to yield the geostrophic motion on a rotating globe (Figure 4.12). As the high-level air over the equatorial belt begins to move poleward, it is deflected to the right (Northern Hemisphere) to become a system of upper westerly winds paralleling the isobars at about the 30th parallel. Correspondingly, in the Southern Hemisphere deflection to the left also turns the poleward flow at high level into a westerly wind system.

But now still another phenomenon can be anticipated. Because air moving at high levels poleward from the equatorial belt has been turned into westerly flow, following the earth's parallels of latitude, the air here tends to accumulate more rapidly than it can escape poleward. This accumulation, or banking up, of air constitutes a *convergence* and takes place in zones between latitudes 20° N and 30° N and between latitudes 20° S and 30° S—the tropical zones. Here convergence aloft produces at the surface two belts of high barometric pressure known as the *subtropical high-pressure belts,* one in each hemisphere.

Air subsiding within the subtropical high-pressure zone spreads both equatorward and poleward, producing systems of prevailing surface winds. That air which follows the barometric pressure gradient from subtropical high to equatorial low is deflected westward to create a system of prevailing winds known as the *tropical easterlies,* or *trade winds* (Figure 4.12). The tropical easterlies form a broad,

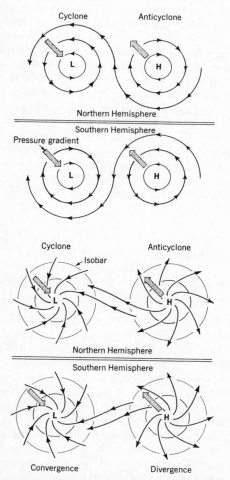

Figure 4.11. Flow paths of air in cyclones and anticyclones in Northern and Southern hemispheres. Upper diagrams are for upper-air winds; lower diagrams are for surface winds.

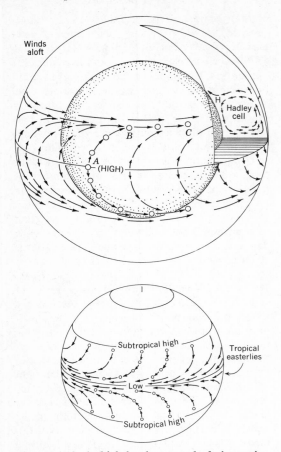

Figures 4.12. At high levels a parcel of air starting northward from a position at rest at *A* over the equator would be deflected to the right until moving due eastward at *B* (*upper figure*). Near the earth's surface air starting to travel equatorward from the subtropical highs is turned westward to produce the tropical easterlies (*lower figure*).

steady, and deep air stream moving around the earth over the equatorial regions and extending to high altitudes. As shown in Figure 4.12, the tropical easterlies at low level tend to converge from both hemispheres upon the equatorial zone of low pressure. This zone is designated as the *intertropical convergence zone* (abbreviated to ITC).

The atmospheric circulation system of equatorial and tropical latitudes thus consists of two cells, one in each hemisphere. Seen in cross section, and neglecting east-west components of motion, the meridional circulation within each cell consists of horizontal and vertical motions, together forming a complete circuit. The existence of such a circulation system was first postulated by George Hadley in 1735 and

is now designated as the *Hadley cell* by meteorologists.

The Hadley cell is not a closed system, for if it were closed there could be no exchange of air and water vapor with the middle and high latitudes of the two hemispheres. At the poleward limit of the Hadley cell, at about latitude 25°, part of the low-level air migrates poleward, carrying with it sensible heat and water vapor. Of the total quantity of water vapor moving within the cell about one-third escapes poleward, constituting the latent energy flux required to satisfy the global energy balance.

## TRANSPORT OF ANGULAR MOMENTUM BY ATMOSPHERIC MOTIONS

Thus far, the discussion of winds has been treated in terms of four forces. Of these, the Coriolis force was called upon to explain why air traveling poleward across the parallels of latitude is deflected to the right (Northern Hemisphere) and becomes a westerly wind, whereas air traveling equatorward, also deflected to the right, becomes an easterly wind. We shall now introduce the concept of *transport of angular momentum* as a basis for understanding the global atmospheric circulation.

Angular momentum was discussed in Chapter 3 in an explanation of the changing speeds of planetary revolution in elliptical orbits. Recall that angular momentum, *L,* is defined as follows:

$$L = M \cdot V \cdot R$$

where *M* is mass of the object in motion,
     *V* is the instantaneous linear velocity,
and *R* is the radius of the circular path of motion.

In the present discussion, we are concerned with small masses on or close to the earth's surface traveling in horizontal paths. Thus the paths of motion conform with a spherical surface (disregarding oblateness). At any instant, then, a small parcel of air has one component of its motion in a circle whose plane is at right angles to the earth's axis of rotation (Figure 4.13). This circle has the radius of the parallel of latitude with which it is identical. In the case of the rotating earth, angular momentum is a vector quantity directed toward the north polar axis. The angular momentum of a stationary particle at point *B* in Figure 4.13 will be less than that of a particle at point *A* be-

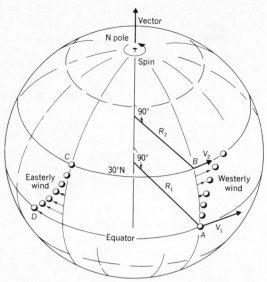

Figure 4.13. Angular momentum and zonal winds.

cause both radius and linear velocity are less than at $A$. For the earth as an entire planet, the total angular momentum must remain constant, in accordance with the law of conservation of angular momentum. In discussing circulation of the atmosphere and oceans, we can consider the total angular momentum to be the sum of three parts:

$$L_{total} = L_{earth} + L_{oceans} + L_{atmosphere}$$

The term $L_{earth}$ denotes the solid earth, or lithosphere, which can be regarded (for short periods of time) as a rigid body within which there is no transfer of mass from one place to another. In both the atmosphere and the oceans mass transfer occurs readily. Should the angular momentum of any one of the three parts be changed by mass transfer, there must be compensating changes in one or both of the other parts.

Consider that a parcel of air is located at point $A$ on the equator (Figure 4.13) and has no motion relative to the earth's surface, which is to say that there is no wind at this point. Let the parcel of air be of unit mass, which remains unchanged throughout the analysis. The only two variables will then be radius and velocity.

As the air parcel begins to move poleward from the equator, its horizontal path, paralleling the earth's curvature, traverses parallels of latitude of decreasing radius. (Radius of parallels decreases proportionately to the cosine of

the angle of latitude.) Therefore, the value of $R$ in the equation of angular momentum decreases with poleward travel, whereas the angular momentum of the parcel must remain a constant. Therefore the linear velocity ($V$) from west to east must increase, with the result that the parcel of air moves eastward at a rate faster than the eastward motion of a point beneath it on the earth's surface. Consequently, a westerly wind component is generated and angular momentum is transported poleward across the parallels.

In reverse motion, toward the equator, the air parcel at point $C$ in Figure 4.13 will cross parallels of both increased radius and increased linear velocity. The parcel will tend to drop behind the surface motion of the earth beneath it and will develop a relative westward motion—which is to say, an easterly wind component. The transfer of angular momentum across the parallels is now a negative quantity.

In the case of the Hadley-cell circulation, the necessity for conservation of angular momentum requires that upper air, moving poleward in the cell, acquire a west-to-east motion. The result is a strong westerly wind at high levels in the troposphere in subtropical latitudes, over about the 30th parallels north and south. This high-speed flow will be discussed in later paragraphs. Air moving equatorward at low levels in the Hadley-cell circulation is required to develop into an easterly wind, but because of friction with the earth's surface it attains only moderate speeds.

We have now accounted for both the meridional (north-south) and zonal (east-west) components of motion in the atmospheric circulation system of low latitudes. We turn next to global circulation at middle and high latitudes.

## GLOBAL CIRCULATION IN MIDDLE AND HIGH LATITUDES

Poleward of the subtropical high pressure belts, average circulation in the troposphere takes the form of a prevailing system of *upper-air westerlies*, shown schematically in Figure 4.14. This flow constitutes a great vortex moving counterclockwise (Northern Hemisphere) around a prevailing center of low barometric pressure, the *polar low*. A corresponding system of upper air westerlies exists in the Southern Hemisphere.

The simple zonal flow of the westerlies is disturbed by a ceaseless succession of wavelike

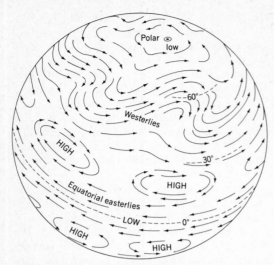

Figure 4.14. Generalized pattern of global circulation at high levels in the troposphere.

undulations and by the formation and dissolving of large eddies, which are lows or highs of barometric pressure. In this way advection occurs on a large scale in the troposphere. Figure 4.15 is a map of the Northern Hemisphere showing the distribution of barometric pressure and winds at high altitude on a particular day.

Winds parallel the isobars and are strongest where the isobars are most closely spaced. Notice, first, that the isobars in middle latitudes are sinuous in pattern and form large waves, of which some five or six can be identified. These undulations are *upper-air waves,* or *Rossby waves* (named for C. G. Rossby, a meteorologist who developed the mathematical equations for parameters governing the waves).

The upper-air waves may grow, change in form, and dissolve. They may remain essentially stationary for many days and may also drift slowly in the east-west direction. An upper-air wave may deepen to the extent that the crest, bulging equatorward, is detached and becomes a *cutoff low* (several are depicted by concentric isobars labeled *L* on Figure 4.15). A wave trough may also become detached to form a *cutoff high.* Where the isobars of upper-air waves are closely spaced, a narrow meandering band of high-speed air flow is generated, a phenomenon known as the *jet stream.* Notice that a ring of weak anticyclones surrounds the earth at subtropical latitudes; these are the subtropical high-pressure centers of subsiding air on the poleward side of the Hadley cell.

Speed of the upper-air westerly winds varies

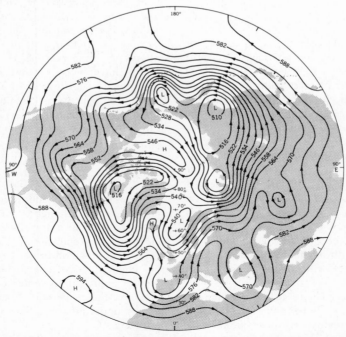

Figure 4.15. Isobaric map at the 500-mb (18,000-ft) level for April 28, 1969, drawn from infrared spectrometer data obtained by *Nimbus III* satellite. Pressures in millibars. Arrows show upper-air winds. (Data from NOAA and NASA. See *Amer. Meteorological Soc. Bull.,* vol. 50, no. 7, July, 1969, cover and p. 544.)

greatly from time to time and place to place. Maximum speeds in the range of 180 to 230 mph (290 to 370 km/hr) are found in the jet stream. The core of maximum speed is found at an altitude of about 35,000 to 40,000 ft (11 to 12 km). The speed is about twice as fast in winter as in summer and the core in winter lies at somewhat lower latitude than in summer.

Figure 4.16 is a schematic diagram of the general east-west, or *zonal,* components of winds in the troposphere. This diagram does not show the north-south, or *meridional,* components of the circulation, nor does it suggest the changing patterns of Rossby waves, cyclones, and anticyclones.

Notice in Figure 4.16 that in winter, poleward of about 70° N latitude, average winds are shown as moving from east to west. These winds are referred to as the *polar easterlies.* Their average speed is small, and they are not as persistent as the tropical easterlies.

## CAUSE OF THE WESTERLIES

Poleward of the Hadley cell in each hemisphere, winds are persistently westerly at all levels of the troposphere (except for local reversals connected with moving cyclones and anticyclones). Consequently, a simple thermally driven cellular circulation will not explain the westerlies. We must turn instead to a mechanism by which angular momentum is transferred from low latitudes to high latitudes by the action of cyclones and anticyclones.

Consider, first, that the system of tropical easterlies is a westward air flow, opposite to the direction of the earth's eastward rotation. Friction of these winds with the earth's surface must tend to slow the earth's rotation. Angular momentum is transferred from the solid earth into the tropical easterlies by this friction. On the other hand, the same friction draws energy from the easterlies at low levels, and these winds are much weaker than would be predicted on the basis of angular momentum transfer. In contrast, in the westerlies the atmosphere is rotating faster than the earth's surface beneath, and the earth will thus draw angular momentum from the atmosphere. Such withdrawal of angular momentum would quickly slow the westerly winds and reduce them to nothing unless momentum were brought into the westerlies at a rate equal to its withdrawal. It is therefore necessary that a mechanism be present in which angular momentum can be transferred poleward across the parallels of latitude from the easterlies into the low-level westerlies. Such transfer must be sustained if the general atmospheric circulation is to be maintained in the form we find it.

Transfer of angular momentum is accomplished by the mechanism of large-scale cyclones and anticyclones of the middle latitudes and takes place largely at about the 30th parallel of latitude. Figure 4.17 shows how momentum transfer operates. An upper-air wave in the westerlies lies toward the left and appears as a trough of low pressure whose axis is slanted from southwest to northeast. Adjacent to the low trough is a center of high pressure, or anticyclone, whose axis of elongation is also from southwest to northeast. This orientation is typical in the Northern Hemisphere. Air crossing the 30th parallel of latitude at the point *A* has both northward and eastward components of motion, while air crossing the same parallel at point *B* has both westward and southward components of motion. Whereas the northward and southward components are equal at *A* and *B*, respectively, the eastward component at *A* is greater than the westward component at *B*, because of the

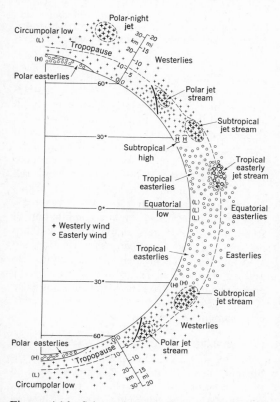

Figure 4.16. Schematic diagram of zonal wind directions and jet streams along a meridian from pole to pole.

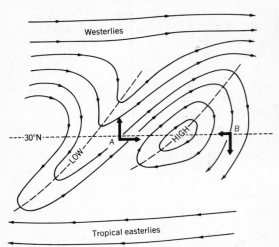

Figure 4.17. Wave theory of angular momentum transfer to sustain westerly winds. [Based on a diagram by R. L. Pfeffer (1967), in *Encyclopedia of Atmospheric Sciences and Astrogeology*, R. W. Fairbridge, ed., New York, Reinhold, p. 74, Figure 6.]

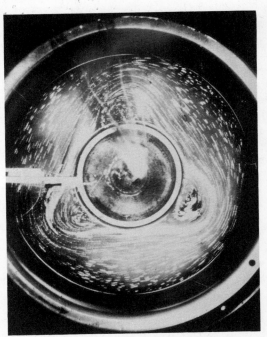

Figure 4.18. Photograph of a laboratory "dishpan" experiment showing waves generated in a fluid in a rotating container. Flow pattern is revealed by particles of aluminum scattered on the water surface. (Photograph by courtesy of Dave Fultz, Hydrodynamics Lab., Univ. of Chicago.)

earth's eastward rotation. The vector sum of the eastward and westward components will therefore give a net difference that is directed eastward and represents the transport of angular momentum northward across the parallel of latitude. In this way, the kinetic energy is furnished for the driving of the westerly winds. This hypothesis of westerly winds is designated the *wave theory*. This form of poleward transport of angular momentum is described as an *eddy transport mechanism*.

The polar easterlies, which are comparatively weak winds and occur largely at low levels, may be explained through the spreading of dense, cold polar air toward lower latitudes, with deflection toward the west by the Coriolis force. This explanation represents a recourse to the cellular convection theory.

It is interesting to note that model experiments have proved successful in reproducing the main features of the general circulation of the troposphere (Figure 4.18). A circular pan of fluid is used to represent a hemisphere. Heat is applied to the fluid around the periphery, or equatorial zone, while the fluid in the center of the pan is cooled. The entire apparatus, together with an attached overhead motion-picture camera, is rotated clockwise. Particles of aluminum powder moving with the fluid permit flow paths to be photographed.

When the thermal gradient and rate of rotation are properly adjusted in the model, a westerly flow sets in and develops a number of waves resembling the Rossby waves. Anticyclonic centers ring the westerly current zone in a manner analogous to the subtropical highs. Experimentation has shown that when the rotation rate is sufficiently slow and the temperature gradient is sufficiently high, a single convectional cell resembling the Hadley cell extends from equator to pole. These results suggest that our earth owes its atmospheric circulation pattern to a unique combination of rotation rate and thermal imbalance. Perhaps on Venus, a planet with very slow rotation and a strong thermal gradient from equator to poles, a Hadley-cell circulation dominates the entire planet and strong westerlies do not exist. Again, the special nature of our own planetary environment asserts itself.

## DEVELOPMENT OF UPPER-AIR WAVES

Let us analyze further the patterns of development of upper-air, or Rossby, waves and their relation to atmospheric temperatures. Figure 4.19 is a schematic diagram showing wave evolution in four stages. Long, heavy

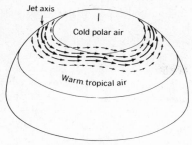

A. Jet stream begins to undulate

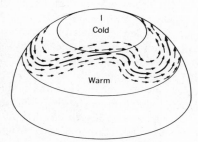

B. Rossby waves begin to form

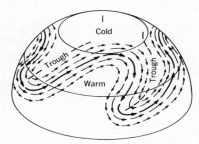

C. Waves strongly developed

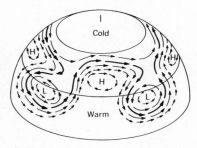

D. Cells of cold and warm air bodies are formed

Figure 4.19. Four stages in the development of upper-air waves in the Northern Hemisphere. (After J. Namias, NOAA National Weather Service.)

arrows show the location of a jet stream whose axis defines the position of the waves. Conditions shown are those existing near the top of the troposphere.

The troposphere lying poleward of the jet

axis consists of cold polar air, whereas that on the equatorward side consists of warm tropical air. Such large bodies of the atmosphere are referred to by the term *air mass.* Air masses are identified on the basis of both temperature and water-vapor content. As will be explained in greater detail in Chapter 5, the polar air masses, because they are cold, can hold little moisture, whereas warm tropical air masses can hold comparatively large quantities. The jet stream in middle latitudes occupies a position at the contact between the polar air mass and the tropical air mass. A contact surface between adjacent air masses is termed a *front,* and in the case under discussion the front lying beneath the jet stream is known as the *polar front.*

Diagram *A* of Figure 4.19 shows the jet stream lying over the high latitudes and with only small undulations. As waves form (diagram *B*), the polar air pushes south at one place and the tropical air moves north at another. Soon great tongues of air form an interlocking pattern, with the jet stream taking a sinuous path between them (diagram *C*). Finally, a wave constricts at the base, and a mass of cold or warm air is detached, forming an isolated mass, or *cell.* A cell of stranded cold air aloft at subtropical latitudes forms a low-pressure center with counterclockwise circulation. An isolated cell of warm air aloft at the higher latitude becomes a high-pressure center with clockwise air flow. At the close of the wave-development cycle, which takes four to six weeks to complete, the isolated cells dissolve, and the jet stream resumes its simple course over the high latitudes as shown in diagram *A.*

The cycle of upper-air wave development explains how great quantities of heat are transferred from equatorial regions to polar regions. North-moving tropical air carries heat to the high latitudes where the heat is lost, whereas south-moving tongues bring cold air to the low latitudes where it absorbs part of the excess heat. Although this form of heat and moisture transfer is fluctuating in intensity and location, the average effect, year in and year out, is to maintain in balance the earth's heat budget. Transfer of heat and water vapor throughout the middle and high latitudes by the growth of upper-air waves and the formation of cyclones and anticyclones is dominantly a process of advection; the horizontal movements are vast and take place within a relatively thin troposphere. In contrast, Hadley cell mixing of air in equatorial and tropical latitudes is dominantly by convection in a relatively thick troposphere.

## THE JET STREAM

We now return to a more detailed consideration of the jet stream as a powerful, but narrow, stream of fast-moving air in the upper troposphere. One might think of this jet stream as resembling the high-pressure flow of water from a hose nozzle held submerged and pointed horizontally in the direction of flow of a slowly moving stream (Figure 4.20). Rather than being a layer, the jet stream is shaped more like a tube which lies roughly horizontally, but which may be curved in plane to change direction from, say, northwest to west to southwest. Figure 4.21 is a map of the United States showing wind speeds at the 30,000-ft (9-km) level on a particular day. The heavy arrows show the jet core as making a great loop southward over the central United States, then curving north over New England. Wind speed is over 200 mph (320 km/hr) in the fastest section of the stream.

Within the past decade or so an enormous expansion in information about winds and temperatures of the upper air has revealed the existence of three important jet-stream systems

in the troposphere of the Northern Hemisphere.

The jet stream described in previous paragraphs as associated with the Rossby waves is known as the *polar-front jet*. Its core lies at the top of the troposphere, and it is classified as a *tropopause jet stream*. Figure 4.22 shows the broad band in which the principal activity of the polar-front jet takes place during the winter.

A second westerly jet system is found in subtropical latitudes and occupies a position at the tropopause level, 43,000–46,000 ft (13–14 km), on the poleward sides of the subtropical high-pressure centers. The mean axis of this *subtropical jet stream* is shown in Figure 4.22. A third system, discovered more recently at still lower latitudes, differs from the first two in that it runs in the opposite direction, namely, from east to west. This *tropical easterly jet stream* occurs only in the summer (high-sun) season and is limited to Northern Hemisphere locations over Southeast Asia, India, and Africa.

For an understanding of the driving mechanism of the polar jet stream we must look into the distribution of both temperature and pressure in a north-south cross section through the atmosphere in the region of the jet stream.

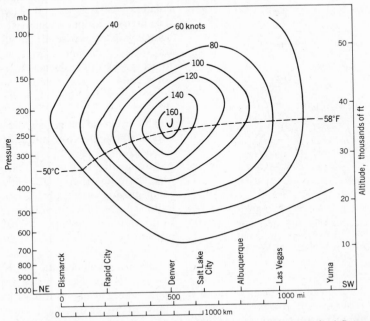

Figure 4.20. Cross-sectional diagram through a jet stream over the western United States. See Figure 4.21 for line of section and accompanying map data. [After H. Riehl (1962), *Jet Streams of the Atmosphere*, Fort Collins, Colo., Colorado State Univ., p. 12, Figure 2.16.]

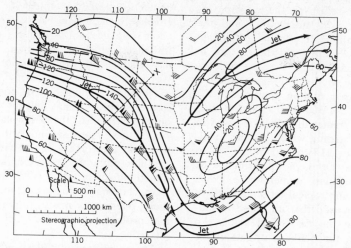

Figure 4.21. Isotachs (knots) and wind arrows at the 300-mb (30,000-ft) level on April 22, 1958. Solid arrows mark jet-stream axis. Cross section along the line X–Y is shown in Figure 4.20. On wind symbols one pennant means 50 knots; one whole feather means 10 knots. [After A. Riehl (1962), *Jet Streams of the Atmosphere*, Fort Collins, Colo., Colorado State Univ., p. 9, Figure 2.12.]

Figure 4.23 is such a cross section of the polar-front region. The polar front is shown by a shaded band, the tropopause by a narrow band above it. Two sets of lines are superimposed— isothermal surfaces (dashed lines) and isobaric surfaces (solid lines). From south to north, temperatures drop sharply across the front, as shown by the steplike bend in an isothermal surface where it crosses from warm air to cold

air. Correspondingly, barometric pressure drops sharply at the front, but this effect is present only in the upper troposphere and above the tropopause. Where the isobaric surface makes its steep descent the pressure gradient is greatly strengthened in a narrow zone. Because wind speed depends upon pressure gradient, the gradient wind paralleling the isobars is greatly intensified and forms the jet-stream core, indicated in the diagram by a circle placed at the steepest point on the isobaric surface.

To understand the existence of the subtropi-

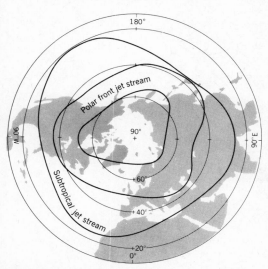

Figure 4.22. Mean winter position of the axis of the subtropical jet stream and the belt of principal winter activity of the polar-front jet stream. [After H. Riehl (1962), *Jet Streams of the Atmosphere*, Fort Collins, Colo., Colorado State Univ., p. 2, Figure 1.2.]

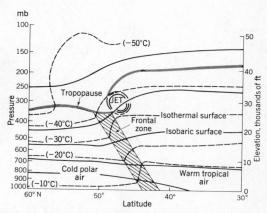

Figure 4.23. Schematic cross section through a frontal zone, showing jet axis in relation to isothermal and isobaric surfaces. [After E. R. Reiter (1967), *Jet Streams*, Garden City, N.Y., Doubleday, p. 122, Figure 57.]

cal jet stream, we return to the principle of conservation of angular momentum and the Hadley-cell circulation. It can be calculated that air moving poleward from the equator to latitude 30° (N or S) will, because of conservation of angular momentum alone, attain a speed of west-to-east motion relative to the earth surface of about 300 mph (480 km/hr). This speed is even greater than that observed in the subtropical jet stream, which reaches maximum core speeds of 215 to 240 mph (345 to 385 km/hr). Thus, although the principle of conservation of angular momentum explains the existence of a subtropical jet stream, there must be found a reason that air speed is substantially less than the theoretical value. An explanation lies in the banking up of air, or convergence, which takes place at the tropopause in the region of maximum westerly wind speed. This convergence sets up a force (known as a pressure force) that resists westerly air flow and detracts from the theoretical speed, as well as limiting further poleward extension of the upper-air westerlies in the Hadley cell.

## GLOBAL PATTERNS OF SURFACE WINDS

Thus far, our approach to global circulation has been one of generalization about very large circulation patterns affecting the atmosphere

above the level at which surface friction is effective in modifying winds. We have also not taken into account low-level atmospheric disturbances, which by their motion cause day-to-day changes in wind direction and strength. Nor have we taken up seasonal effects in which the heating and cooling of continents relative to the adjacent oceans induces winds that seem quite unrelated to the basic planetary patterns. All of these many secondary forms of circulation near the surface of the earth make up the complex patterns of weather and climate that directly affect Man in his surface environment. In our attempt to focus upon basic systems and their operation, many important details of meteorology and climatology must be neglected.

The characteristic pattern of surface winds is shown in Figure 4.24. Note first that the subtropical high-pressure belt is actually composed of a number of centers, known as *cells*. Typically one or two cells are centered over each ocean, while other cells are centered over tropical portions of the continents. Each cell is a persistent site of subsiding air, which is dry. The world's great tropical deserts lie beneath the high-pressure cells. Air movement equatorward from the high-pressure cells constitutes the trade winds, as already noted. These winds are remarkably persistent over the tropical

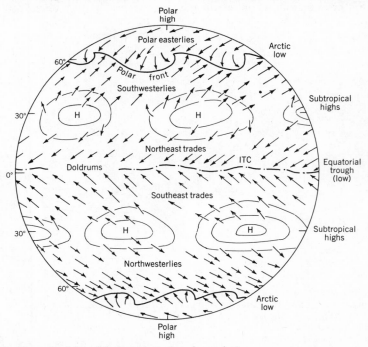

Figure 4.24. Schematic diagram of the global pattern of surface winds.

oceans. Near the equator, the trades converge in the *equatorial trough.* Here barometric pressure is somewhat lower than normal. Locally, the line of trade-wind convergence is sharply defined. Elsewhere there exists a zone of stagnant air, the *doldrums,* in which winds can be described as being light and variable, or absent in extended periods of calms. It is within the equatorial trough that the convectional rise of heated air takes place in the Hadley-cell circulation.

Poleward of the subtropical cells of high pressure the lower air tends to move toward higher latitudes as a southwest wind. This wind pattern, which is intensified in summer of the respective hemisphere, has given rise to the labels *southwesterlies* (Northern Hemisphere) and *northwesterlies* (Southern Hemisphere) within the latitude belt from about 30° to 50°. The facts are that this latitude belt experiences winds from all quarters, depending upon local storms and seasonal effects. In the sense that west winds are most frequent, this latitude zone can aptly be described as a belt of *prevailing* westerly winds. We have already seen that the development of Rossby waves and their occlusion is the basic cause of surface winds from various directions in middle latitudes. At the earth's surface, the contact between cold air of polar origin and warm air of tropical origin is usually a sharply defined line, the *polar front.* As depicted in Figure 4.24, the polar front has a deeply indented pattern. The front is constantly shifting. It may at one time sweep far equatorward; at another time it is formed in arctic latitudes. The cold air motion is associated with winds from a northerly quarter. Hence northwest, north, and northeast winds occur from time to time from middle latitudes to polar regions. The *polar easterlies,* as labeled on the illustration, should not be thought of as persistent winds, such as are the trades, but rather as frequent winds associated with traveling disturbances of the lower atmosphere.

## MONSOON CIRCULATION PATTERNS

The seasonal thermal contrasts between continents and oceans have been emphasized in Chapter 1. Barometric pressure at low levels in the atmosphere reflect air temperatures. For example, over a highly heated continent, low pressure prevails. Over a cold continent in winter, high pressure prevails. Adjacent oceans at the same season show an opposite barometric tendency. Consequently, a pressure

gradient is set up from high to low pressure. Winds develop in response to these gradients. The result is a seasonal flow of air into a continent from the surrounding ocean, alternating with a reversal of this flow at the opposite season. Such seasonal patterns go by the general term *monsoon systems.* Actually, the monsoon circulation of southwestern Asia is by far the most important example of its kind. Much weaker displays of the monsoon effect can be observed in northern Australia, and in the central United States.

Figure 4.25 is a schematic diagram of the monsoon system over a continent in the Northern Hemisphere. The summer cyclone tends to be displaced toward the southern side of the continent, while the winter anticyclone tends to occupy a position north of the continental

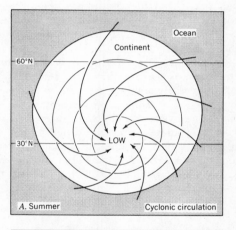

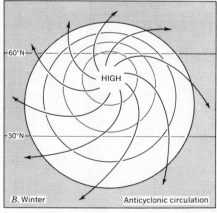

Figure 4.25. Schematic diagram of yearly alternations in surface pressure and air flow over a large middle-latitude continent in the Northern Hemisphere. [After S. Petterssen (1958), *Introduction to Meteorology,* New York, McGraw-Hill, p. 173, Figure 121.]

interior. In Figure 4.26, the surface winds of eastern Asia are shown for July and January. Compare the schematic diagram with this map. The system is well developed only over the southern and eastern parts of Asia. The western part of the Eurasian continent does not show the effect appreciably. Note the placement of the July low-pressure region over northern India, West Pakistan, and Afghanistan. In contrast, the strong winter high of Siberia lies far to the north and coincides with a center of intense cold.

### WINDS AND WAVES

Winds blowing over the ocean surface transfer vast quantities of kinetic energy from the atmosphere to the oceans. One can think of the atmospheric circulation systems, such as the Hadley cell and the prevailing westerlies, as great gear wheels. Meshed with the sea, these wheels turn related systems of surface water motion.

Kinetic energy of water motion takes two forms. One is wave motion, the other a slow drift of water resembling that of a broad river. Both types of motion are powered by wind. As wind blows over a smooth water surface a frictional drag, or *skin drag,* is exerted by the air upon the water. As the air is in turbulent motion it consists of innumerable eddies continually forming and dissolving. Because of

eddies, the skin drag will not be uniformly applied to the water surface and there will be variations in pressure of the air upon the water. The result is the formation of small ripples and longer waves of various amplitudes. Once a wave is formed, it may be reinforced by the pressure of the wind on its sloping surfaces. Kinetic energy continues to flow from the wind into the wave and its height builds.

Wind-generated water waves belong to a type known as *progressive oscillatory waves*. In this type of wave, particles are in constant motion in vertical, circular paths. The motion is greatest at the water surface and dies out rapidly with depth. Figure 4.27 shows the nature of the orbital motion. Particles on the wave crest are moving forward, in the direction of the wave motion, while particles in the trough are moving in the opposite direction. Midway between crest and trough the motion is vertical. With the passage of one wavelength (measured crest-to-crest, or trough-to-trough) the particle completes one orbital circle. The circular particle motion, being of constant velocity, accounts for half of the total kinetic energy of the wave and remains constant as a succession of waves passes. The other half of the wave energy is potential energy due to the fact that particles are lifted above the still-water level or are depressed below that level. The quantity of potential energy fluctuates from zero value to its maximum value and back to zero twice as each wave passes. This energy travels forward with the wave at the wave velocity. Thus the progressive oscillatory wave is capable of conducting a horizontal flow of energy, even though there is no net forward motion of the water particles. Energy of a wave is proportional to the square of the wave height (elevation difference between crest and trough) and directly proportional to the wave-

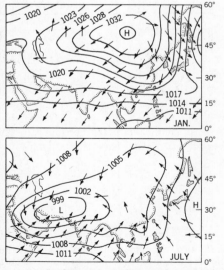

Figure 4.26. Surface maps of pressure and winds over southeastern Asia in January and July. Pressure in millibars. Mercator projection. (Based on data compiled by John E. Oliver, Columbia University.)

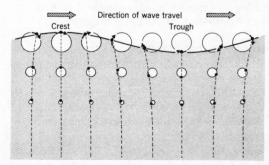

Figure 4.27. Circular orbits in simple waves of low steepness in deep water. (© 1960, John Wiley & Sons, New York.)

length. Knowing the wave period length, and height, the energy flux can be calculated.

Wave height is increased as wind pressure is exerted upon the windward slope of the wave. However, wave speed also increases as it grows and lengthens. It is an observed fact that some groups of waves travel at speeds faster than the wind which sustains them. Obviously, another mechanism besides pressure accounts for energy transfer. This mechanism is the skin drag already referred to. Drag of air over the wave crest tends to speed up the orbital motion of the water (Figure 4.28). Drag upon the water of the trough opposes the water motion and tends to slow orbital motion. However, as the drag is more intense over the crests than over the troughs (because the troughs are sheltered), the net effect is to feed energy into the wave.

Waves will reach a certain limiting height, depending upon the duration and strength of the wind and upon the length of the water surface over which the wind can operate. Maximum wave height is approximately proportional to wind speed.

Wind waves that are no longer in the process of growing or being sustained by wind are transformed into long, low waves of uniform spacing, known as *swell*. These decaying waves travel enormous distances across the ocean. For example, a storm wave of 30-ft height and 9-sec period will, after traveling 3000 mi, be reduced to a height of 4 ft and a period of 18 sec. Long swells on an otherwise calm sea constitute an example of a simple train of ideal progressive oscillatory waves. Waves in process of growth, by contrast, consist of wave elements of many periods, heights, lengths, and directions superimposed upon one another.

## WINDS AND OCEAN CURRENTS

The same frictional drag, or skin drag, that contributes to wave growth also sets the surface water in motion. As the uppermost water

layer is dragged in the down-wind direction, it in turn drags along the next lower layer. Thus the motion is propagated toward increasing depth. However, in following this motion to lower depths, we must take into account the Coriolis effect. Each layer is subjected to the Coriolis effect, which acts as a force pulling toward the right in a direction perpendicular to the direction of motion. The action is the same as for air in motion (see Figure 4.9).

The Coriolis effect upon motion of the ocean surface was observed by Fridtjof Nansen, the arctic explorer, as his vessel, the *Fram,* was drifting upon the polar sea, firmly held in pack ice. Nansen noted that the pack ice was moving in a direction some 20° to 45° toward the right of the wind direction, a phenomenon that he correctly attributed to the Coriolis effect. To the oceanographer Ekman is attributed the mathematical analysis of water motions with increasing depths. As shown in Figure 4.29, each layer is deflected to the right with respect to the layer above it. Therefore, the angle with respect to the surface water motion also increases with depth, while at the same time speed of the motion decreases. When vector arrows are drawn to represent direction and speed at equal units of depth, their points form a spiral of diminishing radius. This spiral has been named the *Ekman spiral.* Whereas the surface-water motion is about 45° to the right of the wind direction, the motion of water with greater depth gradually turns until the direction is exactly opposite to the surface motion. This depth is referred to as the *friction depth* and is encountered at a distance from 300 to 600 ft (90 to 180 m) below the surface.

Taking into account the changed speed and direction within the Ekman spiral, it can be computed that the average direction of motion of the entire layer of moving water is about at 90° to the right of the wind direction in the Northern Hemisphere. In the Southern Hemisphere the deflection is correspondingly toward the left.

Drift of ocean-surface water, as shown on nautical charts, refers to the uppermost water layers. In comparing drift direction with prevailing winds, one finds that direction of water motion is approximately at 45° with respect to wind direction. This relationship is particularly clear in the trade-wind belts. The trades are remarkably persistent winds, being almost entirely from the northeast quarter in the Northern Hemisphere. The water drift here is almost due westward, making a 45° angle.

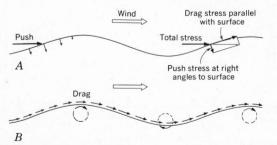

Figure 4.28. Development of wind waves by pressure and surface drag.

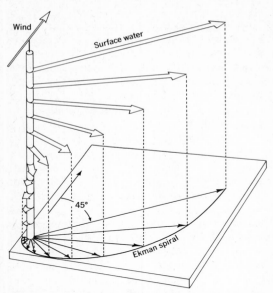

Figure 4.29. The Ekman spiral. Open arrows show current direction and relative speed from the surface downward for equal depth units. The projection of these arrow points upon a horizontal plane, below, produces the Ekman spiral. [After H. U. Sverdrup, *Oceanography for Meteorologists,* copyright 1942, renewed 1970, Englewood Cliffs, N.J., Prentice-Hall, p. 125, Figure 30.]

## CURRENTS PRODUCED BY DENSITY DIFFERENCES

Surface-water motion also occurs when the ocean surface develops a gradient with respect to the ideal or equilibrium surface. One cause of a sloping water surface is the accumulation of water near a coast from an impinging current flow. A surface gradient may also exist where a column of water of less density lies adjacent to a column of greater density. Figure 4.30 illustrates such a case. A layer of less dense water (right) overlies denser water. Surfaces of equal pressure (isobaric surfaces) are horizontal and parallel in the denser water below. However, in the layer of less dense water the isobaric surfaces are raised. The sea surface itself is an isobaric surface sloping from right to left. Just as in the case of a sloping isobaric surface in the atmosphere, a pressure-gradient force ($F$) is directed across the isobars in the down-gradient direction. Water tends to move in the direction of the pressure-gradient force but is deflected by Coriolis force until flow parallels the slope. The current that results resembles the geostrophic wind.

Density of sea water depends upon both its temperature and its salinity. Colder water is more dense than warm. The greater the salinity, the greater is the density. The term *thermohaline* refers to the combined effect of temperature and salinity in varying the density of sea water. Very cold water of arctic and antarctic regions tends to have high density. Warm water from a tropical-desert area where evaporation is rapid will have high density because the salinity is high. We can anticipate that water of the equatorial belt, where temperatures are high but salinity low because of heavy rainfall, will have relatively low density. It is because of such density differences from one area to another that thermohaline currents can be set up.

## GENERAL PATTERN OF OCEANIC CIRCULATION

Within each ocean a characteristic pattern of surface currents and drifts is repeated. Figure 4.31 shows schematically the major elements of the flow system. The major features are two great *gyres,* or circular flow systems. One gyre is located in each hemisphere, centered approximately upon the subtropical cell of high barometric pressure. Water motion is clockwise about the gyres. (Compare with the schematic map of pressure and winds, Figure 4.24.) Note that the trade winds set in motion an *equatorial current,* paralleling the equator, while the prevailing westerlies set in motion a *west-wind drift* in middle latitudes. The gyre is completed by a strong poleward flow at the western side of the gyre. Because of the Coriolis effect, the gyres are pushed toward the west side of the ocean. Consequently, the poleward currents on

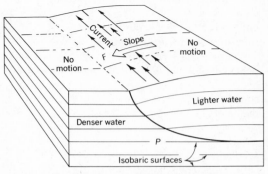

Figure 4.30. Difference of density in adjacent water layers tends to produce a current at right angles to the slope of the water surface. [After H. U. Sverdrup (1942), *Oceanography for Meteorologists,* Englewood Cliffs, N.J., Prentice-Hall, p. 105.]

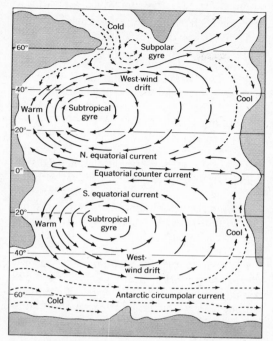

Figure 4.31. Schematic diagram of an ocean with an idealized system of surface currents.

the west sides are intensified. Examples are the Gulf Stream off North America, and the Kuroshio Current off Japan. These currents are relatively warm and serve to transport heat from low to high latitudes.

On the eastern sides of the gyres, the drift is turned equatorward, bringing cool water of arctic and antarctic origin into low latitudes. In combination with up-welling of colder water from depth, these equatorward currents bring unusually cool air temperatures to continental west coasts at low latitudes. The effect of the great oceanic gyres upon the earth's heat budget is most important, for enormous quantities of water are exchanged by the flow.

Configuration of the Antarctic continent, a pole-centered landmass completely surrounded by the great belt of southern ocean, results in a simple circulation system quite unlike that of the Northern Hemisphere. Strong prevailing westerly winds set in motion an *antarctic circumpolar current,* which encircles Antarctica in a continuous stream.

Surface water close to the antarctic continent becomes intensely chilled and, because of its greater density, subsides from the surface to great depths, spreading out slowly upon the ocean floor and gradually moving toward lower

latitudes. The zone in which cold-water sinking takes place is known as a *convergence zone,* for surface water must move in from the flanking regions to replace the sinking water. Thus, we see that oceanic circulation also takes place in the vertical dimension and that heat exchange also occurs through the sinking and rising of waters and their gradual motion at various depths to different latitudes. Space does not permit an analysis of these scientifically important deep-water circulation patterns.

## OCEANIC CIRCULATION AND THE EARTH'S HEAT BALANCE

In Chapter 1 the following heat-balance equation was developed for a unit of soil or water:

$$R = H + LE + G + F$$

where $R$ is net all-wave radiation at the earth's surface,

$H$ is transfer of sensible heat through the upper surface by conduction and turbulent exchange,

$LE$ is latent-heat transfer by evaporation,

$G$ is the net warming or cooling of the column,

and $F$ is horizontal transfer of heat out of the column by mass transport.

The global circulation systems of both the atmosphere and the world ocean have been described in the preceding chapter. Therefore it is appropriate to consider the heat-balance equation as it applies to the earth-atmosphere system. The unit column now includes the entire thickness of both atmosphere and ocean.

First, the net warming or cooling will be very small for the annual cycle at a given place, which means that the term $G$ can be eliminated from the equation. Second, instead of the term $H$, which refers to upward heat flux from the earth's surface, we will substitiute the term $C$, defined as the net flux of sensible heat out of the column by atmospheric motion. The term $F$ will now refer to the net transport of heat out of the column by ocean currents. Instead of the term $LE$, it will be necessary to use for latent-heat flux a corresponding term $L(E - r)$, in which the smaller letter $r$ is the annual precipitation (rain or snow). Therefore the quantity $(E - r)$ is the difference between water evaporated and water precipitated and represents the net quantity of water that enters or leaves the atmospheric column in vapor form. A positive value of $(E - r)$ indicates that evaporation is in excess and that water vapor must be exported from the atmospheric column.

With terms thus redefined, the global heat-balance equation becomes:

$$R = C + L(E - r) + F$$

Notice that the three terms on the right represent the three mechanisms of meridional heat transport by (1) sensible heat carried by moving air, (2) latent heat carried in atmospheric water vapor, and (3) sensible heat carried by moving water.

Figure 4.32 shows the average annual values of all four terms of the heat-balance equation for each 10° belt of latitude from pole to pole. Figure 4.33 corresponds to the preceding figure

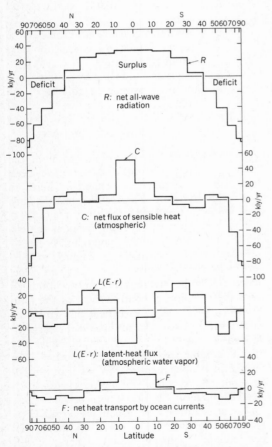

Figure 4.32. Latitudinal distribution of components of the global heat-balance equation. [Data from W. D. Sellers (1965), *Physical Climatology*, Chicago, Univ. of Chicago Press, p. 115, Figure 34.]

but shows annual total meridional transport of heat for each term in the heat-balance equation. The units used in Figure 4.33 are kilocalories per year times $10^{19}$. Smooth curves are used in this illustration, instead of step graphs, because flow is continuous across the parallels of latitude. Where the curves lie above the zero line, flow is northward, while below the zero line flow is southward.

The explanations of each curve in the two figures have been fully explored in this chapter and Chapter 1. Notice that the net-radiation graph $(R)$ in Figure 4.32 is identical with that shown as the middle graph in Figure 1.21, conveying the information that there is a radiation surplus between latitudes 40° N and 40° S and a radiation deficit poleward of those parallels.

Consider next the distribution of the term $C$, representing sensible-heat flux (Figure 4.32). A sharp peak between the equator and 10° N latitude shows that a great surplus of atmospheric heat is generated in a narrow zone. Appropriately named the "firebox" of the earth's atmosphere, this zone obtains its heat surplus both from radiation and from the conversion of latent heat into sensible heat in cloud condensation (a process explained in Chapter 5). Negative values of sensible-heat flux occur in two subtropical latitude belts. For an explanation, we look to the graph for latent-heat flux, $L(E - r)$. At a glance, it is evident that this graph is opposite in phase with the graph above it. A strong negative value of latent-heat flux in the zone 0° to 10° N shows that water vapor is imported into the equatorial trough, there to be converted into sensible heat by condensation. Recall that in discussion of the Hadley cell it was stated that large amounts of water vapor are brought equatorward in the converging trades (tropical easterlies).

Over the subtropical high-pressure belts, peaking in the belt 20° to 30°, a surplus in the latent-heat flux signifies that water vapor is entering the atmosphere by evaporation from the sea surface (Figure 4.32). In the graph of sensible-heat flux, above, these same belts show slightly negative values, for here air in the descending limb of the Hadley cell divides and flows out of the belt both poleward and equatorward.

The middle-latitude belts, 40° to 60°, gain sensible heat by poleward air movement in the westerlies but lose latent heat by condensation in cyclonic storms, which are common in this

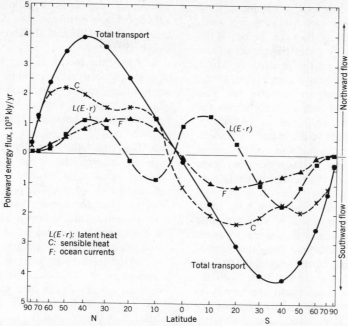

Figure 4.33. The earth's meridional heat transport. [Data from W. D. Sellers (1965), *Physical Climatology*, Chicago, Univ. of Chicago Press, p. 115, Figure 34.]

belt. (See Chapter 5.) In the two polar zones, sensible heat is lost by transformation into radiant energy, which leaves these regions by longwave radiation into outer space.

Finally, the meridional transfer of sensible heat from equatorial latitudes to middle latitudes by ocean currents is clearly evident in the lowermost graph in Figure 4.32 and in Figure 4.33. Transport out of the belt between 20° N and 20° S occurs largely in the poleward water movements on the western sides of the great oceanic gyres. As shown in Figure 4.33, peak values of poleward transport by ocean currents occur at about 20° to 25° latitude.

We have now completed an evaluation of the earth's heat balance, including estimates of the quantities of energy flux involved. Keep in mind that these estimates will be revised from time to time and should serve only as a guide to relative amounts. The heat balance is, of course, entirely that of an energy budget and includes no evaluation of masses in motion except with regard to their roles as transporters of sensible heat and latent heat.

There exists a second great global budget, consisting of transport systems of both air and water and reflected in a *mass balance*. The latter is referred to as the *water balance* and will be developed further in the next chapter,

following a discussion of atmospheric moisture and its changes of state. Final details of the water balance must be deferred until the flow of water upon the lands and below the ground surface are treated in Chapter 6.

## A SYSTEM IN REVIEW

This chapter has dealt with transport systems that are entirely mechanical in action. Starting with large-scale atmospheric motion in response to pressure-gradient differences, kinetic energy of a gaseous layer in motion is transferred by mechanical linkage to a liquid surface beneath it. Both atmospheric and oceanic flow systems are characterized by fluid flow circuits which involve advective transfer of heat. In terms of the earth's heat budget, advection is of enormous importance in moderating the earth's thermal regime by carrying excess heat of the equatorial latitudes, where radiation input is large, to cold polar regions, where there is a radiation deficit.

The flow systems of atmosphere and oceans are thermally powered. As such, they are subsystems of the sun-earth-space radiation system and are dependent upon the larger system for sustained operation. Kinetic energy of air and water in motion is eventually transformed into heat energy through resistance offered to the flow. Much of this resistance is within the fluid itself, because fluids possess viscosity and work must be done to sustain flowage. Some of the resistance is offered by zones of contact of the fluids with solid land of the continents. Much energy is dissipated when waves arrive at the continental shores and are transformed into surges and currents which in turn erode the lands and transport sediment (Chapter 9). Much energy of winds is dissipated in friction over unyielding land surfaces, with minor amounts of work done through transportation of solid particles over the land surface (Chapter 9).

Heat generated by resistance within the moving fluids and at their contacts with the solid land surface is eventually dissipated to outer space as longwave radiation. Thus the flow of energy is completed and the essential terms of the global heat balance are satisfied. Both the input and output of this system are wholly in the form of energy, since matter remains entirely within the system boundaries and is recirculated without appreciable gain or loss.

### References for further study

Williams, J. (1962), *Oceanography: An Introduction to the Marine Sciences,* Boston, Little, Brown, 242 pp., chaps. 9–11.

Bascomb, W. (1964), *Waves and Beaches,* Garden City, N.Y., Doubleday, 260 pp.

Riehl, H. (1965), *Introduction to the Atmosphere,* New York, McGraw-Hill, 365 pp., chaps. 3, 6.

Sellers, W. D. (1965), *Physical Climatology,* Chicago, Univ. of Chicago Press, 272 pp., chap. 8.

Reiter, E. (1967), *Jet Streams,* Garden City, N.Y., Doubleday, 189 pp.

Petterssen, S. (1969), *Introduction to Meteorology,* 3rd ed., New York, McGraw-Hill, 333 pp., chaps. 9–11.

Strahler, A. N. (1971), *The Earth Sciences,* 2nd ed., New York, Harper & Row, 826 pp., chaps. 15–17.

### Review questions

1. What is the standard value of sea-level barometric pressure? At what rate does pressure change with increasing altitude? Does the form of the pressure-altitude curve reflect the position of the tropopause?

2. Describe a pressure gradient in the horizontal direction. How is the gradient shown on a map? in cross section? What is the pressure-gradient force? How is this force generated?

3. Describe the formation of a simple convective wind system resulting from unequal heating of an air layer. Show how pressure differences are developed, causing air motion. Use this model to explain the sea breeze and land breeze.

4. Apply the model of the previous question to a simple convective system of winds on a nonrotating earth. Describe the meridional winds of such a system. What real global pressure phenomena are explained by this model?

5. Describe the Coriolis effect. Illustrate with an example from the earth-trace of an orbiting satellite. What variable factors affect the magnitude of the Coriolis force? In what direction does the force act with respect to the path of motion? Show how a parcel of air moving horizontally is acted upon by the Coriolis force to produce the geostrophic wind.

6. What third force acts upon air moving in a curved path? How does the force of friction influence air movement near the ground? How does frictional force affect the flow paths within a cyclone? Within an anticyclone? Relate these effects to convergence and divergence.

7. Describe the Hadley-cell circulation system of low latitudes. Why does upper-air convergence develop in the subtropical belt? What pressure effects has this convergence? How are tropical easterlies formed? What is meant by ITC? What role does the Hadley cell play in the global heat balance?

8. How does the law of conservation of angular momentum apply to the earth's atmosphere? Explain the transport of angular momentum across parallels of latitude by moving air. How are westerly winds developed by poleward flow of air? What change in angular momentum accompanies equatorward air flow?

9. Describe the upper-air westerlies of middle and high latitudes. With what barometric pressure system is this flow associated? What departures from simple zonal flow develop within the westerlies? What is a cutoff low? a cutoff high? What are the polar easterlies? How are they generated?

10. Explain the maintenance of the system of westerlies through transfer of angular momentum by the eddy transport mechanism. Describe a laboratory model experiment in which westerlies and upper-air waves can be simulated. What variables affect the circulation patterns in this model? What pattern of atmospheric circulation might be anticipated on the planet Venus?

11. What is the jet stream, and how is it related to upper-air waves of the westerlies? Compare air masses in terms of temperature on poleward and equatorward sides of the jet-stream axis. What is the polar front? Describe the stages in evolution of upper-air waves leading to cutoff and development of cells. Relate these cells to conditions of temperature and pressure. What is meant by advection? How does this activity play a part in the earth's heat balance.

12. Describe three major jet-stream systems and explain their locations with respect to parts of the planetary circulation system. What is the driving mechanism of the polar jet stream? of the subtropical jet stream?

13. Describe the global patterns of surface winds. How are wind patterns related to the subtropical cells of high pressure? What conditions of circulation prevail in the equatorial zone? Are wind directions more persistently from one direction in the westerlies or in the trades? Explain.

14. What is a monsoon circulation? How is it developed? Describe the monsoon circulation of Southeast Asia and relate it to seasonal conditions of air temperature and of barometric pressure.

15. How are water waves generated by winds? What type of wave is produced? Describe the orbital motion within the wave. In what form does energy exist within waves, and how is the energy carried forward? What is a swell?

16. How does wind stress cause motion of surface water? Describe and explain the Ekman spiral. How is average direction of water motion related to wind direction? Illustrate with the case of the trade-wind belt.

17. How can surface water motion be induced by differences in water density? What does the word *thermohaline* mean? How is the density of sea water affected by temperature? by salinity?

18. Describe the general patterns of surface currents and drifts of the oceans of the globe. What is a gyre? Contrast circulation patterns of Northern and Southern hemispheres. What is a convergence zone?

19. Derive a global heat-balance equation that takes into account the three mechanisms of meridional heat transport. Describe the meridional profile of sensible heat flux. How does the profile of latent heat flux relate to that of sensible heat flux? At what latitudes is heat transport by ocean currents most important?

20. Describe in broad terms the transport systems of atmospheric and oceanic circulation. What is the energy source for these circulation systems? How does energy leave the system? What geologic activities depend upon energy derived from atmospheric circulation?

# chapter 5 transport systems: ii. changes in state of atmospheric water

The analysis of atmospheric and oceanic transport systems given in Chapter 4 is incomplete in a highly important sense. Both the air and the water involved in advective and convective circuits were treated primarily as if no change of state of water entered into the picture, although the role of latent heat was included in the earth's heat balance. The air was considered as if it held no water vapor, but simply moved as a gas responding to temperature differences and corresponding changes in density and barometric pressure. Water was assumed to remain below the interface of the sea surface, there to change in temperature and to move in response to wind stress. This chapter emphasizes the mass transport of water from the liquid state in the oceans to the vapor state in the overlying atmosphere, followed by return to the liquid state by condensation and return to the oceans and lands.

Whereas dry air, with its low specific heat,*

* The specific heat of air is about 0.25 cal/gm, or about one-fourth that of water, which is 1.0 cal/gm.

is limited in its capacity to hold and transport heat, the same air can take up and carry water in the vapor state, holding a large quantity of heat energy in the latent form. Through condensation, this latent energy is released to the atmosphere, a process that may take place far from the region where the vapor entered the atmosphere. We have seen in Chapter 4 that water vapor transported in the planetary circulation system plays a major role in maintaining the earth's heat balance as we now find it; Figure 5.1 illustrates this concept. At the same time, condensation of water vapor supplies power for intense storms, which generate local winds differing greatly in direction and strength from the average planetary winds. Large-scale energy release by condensation requires the lifting of huge masses of moist air through large vertical distances. A principle requiring special attention is that the rise of air is accompanied by spontaneous cooling, enabling condensation to take place on a massive scale.

The cycle of exchange of water vapor be-

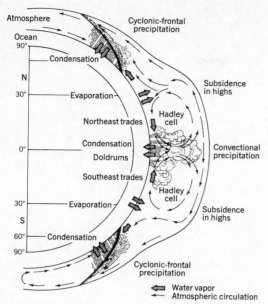

Figure 5.1. Schematic diagram of the role of water vapor in meridional heat exchange. (From A. N. Strahler, "The Life Layer," *Jour. of Geography*, vol. 69, no. 2, p. 74, Figure 3. © 1970 by The Journal of Geography; reproduced by permission.)

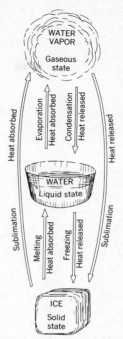

Figure 5.2. Three states of water.

tween the atmosphere and the oceans does not constitute an independent physical system, but rather it is an integral part of the atmospheric transport system. An investigation of water vapor in the atmosphere therefore leads us farther along toward completion of an analysis of the earth's fluid transport systems. Paths taken by water molecules from ocean to air and return are many and varied. Treated apart, these circuits of water movement are part of the total *hydrologic cycle,* which also includes the flow paths and storage reservoirs of liquid and solid water on and within the solid earth, as streams, glaciers, lakes, and ground water. This aspect of the hydrologic cycle is treated in Chapter 6. Only when the gravity-flow subsystems are included will our study of the total system of matter and energy flow, powered by solar radiation, be fully completed.

## WATER STATES AND HEAT

Water occurs in three states: (1) frozen as ice, a crystalline *solid;* (2) *liquid* as water; and (3) *gaseous* as water vapor (Figure 5.2). From the gaseous-vapor state, molecules may pass into the liquid state by *condensation* or, if temperatures are below the freezing point, by *sublimation* directly into the solid state to form ice crystals. By *evaporation,* molecules can

leave a water surface to become gas molecules in water vapor. The analogous change from ice directly into water vapor is also designated sublimation. Then, of course, water may pass from liquid to solid state by *freezing,* and from solid state to liquid state by *melting.*

Of great importance in atmospheric science are the exchanges of heat energy accompanying changes of state. For example, when water evaporates, *sensible heat,* which we can feel and measure. by thermometer, passes into a hidden form held by the water vapor and known as the *latent heat of vaporization.* This change results in a drop in temperature of the remaining liquid. The cooling effect produced by evaporation of perspiration from the skin is perhaps the most obvious example. For every gram of water that is evaporated, about 600 cal pass into the latent form. In the reverse process of condensation, an equal amount of energy is released to become sensible heat, tending to increase the temperature of the air in which condensation is taking place. Similarly, the freezing process releases heat energy in the amount of about 80 cal/gm of water, whereas melting absorbs an equal quantity of heat, referred to as the *latent heat of fusion.* When sublimation occurs, the heat absorbed by vaporization or released by crystallization is even greater for each gram of water, because the latent heats of vaporization and fusion are added together.

## ATMOSPHERIC HUMIDITY

The amount of water vapor that may be present in the air at a given time varies widely from place to place. It ranges from virtually nothing in the cold, dry air of arctic regions in winter to as much as 4% or 5% of the volume of the atmosphere in warm, humid, equatorial areas.

Water vapor enters the atmosphere by evaporation from exposed water surfaces such as oceans, lakes, rivers, or moist ground. Some is supplied by plants which transpire water (a form of evaporation) as a physiological function. With large expanses of ocean and densely forested lands over the globe, there is no lack of surface for evaporation.

The term *humidity* refers generally to the degree to which water vapor is present in the air. For any specified temperature there is a definite limit to the quantity of moisture that can be held by the air. This limit is known as the *saturation value*. The proportion of water vapor present relative to the maximum quantity is the *relative humidity,* expressed as a percentage. At the saturation value, relative humidity is 100%; when half of the total possible quantity of vapor is present, relative humidity is 50%, and so on.

A change in relative humidity of the atmosphere can be caused in one of two ways. If an exposed water surface is present, the humidity can be increased by evaporation. This is a slow process, requiring that the water vapor diffuse upward through the air. The other way is through a change of temperature. Even though no water vapor is added, a lowering of temperature results in a rise of relative humidity. This is automatic and is a logical consequence of the fact that the capacity of the air to hold water vapor has been lowered by cooling; thus the existing amount of vapor represents a higher percentage of the total capacity of the air. Similarly, a rise of air temperature results in decreased relative humidity, even though no water vapor has been taken away. The principle of relative-humidity change caused by temperature change is illustrated by a graph of these two properties throughout the day (Figure 5.3). As air temperature rises, relative humidity falls and vice versa.

A simple example illustrates these principles. At a certain place the temperature of the air is

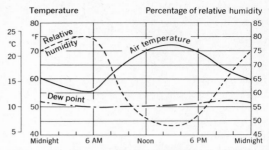

Figure 5.3. Curves of mean hourly air temperature, dew point, and relative humidity for the month of May at Washington, D.C. (Data of NOAA, National Weather Service.)

60° F (16° C); the relative humidity is 50%. Should the air become warmed by longwave radiation from the sun and ground surface to reach 90° F (32° C), the relative humidity automatically drops to 20%, which is very dry air. By outgoing longwave radiation the air becomes chilled during the night and its temperature falls to 40° F (5° C); the relative humidity then automatically rises to 100%, the saturation value. Any further cooling will cause condensation of the excess vapor into liquid form. As the air temperature continues to fall, the humidity remains at 100%, but condensation continues, taking the form of minute droplets of dew or fog. If the temperature falls below freezing, condensation occurs as frost upon exposed surfaces.

The term *dew point* is applied to the critical temperature at which the air is fully saturated and below which condensation normally occurs. An excellent illustration of condensation due to cooling is seen in summertime when beads of moisture form on the outside surface of a pitcher or glass filled with ice water. Air immediately adjacent to the cold glass or metal surface is sufficiently chilled to fall below the dew-point temperature, causing moisture to condense on the surface of the glass.

Although relative humidity is an important indicator of the state of water vapor in the air, it is a statement only of the relative quantity with respect to a saturation quantity. The actual quantity of moisture present is denoted by *absolute humidity,* defined as the weight of water vapor contained in a given volume of air. Weight is stated in grams, volume in cubic meters. For any specified air temperature, there is a maximum weight of water vapor that a cubic meter of air can hold (the saturation quantity). Figure 5.4 is a graph showing this maximum moisture content of air for a wide range of temperatures.

In a sense, absolute humidity is a yardstick of a basic natural resource—fresh water—to be applied from equatorial to polar regions. It is a measure of the quantity of water that can be extracted from the atmosphere as precipitation. Cold air can supply only a small quantity of rain or snow; warm air is capable of supplying large quantities.

## VAPOR PRESSURE

When water vapor is added to otherwise pure, dry air, the water molecules diffuse perfectly among the other gas molecules. Because the molecular weight of water vapor is less than that of pure, dry air, moist air is lighter (less dense) than dry air, if equal volumes are compared at a given temperature and pressure. That part of the total barometric pressure that is due to the water vapor alone is termed the *vapor pressure* and can be stated in terms of the part of a mercury column sustained by the vapor alone. For cold, dry air, the vapor pressure may be as low as 0.05 in. (0.013 cm); for very warm, moist air of the equatorial regions, it may be as high as 0.80 in. (2 cm). This latter figure says that if the mercury column stands at 30.0 in. (76.2 cm) height, 0.8 in. (2 cm) of that height is counterbalanced by the weight of water vapor in the air.

Figure 5.4 shows the maximum possible vapor pressure for air of a range of temperatures from very cold to very warm. Both vapor pressure and absolute humidity tell the quantity of water vapor present in the air but in somewhat different ways.

## SPECIFIC HUMIDITY

One disadvantage of using absolute humidity as a measure of atmospheric moisture is that when air rises or sinks in elevation, it undergoes corresponding volume changes of expansion or contraction. Consequently, the absolute humidity cannot remain a constant figure for the same body of air. Modern meteorology therefore makes use of another measure of moisture content, *specific humidity,* which is the ratio of weight of water vapor to weight of moist air (including the water vapor). Units are grams of water vapor per kilogram of moist air. When a given parcel of air is lifted to higher elevations without gain or loss of moisture the specific humidity remains constant, despite volume increase.

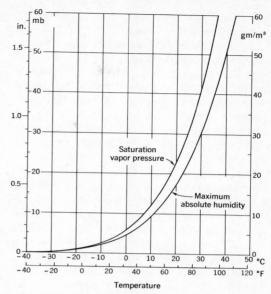

Figure 5.4. Vapor pressure of saturated air and the equivalent values of absolute humidity.

Specific humidity is used to describe the moisture characteristics of a large mass of air. For example, extremely cold, dry air over arctic regions in winter may have a specific humidity of as low as 0.2 gm/kg, whereas extremely warm moist air of tropical regions may hold as much as 18 gm/kg. The total natural natural range on a world-wide basis is such that the largest values of specific humidity are from 100 to 200 times as great as the least.

## AIR MASSES

A fundamental concept in understanding the role of water vapor in transport of energy and matter through the atmospheric circulation system is that of the *air mass.* In terms of dimensions, a single air mass is a body of air extending horizontally over a substantial part of a continent or ocean and vertically through a major fraction of the troposphere. In terms of its properties, a given air mass possesses an approximately uniform temperature and water-vapor content in all horizontal directions at any given elevation. An important descriptive property of an air mass is the manner in which its temperature changes with elevation.

Typically, a given air mass has a sharply defined boundary in contact with a different air mass adjacent to it. Such a discontinuity is termed a *front.* Fronts may be essentially vertical, or may be inclined almost to horizontality. In the latter case, one air mass will overlie another. Fronts may also be in rapid motion, as one air mass displaces another.

An air mass is a product of its *source region,* the ocean or land surface from which it derives its physical properties. For example, over a warm ocean, the air mass derives a high water-vapor content in combination with high temperature. Over a cold continent in winter, an air mass is not only intensely cold, especially in the lower layer, but its water-vapor content is extremely small as well.

Although an air mass develops its unique properties over the source region, the mass can travel into other regions, following the movement of regional winds in response to the pressure gradient. Modification of air-mass characteristics gradually takes place during migration, depending upon whether heat is gained or lost to the ground surface through longwave radiation or sensible heat flux. Water vapor may be added by evaporation from a sea surface below and find its way upward by diffusion and turbulent air motions. Water vapor may also be lost by condensation and precipitation.

Classification of air masses is based upon the latitudinal position of the source area and the nature of the underlying surface, whether continent or ocean. Latitudinal position relates closely with air temperature, nature of the surface below with water-vapor content. In tabular form, the types of air masses based on latitude are as follows:

| Air Mass | Symbol | Source Region |
|---|---|---|
| Arctic | *A* | Arctic Ocean and fringing lands |
| Antarctic | *AA* | Antarctica |
| Polar | *P* | Lands and oceans, 50° to 65°, N and S latitudes |
| Tropical | *T* | Lands and oceans under subtropical high-pressure cells, 20° to 35°, N and S latitudes |
| Equatorial | *E* | Oceans close to the equator, in equatorial trough and doldrums |

Temperatures of these air masses range from extremely cold for the arctic types to very warm for the tropical types.

In terms of source region characteristics and moisture content, two further subdivisions are recognized as follows:

| Air Mass | Symbol | Source Region |
|---|---|---|
| Maritime | *m* | Oceans |
| Continental | *c* | Continents |

As expected, maritime air masses have high water-vapor content; continental air masses have low water-vapor content.

The principal combinations of latitudinal and source-region divisions are shown in Table 5.1, with typical examples to illustrate the conditions of temperature and specific humidity that may be expected. Notice that the moisture content of the *mE* air mass is almost 200 times as great as that of the *cA* air mass. The example of *cT* air mass, with 11 gm/kg specific humidity, illustrates that air of the tropical deserts, although of low relative humidity when highly heated during the daytime, actually holds substantial quantities of water vapor. The *mP* air masses, shown in the example with a specific humidity of 4.4 gm/kg, are capable of yielding large amounts of precipitation under favorable conditions, whereas the polar and arctic air masses can produce little or none.

Figure 5.5 is a schematic global diagram to show the principal air-mass regions. The subtropical high-pressure cells form source regions of *mT* air masses over the oceans but of *cT* air masses over continents. The source regions of *mP* air masses coincide with great centers of low pressure over the Aleutian region in the north Pacific, the Icelandic region in the north Atlantic, and the Southern Ocean surrounding Antarctica. Important frontal zones of interaction between unlike air masses are shown on the diagram by heavy lines. These fronts are shown diagrammatically, however, and in reality shift widely over middle and high latitudes.

## CONDENSATION, CLOUDS, AND PRECIPITATION

Actively falling rain, snow, sleet, or hail, referred to collectively as *precipitation,* can result only where large masses of air are experiencing continued drop in temperature below the dew point. This condition cannot be brought about by the simple process of chilling of the air through loss of heat by radiation during the night. Instead, it is necessary that the large mass of air be rising to higher elevations. This statement requires that an essential physical principle be explained.

One of the most important laws of meteorology is that rising air (or any gas) experiences a drop in temperature, even though no heat energy is lost to the outside (Figure 5.6). The drop of temperature is a result of the decrease

Table 5.1.  EXAMPLES OF AIR-MASS CHARACTERISTICS

| Air Mass | Symbol | Properties | Temperature (°F) | (°C) | Specific Humidity (gm/kg) |
|---|---|---|---|---|---|
| Continental arctic and continental antarctic | cA (cAA) | Very cold, very dry (winter) | −50° | −46° | 0.1 |
| Continental polar | cP | Cold, dry (winter) | 12° | −11° | 1.4 |
| Maritime polar | mP | Cool, moist (winter) | 39° | 4° | 4.4 |
| Continental tropical | cT | Warm, dry | 75° | 24° | 11 |
| Maritime tropical | mT | Warm, moist | 75° | 24° | 17 |
| Maritime equatorial | mE | Warm, very moist | 80° | 27° | 19 |

in air pressure at higher elevations, permitting the rising air to expand. Individual molecules of the gas are more widely diffused and do not strike one another so frequently; hence they impart a lower sensible temperature to the gas. When no condensation is occurring, the rate of drop of temperature, termed the *dry adiabatic rate,* is about 5½° F per 1000 ft of vertical rise of air. In metric units the rate is 1 C° per 100 m. The dew point also declines with rise of air; the rate is 1 F° per 1000 ft (0.2 C° per

100 m). In Figure 5.6 the drop in dew-point temperature is labeled *dew-point lapse rate.*

When water vapor in the air is condensing, the adiabatic rate is less, about 3.2 F° per 1000 ft (0.2 C° per 100 m), owing to the partial counteraction of temperature loss through the liberation of latent heat during the condensation process. This modified rate is referred to as the *wet adiabatic,* or *saturation adiabatic, rate* (Figure 5.6). Adiabatic cooling rate should not be confused with the normal tem-

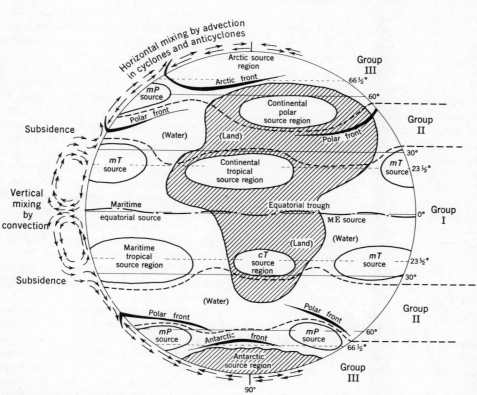

Figure 5.5. Schematic diagram of climate groups in relation to frontal zones, air masses, and source regions. (© 1960, John Wiley & Sons, New York. Data from Petterssen and others.)

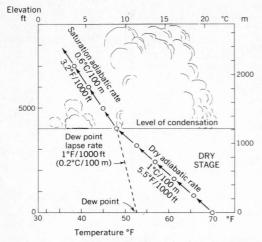

Figure 5.6. Dry adiabatic lapse rate and dew-point lapse rate.

perature-lapse rate, explained in Chapter 1. The lapse rate applies only to still air whose temperature is measured at successively higher levels. When an air mass has been cooled by lifting to the point that the dry adiabatic curve intersects the dew-point curve, condensation begins and clouds appear (Figure 5.6).

Clouds consist of extremely tiny droplets of water, 0.0008 to 0.0024 in. (0.02 to 0.06 mm) in diameter, or of minute crystals of ice. These are sustained by the slightest upward movements of air. In order for cloud droplets to form, it is necessary that microscopic dust particles serve as centers, or *nuclei*, of condensation. Dusts with a high affinity for water (i.e., *hygroscopic*) are abundant throughout the atmosphere.

Where the air temperature is well below freezing, clouds may form of tiny ice crystals. Water in such minute quantities can remain liquid far below normal freezing temperatures and is said to be *supercooled*. Water droplets exist in clouds at temperatures down to 10° F (−12° C), a mixture of water droplets and ice crystals from 10° to −20° F (−12° to −30° C) or even lower, and predominantly ice crystals below −20° F (−30° C). Below −40° F (−40° C) all of the cloud particles are ice. Clouds appear white when thin or when the sun is shining upon the outer surface. When dense and thick, clouds appear gray or black underneath simply because this is the shaded side.

Cloud types may be classified on the basis of two characteristics: general form and altitude.

On the basis of form there are two major groups: *stratiform,* or layered, types; and *cumuliform,* or massive, globular, types. High clouds, in the altitude range of 20,000 to 40,000 ft (6 to 12 km), are *cirrus* and related types, usually indicative of jet-stream activity. These thin, wispy or veillike clouds produce no precipitation, but are important indicators of upper-air movement. In middle-altitude range (6500 to 20,000 ft; 2 to 6 km) a particularly important cloud form is *altostratus,* a blanket-like formation that signifies condensation within a gradually rising moist air layer. In the low-altitude range, under 6500 ft (2 km), the thick, dense *nimbostratus* cloud is a producer of widespread precipitation. In contrast, *cumulus,* the isolated pufflike masses of cloud in low- and middle-altitude ranges, indicates condensation in local updrafts induced by solar heating or turbulence over rough terrain (Figure 5.7). *Cumulonimbus,* a stalklike cloud with a large vertical range but limited horizontal dimensions, represents a powerful updraft in which rapid condensation is producing heavy rain, often with hail, and at the same time generating lightning discharges. Cumulonimbus is the expression of intense convection, or rapid vertical mixing of the atmosphere, in contrast with advective motions indicated by the broad stratiform cloud layers.

*Fog* is simply a stratiform cloud lying very close to the ground. One type, known as a *radiation fog,* commonly forms at night when temperature of the basal air falls below the dew point. Another type, *advection fog,* results from the movement of warm, moist air over a cold or snow-covered ground surface. Losing heat to the ground, the air layer undergoes a drop of temperature below the dew point, and condensation sets in. A similar type of advection fog is formed over oceans where air from over a warm current blows across the cold surface of an adjacent cold current. Fogs of the Grand Banks off Newfoundland are largely of this origin because here the cold Labrador current comes in contact with warm waters of Gulf Stream origin.

Precipitation consists of water drops or ice particles sufficiently large to fall rapidly to lower levels. *Rain* is formed when cloud droplets in large numbers are caused to coalesce into drops. The drops may then grow by colliding with other drops and joining with them to become as large as 0.25 in. (7 mm) in diameter; but above this size they are unstable and break into smaller drops. Other forms of precipitation are *sleet,* ice particles formed by freezing of raindrops; *snow,* ice crystals formed by direct condensation at below-freezing temperatures; and *hail,* ice pellets produced in strong updrafts within a cumulonimbus cloud.

Precipitation occurs only when large masses of air are induced to rise to higher elevations. Consider three possible situations in which such lifting can take place: (1) *convectional;* (2) *orographic;* and (3) *cyclonic,* including *frontal.*

## CONVECTIONAL PRECIPITATION AND THUNDERSTORMS

Convectional precipitation takes place within a *convection cell,* which contains a succession of rapidly rising masses of warmer air, seeking higher altitude because they are lighter than surrounding air. Suppose that on a warm summer morning the sun is shining upon a landscape consisting of patches of open fields and woodlands. Certain of these types of surfaces, such as the bare ground, heat more rapidly and transmit longwave radiation to the overlying air, which is warmed more than adjacent air and begins to rise as a bubblelike mass (Figure 5.7). Vertical currents of this type are often called *thermals* by sailplane pilots, who use them to obtain lift.

With sufficient rise the air bubble may be cooled below the dew point. At once condensation begins, and the rising air column appears as a cumulus cloud whose flat base shows the critical level above which condensation is occurring (Figure 5.7). The bulging "cauliflower" top of the cloud represents the top of the rising warm-air body, pushing into higher levels of the atmosphere. Under fair-weather conditions, the cumulus cloud moves down-

wind and dissolves. Under favorable conditions the convection intensifies, producing a towering cumulonimbus mass, or *thunderstorm,* from which heavy rain issues.

Actually, the unequal heating of the ground serves only as a trigger effect to release a spontaneous rise of air, fed by latent heat energy liberated from the condensing water vapor. Recall that for every gram of water formed by condensation 600 cal of heat are released.

Graph A in Figure 5.8 is a plot of altitude against air temperature. The small circles represent a small parcel of air being forced to rise steadily higher, following the same dry adiabatic rate of cooling shown in Figure 5.6. To the right of this line is a solid line showing the temperature of the undisturbed surrounding air; it is the normal lapse rate. Suppose that the air parcel is lifted from a point near the ground, where its temperature is 90° F (32° C). After the air parcel has been carried up 2000 ft (600 m), its temperature has fallen about 11 F° (6 C°) and is now 79° F (26° C); whereas the surrounding air is cooler by only about 7 F° (4 C°) and has a temperature of 83° F (28° C). The air parcel would thus be cooler than the surrounding air at 2000 ft (600 m) and, if no longer forcibly carried upward, would tend to sink back to the ground. These conditions represent *stable* air, not likely to produce convection cells, because the air would resist lifting.

When the air layer near the ground is excessively heated by longwave radiation and sensible heat flux, the lapse rate is increased* (Figure 5.8B). The air parcel near the ground begins to rise spontaneously because it is lighter than air over adjacent, less intensely heated ground areas. Although cooled adiabatically while rising, the air parcel at 1000 ft (300 m) has a temperature of 85° F (29° C), but this is well above the temperature of the surrounding still air. The air parcel, therefore, is lighter than the surrounding air and continues its rise. At 2000 ft (600 m), the dew point is reached and condensation sets in. Now the rising air parcel is cooled at the reduced wet adiabatic rate of 3.2 F° per 1000 ft (0.6 C° per 100 m), because the latent heat liber-

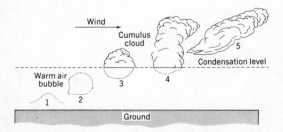

Figure 5.7. Rise of a bubble of heated air to form a cumulus cloud. [Modified from a drawing of F. H. Ludlam and R. S. Scorer (1957), *Cloud Study: A Pictorial Guide,* London, Murray, p. 12, Figure 2.]

* The meteorologist would say the lapse rate is "steepened." This word may be confusing, since the line has reclined to a lower slope on the graph. If coordinates were transposed on the graph the word *steepened* would seem correct in usage.

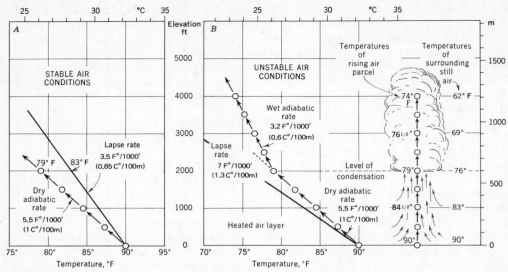

Figure 5.8. Stable and unstable air conditions. (© 1965, John Wiley & Sons, New York.)

ated in condensation offsets the rate of drop due to expansion. At 3000 ft (900 m), the rising air parcel is still several degrees warmer than the surrounding air and therefore continues its spontaneous rise.

The air described here as spontaneously rising during condensation is *unstable* in properties. In such air the rise of air tends to increase in intensity as time goes on, much as a bonfire blazes with increasing ferocity as the updraft draws in greater supplies of oxygen. Of course, when very high altitudes are reached, the bulk of the water vapor will have already condensed and fallen as precipitation. The energy source is then gone; the convection cell weakens and air rise finally ceases.

Detailed studies show that thunderstorms consist of individual parts, called *cells*. Within each cell air rises in a succession of bubblelike masses, rather than in a single continuous column. At all levels air is brought into the cell from the sides in the wake of the rising bubble by a process called *entrainment*.

Vertical air speeds up to 3000 ft/min (900 m/min) commonly develop. Condensation goes on rapidly and ranges in type from droplets of water in the lower and middle parts, through mixed rain and snow, then wet snow, to dry snow in the extremely cold upper part.

As the rising air bubble travels upward to high levels, heavy precipitation occurs. The top of the cloud, above the freezing level, spreads laterally to form an *anvil top* (Figure 5.9). Falling ice particles, cooling and seeding the

cloud, cause rapid condensation. Falling drops or ice particles actually drag the air downward to produce a strong downdraft of cold air, which strikes the ground at the time of the heavy initial burst of rain (Figure 5.10). This gusty squall wind spreads out horizontally along the ground.

The downdraft creates an area of higher barometric pressure at ground level, the *thunderstorm high*. Air turbulence within the storm is violent and will seriously damage or destroy light aircraft that venture into the cell. Raindrops may be caught in the updraft and carried above the freezing level, where they become frozen pellets. Coated by supercooled water, these pellets grow into hailstones (Figure 5.11). Hailstones up to 3 in. (8 cm) in diameter fall in rare cases.

Another familiar effect of the thunderstorm is *lightning,* an electrical discharge—or simply a great spark, or arc—from one part of a cloud

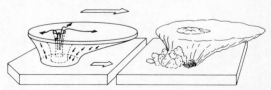

Figure 5.9. Schematic diagram (*left*) and sketch (*right*) of anvil cloud formation. Underside of anvil overhang is formed of trails of ice and snow crystals falling from the spreading cloud top. [Modified from drawings by F. H. Ludlam and R. S. Scorer (1957), *Cloud Study: A Pictorial Guide,* London, Murray, p. 16, Figure 5.]

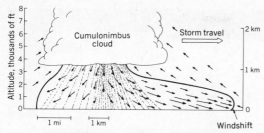

Figure 5.10. Schematic diagram of downdraft beneath a thunderstorm. A cold air wedge with strong wind gusts spreads along the ground in advance of the cloud. [After H. R. Byers and R. R. Braham (1949), *The Thunderstorm,* Washington, D.C., U.S. Govt. Printing Office.]

to another or from the cloud to the ground. In a manner not yet established, but subject to a number of hypotheses currently under intensive investigation, regions of positive and negative electrical charges accumulate in the cumulonimbus cloud (Figure 5.12). Generally the upper portion of the thunderstorm is positively charged, whereas centers of negative and positive charges form below.

The ground beneath the negatively charged parts of cloud in turn develops a positive charge. When the electrical potential has reached sufficient magnitude (some 20 to 30 million volts), a lightning stroke occurs, traveling first from cloud to ground, then returning to the cloud. Several alternations between cloud and ground eliminate the difference in electrical pressure. The whole process takes less than one-tenth of a second and appears as a single flash.

An electric current of perhaps 60,000 to 100,000 amperes may flow during a lightning

Figure 5.11. Hailstones, larger than a hen's egg (center foreground). (Courtesy of NOAA, National Weather Service.)

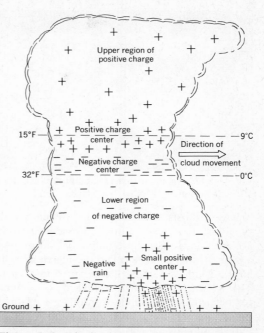

Figure 5.12. Distribution of electrical charges inside a typical thunderstorm cell. [After U.S. Dept. of Commerce (1955), *C. A. A. Technical Manual 104,* Washington, D.C., U.S. Govt. Printing Office, p. 60, Figure 95.]

discharge. The thunder which we hear is the shock wave of sound sent out by the lightning stroke, whose great heat causes a sudden expansion of the air along the path of the stroke. Because sound travels at a rate of roughly 1 mi for every 5 sec (330 m/sec), the thunder follows the lightning flash by a time interval depending upon distance. If both seem to occur at the same instant, the strike is very close by, whereas a delay of 5 sec in the sound would indicate a strike roughly 1 mi away. Very distant diffuse flashes reflected from high cumulonimbus clouds may be too far away to be heard, because sound waves die out rapidly as they travel.

After a thunderstorm has experienced the rise of a number of successive bubblelike air masses, the uppermost portion of the thunderstorm has developed an anvil top in the altitude zone 40,000 to 60,000 ft (15 to 18 km). The anvil, formed of ice crystals, drifts downwind in the prevailing upper-air flow and may result in an extensive cirrus layer (Figure 5.13).

Large thunderstorms may consist of several cells, developing in succession at adjacent positions, thus giving the storm long duration and

Figure 5.13. An anvil-topped cumulonimbus cloud. (Sketched by A. N. Strahler from a photograph by NOAA, National Weather Service.)

repeated bursts of heavy rain. When many thunderstorms occur along a broad belt, it is not feasible to distinguish individual storms. As a general rule, a single-celled thunderstorm will have a width of perhaps 3 to 5 mi (5 to 8 km). The characteristic meteorological conditions for occurrence of thunderstorms are explained in later paragraphs.

Because convectional, or thunderstorm, rainfall requires favorable air conditions in the form of moist, usually warm, unstable air, it is a dominant type in equatorial and tropical regions. It generally becomes less important in the higher latitudes and is conspicuously absent in the polar regions. Thunderstorms are also most frequent in summer. Because convectional rainfall is formed in cells, the rainfall pattern is spotty—some localities receive as much as 1 to 3 in. (25 to 75 mm) of rain in a single storm, whereas localities a few miles away may have none at all. Although convectional rainfall is produced in storms of small areal extent, these in turn can constitute the numerous parts of much larger atmospheric disturbances.

## OROGRAPHIC PRECIPITATION

The second precipitation-producing mechanism is described as *orographic*, which means "related to mountains." Prevailing winds or other moving masses of air may be forced to flow over mountain ranges (Figure 5.14). As the air rises on the windward side of the range, it is cooled at the adiabatic rate. If cooling is sufficient, precipitation will result. After passing over the mountain summit, the air will begin to descend the lee side of the range. Now it will undergo a warming through the same adiabatic process and, having no source from which to draw up moisture, will become very

dry. A belt of dry climate, often called a *rain shadow,* may exist on the lee side of the range. Several of the important dry deserts of the earth are of this type.

Much orographic rainfall is actually of the convectional type, in that it takes the form of heavy convectional showers and storms. The storms are induced, however, by the forced ascent of unstable air as it passes over the mountain barrier.

## CYCLONIC STORMS

Much of the unsettled, stormy weather experienced in middle and high latitudes is associated with traveling cyclones. The convergence of air masses toward these centers is accompanied by lift of air and adiabatic cooling, which, in turn, produces cloudiness and precipitation. By contrast, much fair, sunny weather is associated with traveling anticyclones. Here the air tends to subside and spread

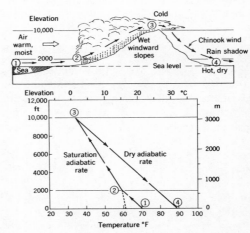

Figure 5.14. Cooling, condensation, and subsequent warming within a mass of air forced to pass over a mountain barrier.

outward, causing adiabatic warming, a process unfavorable to condensation.

Cyclones may be very mild in intensity, passing with little more than a period of cloud cover and light rain or snow. On the other hand, if the pressure gradient is strong, winds ranging in strength from moderate to gale force may accompany the cyclone. In such a case, the disturbance may be called a *cyclonic storm.*

Moving cyclones fall into three general classes. (1) The *extratropical cyclone* is typical of middle and high latitudes. It ranges in severity from a weak disturbance to a powerful storm. (2) The *tropical cyclone* is found in low latitudes over ocean areas. It ranges from a mild disturbance to the terribly destructive *hurricane,* or *typhoon.* (3) The *tornado,* although a very small storm, is an intense cyclonic vortex of enormously powerful winds. It is on a very much smaller scale of magnitude than other types of cyclones and must be treated separately.

The thunderstorm, as already noted, is a localized disturbance connected with a large cumulonimbus cloud in which there is a rapid convectional rise of air. It lacks the cyclonic spiral flow of winds. Thunderstorms often occur in large numbers within a single cyclonic storm, and occasionally tornadoes develop within the thunderstorms at the same time.

### WAVE THEORY OF CYCLONES

During the First World War a Norwegian meteorologist, J. Bjerknes, brought forward a new theory to explain moving extratropical cyclones and anticyclones. We have seen that there exists in middle latitudes a line of contact between cold air masses of arctic or polar origin and warm air masses of subtropical origin. This fluctuating line of contact is the polar front (Figure 5.5).

The term *front,* as used by Bjerknes, was particularly apt because of the resemblance of this feature to the fighting fronts in western Europe, then active. Just as vast armies met along a sharply defined front which moved back and forth, so masses of cold polar air meet in conflict with warm, moist air from the subtropical regions. Instead of mixing freely, these unlike air masses remain clearly defined but interact along the polar front in great whorls whose structure is not unlike the form of an ocean wave seen in cross section.

A series of individual blocks, Figure 5.15, shows the various stages in the life history of an extratropical cyclone. Originally, the polar front is simply a smooth boundary along which air of unlike physical properties is moving in opposite directions. In block *A* of Figure 5.15, the polar front shows a bulge, or *wave,* beginning to form. Cold air is turned in a southerly direction, warm air in a northerly direction, as if each would penetrate the domain of the other. It is now necessary to digress from the series of diagrams of Figure 5.15 to consider what occurs when cold air moves into an area of warm air, or vice versa.

### COLD AND WARM FRONTS

The structure of a frontal contact zone in which cold air is invading the warm-air zone is shown in Figure 5.16. A front of this type is termed a *cold front.* The colder air mass, being heavier, remains in contact with the ground and forces the warmer air mass to rise over it. The slope of the cold-front surface is greatly exaggerated in the figure, being actually of the order of slope of 1 in 40 to 1 in 80 (meaning that the slope rises 1 ft vertically for each 80 ft of horizontal distance). Cold fronts are associated with strong atmospheric disturbance, the warm air thus lifted often breaking out in thunderstorms. In some instances violent thunderstorms occur along a line well in advance of the cold front, a *squall line.* Such lines of thunderstorms can be seen on the radar screen (Figure 5.17).

Figure 5.18 illustrates a *warm front,* in which warm air is moving into a region of colder air. Here, again, the cold air mass remains in contact with the ground, and the warm air mass is forced to rise as if ascending a long ramp. Warm fronts have lower slopes than cold fronts, being of the order of 1 in 80 to as low as 1 in 200. Moreover, warm fronts are commonly attended by stable atmospheric conditions and usually lack the turbulent air motions of the cold front. A dense stratiform cloud layer is typical. Of course, if the warm air is unstable, it will develop convection cells, and there will be heavy showers and thunderstorms.

Cold fronts normally move along the ground at a faster rate than warm fronts. Hence, when both types are in the same vicinity, as they are in the cyclonic storm, the cold front normally overtakes the warm front. A curious combination, known as an *occluded front,* then results (Figure 5.19). The colder air of the fast-moving cold front remains next to the ground,

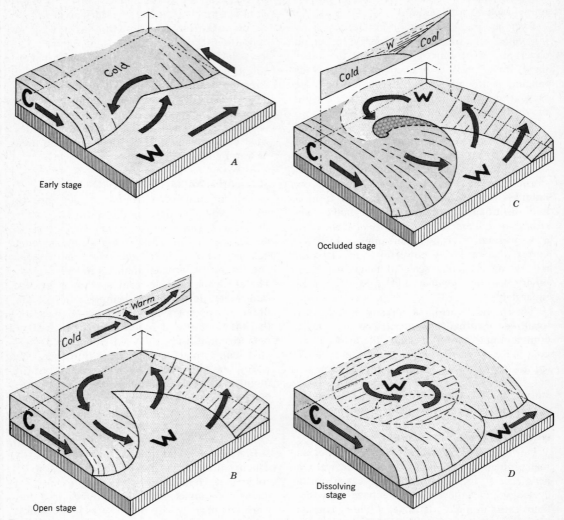

Figure 5.15. Four stages in the life history of a wave cyclone of middle latitudes. (© 1960, John Wiley & Sons, New York.)

forcing both the warm air and the less cold air to rise over it. The warm air mass is lifted completely free of the ground. The relations between warm, cold, and occluded fronts can now be introduced into the life history of the wave cyclone.

In block *B* of Figure 5.15 the wave disturbance along the polar front has deepened and intensified. Warm air is now actively moving northeastward along a warm front, while cold air is actively pushing southward along a cold front. Each front is convex in the direction of motion. The zone of precipitation is now considerable, but wider along the warm front than along the cold front. In a still later stage the

more rapidly moving cold front has reduced the zone of warm air to a narrow sector. In block *C*, the cold front has overtaken the warm front, producing an occluded front and forcing the warm air mass off the ground, isolating it from the parent region of warm air to the south. The source of moisture and energy thus cut off, the cyclonic storm gradually dies out and the polar front is reestablished as originally (block *D*).

Long observation of the movements of cyclones has revealed that certain tracks are most commonly followed. Some cyclonic storms travel across the entire United States from places of origin in the North Pacific, such as

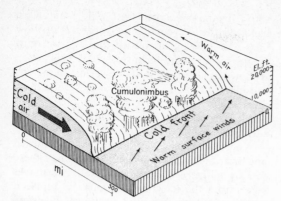

Figure 5.16. Diagram of a cold front. (© 1960, John Wiley & Sons, New York.)

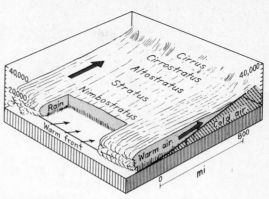

Figure 5.18. Diagram of a warm front. (© 1960, John Wiley & Sons, New York.)

the prevailing low-pressure zone over the Aleutians; others originate within the central United States. Most tracks converge toward the northeastern United States and pass out into the North Atlantic, where they tend to concentrate in the low-pressure region over Iceland. General world distribution of paths of cyclonic storms is shown in Figure 5.20. Notice the

heavy concentration in the neighborhood of the Aleutian Islands and Iceland, where low barometric pressure prevails in winter. Extratropical cyclones commonly form in succession to travel in a chain across the North Atlantic and North Pacific oceans. Figure 5.21 shows two such *cyclone families.*

In the Southern Hemisphere, storm tracks occur more nearly along a single circumglobal lane, following the parallels of latitude. This pattern appears to be the result of uniform ocean surface throughout the middle latitudes, only the southern tip of South America breaking the monotonous oceanic expanse. Furthermore, the polar-centered icecap of Antarctica provides a centralized source of polar air.

Families of wave cyclones are closely tied to Rossby waves and the jet stream. Wave cyclones form beneath the jet stream and are carried along by that stream. Characteristically, the wave cyclone begins to form at the southern bulge of the Rossby wave, then

Figure 5.17. Lines of thunderstorms show as light patches on this radar screen. The heavy circles are spaced 50 nautical mi (70 km) apart. (Courtesy of NOAA, National Weather Service.)

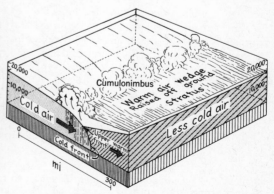

Figure 5.19. Diagram of an occluded warm front. (© 1960, John Wiley & Sons, New York.)

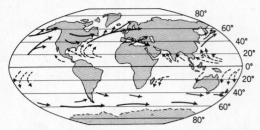

Figure 5.20. Solid lines on this world map show principal tracks of middle-latitude cyclones, and dashed lines show the characteristic tracks of tropical cyclones. (© 1960, John Wiley & Sons, New York. Based on a map by Petterssen.)

sweeps northeastward (Northern Hemisphere) with the jet stream along the eastern flank of the Rossby wave. Figure 5.22 shows four families of wave cyclones, each associated with a Rossby wave. Notice the flanking relationship of wave-cyclone families (shown by fronts) to upper-air waves (shown by the isobars).

## CONVERGENCE AND DIVERGENCE

At the risk of oversimplification, the connection between cyclones and anticyclones at low level and the jet stream within an overlying Rossby wave can be shown by a rather simple model. Figure 5.23 shows what is going on simultaneously at upper and lower levels in the troposphere. In the upper diagram, which is a sketch-map, streamlines of air flow at high level are shown to make a southward bend in a typical upper-air wave (see Figure 4.21). The jet-stream core is indicated by the central streamline. Associated with the southward bend of the wave is a *convergence* of flow lines. Air moving in toward the jet core must escape by subsiding to lower levels. This action is shown in side view in the lower diagram. The subsiding air, as it reaches lower levels, must diverge. In so doing the flow develops an outward spiral and becomes an anticyclone at the surface.

Where the upper-air streamlines are turned northward after leaving the wave trough, there sets in a *divergence* of flow lines. Air moves away from the jet core and must be replaced by rising air, as shown in the lower diagram. The rising air must in turn be replaced by air moving in from all sides at low level. As this air converges, it develops an inward spiral and forms a cyclone (fronts are not shown). At ground level, air moves from anticyclones to cyclones; at high level from zones of divergence to zones of convergence. Thus the circulation cycle is completed.

## TROPICAL CYCLONES

One of the most powerful and destructive types of cyclonic storms is the *tropical cyclone,* otherwise known as the *hurricane* or *typhoon.* The storm develops over oceans in latitudes 8° to 15° N and S, but not close to the equator, where the Coriolis force is extremely weak. In many cases weak upper-air disturbance known as an *easterly wave* simply deepens and intensifies, changing into a deep, circular low. High sea-surface temperatures, which are over 80° F

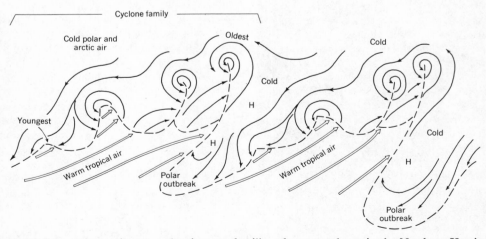

Figure 5.21. Schematic weather map showing two families of wave cyclones in the Northern Hemisphere. Surface fronts are shown by dashed lines. Solid arrows show streamlines of flow of cold air, and open arrows show the flow of warm air. [After S. Petterssen (1958), *Introduction to Meteorology,* New York, McGraw-Hill, p. 223, Figure 163.]

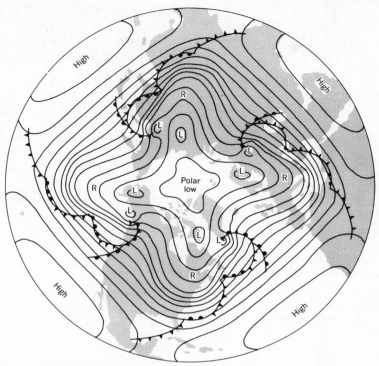

Figure 5.22. This map, centered on the north pole, shows four families of wave cyclones associated with four Rossby waves (labeled $R$). Cyclones are indicated by frontal systems at sea level, whereas the upper-air waves are shown by high-level isobars (smoothly curving, solid lines). [After S. Petterssen (1958), *Introduction to Meteorology*, New York, McGraw-Hill, p. 226, Figure 166.]

(27° C) in these latitudes, are of basic importance in the environment of storm origin. Warming of air at low level creates instability and predisposes toward storm formation. Once formed, the storm moves westward and then turns poleward through the trade-wind belt, often penetrating well into the belt of westerly winds. The tropical cyclone is an almost circular storm center of extremely low pressure into which winds are spiraling with great velocity accompanied by very heavy rainfall.

Figure 5.24 is a surface-weather map showing details of a hurricane of the West Indies. Although based on an actual hurricane, several wind arrows have been added and the precipitation pattern is inferred from similar examples. The pressure of 952 mb in the storm center is equivalent to about 28.3 in. (72 cm) of mercury, a low pressure rarely found in even the deepest of middle-latitude cyclones. Surface winds blow in toward the center with a counterclockwise spiral (Northern Hemisphere), making an angle of about 30° to 40° with the isobars. Wind speeds are commonly from 75 to 125 mph (120 to 200 km/hr), but

much higher gusts have been reported. These extreme winds may affect a circle of radius as great as 200 mi (300 km) for a very large storm.

Precipitation occurs in spiral bands, as shown in Figures 5.24 and 5.25. Air temperatures in the central part of the storm are abnormally high, from 9 to 18 F° (5 to 10 C°) higher than the average value of the tropical atmosphere. This fact shows that large quantities of heat are being absorbed into the storm from the ocean surface below.

Figure 5.26 is a schematic cross section through a tropical cyclone, showing cloud formations and rain bands. Upon reaching high levels, air flows outward, producing a cirrus-cloud cap.

The passage of a severe tropical storm at sea usually follows the same pattern of events. On the day preceding the storm, the weather is fair and calm, with barometric pressure somewhat above normal and fewer cumulus clouds than normal. A long sea swell, produced by great storm waves which have outrun the slowly moving storm, gives warning of what is to

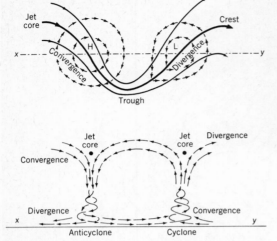

Figure 5.23. Coupling of upper-air zones of convergence and divergence with surface anticyclones and cyclones, respectively. The upper drawing is a schematic weather map. The lower drawing is a cross section on the line *x–y*, extending up to 10 km (33,000 ft). [After H. Riehl (1965), *Introduction to the Atmosphere*, New York, McGraw-Hill, p. 154, Figure 7.7.]

come. Where this swell reaches a coast, the breakers are powerful but less frequent than usual, breaking perhaps 4 or 5 to the minute. The sky in this period preceding the storm shows a sequence of clouds much like that of

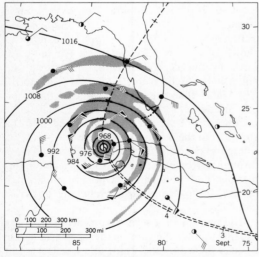

Figure 5.24. Surface-weather map of a typical hurricane of the West Indies. Eye of storm is located over the western tip of Cuba. [After A. N. Strahler (1969), *Exercises in Physical Geography,* New York, John Wiley & Sons, p. 110.]

Figure 5.25. Hurricane Gladys located about 150 mi (240 km) southwest of Tampa, Florida, on October 8, 1968, photographed from *Apollo 7* spacecraft at an altitude of about 110 mi (180 km). View is southeast, toward Cuba. (NASA photograph.)

an approaching warm front—cirrus bands reach across the sky, then thicken to form cirrostratus and altostratus. The cirrus layer is carried downwind in the high-level easterlies. The clouds continue to thicken; congested cumulus forms; showers begin. Now the barometer falls rapidly and the wind increases. Finally, a great dark wall of dense clouds approaches; when it reaches the observer, the storm is unleashed in full fury. Great waves break over the ship and sea-water spray is blown in sheets that reduce visibility almost to zero.

After several hours of raging storm an abrupt calm sets in. This is the *central eye* of the storm, a strange hollow vortex several miles wide surrounded by a dense cloud wall (Figure 5.26). Although the air is almost calm and the sky may clear, waves are mountainous and especially perilous to ships at sea because they intersect in great peaklike masses. In the central eye, air is subsiding rapidly and at the same time is being adiabatically heated. This process explains the remarkably rapid warming often reported in the eye, as well as the tendency for clouds to evaporate and skies to clear. The period of calm may last perhaps half an hour, then the dark cloud wall of the eye approaches and a ship at sea will again be enveloped in violent storm, except that now the wind direction is exactly reversed from that in the first part of the storm. After many hours the winds lessen and subside, the clouds break up, and the storm is over.

Tropical cyclones occur in seven ocean

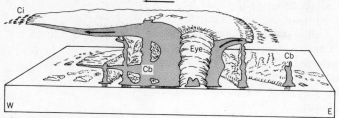

Figure 5.26. Schematic diagram of a hurricane. The cross section cuts through the eye. Cumulonimbus clouds in concentric rings rise through dense stratiform clouds in which the air spirals upward. Width of the diagram represents about 600 mi (1000 km). Highest clouds are at elevations often over 30,000 ft (9 km). [Redrawn from NOAA, National Weather Service, R. C. Gentry (1964), *Weatherwise*, vol. 17, p. 182.]

regions of the world (Figure 5.27): (1) Caribbean Sea and Gulf of Mexico; (2) western North Pacific, including the Philippine Islands and China Sea; (3) the Arabian Sea and Bay of Bengal; (4) eastern Pacific Ocean, off the coast of Mexico and Central America; (5) the South Indian Ocean, east of Madagascar; (6) the western South Pacific, in the region of Samoa, the Fiji Islands, and the northeast coast of Australia; and (7) off the northwest coast of Australia. Severe tropical storms are not known in the South Atlantic.

When the average paths of many tropical cyclones are plotted on a chart (Figure 5.27), it will be seen that they tend to originate in latitudes 10° to 20° N and S and to travel westward, following the tropical easterlies. The paths then turn poleward, bringing the storms into the regions of westerlies. There they recurve eastward, become broadened and weakened into middle-latitude cyclones and are carried eastward across the oceans. In taking the curving path, many storms stay entirely over the ocean, but others travel over the eastern margin of the adjoining continent.

Tropical cyclones occur in that part of the year including and immediately following the period of high sun, or summer season, in the hemisphere in question. Thus the hurricanes and typhoons of the Caribbean and northwestern Pacific occur from June through November. Those of the western South Pacific and South Indian oceans occur from December through March.

The reasons for development of an intense tropical cyclone from the much more frequent weak tropical disturbances are not yet fully understood. As Figure 5.27 shows, high sea-surface temperatures are an important contributing factor, permitting a high rate of heat flow from ocean surface to atmosphere. That tropical cyclones do not occur in the South Atlantic, which does not attain maximum temperatures over 82° F (28° C), seems to confirm the importance of the temperature factor. Only a small fraction of the weak cyclonic disturbances of low latitudes develop into intense tropical cyclones, and the number of storms per season in each locality varies greatly from year to year. Perhaps the controlling factors will be revealed through analysis of upper-air winds.

Vast destruction and loss of life brought about by tropical storms cause them to rank

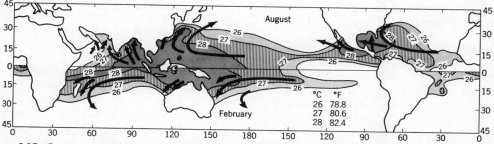

Figure 5.27. Common paths of tropical cyclones as related to sea-surface temperatures (°C) in summer of the respective hemisphere. [© 1965, John Wiley & Sons, New York. After Palmen (1948).]

among the great catastrophes which nature inflicts upon Man. Although of prime importance as a hazard to ships at sea, these storms do their greatest damage when passing over densely inhabited islands and coasts. Destruction of harbor facilities and small craft is especially great because the great waves may be accompanied by abnormally high tides, bringing both wave attack and *storm surges* upon places usually far above the reach of the sea. A storm surge (erroneously referred to as a "tidal wave") is a rapid rise of sea level associated with the passage of the cyclone across shallow coastal water.

In November, 1970, a tropical cyclone moving northward in the Bay of Bengal struck the low-lying deltaic coast of East Pakistan with winds exceeding 150 mph (240 km/hr). A storm surge, estimated to have been 16 to 20 ft (5 to 6 m) high, completely inundated a number of islands, drowning tens of thousands of persons. Total deaths from the storm were estimated to exceed 300,000 persons, with many more ensuing deaths from starvation and disease. This event has been labeled the worst natural disaster of the twentieth century.

Another important environmental effect of tropical cyclones reaching land is the heavy fall of rain, which may total as much as 6 to 12 in. (15 to 30 cm) in a 24-hr period. Summer floods of the Gulf Coast and eastern-seaboard states are usually of this origin. A striking example was provided by hurricane Diane in August, 1955. This storm, which took altogether about 200 lives and did property damage amounting to 1½ million dollars in its sweeping path over the eastern states, passed eastward over southern New England. Torrential rains on the watersheds of New England rivers produced unprecedented floods by the rivers of Connecticut, Rhode Island, and Massachusetts. Similar flooding rains are brought to Japan and the coast of China by summer typhoons.

## TORNADOES

The smallest but most violent of all known storms is the *tornado*. It seems to be a typically American storm, being most frequent and violent in the United States, although occurring in Australia in substantial numbers. Tornadoes are also known throughout tropical and subtropical regions of the globe.

The tornado is a small, intense cyclone in which the air is spiraling at tremendous veloc-

Figure 5.28. A tornado funnel cloud seen at Hardtner, Kansas. (Photograph by Blacklock, courtesy of NOAA, National Weather Service.)

ity. It appears as a dark *funnel cloud* (Figure 5.28), hanging from a large cumulonimbus cloud. At its lower end the funnel may be from 300 to 1500 ft (90 to 460 m) in diameter. The funnel appears dark because of the density of condensing moisture, dust, and debris swept up by the wind. Wind velocities in a tornado exceed anything known in other storms and are estimated to be as high as 250 mph (400 km/hr).

Tornadoes occur as parts of cumulonimbus clouds in the squall line that travels in advance of a cold front. They seem to originate where turbulence is greatest. They are commonest in the spring and summer but may occur in any month. Where polar air lifts warm, moist tropical air on a cold front, conditions may become favorable for tornadoes. They occur in greatest numbers in the Mississippi Valley region.

## WATER BALANCE OF THE ATMOSPHERE

This chapter has dealt with basic principles of evaporation, condensation, and precipitation, so it is appropriate at this point to take another step in evaluating the global balance of energy and matter developed in Chapters 1 and 4. The role of latent heat in the earth's energy balance has already been treated. Figure 4.32

shows the latent-heat flux for each belt of latitude, and Figure 4.33 shows the transport of latent heat across the parallels of latitude. That analysis dealt with energy alone, not with mass, the units used for energy transfer being kilocalories per unit of time.

The earth's water balance is concerned with the transfer of mass in the form of water from place to place in the atmosphere, oceans, and lands. Units used in water-balance analysis are kilograms of water, thus the transport of water is given in kilograms per unit of time (hour, day, month, or year).

At this point, let us consider only the water balance of the earth's atmosphere, deferring to the next chapter a consideration of the water balance of the total global system, involving continents and oceans as well as the atmosphere.

A simple equation can be developed for the water balance of the atmosphere by considering the ways in which water can enter and leave a unit column of the atmosphere extending from the earth's surface to the top of the atmosphere. For practical purposes, the atmosphere above the 400-mb level (which lies at about 24,000 ft, or 7.4 km) can be disregarded.

Water can enter the atmospheric column by evaporation from the ocean or land surface beneath; let this quantity be designated by the symbol $E$ (kilograms per year). Second, water may be imported horizontally into the column in vapor form by atmospheric circulation; let this quantity be designated as $c$. Water may also be exported from the column by the same process, and a negative value of $c$ will suffice to denote a loss. Another form of water loss is by precipitation (dew and hoarfrost can be included), designated by $P$.

The rate of increase or decrease of water vapor within the atmosphere column, designated by the term $g$, can be grouped with the four terms in the preceding paragraph into the following water-balance equation:

$$g = E - P - c$$

Consider, next, that the average annual value of $g$ will be close to zero, therefore

$$0 = E - P - c$$
$$\text{and } c = E - P$$

Consequently, on an annual basis the horizontal transport of water through atmospheric circu-

lation must equal the difference between evaporation and precipitation. The principles of evaporation from continental surfaces, as well as the disposal of precipitation by flow of water over and beneath the ground surface, are treated in Chapter 6.

Consider at this time only the term $c$, as the net annual transport of water across the parallels of latitude for the entire earth. Figure 5.29 is a graph resembling the graph of the meridional energy transport of Figure 4.32, except that the units on the vertical axis are in kilograms of water per year, rather than kilocalories per year. Where the curve lies above the zero line, transport is northward; where below the line, transport is southward. Notice that from about latitude 20° N and S transport is toward the equator. This transport represents movement of water vapor in the Hadley-cell circulation, in which the tropical easterlies meet in the intertropical convergence zone. Here the vapor is condensed, largely as convectional precipitation, and leaves the atmosphere to become water on the lands and oceans. Above latitude 25° N and S, water-vapor transport is poleward, as descending air in the poleward limb of the Hadley cell is transferred across parallels of higher latitude by advection in cyclones and anticyclones of middle latitudes. Poleward of latitude 40° losses of water vapor through precipitation are large and evaporation is reduced by cold. Thus the trans-

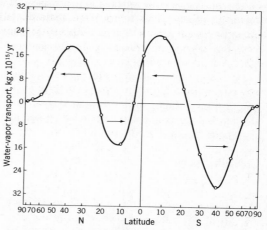

Figure 5.29. Graph of mean annual meridional transport of water vapor. A smooth curve has been drawn through values calculated for each 10° parallel of latitude. [Data from W. D. Sellers (1965), *Physical Climatology*, Chicago, Univ. of Chicago Press, p. 94, Figure 29.]

port of water vapor drops off sharply, to become zero at each pole.

## SYSTEMS IN REVIEW

Systems of atmospheric disturbance, examined in this chapter, represent both advective and convective motions of large masses of air. An integral part of these instability systems is the change of state of water, from the vapor state to the liquid state, resulting in the release of enormous quantities of energy from the latent form to yield sensible heat. In convective cells (thunderstorms) and in lift of air masses in cyclones and their related fronts, the energy for growth and intensification of the disturbance is furnished by latent heat of water vapor.

We may regard these storms as analogous to conflagrations in which hydrocarbon fuels are oxidized at rapid rates. A great city fire draws in oxygen from the surrounding atmosphere. Once started by even a trivial blaze, the conflagration intensifies out of all control. Only when the fuel is oxidized does the fire cease. Similarly, great storms feed upon the latent energy of water vapor, growing to huge proportions and out of all control. Storms must run their courses. Only when the water-vapor source is expended does the storm weaken. We have seen that occlusion of the warm air mass, separating it from the parent body of warm tropical air, leads to weakening and decay of a cyclonic storm. A tropical cyclone, upon passing across a coast and into the heart of a continent, will weaken and dissolve as its moisture source in a warm sea surface beneath it is no longer available. The updraft of a thunderstorm cell weakens at high altitude, when the available air moisture has condensed and no more is available.

Cyclonic storms fall into the class of *secular* subsystems, running their life cycles through in time periods usually numbered in days. They also represent wave systems produced by boundary shear along the discontinuity that separates fluids of differing physical properties. Cold, dry polar air and warm, moist tropical air cannot maintain smooth, uniform flow in opposite directions along the polar front. Wavelike eddies are self-aggravating phenomena of fluid instability. They must develop, grow in size, and be occluded along the fluid discontinuity. Ocean waves are a related phenomenon, in which wind blowing over a water surface produces instability. Horizontal eddies, not greatly unlike cyclonic storms in their flow patterns, are also generated within ocean-current systems, where the faster-moving threads of current shear past the adjacent slower-moving water bodies.

Looking back over the patterns of atmospheric circulation, three orders of magnitude of systems can be recognized. First, there is the average planetary zonal circulation, consisting of the westerly winds around the polar cyclones and the tropical easterlies over low latitudes, with the Hadley-cell motions included. Second, there is the system of Rossby waves that form, intensify, and dissolve on a large scale within the upper-air westerlies. This wave system involves a jet stream and the occlusion of large waves to produce an advective pattern on a large scale. Third and smallest, there are the wave cyclones that form in the lower atmosphere, below the jet stream, and on the flanks of larger Rossby waves. These cyclones provide the mechanism of air-mass lift and energy release. Similarly, convection cells provide the mechanism of air-mass lift and energy release within the larger movements of the Hadley cell in equatorial waters and along fronts in unstable air in the structure of the cyclone. The role of the tropical cyclone is essentially the same as that of the middle-latitude cyclone in condensing water vapor, but it acts in lower latitudes. The tornado represents an eddy system of much smaller order of magnitude than any of the above and as such is an isolated and localized phenomenon, albeit one of enormous intensity.

As a final observation, notice that the atmospheric disturbances we have analyzed are characterized by unpredictability both in time and in place. As yet no long-range prediction of these events is possible. The cyclonic and convective disturbances are phenomena of random occurrence when viewed as events of the future.

### References for further study

Ludlam, F. H., and R. S. Scorer (1957), *Cloud Study: A Pictorial Guide,* London, Murray, 80 pp.

Battan, L. J. (1961), *The Nature of Violent Storms,* Garden City, N.Y., Doubleday, 158 pp.

Dunn, G. E., and B. I. Miller (1964), *Atlantic Hurricanes,* Baton Rouge, Louisiana State Univ. Press, 377 pp.

Federal Aviation Agency and Civil Aeronautics Administration, U.S. Dept. of Commerce (1965), *Aviation Weather,* Washington, D.C., U.S. Govt. Printing Office, 299 pp.

Riehl, H. (1965), *Introduction to the Atmosphere,* New York, McGraw-Hill, 365 pp., chaps. 4, 5, 7, 8.

Petterssen, S. (1969), *Introduction to Meteorology,* 3rd ed., New York, McGraw-Hill, 333 pp., chaps. 4–8, 12–14, 16.

## Review questions

1. Describe the three states of water. What terms are applied to the various changes of state of water? What is sensible heat? latent heat? What quantities of heat are involved in evaporation? in melting?

2. Define humidity in the general sense. What is the saturation value? What is relative humidity, and how does it change with temperature change? What is the dew point, and how can it be observed?

3. Define absolute humidity, vapor pressure, and specific humidity. What advantage has the use of specific humidity in the description of an air mass?

4. What is an air mass? What properties serve to distinguish one air mass from another? What relationship does a front bear to air masses? How does an air mass acquire its characteristics from a source region, and how are these characteristics changed during migration? Give examples. Describe the classification of air masses and the symbols used. What is the global plan of distribution of air-mass source regions?

5. Describe and explain the adiabatic cooling of rising air. What values apply to the dry and wet adiabatic rates and to the dew-point lapse rate?

6. Describe the particles that compose clouds. What is the relationship between temperature and the composition of a cloud? What are the two major groups of clouds? Describe cirrus, altostratus, nimbostratus, cumulus, and cumulonimbus clouds. What atmospheric condition or activity does each signify?

7. What kinds of fogs occur, and why does each develop? What is precipitation? What are the forms of precipitation? What are the three basic situations in which precipitation can occur?

8. Describe the formation of a cumulus cloud by convection. Under what conditions can a thunderstorm develop? What is the energy source? Describe and explain stable and unstable conditions within an air mass. Base your analysis upon lapse rates.

9. Describe a thunderstorm, giving details of structure, height, air speeds, cloud form, barometric-pressure effects, rainfall, winds, hail, and lightning. What world regions and seasons favor thunderstorm development? Why?

10. Describe orographic precipitation, using adiabatic rates as the basis of an explanation. What is a rain shadow? How may a desert climate be associated with orographic precipitation?

11. What is a cyclonic storm? What are the several varieties of cyclonic disturbances and storms, and in what parts of the world are they found? Describe the wave theory of cyclone development. What are cold fronts, warm fronts, and occluded fronts? What part does each front play in the development of the cyclone? Describe the tracks of cyclones. What are cyclone families? Where do middle-latitude cyclones tend to be concentrated?

12. How are wave cyclones related to upper-air flow and the jet stream? Explain the role of upper-air convergence and divergence in controlling the development of cyclones and anticyclones.

13. Describe a tropical cyclone, giving details of form and structure, pressures, winds, clouds, and precipitation. What is the central eye, and how is it produced? What are the seven world regions of occurrence of tropical cyclones? What are the seasons of occurrence? Describe the characteristic paths of these storms. What role does sea-surface temperature play in genesis of tropical cyclones? Distinguish a storm surge from a seismic sea wave.

14. Describe a tornado. What is the season of their most frequent occurrence? What region has the most tornadoes?

15. Explain the concept of the earth's water balance. Describe the water balance of the atmosphere, giving the equation of balance and defining each term. Describe the average meridional profile of transport of water vapor across the parallels of latitude. Relate direction of transport to atmospheric circulation systems.

16. Describe in broad terms the basic nature of the systems of atmospheric disturbance superimposed upon the planetary circulation. Emphasize the role of water vapor in these atmospheric disturbances. Comment upon the time and distance scales involved and upon the element of predictability of occurrence.

# chapter 6 transport systems: iii. gravity flow of water on the lands

The total plan of movement, exchange, and storage of water is called the *hydrologic cycle*. In the word *cycle* is the implication that there exists a full circuit of mass transport, through which water can flow but cannot be gained or lost. In an approximate sense over secular spans of time, the earth's total water resource is a constant. When the hydrologic cycle is regarded as an open system, it is because energy in its various forms, rather than matter, enters and leaves the system boundaries. Flow of water as matter in this system requires that energy be imported and exported. Sensible heat of water in liquid, solid, and gaseous states as well as latent heat of vaporization and fusion are stored and exchanged. Potential and kinetic forms of mechanical energy are likewise involved, because of the changes of elevation of water above the sea-level base of reference.

## A GRAVITY-FLOW SYSTEM

In its broadest sense, the hydrologic cycle involves all possible paths of water movement: through the atmosphere and oceans, over the lands, and below the ground surface (Figure 6.1). The concern of this chapter is with two subsystems, both involving the gravity flow of water from higher to lower levels upon the surfaces of the continents. The water may be in the liquid form (to constitute streams) or in the solid state as ice (to constitute glaciers). Both water streams and ice streams have much in common. The system intake boundary is the interface between atmosphere and land. Here water enters through precipitation, whether as rain or snow.

At the instant of its arrival, precipitation has potential energy by virtue of its position above sea level. If the water does not return to the atmosphere by evaporation and sublimation (a reversal of flow through the system boundary), it inevitably flows to lower levels under the influence of gravity. In the case of the water system, systematic convergences of the flow paths result in concentration of flow in an increasingly larger trunk stream. Exit from the

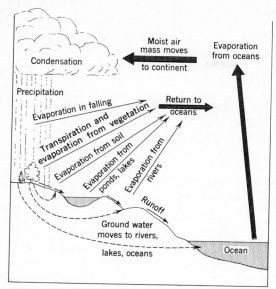

Figure 6.1. The hydrologic cycle. (© 1960, John Wiley & Sons, New York.)

system is accomplished through a single point, where the trunk stream reaches the sea.

Glaciers of a particular class (those that originate in high mountains) likewise show convergences to a single massive trunk. In some cases, this trunk flow reaches the sea; more commonly it does not. In the latter case, exit of matter from the system boundary occurs by direct evaporation into the atmosphere, and by melting. Emergence of the meltwater as a stream represents an abrupt transition from a glacier system to a stream system.

Systems of gravity flow of water on the lands belong to the class of *irreversible* (one-way) *systems,* in which work is done by conversion of potential energy of position to kinetic energy of matter in motion. To overcome frictional resistance, kinetic energy of downslope motion is converted into heat, thence lost from the system by conduction and radiation.

## A DECAY SYSTEM

If the land surfaces of the world were absolutely unyielding and changeless, the system of gravity flow on the lands would be sustained by solar energy, constantly bringing water to elevated points and thereby constantly replenishing the potential energy. An average steady state of the system could then be easily maintained, assuming a constant source of solar energy for vast spans of time.

As we shall find in the next two chapters, the land surfaces of the earth are not unyielding and changeless. Two forms of landscape change are to be dealt with in our real world. One is the movement of the rock crust (lithosphere) itself, either upward or downward, to alter the position of the land with respect to sea level and thus to change the supply of potential energy at the input boundary of the flow system. Such crustal changes may be in the truest sense accidental from a systems point of view. The crust is elevated at a particular place by action of enormous and deep-seated forces involved with quite another energy system—that of radiogenic heat and its accumulation and escape from the earth's lower crust and upper mantle (Chapter 7).

Another class of crustal changes is causally tied in with the system of gravity flow. This is a spontaneous rise of the crust in response to removal of material from the surface and is explained in Chapter 7.

The second form of landscape change, which we can refer to simply as *denudation,* is the geologic phase of the flow system itself. Denudation is the lowering of the land surface as rock yields to the forces that tend to decompose and disintegrate it, to wear it away, and to transport the resulting particulate matter to lower levels along with the flow itself. Denudation is the subject of Chapters 8 and 9.

It should be obvious that geologic and hydrologic processes and forms within the system are interacting and interdependent. Flow of water shapes the configuration of the land surface, creating distinctive landscape elements that can be designated simply *landforms.* But the landforms control the flow paths of the water. Thus a winding river gorge is carved by the river, but at the same time the gorge confines and directs the flow of the river. Neither the hydrologic nor the geologic process comes first; neither is primary in role with respect to the other. Instead, both evolve together.

As denudation progresses, the reduction of the land surface by removal of its own substance continually decreases the potential energy of the flow system, since precipitation falls upon a surface of progressively lower elevation. We shall see that reduction in average elevation of the surface must also be accompanied by a reduction in the rate of further changes. It now becomes obvious that this system belongs to the class of *decay systems,* which we have not thus far encountered. The processes of denudation diminish in intensity as the average rate of descent in elevation is reduced. Processes require increasingly longer intervals of time to accomplish a given unit of geologic work. Under such a program, the total destruction of a continent could never truly reach an end; it could only approach an ultimate goal. Meantime, the gravity-flow system of water on the lands must become ever more feeble. Consider also that lowering of highlands and mountain chains will reduce the orographic effect in production of precipitation; but there will be no lack of precipitation of convectional and cyclonic forms.

With this general introduction to the broadest concepts of gravity flow of water as an open system acting upon the lands, we turn to some of the particulars relating to the flow itself.

## SURFACE WATER AND SUBSURFACE WATER

Our investigation begins where the last chapter left off—with the arrival of precipitation at the ground surface. The hydrologist (water scientist) classifies water that flows on the land surface or lies ponded in lakes and marshes as *surface water;* water that lies beneath the land surface, enclosed in pores or cracks in soil and rock, as *subsurface water.* The flow of surface water is included under the general heading of *runoff,* which covers the disposal of surplus water from the continents in liquid or solid form (as distinguished from return to the atmosphere by evaporation).

## INFILTRATION AND OVERLAND FLOW

In the natural undisturbed state most soil surfaces can absorb the water from light to moderate rains and transmit it downward by a process termed *infiltration.* Natural passageways are available between individual soil grains and between the larger aggregates of soil where previous drying has caused cracks to form, where borings by worms and other animals have been made, where decay of plant roots has left openings, and where the alternate growth and melting of ice crystals has disrupted the soil. Such openings tend to be kept clear by the protective mat of decaying leaves and plant stems, and the mat also acts to break the force of falling raindrops. When rain falls too rapidly to escape downward through the soil passages, the excess quantity escapes as a form of runoff called *overland flow*—a surface layer of water following the slope of the ground.

Intensity of rainfall is measured in depth of water accumulated per unit of time. Imagine that the rain is caught in a straight-sided, flat-bottomed container and that none is lost by splashing out or by evaporation. The depth in inches of accumulation per hour represents rainfall intensity (Figure 6.2). If the container is imagined to have a porous bottom, like a sieve, the water will leak through, lowering the level at a certain rate, representing the rate of infiltration into the soil, the *infiltration capacity.* Now, if the rainfall rate exceeds the infiltration rate, the container will fill until it can hold no more. When both the storage capacity and the ability of the soil to transmit water to greater depth are exceeded, the excess escapes as overland flow. Thus we can also measure runoff by overland flow in units of inches or centimeters per hour.

The ability of soils to absorb rainfall, or the infiltration capacity, is ordinarily rather great at the very outset of a rain that follows a period of dryness. This is because the soil is in a contracted state and has many large openings. As wetting proceeds, however, the soil takes up water and swells, closing the larger openings. Moreover, the spongelike capacity of the soil pores to hold water is quickly met, after which the infiltration capacity is sharply reduced. Thus the infiltration capacity changes with time; the initial value is high—perhaps 2 to 3 in./hr (5 to 8 cm/hr)—but falls rapidly within the first hour and thereafter levels off and becomes relatively constant at a much lower rate.

At this point we have to choose between two alternatives: the first is to pursue the overland flow until it reaches the oceans; the second is

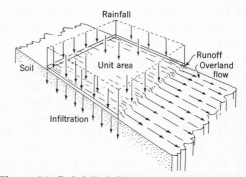

Figure 6.2. Rainfall, infiltration, runoff, and overland flow.

to trace the course of infiltrated water until it reemerges as surface water. We choose the second alternative, since it takes the more limited of the flow paths.

## ZONES OF SUBSURFACE WATER

Water is held in the soil and underlying rock in different ways, depending upon the degree to which it occupies the available interconnected pore spaces. Lacking in an understanding of soil and rock varieties and their properties, treated in later chapters, it will be necessary to refer to some idealized body of mineral matter beneath the ground surface. A good model will be that of a densely packed mass of pure sand (such as beach sand or dune sand) extending downward indefinitely. In such sand about 35% of the bulk volume is open space; the voids are fully interconnected and are large enough to permit movement of water through the mass. Such a body is described by hydrologists as being *permeable.*

Under typical conditions of a humid climate, such as that of the eastern United States or western Europe, there is present an upper zone of soil and rock in which water is held in the form of small films or droplets clinging to mineral surfaces with a force stronger than the force of gravity. This water is described as *capillary water,* because the adhesive force is capillary tension. Air occupies the remaining volume of the pore spaces, either as a connected network of air spaces or as separate air bubbles. This subsurface region of capillary water and air is known as the *zone of aeration* (Figure 6.3). It is geologically significant as a zone in which oxidation of mineral matter can take place.

Below the zone of aeration lies the *zone of saturation,* in which all pore space is occupied by water. The upper surface of this zone is the *water table* (Figure 6.3). Water in the zone of saturation is known as *ground water* and moves slowly in response to gravity.

The zone of aeration can be subdivided into two subzones. That moisture which is within range of plant roots defines the *soil-water belt* and can be extracted by plants. This water can be released into the atmosphere by transpiration. Some of this capillary water can also evaporate directly through the soil surface in dry weather. The combined processes of direct evaporation and plant transpiration can be designated as *evapotranspiration.* However, there may be present an underlying zone of capillary water too deep to be reached by plants and not subject to appreciable evaporation; it is said to occupy the *intermediate belt* (Figure 6.3).

The capillary state of water above the water table is temporarily destroyed whenever prolonged and copious rain or rapidly melting snow allows large amounts of water to infiltrate. At such times the soil openings are fully saturated, and the water moves down as a wave under the influence of gravity to reach the water table. The ground-water body is thus *recharged.* Most of this excess water drains out of the zone of aeration soil in a period of days and the capillary state takes over again.

## GROUND-WATER MOVEMENT AND RECHARGE

The position of the water table can be determined by noting the level at which the water surface stands in a well that penetrates the

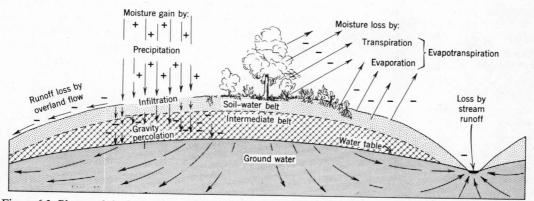

Figure 6.3. Phases of the hydrologic cycle in the zones of soil water and ground water. (© 1960, John Wiley & Sons, New York.)

ground-water zone. Where there are many wells closely spaced over an area, the configuration of the water table can be shown by connecting the levels of standing water in the wells (Figure 6.4). The water table will be found to be highest in elevation under the interstream divides and lowest along the lines of valleys, where it may intersect the surface in the channels of streams or at the shores of lakes and marshes.

Water in an open body, such as a lake, assumes a horizontal surface because there is little resistance to flowage. In the ground-water zone, however, gravity movement is through the very tiny spaces between mineral grains and along thin cracks in bedrock, which greatly resist flowage. Consequently, percolating water reaching the water table under the divides cannot escape readily and tends to accumulate, raising the water table and causing it to maintain a sloping surface in rough conformity with the ground surface (Figure 6.4). Difference in level between the water table under a divide and at the low point of a valley constitutes a *hydraulic head* and causes the water to flow very slowly within the ground-water body, following curved paths much like those shown in Figure 6.5. A particular molecule of water, if it could be traced, might follow a curving path that carries it deep into the rock and returns it by upward flow to the line

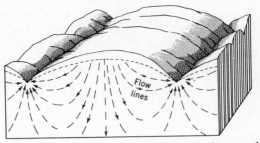

Figure 6.5. Ground water follows strongly curved paths of travel where the subsurface material is uniform throughout. (© 1960, John Wiley & Sons, New York. Based on data of M. K. Hubbert.)

of a stream channel, where the water escapes into the stream as surface runoff. Flow velocity is highest near the line of escape, as suggested by the close crowding of arrows in Figure 6.5.

With a generally constant climatic environment the water table will become approximately fixed in position, and the rate of recharge will on the average balance the rate at which water is returned to surface flow by seepage in streams, lakes, and marshes. But should there occur a period of unusually dry years, the water table will slowly fall; if there is a period of unusually wet years, it will gradually rise (Figure 6.4).

Smaller seasonal fluctuations in the level of the water table are to be expected in climates having alternately dry and wet seasons or alternately warm and cold seasons. A seasonal decline in the water table results from the cutting off of recharge during a dry season or when soil moisture is solidly frozen. A seasonal rise results from the percolation of excess infiltration through the zone of aeration.

### OVERLAND FLOW AND CHANNEL FLOW

*Overland flow* is the movement of runoff downslope on the ground in a more or less broadly distributed sheet (Figure 6.6). Overland flow may take the form of a thin continuous film over relatively smooth soil or rock surfaces. Where the surface is pitted or has obstructing masses in the form of soil mounds, boulders, or fallen vegetation, runoff takes the form of small rivulets overflowing from one hollow to the next. On a grass-covered surface the countless stems cause the flow to be subdivided into a pattern of many intertwining flow lines. Such flow may not be noticed, even in a heavy rain yielding much runoff. Similarly, in a heavy forest the accumulation of fallen vegetation may completely mask from view a substantial rate of overland flow.

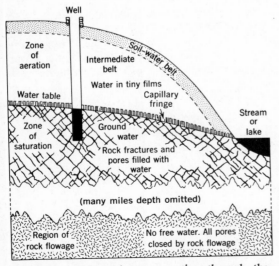

Figure 6.4. Schematic cross section through the various moisture zones and belts of soil and bedrock. (© 1960, John Wiley & Sons, New York. Based on data of Ackerman, Colman, and Ogrosky.)

Figure 6.6. This heavy overland flow from a corn field occurred on an 8% slope following a torrential summer thunderstorm rain. Channel flow is seen in the ditch in the foreground. (Photograph by Soil Conservation Service, U.S. Dept. of Agriculture.)

A *stream channel* is essentially a long, narrow, sloping trough shaped by the concentrated flow of water in a manner most effective for moving the mixture of water and sediment supplied by runoff and by ground-water seepage from the enclosing drainage basin. Channels range in size from insignificant brooks one can step across in a single stride to the trenches of great rivers hundreds of feet wide. Taking the mile-wide Mississippi River as an extreme example, we see that natural stream channels can range from 1 ft (0.3 m) or less to 5000 ft (1500 m) or more in width, a 5000-fold ratio in size.

Channels do not necessarily need to contain flowing water to be so defined. Many channels of desert streams are dry most of the time, yet they bear the unmistakable markings of rapidly flowing water and are occupied by raging torrents on the rare occasions of flood.

To describe a stream channel and the flow of water in it, hydraulic engineers use a set of terms and definitions that constitute, collectively, the *hydraulic geometry* (Figure 6.7). Stream *depth, d,* is measured at any desired point. *Width, w,* is the distance across the stream from bank to bank. *Cross-sectional area, A,* is given for a vertical cross section at right angles to direction of flow. The length of the line of contact of water with channel, measured along the cross section, is termed the *wetted perimeter, P.*

Of great importance in describing a stream

channel is the *gradient,* or *slope, S.* The slope of a large river can be given as the angle of the water surface with respect to the horizontal. In giving the gradient of a small shallow stream or of a dry channel, the gradient of the channel floor is determined; it would differ little from the water-surface gradient if averaged over an appreciable distance.

## STREAM FLOW

Every particle of water in a stream is drawn vertically downward under the force of gravity, so that the water exerts a pressure upon the channel walls proportional to the water depth. A part of the force of gravity acts in the downstream direction, parallel with the stream bed, tending to cause flow of one water layer over the next lower layer in a type of motion known as *shear.* The fluid may be thought of as having almost infinitely thin layers of water molecules, each layer slipping over the layer below, much as playing cards slip over one another when the deck of cards is pushed along a table top. The layer immediately in contact with the solid bed does not slip, but each higher layer slips over the one below, so that the forward motion, or *velocity, V,* increases from the bed upward into the stream.

Dotted lines in Figure 6.7 show the successive positions that would be occupied by water particles starting out together on a vertical line. We see that velocity increases very rapidly

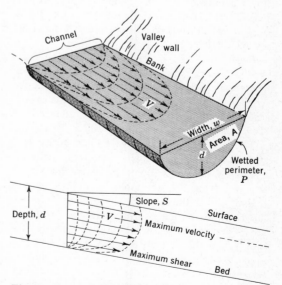

Figure 6.7. Geometric elements of a stream channel and distribution of speeds of flow. (© 1960, John Wiley & Sons, New York.)

from the bed upward, then increases less rapidly, so that the maximum velocity is found at a point about one-third of the distance from the surface. Similarly, on the stream surface velocity increases from zero at the banks to a maximum near the center line. The rate of shear, which is the same as the rate of change in velocity, is greatest near the bed and banks of the stream.

The foregoing statements imply that each particle of water moves downstream in a direct simple path. Such would be the case in true *laminar flow*, or *streamline flow*, which occurs in fluids when their motion is very slow. In most forms of runoff, including most overland flow and nearly all stream-channel flow, the water particles describe highly irregular paths of travel, resembling a tortuous corkscrew motion including sideways and vertical movements. Such motion, described as *turbulent flow*, consists of innumerable eddies of various sizes and intensities continually forming and dissolving. The velocity, $V$, referred to above, and the simple paths of flow shown by the arrows in Figure 6.7 are merely the average velocities and average paths of the particles at given levels in the stream.

Turbulent flow in fluids is of great importance in the processes of erosion by running water, waves and tidal currents, and wind, because the transportation of fine particles held in *suspension* in the fluid depends upon the upward currents in turbulence to support the particles. Without turbulence particles could only be rolled or dragged upon the bed or lifted a short distance above it.

Because of the differences in average flow velocity from point to point in a stream, a single statement of velocity is needed to apply to the stream as a whole. This is the *mean velocity* and is approximately equivalent to six-tenths of the maximum velocity.

The quantity of water that flows through a stream channel in a given period of time, the *discharge*, is a most important characteristic of the flow from the standpoint of describing the magnitude of the stream. Discharge, $Q$, is defined as the volume of water passing through a cross section in a short unit of time. Commonly the units are in terms of cubic feet per second, abbreviated as *cfs*, or simply stated as *second-feet* (in metric units—cubic meters per second, *cms*). Discharge is computed by multiplying the mean velocity, $\bar{V}$, times the cross-sectional area, $A$, in the formula $Q = A\bar{V}$.

If a long stream channel is to conduct a given discharge through its entire course, the discharge must be constant at all cross sections, otherwise water would accumulate by ponding. It follows that the product of cross-sectional area and mean velocity must be constant in all cross sections along the stream (Figure 6.8). If the stream becomes narrower, with reduced cross section, it must have a proportional increase of velocity. If the velocity should increase because of a steepened gradient, the cross-sectional area of the stream will become smaller. The same river that flows slowly in a broad channel on a low gradient will flow swiftly in a narrow stream when it enters a gorge of steep gradient. The equation $Q = A\bar{V}$ is known as the *equation of continuity* of flow, because a stream that is neither gaining nor losing water at any point on its course must keep the discharge constant by appropriate combinations of cross-sectional area and velocity.

## STREAM ENERGY AND VELOCITY

The flowing of a stream requires that energy be changed continuously from one form to another. Shear within the water is resisted by a property of stickiness in the fluid, known as *viscosity*. Energy must be consumed in overcoming this resistance to flow. At first, stream energy exists in the potential form, by reason of the stream's height or altitude at the upper end of the course. As the water drops in level downstream, the potential energy is transformed into kinetic energy, the energy of motion.

If the stream offered no resistance to flow, the water would accelerate continuously, just as an object accelerates when falling in a vacuum. But the increasing rate of flow in the stream is met by increasing internal resistance

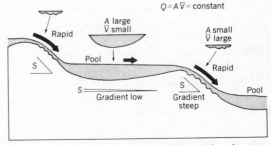

Figure 6.8. Relations among cross-sectional area ($A$), mean velocity ($\bar{V}$), and gradient ($S$) in a stream of uniform discharge.

from the viscosity of the water, so that the velocity quickly reaches a constant value. In overcoming resistance kinetic energy is transformed into heat energy at a constant rate. Actually, the stream should become warmer by its own flow, but the rise in temperature is not measurable.

We have seen that stream velocity increases when the slope, or gradient, increases, for then the downslope force component of gravity is greater. A stream will also become swifter if its channel shape is altered to offer less resistance to flow along its wetted perimeter. If the stream becomes broader and shallower, its perimeter becomes longer, compared with the area of cross section, thus offering more resistance to flow and causing a decrease in velocity. A channel is most efficient when it has the least perimeter for the given cross-sectional area. A semicircular channel is the most efficient form but is rarely approached in nature. Other considerations, such as the necessity of transporting sediment and the weakness or strength of the materials composing the channel walls, enter into the form of a natural stream channel.

Still another primary factor controlling velocity is the roughness of the stream bed. Flow over a bed consisting of cobbles or boulders or having wavelike ripples of sand will be less efficient than flow over a very smooth bed, such as one of fine clay or of highly polished rock.

In summary, a stream whose discharge is kept constant throughout its length will have its mean velocity determined by the stream gradient and by the cross-sectional area, form, and roughness of its channel.

## DRAINAGE SYSTEMS

Let us examine a fully developed and active drainage system. From the stream mouth, where all discharge exists, the system perimeter is located by following out the natural *drainage divide,* a continuous line with respect to which overland flow is directed either toward the system or away from it (Figure 6.9). The drainage divide outlines a natural *drainage basin,* which is normally of elliptical or pear-shaped outline. Abnormalities of basin shape are commonly present, where geological controls exert strong action, but we will assume these controls are at the minimum.

Dominating the drainage basin is a treelike, branched system of stream channels. Overland flow, originating at the divide of the drainage basin and along the many subsidiary divides between channel branches, makes its way by the most direct downslope trajectory to the nearest channel. A given element of channel thus receives sustenance both from the channel lying upstream and from the adjacent land surfaces, which can be called simply the *valley-side slopes.* It will also be evident that at the upper extremity of each branch a channel is dependent for survival upon the contribution of the overland flow derived from the land surface between it and the enclosing divide. For a particular region, with its unique combination of soil, rock, and vegetation, a particular average surface area is required to initiate and sustain a permanent channel. Figure 6.10 shows a typical landscape with fully developed stream networks.

Overland flow exerts a stress upon the ground over which it flows. This stress can loosen particles of rock and soil, dragging them

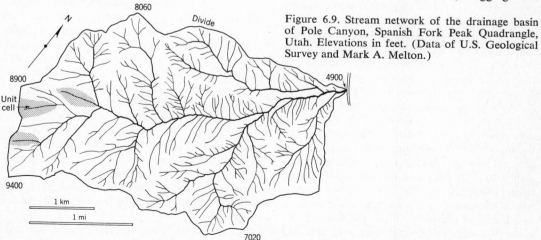

Figure 6.9. Stream network of the drainage basin of Pole Canyon, Spanish Fork Peak Quadrangle, Utah. Elevations in feet. (Data of U.S. Geological Survey and Mark A. Melton.)

Figure 6.10. Air view of a fluvially dissected landscape in southern California. (Copyrighted Spence Air Photos.)

downslope to the channels. Thus overland flow erodes and thereby furnishes to the stream its *load* of debris, discussed in Chapter 9.

In areas of humid climates, where annual rainfall is far in excess of annual evaporation, ground water seeps into the channels, making an important contribution to stream flow. This increment is described as *base flow* and sustains perennial streams in periods between rains. Arid lands lack a ground-water system and produce no base flow. Consequently, most streams of arid lands are *ephemeral,* flowing only spasmodically in direct response to overland flow. Even in humid regions, the smallest channel elements are normally dry in summer because they lie above the water table.

Study of a stream channel system is most instructive in showing how a flow system adjusts itself to some optimum compromise between various conflicting requirements. The channel system must dispose of all water furnished to it. It must also dispose of all mineral matter supplied to it. The treelike pattern which we see represents a compromise between two forms of efficiency. First, the shortest distance between the intake area and the exit point represents the most rapid rate of fall and the least total resistance. But a large number of separate parallel channels, each taking the shortest distance, is in itself a violation of a second principle of stream efficiency, namely, that a single large channel is much more efficient for water transport than the total of several small channels. As a compromise, the system develops a habit of junctions, wherein larger channels are continually created. Lengths of overland-flow paths tend to be adjusted to a rough degree of equalization, resulting in a tendency toward uniform spacing of channels. Each finger-tip channel competes with its neighbors for surface area. An equilibrium is easily established, based upon a principle of mutual repulsion. Each finger-tip channel with its contributing surface for overland flow can be thought of as a unit cell, or building block, for the system (Figure 6.9). The actual dimensions of each cell vary greatly from one region to another depending upon the ease of erosion of the material underlying the surface and the degree of resistance offered by vegetation.

Channel gradients in the drainage network

show a systematic adjustment with respect to the magnitude of the channel in terms of its discharge of water and rock waste. The finger-tip channels have the steepest gradients. At each junction between channels of comparable orders of magnitude the channel gradient abruptly decreases to a lower slope. This gradient decrease is a result of the increased efficiency of a larger channel as compared with a smaller one, a subject that will be explored more fully in Chapter 9. The gradient of the trunk segment nearest the mouth of the drainage basin is therefore the lowest of the entire system.

From what has been said in an earlier paragraph one might be led to think that the large trunk stream would move sluggishly in comparison with the small steep-gradient streams in the headwater region. Perhaps we do tend to associate swiftness with a mountain torrent in contrast to the seemingly slow and stately flow of a great river. Actually, mean velocity of stream flow increases slightly in the downstream direction. While it is true that reduced slope tends to give reduced velocity, the increasing depth of the stream in the downstream direction tends to give increased velocity. Depth is the more important factor of the two, and an increase in velocity is the net result.

## RELATION OF STREAM FLOW TO RAINFALL

One important aim of the science of hydrology is to relate the changes in discharge of streams to the characteristics of rainfall and to variations in runoff attributed to overland flow and to influent seepage from the ground-water body. When rainfall records are compared with runoff records by means of graphs, certain basic principles emerge.

Take for example the drainage basin of Sugar Creek, Ohio, with 310 mi² (805 km²) of watershed area. The outline of the basin is shown by a dashed line in Figure 6.11, which is a map of the Muskingum River watershed with isohyets (lines of equal rainfall) drawn for a rainstorm of August 6 and 7, 1935. Rainfall on the Sugar Creek watershed ranged from 5 to 9 in. (13 to 23 cm), but the average accumulated depth for the watershed was 6.3 in. (16 cm). Figure 6.12 is a hydrograph based on the records of a stream gauge at Strasburg, Ohio. Here discharge is plotted in depth equivalent in inches per hour, the same units used for rainfall, so that the rainfall and runoff

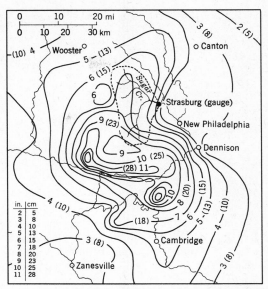

Figure 6.11. Isohyets in inches of a 1-day summer rainstorm in northern Ohio, August 6–7, 1935. Centimeters in parentheses. [© 1965, John Wiley & Sons, New York. Based on a map by W. G. Hoyt and W. R. Langbein (1955), *Floods,* Princeton, N.J., Princeton Univ. Press, p. 44, Figure 12.]

can be compared directly. Notice that Sugar Creek was carrying a small discharge before the rainstorm. That flow may be attributed to the seepage of ground water into the channel, providing *base flow.* Runoff at the gauge did not begin to increase sharply until the rain was almost over, a lag of many hours. The peak discharge was reached about 18 hr after the rain began, then decreased gradually. Lag in this case is due in part to the initial infiltration rate, but more particularly to *channel storage,* which is the ability of many branching stream channels to hold water in the manner of a temporary reservoir and hence to store water as runoff increases.

During the prolonged rainstorm over the Sugar Creek watershed, water infiltrating the ground percolated down to the water table, recharging the groundwater body and causing an increase in the contribution to streams by base flow. The dashed line in Figure 6.12 shows the slow rise of base flow during August 7 and 8, with the cessation of surface runoff, until it provided almost the entire flow of the stream.

A computation of the total storm runoff showed that only about 3 in. (8 cm) of water was discharged by the stream through the Strasburg gauge, whereas an average of 6.3 in.

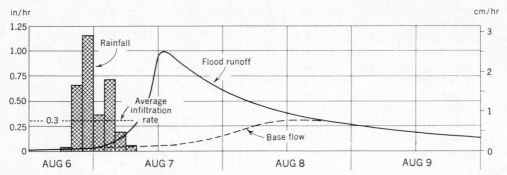

Figure 6.12. Hydrograph of the Sugar Creek watershed, showing the relation of flood crest to period of rainfall. [© 1965, John Wiley & Sons, New York. Data from W. G. Hoyt and W. R. Langbein (1955).]

(16 cm) had fallen. The missing 3.3 in. (8 cm) was lost by evaporation, or infiltrated the surface to be held as capillary moisture in the zone of aeration, or was added to the ground water.

The larger the watershed, the longer the lag between rainfall period and peak discharge, and the slower the rate of decline of discharge after the peak has passed. In other words, with increasing basin size the discharge is both delayed in time of peak and drawn out in duration.

## FLOODS

Despite the fact that everyone is familiar with river floods through photographs seen in newspapers and on television, it is not easy to give a simple and widely acceptable definition of what constitutes a flood. Most streams have a rather clearly defined channel whose walls are scoured sufficiently by high discharges that little or no vegetation can flourish there, whereas the adjoining ground normally supports a vegetative cover of forest, grasses, or crops. A stream whose discharge just fills the clearly defined channel is said to be in the *bank-full* stage. Closely coinciding with the bank-full stage is a stream height designated by hydrologists as *flood stage,* the critical upper limit above which overbank flooding sets in, inundating the adjoining flat ground known as the *floodplain,* and thereby constituting a *flood*. A floodplain may be present on one or both sides of the channel and is inundated by flood water about once a year, on the average, in those climates where a season of water surplus is characteristic. Where a river occupies a narrow rock gorge, there may be no convenient reference level, such as a floodplain, by which to judge the occurrence of a flood.

At long intervals—such as every 20, 50, or 100 yr, on the average—there occur discharges of far greater magnitude than those expected annually. Such rare floods inundate ground surfaces lying well above the floodplain and may cover broad, flat, steplike expanses of adjacent ground (Figure 6.13).

The rise and fall of a river surface during passage of a flood is termed the *flood wave.* The highest point, or *crest*, travels downstream to reach progressively lower elevations along the system. Principles governing the form and height of the flood wave are the same as those governing the lesser peak discharges already discussed. An example is taken from the Savannah River and its tributaries in South Carolina and Georgia (Figure 6.14). Near Clayton, Georgia, the Chattooga River, draining only 203 mi$^2$ (526 km$^2$), experienced its peak discharge of about 7000 cfs (200 cms) only about one day after the occurrence of the storm, then quickly subsided.

The flood wave continued downstream for 65 mi (105 km) to Calhoun Falls, South Carolina, where the flood crested late on the second day with a peak discharge of 46,000 cfs (1400 cms) derived from a watershed of almost 2900 mi$^2$ (7500 km$^2$). At Clyo, Georgia, 95 mi (153 km) farther downstream, where the watershed area is almost 10,000 mi$^2$ (26,000 km$^2$), the flood crest of 64,000 cfs (2000 cms) arrived on the fifth day. As plotted on the upper hydrograph of Figure 6.14, it is clear that the lag in arrival of flood crest increased downstream and that peak discharge also increased. The duration of the flood also increased downstream.

To compare the characteristics of the three stations independent of the magnitude of the flood, the lower part of Figure 6.14 shows the

Figure 6.13. The Connecticut River flood of March, 1936, inundated a part of the city of Hartford. A line of trees at left marks the river bank. (Official photograph, 8th Photo Section, A. C., U.S. Army.)

discharge per square mile of watershed plotted against time in days. The area under each line on the graph is the same, only the curve form differs. Here we see clearly the sharp peaking and rapid dropoff of discharge in the small watershed, in contrast to the broadly attenuated flood wave farther downstream.

## GLACIERS

To complete a study of the terrestrial circuits of the hydrologic cycle we must include a study of *glaciers,* those enormous accumulations of land ice that once overwhelmed parts of the continents and still persist over Greenland, Antarctica, and in many high mountain ranges of the globe.

Glaciers can be viewed as parts of the grav-

ity-flow system of water, provided we recognize the fundamental differences between the physical characteristics of ice and water. Ice at ordinary atmospheric pressures is a brittle solid, seemingly incapable of yielding by flowage. Under a sharp blow it fractures into bits. Examined under a microscope it shows clearly the crystalline properties of a mineral. Yet, when ice has accumulated to a thickness of perhaps 200 to 300 ft (60 to 90 m) and is resting on a sloping surface, the lower layers of ice respond to the force of gravity by slow flowage. That is to say, layers the thickness of molecules glide over one another, allowing ice layers higher in the glacier to travel downslope over those below and enabling the entire mass to move downhill. A surface layer some 100 to

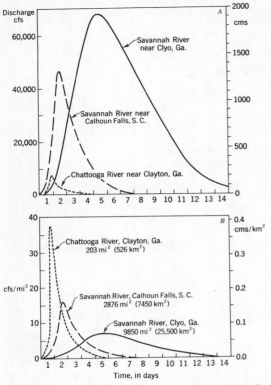

Figure 6.14. A flood wave traveling downstream is shown in these hydrographs of the Savannah River system in South Carolina and Georgia. [© 1965, John Wiley & Sons, New York. After W. G. Hoyt and W. B. Langbein (1955), *Floods*, Princeton, N.J., Princeton Univ. Press, p. 39, Figure 8.]

150 ft (30 to 45 m) thick will, however, remain brittle and will be carried along upon the deeper ice.

The flow of glacial ice is always of the *laminar* type, found in water streams only at very low speeds. Turbulent flow never occurs. Consequently, glaciers, such as that shown in Figure 9.19, exhibit uniform parallel banding in the direction of flow. Rock debris lying on the ice makes up these bands and shows strikingly the nature of streamline flow without cross currents.

Glaciers come in two basic forms (Figure 6.15). The *valley glacier,* or *alpine glacier,* is the true member of the water-stream family, for it has branches. Actually, the valley-glacier pattern is imposed by a previous stream-valley system, which the glacier has occupied. The second basic form is seen in the *icecap* and its former extension into a vast *continental ice sheet.* We can think of the icecap and ice sheet

as essentially circular plates of ice that spread radially outward. Unlike the valley-glacier system, which requires a steep down-valley gradient to cause flow, the icecap and ice sheet flow because the ice surface has a gradient from a higher central area to a lower periphery. A simple model for such flow would be a spoonful of pancake batter poured onto a skillet. Add more batter at the center and the pancake will increase in diameter.

## GLACIERS AS OPEN SYSTEMS

As open systems, all glaciers have much in common. Matter, in the form of snow, is received upon the upper surface in the zone of highest elevation. Here the rate of loss of snow by evaporation and melting in summer is on the average less than the rate at which the snow is received. This region is the *zone of accumulation* (Figure 6.16). As snow layers accumulate, they are altered to a dense granular ice (known as *firn*), which is gradually compacted to true glacial ice. At sufficient depth this ice begins its slow downslope flow-

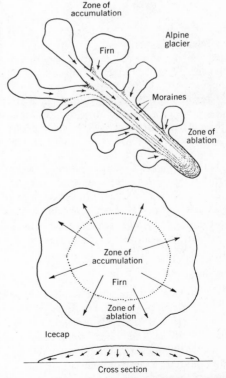

Figure 6.15. Schematic maps comparing the form of an alpine glacier with that of an icecap.

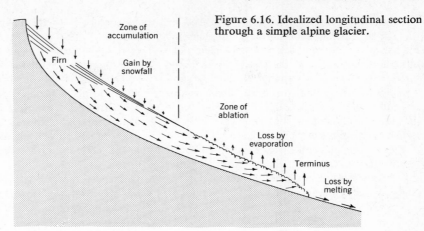

Figure 6.16. Idealized longitudinal section through a simple alpine glacier.

age. Rates of surface motion may be at most a few inches per day. At the lower end or periphery of the glacier, loss by combined melting and evaporation exceeds the rate at which snow accumulates. This imbalance is the greater as the glacier is followed to lower, warmer elevations. Consequently, the ice disappears at the lower end or border (*terminus*) of the glacier. This region of net loss is the exit boundary of the system and is known as the *zone of ablation*.

As a flow system, the motion of ice from the zone of nourishment to the zone of ablation is dependent upon the ice thickness, which in turn depends upon rates of nourishment and ablation. A glacier easily adjusts its form and dimensions to reach a steady state, in which the terminus remains essentially fixed in position for long periods of time. Such a condition is known as *glacier equilibrium*. Equilibrium may be upset by changes in the rates at which ice accumulates or disappears; hence glaciers are remarkably sensitive indicators of climatic changes and are studied for the information they can give as to past periods of colder or warmer climate; or of wetter or drier periods.

Comparing the cross section of a valley glacier with that of a water stream, the equation of continuity ($Q = A\bar{V}$) applies to both. The discharge, $Q$, of a stream system is probably nearly the same as that of a glacier system that would occupy the same valley system in a period of colder climate. The difference then lies in the relative values of cross-sectional area ($A$) and mean velocity ($\bar{V}$). As Figure 6.17 shows, a glacier has a very large cross-sectional area but a very low velocity; a stream has a very small cross section but much higher veloc-

ity. Velocity is largely controlled by the basic properties of the two substances: low viscosity for water and extremely high viscosity for ice. Consequently, the cross sections are adjusted to suit the velocities.

## GREENLAND AND ANTARCTIC ICE SHEETS

From the study of small streamlike valley glaciers we turn our attention to the two enormous ice masses of subcontinental size that exist today. Greenland and Antarctica bear these great ice sheets.

The Greenland Ice Sheet occupies some 670,000 mi² (1,740,000 km²)—which is 80% of the entire area of the island of Greenland—covering all but narrow land fringes (Figure 6.18). Altogether the ice sheet comprises some 672,000 mi³ (2,800,000 km³) of ice. In a general way the ice forms a single broadly arched,

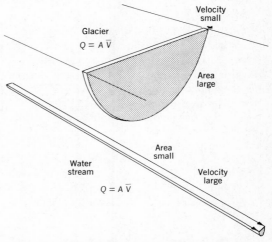

Figure 6.17. Velocity and cross-sectional areas of a glacier and a water stream compared.

doubly convex ice lens, smoothly surfaced on the upper side and considerably rougher and less strongly curved on the underside. The mountainous terrain of the coast passes inland beneath the ice with steadily descending summit elevations, giving a central lowland area close to sea level in elevation. The ice margin is in places gently sloping, but elsewhere it forms a steep ramp or a sheer cliff (Figure 6.19).

The ice thickness measures close to 10,000 ft (3 km) at its greatest. It is not surprising that the earth's crust beneath the center of Greenland is actually depressed under such a load, in conformity with the principle of isostasy (see chapter 7), for 10,000 ft (3 km) of glacial ice is roughly equivalent to a rock layer at least 3000 ft (0.9 km) thick.

The central area of the Greenland Ice Sheet is in the glacial zone of accumulation: It is a vast firn field of compacting snow in process of transformation into glacial ice. The firn limit lies some 30 to 100 mi (50 to 160 km) inland of the ice margin; thus the ablation area constitutes only 15% to 20% of the entire ice sheet.

Because the ice surface slopes seaward, the ice creeps slowly downward and outward toward the margins, where it discharges by glacial tongues—called *outlet glaciers*—closely resembling valley glaciers in form, but fed from a vast ice sheet rather than from a cirque. Some of the outlet glaciers have unusually fast rates of flow, on the order of 100 ft (30 m) per day. Outlet glaciers, reaching the sea in fiords, are the source of North Atlantic icebergs. Near the ice borders, where coastal terrain is most mountainous, occasional peaks of bedrock project from beneath the ice sheet.

The Greenland Ice Sheet is nourished by snowfall occurring in cyclonic storms traveling generally from west to east across the landmass. For some time in the recent past the Greenland Ice Sheet was losing mass steadily, but very slowly, as judged from the observed recession of its outlet glaciers and a lowering of ice level along its fringes. However, the ice sheet as a whole is judged to be close to equilibrium at the present time.

Like Greenland, the Antarctic continent is almost entirely buried beneath glacial ice. This is an ice area of just over 5 million mi² (13

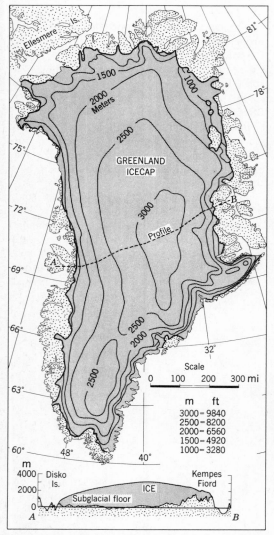

Figure 6.18. Greenland and its ice sheet. (© 1960, John Wiley & Sons, New York. Based on a map by R. F. Flint.)

Figure 6.19. Ice cliff 50 to 150 ft (15 to 45 m) high at the margin of the Greenland Ice Sheet, Nunatarssuaq, Greenland. The cliff moves forward at about 0.5 in. (1.3 cm) per day. (Photograph by L. H. Nobles.)

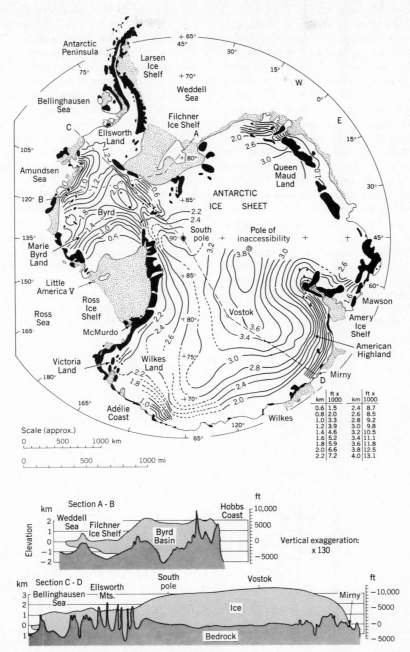

Figure 6.20. Map of Antarctica showing ice-surface elevations by contours with interval of 0.2 km (660 ft). Areas of exposed bedrock shown in black; ice shelves by stipple pattern. [Map redrawn and simplified from C. R. Bentley (1962), *Geophysical Monograph No. 7,* Washington, D.C., Amer. Geophys. Union, p. 14, Figure 2. Cross sections after Amer. Geog. Soc. (1964), *Antarctic Map Folio Series,* Folio 2, Plate 2.]

million km²), or about 1½ times the total area of the contiguous 48 United States (Figure 6.20). Ice volume is about 6 million mi³ (25 million km³), which is over 90% of the total volume of the earth's glacial ice. (In compari-

son, the Greenland Ice Sheet has about 8%.)

The Antarctic Ice Sheet reaches its highest elevation, almost 13,000 ft (4 km), in a broadly rounded summit located about latitude 82° S, longitude 75° E (Figure 6.20). Surface slope is gradual to within 200 mi (320 km) of the edge of the continent, where a marked steepening occurs, as the crowding of elevation contours on the map indicates. Ice thickness is shown on a second map of America (Figure 6.21). The greatest thicknesses are over 10,000 ft (3000 m). Although in general the ice is thickest where surface elevation is highest (compare the maps), there are important exceptions to this statement. A great subglacial channel, or valley, named the Byrd Basin, has been discovered in the area of Marie Byrd Land. Here an ice thickness of nearly 13,000 ft (4000 m) has been measured, and the rock floor lies some 6500 ft (2000 m) below sea level. (See cross sections accompanying Figure 6.21.)

The subglacial topography of Antarctica, where known from profiles of traverses along which the ice has been probed by geophysical methods, is in large part mountainous. Mountain peaks and ranges rise above the ice in several belts, mostly close to and parallel with the continental margins. Here the ice moves in outlet glaciers from the interior polar plateau to reach the coast (Figure 6.22). This terrain distribution suggests that the central region has subsided greatly under ice load, as the interior of Greenland seems to have done.

A characteristic feature of the Antarctic coast is the presence of numerous *ice shelves,* which are great plates of floating ice attached to the land (Figure 6.20). Largest is the Ross Ice Shelf, about 200,000 mi² (520,000 km²) in area, with its surface at an average elevation of about 225 ft (68 m) (Figure 6.23). Almost as large is the Filchner Ice Shelf, bordering the Weddell Sea. Smaller ice shelves occupy most of the bays of the Antarctic coast and in places form a continuous but narrow ice fringe. In general, the ice shelves represent those parts of the ice sheet that have been pushed seaward into water of sufficient depth that the ice is floated off the bottom. The ice shelves are largely maintained by snow accumulation on their surfaces. These ice shelves are the source

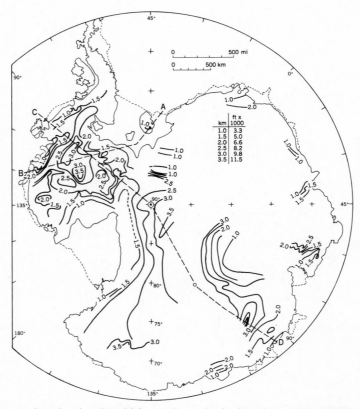

Figure 6.21. Map of Antarctica showing ice thickness. Isopachs in km; interval is 0.5 km (1640 ft). Dashed shorelines are on ice shelves. [Data from Amer. Geog. Soc. (1964), *Antarctic Map Folio Series,* Folio 2, Plate 3.]

Figure 6.22. Oblique air view of the head of Shakleton Glacier, Queen Maud Mountains, Antarctica (latitude 85° S, longitude 177° W). The polar ice plateau is seen in the distance. (U.S. Geological Survey photograph.)

of great tabular icebergs of the Antarctic Ocean.

## PLEISTOCENE ICE SHEETS

In the last hundred years, field observations (see Chapter 9) in many parts of the world have provided abundant evidence to show beyond doubt that large parts of North America, Eurasia, and South America were covered by great ice sheets in the *Pleistocene Epoch,* a unit of geologic time spanning approximately the last 2 to 2.5 million years (m.y.). Only within the last 10,000 to 15,000 yr did these ice sheets disappear from over much of the now heavily populated lands of North America and Europe.

The maximum extent of ice sheets of the Pleistocene Epoch in North America and Europe is shown in Figures 6.24 and 6.25. In North America, all of Canada and the mountainous areas of Alaska were covered. Over the Cordilleran ranges, alpine glaciers coalesced into a single icecap, which spread westward to the Pacific shores and eastward down to the foothills of the mountains. Much larger was the great *Laurentide Ice Sheet,* which was centered over Hudson Bay and spread radially. The Laurentide Ice Sheet inundated the Great Lakes area and spread south into the United States as far as about the line of the Missouri and Ohio rivers.

In Europe (Figure 6.25), the *Scandinavian Ice Sheet,* centered over the Baltic Sea, covered all of the Scandinavian peninsula and reached southward and eastward into the Low Countries, Germany, Poland, and Russia. This ice mass also spread westward across the North Sea, where it joined with an ice sheet that covered much of the British Isles. The Alps and Pyrenees ranges bore small icecaps formed of the coalescence of many individual valley glaciers. As would be expected, glacial activity in all the world's high mountain ranges was greatly intensified, with valley glaciers increas-

Figure 6.23. The Ross Ice Shelf, Antarctica. The steep ice cliff, from 50 to 150 ft (15 to 46 m) high, presents a formidable barrier. (Official U.S. Coast Guard photograph.)

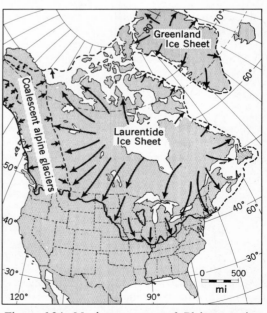

Figure 6.24. Maximum extent of Pleistocene ice sheets of North America. (© 1960, John Wiley & Sons, New York. Based on data of R. F. Flint.)

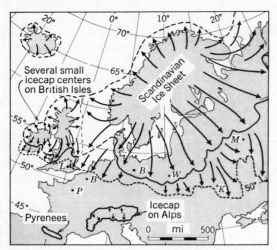

Figure 6.25. Limit of glacial ice of Europe in the last glaciation (solid line) and maximum extent in the entire Pleistocene Epoch (dashed line). (© 1960, John Wiley & Sons, New York. Based on data of R. F. Flint.)

ing in size and extending into lower altitudes than they do today.

In Siberia, icecaps formed upon the uplands east of the Ural Mountains. Mountain ranges of northeastern Siberia supported icecaps formed by the coalescence of complex systems of smaller icecaps and valley glaciers. Smaller icecaps also existed over a number of the higher mountain and plateau areas of central and eastern Asia.

In South America, the only large ice sheet of the Southern Hemisphere (exclusive of Antarctica) was formed over the Andean range of Chile and Argentina, largely southward of latitude 40°, by coalescence of valley glaciers and icecaps. At its maximum extent the ice sheet reached to the Pacific Ocean on the west and spread eastward upon the pampas (piedmont plains) of Patagonia for a distance of 100 mi (160 km) or so beyond the base of the Andes.

Details of ice limits in the last major ice advance are given in Chapter 14.

Cause of growth of the Pleistocene ice sheets is not yet established; several hypotheses are currently under debate, with no hope in sight for any substantial area of agreement among the scientists. We can, however, name some general mechanisms that have been suggested as capable of explanation of this remarkable upset in our planetary environment. *Glaciations,* as these periods of ice growth and spread are called, have occurred a few times in the

geologic past, but their durations have probably been comparatively short. Certainly they do not point to a progressive change in the earth's heat balance in the direction of declining planetary temperature.

A general requirement of glaciation is a lowering of the earth's average atmospheric temperature along with sustained or increased levels of precipitation. It is well established by world-wide evidence that during the Pleistocene Epoch the *snow line* (elevation above which snowbanks remain throughout the year) was lowered in elevation by about 200 ft (600 m) in equatorial latitudes and by 3000 to 4000 ft (900 to 1200 m) in middle and high latitudes. This world-wide phenomenon clearly indicates a generally colder climate for the earth as a whole at times of glaciation. A reduced average temperature would, in general, reduce rates of ablation at those places where snow could accumulate in large quantities, thus causing growth of glacial ice bodies.

Another requirement of ice-sheet growth is that there be present an elevated landmass—a plateau or mountain range—favorably situated to receive snowfall derived from cyclonic storms into which maritime air masses are drawn. Low-lying continental plains would not be likely to accumulate enough snowfall to initiate ice-sheet growth, even if the climate were sufficiently cold.

Favorable topographic conditions are found in Greenland and Antarctica, where ice sheets exist today, and in the Labrador Highlands, the northern Cordilleran ranges, Scandinavia, the Urals, and the southern Andes, where Pleistocene icecaps grew. Once formed, a small icecap might be expected to grow into a large ice sheet, the ice body itself functioning as a highland to induce the necessary orographic precipitation. Assuming a favorable global topography, what mechanisms can be invoked for repeated cycles of atmospheric cooling and warming?

A supposed change in rate of output of solar energy has provided the basis for several hypotheses of glaciation. Although minor fluctuations are observed in incoming radiation, we do not as yet have evidence of any long-range trend of change in its value; the concept of a solar constant of 2 ly/min remains essentially valid. As noted in Chapter 1, the use of earth satellites to measure solar radiation beyond the limits of the earth's atmosphere may yield valuable new information. There is as yet no reason to doubt the constancy of the sun's energy output for the span of geologic time in which glaciations have left a record. We can, nevertheless, speculate that reductions of the sun's energy output have occurred and that the planetary temperature was correspondingly lowered, bringing on the growth of ice sheets.*

When the hypothesis of fluctuation in solar-energy output is combined with the topographic effect of mountain and plateau areas, an explanation of ice-sheet growth and disappearance results that can be labeled the *solar-topographic hypothesis*. In essence, the hypothesis states that formation of highlands created a favorable topographic configuration for ice-sheet development but that fluctuations in the sun's energy output, causing world-wide atmospheric temperature changes, governed the actual growth and disappearance of ice sheets. In the complete absence of any time schedule of variations in solar radiation, should such variations have occurred, no further development of this hypothesis is possible.

A different approach to the possibility of variations in the intensity of solar energy received at the earth's surface has been to invoke systematic changes in geometrical relations of the earth's axis and orbit known through astronomical observations.

Without much more information on the earth's orbital motions than we provided in Chapter 3, it is not possible to give a meaningful statement of details of this hypothesis. It can simply be noted that there are very slow cycles of change in the distance separating earth from sun and in inclination of the earth's axis. For given distances and angles of the sun's rays, the incoming solar radiation can be calculated for a given latitude. When this is done, there are found variations in radiation amounting to about 5% above or below the present value at middle latitudes in the Northern Hemisphere. It is presumed that glaciations would be initiated during the periods of minimum incoming solar radiation. It is claimed that a meaningful relationship exists between repeated glaciations and cycles seen in the radiation curve.

* This speculation may have been laid to rest by studies of radioactive isotopes in lunar rocks. These studies show that solar-flare activity has been at a level comparable with that at present for at least the past 1 to 2 m.y., without any indication of fluctuations of long period that could cause corresponding climatic changes on earth.

A widely supported hypothesis, relatively simple in concept, attributes world-wide temperature drop and ice-sheet growth to a decrease in the carbon-dioxide content of the atmosphere. The average content (about 0.032% by volume), variations in content, and importance of carbon dioxide have been discussed in Chapter 1. Along with water vapor, carbon dioxide is an important gas in causing the greenhouse effect, in which terrestrial radiation is absorbed in the lower atmosphere and the average air temperature is thereby considerably increased over what it would be without these gases.

Estimates have been made to show that if the carbon-dioxide content of the atmosphere were reduced to half of the existing quantity, the earth's average surface temperature would drop by about 7 F° (4 C°), enough to bring on the growth of ice sheets under favorable topographic conditions.

The rapid growth of forests would be expected to withdraw carbon dioxide from the atmosphere, causing an initial drop in temperature. This process might also be rapidly reversed by disappearance of plant cover and consequent release of carbon dioxide to the atmosphere. It has been pointed out that the amount of carbon dioxide held in solution in sea water would increase as the water became colder, so that a trend toward reduced atmospheric carbon dioxide would be self-perpetuating and would continue until the necessary drop in atmospheric temperature was achieved.

Whether or not the fluctuation in carbon dioxide is adequate to control glaciation, under any hypothesis its effect in reinforcing temperature fluctuation due to other controls must be taken into account.

Also involving change in atmospheric composition is the hypothesis of glaciation brought about by increase in quantity of volcanic dust in the upper troposphere. Should there be an episode of unusually great volcanic activity, the greatly increased atmospheric dust would reflect back into space a greater part of the incoming solar radiation (increase in earth's albedo), thus reducing the quantity of solar energy received at the earth's surface and, consequently, lowering the average atmospheric temperature. Reductions in quantity of solar radiation received at the ground have been observed for short periods immediately following great volcanic eruptions. Nevertheless, it is doubtful that volcanic eruptions have occurred on the scale needed to produce the growth of ice sheets. Moreover, periods of exceptional volcanic activity have not been shown to be correlated with periods of glaciation.

Yet another explanation given serious consideration is based upon supposed changes in the energy and moisture balances affecting the atmosphere and oceans. The disappearance of sea-ice cover from the Arctic Ocean is said to have played an essential role in initiating a glaciation, since the free-water surface could supply large amounts of water vapor for air masses that nourish an ice sheet. Once developed to full size the ice sheets themselves became refrigerators of the global air temperature. The resultant cooling caused the Arctic Ocean to freeze over, cutting off the moisture supply and starting a reverse trend toward disappearance of the ice sheets.

## THE WORLD WATER BALANCE

Finally, we turn to an assessment of the *world water balance,* which is a quantitative statement of the masses of water exchanged annually in the operation of the hydrologic cycle. An estimated 80,000 mi³ of water evaporates annually from the ocean surface, and about 15,000 mi³ evaporates from the lands, including lakes and marshes (Figure 6.26). Thus a total of 95,000 mi³ of water evaporates, and an equal amount must be returned to the earth's surface annually by precipitation. Of this, about 24,000 mi³ falls as rain or snow upon the land surfaces. These figures show that the quantity precipitated upon the lands is some 60% greater than the amount of water that is returned to the atmosphere by evaporation from the land. We are led to conclude that the remaining precipitation on land, 9000 mi³, or about 40%, is returned annually to the oceans by liquid or glacial flow over and beneath the ground. The most obvious part of this return flow is, of course, by streams emptying into the oceans, but some water seeps into the ground and, as ground water, passes beneath the lands into the coastal ocean waters.

The figures given in Figure 6.26 represent a rough numerical estimate of the components of the earth's water balance. Recall that in Chapter 5 the water balance of the atmosphere was developed in terms of a simple equation, including the terms $P$, for precipitation, $E$, for evaporation, and $G$, for the net gain or loss of water held in the system. Using these same terms, the water balance of either the world continents taken together or the world ocean can be stated as follows:

$$P = E + G + R$$

where, $P$, $E$, and $G$ are defined as above, and $R$ is runoff (positive when out of continents, negative when into oceans). Since the annual change in stored water must be very small on large areas of the globe taken together, the term $G$ can be neglected, simplifying the equation to:

$$P = E + R$$

For the continents: 24 = 15 + 9 (units of 1000 mi³)
For the oceans:    71 = 80 − 9

Taking the entire globe as a unit, the runoff terms sum to zero, leaving only:

$$P = E$$

Substituting the numerical data:

$$24 + 71 = 15 + 80$$

and

$$95 = 95$$

Water in storage is distributed very unevenly among its three states in various places over the globe (Table 6.1). Over 97% is in the world ocean, and most of the remainder is locked up in icecaps and glaciers. Subsurface water constitutes a very much greater volume than surface water on the lands, roughly by a factor of 30 times. Notice how trivial is the volume of water held in the entire atmosphere, yet the hydrologic cycle depends upon atmospheric transport of water in order to function.

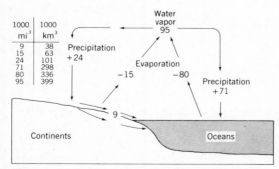

Figure 6.26. Schematic diagram of the world's water balance.

Table 6.1.  ESTIMATED DISTRIBUTION OF THE WORLD'S WATER

| Location | Surface Area (mi²) | (km²) | Water Volume (mi³) | (km³) | % of Total |
|---|---|---|---|---|---|
| Surface water | | | | | |
|   Fresh-water lakes | 330,000 | 860,000 | 30,000 | 125,000 | 0.009 |
|   Saline lakes and inland seas | 270,000 | 700,000 | 25,000 | 104,000 | 0.008 |
|   Average in stream channels | ... | ... | 300 | 1,250 | 0.0001 |
| Subsurface water | | | | | |
|   Soil moisture and intermediate-zone (vadose) water | 50,000,000 | 130,000,000 | 16,000 | 67,000 | 0.005 |
|   Ground water within 0.5 mi (0.8 km) depth | | | 1,000,000 | 4,170,000 | 0.31 |
|   Ground water, deep-lying | | | 1,000,000 | 4,170,000 | 0.31 |
| Total liquid water in land areas | | | 2,070,000 | 8,637,000 | 0.635 |
| Icecaps and glaciers | 6,900,000 | 18,000,000 | 7,000,000 | 29,200,000 | 2.15 |
| Atmosphere | 197,000,000 | 510,000,000 | 3,100 | 13,000 | 0.001 |
| World ocean | 139,500,000 | 360,000,000 | 317,000,000 | 1,322,000,000 | 97.2 |
| Totals (rounded) | | | 326,000,000 | 1,360,000,000 | 100 |

Source: Data from Dr. Raymond L. Nace (1964), U.S. Geological Survey.

## SYSTEMS IN REVIEW

The mass-transport system of gravity flow of water over the lands was summarized in opening paragraphs of this chapter; it might be helpful to reread that statement in the light of details of processes that have been covered. The study of geological products of that gravity-flow system remains to be covered in Chapter 9, but only after a foundation in geological principles and materials has been acquired in the intervening chapters.

Taken together, this chapter and the preceding two chapters make up a trilogy devoted to mass-transport systems within the atmosphere and hydrosphere. Masses in motion have consisted of gases of the atmosphere and of water in its three states. The planetary mass balances have now been completely explored with regard to air and water. These balances define one major segment of the environment of Man and all other life forms. The other major segment is geological and concerns the lithosphere, which is the earth's solid mineral shell. Here, too, we shall find systems of energy exchange and mass transport, but the time spans over which the changes occur are for the most part vastly greater than those analyzed in atmospheric and hydrospheric processes. Be prepared to shift perspective to time realms in which a million years—rather than a day, a month or a year—is the standard unit of periodicity.

### References for further study

Foster, E. E. (1948), *Rainfall and Runoff*, New York, Macmillan, 487 pp.

Flint, R. F. (1971), *Glacial and Quaternary Geology*, New York, Wiley, 892 pp.

Todd, D. K. (1959), *Ground Water Hydrology*, New York, Wiley, 336 pp.

Dyson, J. L. (1962), *The World of Ice*, New York, Knopf, 292 pp.

Morisawa, M. (1968), *Streams: Their Dynamics and Morphology*, New York, McGraw-Hill, 175 pp., chaps. 1–3, 10.

Strahler, A. N. (1969), *Physical Geography*, 3rd ed., New York, Wiley, 732 pp., chap. 28, appendix IV.

Strahler, A. N. (1971), *The Earth Sciences*, 2nd ed., New York, Harper & Row, 826 pp., chaps. 33, 34, 40.

### Review questions

1. Describe the hydrologic cycle. What is the role of streams and glaciers in this cycle? How is potential energy given to the water of streams and glaciers? How is energy transformed in the gravity-flow systems, and where does it go?

2. How do changes in land-surface configuration influence the gravity flow of water on the lands? Explain the interaction between flow systems and landforms. What is a decay system? How do rates of change in such a system change with time?

3. Distinguish between surface water and

subsurface water. What is runoff? Describe the process of infiltration. What factors control infiltration capacity? In what units is it measured?

4. Define the zones of aeration and saturation. How is water held in each of these zones? What is ground water? What is the water table? Distinguish between the soil-water belt and the intermediate belt. What is the role of evapotranspiration in the soil-water belt?

5. How is the position of the water table determined? What is the usual configuration of the water table? Describe the flow paths of ground water under divides and stream valleys. How does the changing level of the water table reflect cycles of precipitation?

6. Describe overland flow. How do plants influence this form of flow? Define a stream channel. What is the range in widths of natural-stream channels? List and define the elements of hydraulic geometry of stream channels. How is stream gradient measured?

7. Describe fluid shear in stream flow. How is velocity distributed in a stream channel. Distinguish between laminar flow (streamline flow) and turbulent flow. What is the importance of turbulence in the activity of a stream? Define discharge in terms of cross-sectional area and mean velocity. What is the significance of the equation of continuity?

8. What is the viscosity of a fluid? How does viscosity influence stream flow? Review the factors that control stream velocity. Describe the conversion of energy during stream flow.

9. Describe a drainage system, including both the stream system and the surface areas it contains. What kinds of form adjustments are required to maintain the system in a stable configuration? Describe the downstream changes in stream gradients within the stream network. How does stream velocity change in the downstream direction?

10. Describe the manner in which stream flow responds to input of precipitation from a heavy rainstorm over the watershed. Why is there a lag in peak discharge? What is the role of base flow in stream flow?

11. What is the relationship between bankfull stage and a condition of flood? What is a floodplain, and what is its role in stream flow? Describe the changes in a typical flood wave as it moves downstream.

12. What is a glacier? Describe glacial ice and its flowage. Compare glacier flow with stream flow. What are the two basic types of glaciers? Compare them in form and gradient. Which is most closely related to a stream of water?

13. Analyze the nourishment, flowage, and wastage of a valley glacier as an open system. What zones can be recognized in the glacier? Describe glacier equilibrium. How can glaciers provide evidence of climatic changes?

14. Describe the Greenland Ice Sheet in terms of area, volume, thickness, surface and bottom configurations, and marginal forms. Compare with the Antarctic Ice Sheet in the same terms. How are these ice sheets nourished? How has the weight of the ice influenced the crust beneath? Describe the ice shelves of the Antarctic coast. What sustains them?

15. Describe the spread and limits of the great ice sheets of the Pleistocene Epoch in North America and Europe. Where were the ice centers situated? What general conditions of topography and atmospheric environment are considered favorable to the onset of glaciation? Briefly review a number of mechanisms that have been proposed as causes or initiating conditions of glaciations.

16. Describe the world water balance. What are the terms in the water-balance equation? How does the global quantity of water present as water vapor in the atmosphere compare with the quantity held as surface fresh water on the lands? with ground water? with water of glaciers? with water of the oceans?

17. Summarize the important characteristics of the gravity-flow systems of water on the lands. What is the energy source, and how is this energy transformed and dissipated? Explain the concept of a mass balance within the energy systems of the atmosphere and hydrosphere.

# chapter 7 geologic systems: i. radiogenic heat and the rise of molten rock

In this chapter we turn to a geologic system quite different in basic nature and effects from those considered in previous chapters. During the early history of the earth certain radioactive elements became concentrated in the rocks of the outer zones of the solid earth. These elements spontaneously generate heat, known as *radiogenic* heat, causing sustained high temperatures within the earth. This accumulated heat gradually escapes to the earth's surface but may locally raise temperatures to exceed the melting point of rock. Where this change of state occurs, rock in the liquid phase moves upward, invading solid rock in shallower crustal zones and even breaking through to the earth's surface to pour out upon the surface in volcanic eruptions. Invasion by molten rock is designated by geologists as *igneous intrusion;* outpouring of rock at the surface as *igneous extrusion,* or simply *vulcanism.*

Radiogenic heat thus causes enormous masses of rock to be displaced and changed. At the same time, the rise of molten rock to the surface permits the escape of large quantities of heat, when measured over long spans of time. This heat is transferred to the oceans and atmosphere, from which it is quickly dissipated into outer space. The system which we are to study is therefore an irreversible, or one-way, flow of energy inherited from the earliest events in the formation of the earth. Although the radioactive-energy source seems limitless and undiminishing over substantial periods of geologic time, it is steadily diminishing and inevitably must run out, just as the sun's energy resource in hydrogen fusion must eventually give out. In this respect, the radiogenic system within our planet has something in common with the fusion system within the sun. Do the other three inner planets and our moon have radiogenic heat sources? If not, their geologic processes and history cannot resemble those of earth, for they would lack the necessary energy for igneous activity.

## RADIOACTIVITY AND HEAT

In order to understand the geologic system of radiogenic heat and its dissipation, a brief discussion of the principles of radioactivity may help those not already familiar with this area of atomic physics.

The *nucleus,* or dense core, of an atom consists of two types of particles, *neutrons* and *protons.* For a given element the numbers of neutrons and protons are approximately constant and exist in a specified ratio. Take, for example, the important radioactive form of the element *uranium.* In the nucleus of this form of uranium there are 146 neutrons and 92 protons. The total of neutrons and protons is therefore 238, which quantity is known as the *mass number* and is designated by a superscript after the symbol for uranium, thus: $U^{238}$. The *atomic number* of an element is equal to the number of protons contained in its nucleus. In the case of uranium the atomic number is 92. Although the atomic number is fixed for each named element, the number of neutrons in the nucleus is subject to some variation. In the case of uranium-238, the number of neutrons is 146, but there exists another form of uranium with 143 neutrons, giving a mass number of 235, and it is designated as *uranium-235.* These differing varieties of the same elements are referred to as *isotopes.* A key to the understanding of radioactivity is that certain isotopes are unstable. This instability can result in the flying off of a small part of the nucleus, reducing the mass number and producing in turn another element. In this spontaneous breakdown, mass is converted into energy, and the release of this energy into the surrounding matter is ultimately in the form of sensible heat.

Let us look further into the nature of the spontaneous radioactive process. Breakdown of the atomic nucleus results in the emission of an *alpha particle,* consisting of two neutrons and two protons. As the alpha particles travel outward through the atoms of the surrounding substance, their energy is transformed into increased activity of the electrons of those atoms, imparting heat to the surrounding substance. Another emission in the radioactive breakdown is the *gamma ray,* an energy form that acts similarly to electromagnetic radiation. Gamma rays are also absorbed by the atoms of the surrounding substance, leading to an increase in heat. A third form of emanation is the *beta particle,* an electron traveling at high velocity. Beta particles also react with surrounding atoms and increase the quantity of heat. The total quantity of heat produced per unit of time in the radioactive process can be exactly calculated for a given quantity of an unstable isotope.

The radioactive disintegration of one parent isotope may lead to the production of another unstable isotope, known as a *daughter* product. This product, in turn, may produce yet another unstable isotope, and so forth, until ultimately a stable isotope results and no further radioactivity occurs. Take as an example the system of uranium-238 and its daughter products, leading finally to the stable lead isotope *lead-206* (Figure 7.1). Arrows show the direction of successive changes. Note that each step in the direction of the arrow to the left marks a decrease in the mass number. Uranium-238 decays to produce *thorium-234.* This is followed by a succession of isotopes of six different elements, listed along the bottom of the graph. The disintegration process achieves a steady rate, or equilibrium, with time. In the case of the uranium-238–lead-206 series, each gram of uranium produces 0.71 cal of heat per year.

Other important heat-producing decay sequences in the rocks of the earth are those of *uranium-235, thorium-232,* and *potassium-40.* Uranium-235 produces 4.3 cal of heat per gram per year, thorium-232 produces 0.20 cal, and potassium-40 produces only 0.000027 cal.

Of great importance in both the thermal history of the earth and the dating of geologic events is a physical law that governs the rate of decay of radioactive isotopes. Once an equilibrium has been reached in the process of radioactive disintegration, the ratio of decrease in the number of atoms of the parent isotope with each unit of time is a constant.

Take, for example, potassium-40, which decays to the stable isotopes *calcium-40* and *argon-40.* We can start at any point in time. Let the number of atoms of potassium-40 at time-zero be designated by unity (1.0), as shown at the upper left corner of the graph in Figure 7.2. After 1.31 billion years (b.y.) have elapsed, the number of atoms of potassium-40 will have been reduced to half of the initial number, designated as 0.5 on the vertical scale. The span of time of 1.31 b.y. is designated as the *half-life.* In a second elapsed span of 1.31 b.y., the number of atoms of potassium-40 will again be halved, reducing the remaining quantity to 0.25 on the vertical scale. Notice that the ratio of reduction is always the same, i.e.,

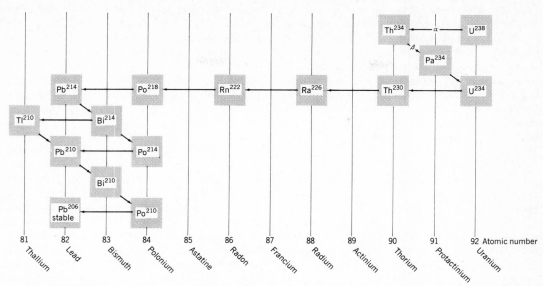

Figure 7.1. Radioactive decay series of U-238 to Pb-206. [After P. M. Hurley (1959), *How Old Is the Earth?* Garden City, N.Y., Doubleday, p. 62, Figure 9.]

one-half. Such a schedule of decrease in quantity with time is known as an *exponential-decay function*. This function applies to all radioactive decay, but the ratio of change, and hence the value of the half-life, is different from one isotope to another. Figure 7.2 also shows the rate at which the daughter isotopes accumulate. Both are rising curves. Both follow an *exponential increase*, which is the inverse of the exponential-decay curve. It should be noted that calcium-40 is produced about 7⅓ times more rapidly than argon-40, hence the curve of calcium-40 rises more steeply. We shall refer to the ratios of parent isotopes to daughter isotopes in the later discussion of methods of rock dating (see Chapter 10).

Table 7.1 gives the half-life of each of the

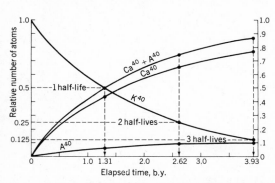

Figure 7.2. Exponential decay and growth curves for $K^{40}$, $Ca^{40}$, and $Ar^{40}$. [After P. M. Hurley (1959), *How Old Is the Earth?* Garden City, N.Y., Doubleday, p. 101, Figure 17.]

important natural radioisotope series. Notice that there are vast differences in the half-lives of these isotopes. In projecting the production of radiogenic heat back into earliest geologic time, these differences will be highly important. Isotopes with the shorter half-lives were then present in very much larger quantities than they are today, in contrast to isotopes having extremely long half-lives.

## IGNEOUS ROCKS AND MINERALS

The next step in analysis of radioactive-heat production in the earth is to evaluate the proportions in which the major radioactive isotopes are present in average kinds of rock. We must therefore turn to a review of the major varieties and compositions of igneous rocks and their component minerals.

As the term *rock* is used here, it refers to the substance of the earth's mantle and crust (see Chapter 2), together making up the outer 1800-

Table 7.1.    HALF-LIVES OF NATURAL
RADIOISOTOPES

| Parent Isotope | Stable Daughter Products | Half-life (b.y.) |
|---|---|---|
| Uranium-238 | Lead-206, plus helium | 4.5 |
| Uranium-235 | Lead-207, plus helium | 0.71 |
| Thorium-232 | Lead-208, plus helium | 14 |
| Rubidium-84 | Strontium-87 | 51 |
| Potassium-40 | Argon-40, calcium-40 | 1.3 |

Source: Data from Brian Mason (1966), *Principles of Geochemistry*, 3rd ed., New York, Wiley, see p. 9.

mi (2895-km) shell of the earth. This rock is composed almost entirely of mineral matter in a crystalline or glassy state, and with a density of from about 2.6 gm/cm³ in near-surface rocks of the crust, to more than 5 gm/cm³ near the inner boundary of the mantle. Whether one wishes to include the liquid iron of the earth's core under the broad definition of "rock" is not a matter of great consequence, but its inclusion may be useful in the planetary sense.

Rock is composed of minerals, of which there are many varieties and many combinations. A *mineral* can be defined as a homogeneous, naturally occurring, inorganic substance, usually having a definite chemical combination and a characteristic atomic structure. For most common minerals it is possible to write a rather rigid chemical formula and to assign to the atomic structure rather definite geometrical specifications.

The various rock groups and individual varieties are distinguished in terms of the mineral varieties present and the proportions in which they occur, along with further distinctions based upon the size of the individual crystal grains, or the lack of any observable crystalline structure. When we consider that hundreds of mineral varieties have been identified, and that the known abundant mineral combinations require the recognition of dozens of varieties of igneous rocks, we realize that any serious study of minerals and rocks is beyond the scope of a general systems approach to the processes acting on our planet. Instead, only the largest categories of rock can be treated.

In examining the radiogenic-heat system and its effects, primary concern is with a class of rocks designated as *igneous,* meaning that the rock has solidified from a high-temperature molten condition, i.e., has undergone a transformation from liquid to solid state. Rock in the molten state is referred to as *magma.*

## CHEMICAL COMPOSITION OF THE EARTH'S CRUST

Before beginning a study of the principal minerals comprising the igneous rocks, it is worthwhile to examine data on the abundance of elements in the earth's crust. The term *earth's crust* is defined later in this chapter. At this point, it should suffice to explain that the crust is the outermost of the earth's solid shells and has an average thickness of about 10 mi

(17 km). Important differences in thickness and composition of the crust exist between the continents and ocean basins. Although the rocks of the crust constitute only about ⁴⁄₁₀ of 1% of the total mass of the earth, they are the only rocks available to the geologist for direct examination and chemical analysis. The great bulk of the crust (about 95%) is composed of igneous rock.

Table 7.2 lists the eight most abundant elements in the earth's crust. The order of listing is according to percentage by weight. Values for percentage by volume and percentage of atoms present are also shown. Keep in mind that these proportions are estimates based on analyses of rock samples and will be subject to minor changes in the light of revised estimates.

Several points are of interest in the data of Table 7.2. Notice, first, that the eight elements constitute between 98% and 99% of the crust by weight and that almost half of this weight is oxygen. Measured in other ways, the importance of oxygen is even greater—in numbers of atoms it makes up over 60% of the total and, being an atom of comparatively large radius, it represents almost 94% by volume. Notice that silicon is in second place with about 28% by weight, or roughly half the value for oxygen. Aluminum and iron occupy intermediate positions, while the last four elements—calcium, sodium, potassium, and magnesium—are subequal in the range of 2% to 4% by weight.

To extend the table we add that the ninth most abundant element is titanium, followed in order by hydrogen, phosphorus, barium, and strontium. It is interesting to note that the metals copper, lead, zinc, nickel, and tin, which play such an important role in our

Table 7.2. THE EIGHT MOST ABUNDANT ELEMENTS IN THE EARTH'S CRUST

| Element | Symbol | Percentage by Weight | Percentage by Volume | Percentage of Atoms Present |
|---|---|---|---|---|
| Oxygen | O | 46.6 | 93.8 | 62.6 |
| Silicon | Si | 27.7 | 0.9 | 21.2 |
| Aluminum | Al | 8.1 | 0.5 | 6.5 |
| Iron | Fe | 5.0 | 0.4 | 1.9 |
| Calcium | Ca | 3.6 | 1.0 | 1.9 |
| Sodium | Na | 2.8 | 1.3 | 2.6 |
| Potassium | K | 2.6 | 1.8 | 1.4 |
| Magnesium | Mg | 2.1 | 0.3 | 1.8 |

Source: Data from Brian Mason (1966), *Principles of Geochemistry,* 3rd ed., New York, Wiley, p. 48, Table 3.4. Figures have been rounded to nearest one-tenth.

modern technology, are present only in very small proportions and are indeed scarce elements. Fortunately, these and other rare but important elements have been concentrated locally into ores from which they can be extracted in useful quantities.

The list of abundances of elements in the crust should be compared with that for the earth as a whole (see Table 12.2). Notice that iron assumes first place in the earth list, while magnesium gains fourth place. Nickel and sulfur, which do not appear in the crustal table, are in fifth and sixth places for the entire earth. Evidently the crust represents a selected assortment of particular elements as compared with the average earth composition. Therefore, an important problem in earth history is to explain how the various shells of our planet acquired unique combinations of abundances of elements. This problem will be considered in later pages.

## THE SILICATE MINERALS

The vast bulk of all igneous rock consists of minerals containing the elements silicon and

oxygen in combination. Collectively, these minerals are known as *silicates*.

We can gain a good appreciation of the nature of igneous rocks as a class by noting the proportions of only seven silicate minerals, or mineral groups, shown in Figure 7.3. The mineral list begins with *quartz,* containing only silicon and oxygen. The next five items are mineral groups; they are silicate compounds, all containing aluminum, and can be designated *aluminosilicates*.

In *potash feldspar,* potassium is the dominant metallic ion. The *plagioclase feldspars* span a continuous range from the *alkalic* plagioclase end of the series, with sodium making up 100% of the metallic ions, to *calcic* plagioclase at the other end, with calcium making up 100% of the metallic ions. Plagioclase of *intermediate* composition contains about equal proportions of sodium and calcium. Quartz and the feldspars are light in color.

*Biotite,* the dark-colored representative of the *mica group,* is a complex aluminosilicate of potassium, magnesium, and iron, with some water. Other dark minerals are *hornblende,*

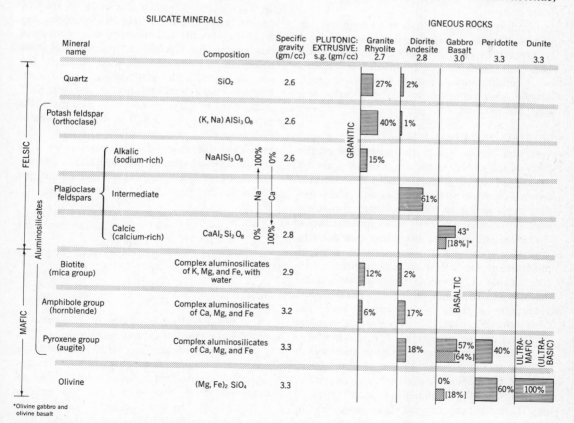

Figure 7.3. Common silicate minerals and igneous rocks.

representing the *amphibole group,* and *augite,* representing the *pyroxene group.* Both of these groups are complex aluminosilicates of calcium, magnesium, and iron. Finally, there is *olivine,* a dense greenish mineral which is a silicate of magnesium and iron, but without aluminum.

Increasing specific gravity from beginning to end of the list is particularly noteworthy and reflects the effect of increasing proportions of iron with its substantially greater atomic weight.

To divide this mineral list into two halves, geologists use the term *felsic* for the light-colored, less dense, quartz-feldspar division; the term *mafic* for the dark-colored, denser division. The derivation of these coined words is obvious: *Fel* and *si* refer to feldspar and silica; *ma* refers to magnesium; and *f* is for iron (symbol Fe).

A number of other important silicate minerals have been overlooked; among them is *muscovite,* a light-colored representative of the mica group. Muscovite lacks magnesium and iron (present in biotite) and is classed as a felsic mineral.

Two important mafic minerals which are not silicates should be mentioned because of their occurrence in a wide variety of igneous rocks. These are *magnetite* (an iron oxide) and *ilmenite* (iron-titanium oxide). Both have high specific gravities ($4\frac{1}{2}$ to $5\frac{1}{2}$ gm/cm³) and are black in color.

## CRYSTALLIZATION OF MAGMA

Igneous rocks, which comprise most of the mass of the earth's crust, are composed almost entirely of the 7 silicate minerals or mineral groups, other minerals being of secondary importance, and it is estimated that the seven make up as much as 99% of all igneous rocks.

One of the first questions that can arise in reviewing these facts concerns the number of minerals involved. Why, with 8 elements available (Table 7.2), should there exist in abundance only 8 minerals or basic mineral groups (including a group not described here, the feldspathoids), instead of the 300-odd possible combinations of groups of 2 through 8 elements? Even assuming that silicon and oxygen will always be linked as a single component, giving 6 components instead of 7, there exists a possibility of 120 combinations, each representing 1 hypothetical mineral. The answer lies in the *mineralogical phase rule,* which states that

for a given number of components (elements) not more than that same number of *phases* (mineral compounds) can coexist in stable form at a given combination of temperature and pressure. In fact, a magma composed principally of 8 elements is not likely to yield the maximum of 8 abundant minerals because certain of the component elements have the tendency to replace certain others on an ion-for-ion basis.

Much of our theoretical knowledge of the formation of silicate minerals from a magma comes from laboratory experiments in which pure mineral ingredients are melted and allowed to crystallize under carefully controlled conditions of temperature and of pressures of different kinds. This type of investigation is one branch of the science of *geochemistry,* which applies the principles of chemistry to solving problems relating to all forms of natural matter in the lithosphere, hydrosphere, and atmosphere.

Magma that upon solidifying yields rock composed of silicate minerals is referred to as a *silicate magma.* The nature of silicate magma as it exists deep within the earth is not, of course, known from direct examination, but much can be inferred from studies of magmas that emerge from volcanoes as lavas and from observations made from silicate melts in the laboratory. Silicate magmas at great depth probably have temperatures in the range of from 900° to 2200° F (500° to 1200° C). At depths of 12 to 25 mi (20 to 40 km) magmas may be under pressures as high as 6 to 12 kilobars (kb) (6000 to 12,000 times the value of atmospheric pressure at sea level). The following figures relate confining pressure to depth below the surface:

| Depth (mi) | (km) | Pressure (kb) | Pressure (atmospheres) |
|---|---|---|---|
| 0 | 0 | 0.0 (approx.) | 1 |
| 5 | 8 | 2.4 | 2,400 |
| 10 | 16 | 4.8 | 4,800 |
| 15 | 24 | 7.2 | 7,200 |
| 25 | 40 | 12.0 | 12,000 |

As a magma rises, it passes into regions of progressively declining confining pressure.

Although a silicate magma is in a liquid or near-liquid state, the elements are by no means completely separated into individual ions of those elements. Instead, silicon and oxygen may be linked to one another in rather complex but irregular chains and networks. The fact that silicate magmas have a high viscosity (resistance to flow) may be explained by the presence of these atomic structures.

All silicate magmas contain additional chemical substances, over and above the elements that yield silicate and nonsilicate minerals. These substances are termed *volatiles,* because they remain in a liquid or gaseous state at much lower temperatures than the mineral-forming compounds and therefore are separated from the magma as temperatures drop and the silicate minerals crystallize into the solid state.

Although we do not know a great deal about the content of volatiles in magmas at depth in the earth, much has been learned by sampling of substances emitted from volcanoes along with the eruption of molten rock (lava). Water is the preponderant constituent of the volatiles emitted as gases from volcanoes. It has been inferred that about 90% by volume of the gas contained in an average magma is water, although some of this may be ground water taken in from near the surface. (The various other volatile substances are discussed in Chapter 12.) Estimates of the proportion of water present in magmas ranges from 0.5% to 8%. Fresh igneous rocks commonly contain about 1% of water entrapped within the minerals during their crystallization.

The importance of water in magma is very great, because even a small amount of water can greatly lower the temperature at which the silicate compounds remain melted. Thus a rising magma experiencing a progressive lowering of temperature can remain molten at considerably lower temperatures with water present than if it consisted only of silicate compounds without water. As a result, intrusions of magmas can reach closer to the earth's surface and can pour out upon the surface in greater amounts than would be possible without the presence of water.

Crystallization, the process of change from liquid state to solid state, begins to take place in a silicate magma at a certain critical combination of temperature and pressure. However, all minerals do not begin to crystallize at the same time. Moreover, a mineral, once formed, does not necessarily remain intact and unchanged from that point on. Instead, the early-formed minerals may subsequently be changed in composition or dissolved and reformed as temperatures continue to fall. This process of change is referred to as *reaction,* and the

orderly series of such changes is referred to as a *reaction series.* A further complexity in the crystallization process may be introduced by the removal of crystallized minerals from the silicate melt, a process termed *fractionation.* For example, early-formed crystals may be left behind as the magma migrates upward, or the crystals may simply settle or rise in the magma body and accumulate. Removal of crystallized minerals changes the average chemical composition of the remaining fluid magma and, consequently, modifies the series of reactions that can follow.

Reaction can take one of two forms. First, there is *continuous reaction,* in which the earlier-formed mineral is gradually changed in composition by the substitution of ions of one element in the magma for another in the mineral. An example is the plagioclase feldspar series (see Figure 7.3). The first feldspar to crystallize is of calcic composition. As the temperature of the magma continues to fall, sodium ions in the magma are substituted for calcium ions in the crystallized feldspar, causing a gradual change in the plagioclase toward the alkalic end of the series. Second, there may be *discontinuous reactions,* in which case a given mineral is dissolved and reconstituted as another mineral at the lower temperature. An example is olivine, which crystallizes at a comparatively high temperature. As the temperature falls, the olivine is dissolved and pyroxene is formed in its place.

## THE BOWEN REACTION SERIES

Assuming a silicate magma of average crustal composition to start with, it is possible to recognize a complete reaction series that will take place during crystallization. Named the *Bowen reaction series*—after N. L. Bowen, the scientist who developed the concept—the total series consists of two converging branches, one of continuous, the other of discontinuous reactions (Figure 7.4).

The mafic minerals follow the discontinuous reaction series, starting with olivine and ending in biotite mica. The feldspars follow a continuous series, in which calcic plagioclase forms about the same time as does olivine, while alkalic plagioclase is formed about at the same time as the amphiboles and biotite mica.

Let us consider how the Bowen reaction series is related to the formation of igneous rocks of various mineral compositions. Suppose that fractionation takes place after olivine

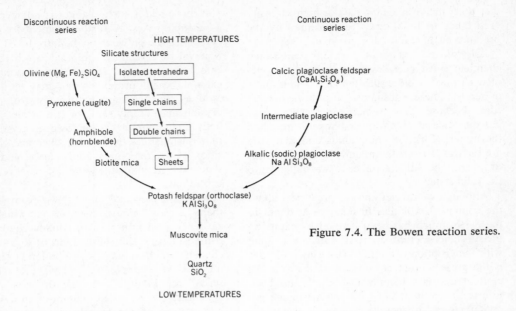

Figure 7.4. The Bowen reaction series.

and pyroxene have been formed. These minerals form a distinctive rock type known as *peridotite* (Figure 7.3). If the reaction series is allowed to progress to the stage in which pyroxene (augite) and intermediate plagioclase feldspar are formed, a rock known as *gabbro* can result.

The remaining components of the magma are now comparatively richer in silicon, aluminum, and potassium because most of the calcium, iron, and magnesium have been used up. This remaining magma may crystallize after migrating to a different physical location from the earlier-formed minerals. The result may be an igneous rock predominantly composed of quartz and potash feldspar. *Granite* is such a rock. The final residual matter of the magma, remaining fluid at comparatively lower temperatures, is a watery solution rich in silica. From this solution are deposited rock veins, of a type known as *pegmatite,* which consist of large crystals of quartz, potash feldspar, and muscovite or biotite mica (Figure 7.5). Ultimately, the water and other minor volatile constituents may reach the earth's surface, to escape in *fumaroles* (vents emitting hot gases) and hot springs.

The general process whereby the original magma with its full range of component elements is separated into rocks of quite different mineral composition is known as *magmatic differentiation.* This process can be responsible for an arrangement of igneous rocks into a series ranging from a mafic group rich in iron, magnesium, calcium, and silica to a felsic group rich in aluminum, sodium, and potassium, and with excess silica. The classification of igneous rocks which we are about to present is thus based upon principles of the Bowen reaction series and processes of mineral fractionation and magmatic differentiation.

**THE IGNEOUS ROCKS**

Now that we can approach the problem of classifying igneous rocks on a meaningful basis, a few important rock varieties can be named and briefly described. Only rocks that figure in later discussions of geologic processes and structures need be included, since the emphasis of this book is on systems.

Consider first, however, that igneous rocks are classified not only by mineral composition, but also in terms of the sizes of individual crystals that make up the rock. The word *texture* covers crystal sizes and arrangements.

Crystal size is largely dependent upon the rate of cooling of the magma through the stages of crystallization. As a general rule, rapid cooling results in small to very minute crystals, while extremely sudden cooling produces a natural glass. Very slow cooling, on the other hand, tends to produce large crystals. From this principle we can deduce that the *plutonic* intrusive igneous rocks, cooling in huge masses at great depths where escape of heat is extremely low, will tend to develop a

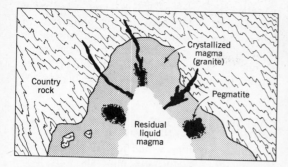

Figure 7.6. A coarse-grained granite, typifying phaneritic texture. The light-colored grains are quartz and feldspar, and the dark grains are largely biotite mica. (Photograph by A. N. Strahler.)

Figure 7.5. (*Above*) Occurrence of pegmatite bodies in relation to an intrusive igneous body and the country rock. (*Below*) Pegmatite from Mitchell County, North Carolina. The specimen is about 4 in. (10 cm) long. The black crystals are tourmaline; the white minerals are quartz and feldspar. (Specimen by courtesy of Ward's Natural Science Establishment, Inc., Rochester, N.Y.)

texture of large crystals, whereas the *extrusive* igneous rocks, which cool rapidly on contact with the atmosphere or ocean water, will be fine-grained or glassy.

The sample of granite pictured in Figure 7.6 illustrates a plutonic rock. It is described as *coarse-grained;* the individual crystals range from 0.2 to 0.4 in. (5 to 10 mm) across.

Most extrusive rocks (lavas) have crystals of such small size that they cannot be individually seen with the unaided eye. Such rocks require microscopic examination for identification. In Figure 7.3, the igneous rock names are placed in two categories: plutonic and extrusive. The gross forms of rock bodies in both categories are described in later paragraphs.

In terms of bulk composition, most igneous rock of the earth's crust belongs to members of the *granite-gabbro series,* which follow closely upon the mineral order of the Bowen reaction series. Customarily, these rocks are presented in sequence from the felsic end toward the

mafic end. We shall follow this practice, although with the knowledge that it is the reverse of the order suggested by the reaction series and magmatic differentiation.

*Granite* is dominated in composition by the feldspars and quartz (Figure 7.7, left). Potash feldspar of the orthoclase variety is the most important mineral, while alkalic plagioclase may be present in moderate amounts or absent (Figure 7.3). Quartz, which accounts for perhaps a quarter of the rock, reaches its most abundant proportions in granite. Biotite and hornblende are common accessory minerals. Magnetite, not shown on the chart, is also a common accessory.

Granite is described as a light-colored igneous rock and is grayish to pinkish, depending upon the variety of potash feldspar present. Its

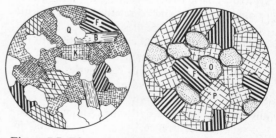

Figure 7.7. Diagrammatic sketch of mineral grains as seen in microscopic thin section, enlarged about five times. (*Left*) Granite. (*Right*) Olivine gabbro. Q—quartz, K—potash feldspar, F—alkali feldspar, B—biotite, H—hornblende, P—pyroxene, O—olivine.

specific gravity, about 2.7, is comparatively low among the igneous rocks. Most granites are sufficiently coarse in texture for the component minerals to be identified with the unaided eye (Figure 7.6). The grayish cast of the quartz grains, with their glassy luster, sets them apart from the milky white or pink feldspars. Black grains of biotite or hornblende contrast with the light minerals. The extrusive equivalent of granite is *rhyolite,* a light-gray to pink form of lava.

The granite-gabbro series progresses through transitional rocks, not named here, as potash feldspar and quartz decrease in proportion while plagioclase feldspar increases and moves from the alkalic end toward the intermediate varieties.

*Diorite* is an important plutonic rock, and its extrusive equivalent, *andesite,* occurs very widely in lavas associated with volcanoes. Diorite is dominated by plagioclase feldspar of intermediate composition, while quartz is a very minor constituent. At this point in the granite-gabbro series pyroxene makes its appearance and is of the augite variety. Amphibole, largely hornblende, is also important, and some biotite is present.

*Gabbro* is an important though not abundant plutonic rock, but it is greatly overshadowed in importance by its extrusive equivalent, *basalt,* which makes up huge areas of lava flows and which is the predominant igneous rock underlying the floors of the ocean basins. Gabbro and basalt are composed almost entirely of pyroxene and intermediate to calcic plagioclase feldspar with or without minor amounts of olivine. As olivine increases, at the expense of reduced plagioclase and pyroxene, *olivine gabbro* and *olivine basalt* appear in the series (Figure 7.7, right). Gabbro and basalt are dark-colored rocks—dark-gray, dark-green, to almost black—and of relatively high specific gravity, 3.0. They are designated as being of *basaltic* (or *mafic*) affiliation, in contrast to the *granitic* (or *felsic*) rocks related to granite.

Continuing the igneous-rock series depicted in Figure 7.3, we arrive at *peridotite,* a rock composed almost entirely of two mineral constituents, olivine and pyroxene. Although widespread in occurrence, peridotite occurs in relatively small plutonic bodies, it is a dark-colored rock of high specific gravity, 3.3, and belongs to a group designated as *ultramafic* (*ultrabasic*) rocks.

The ultramafic rocks include three other varieties, only one of which, *dunite,* is shown in Figure 7.3. All three are *monomineralic* in composition, meaning that a single mineral or mineral group constitutes most of the rock. Dunite is composed largely of olivine. The ultramafic rocks are rather rare in surface exposures.

## COMPOSITION OF THE EARTH'S CRUST AND MANTLE

Simple reasoning would lead us to conclude that if the rock-forming minerals were permitted to assemble freely in respect to the earth's gravity field the three rock groups would be found in a layered sequence with granitic rocks in a surface layer, basaltic rocks next below, and utrabasic (ultramafic) at the bottom. Actually, this general arrangement is accepted as the most reasonable model for the earth's crust and mantle. Figure 7.8 shows this arrangement in a very rough way for continents and ocean basins. Granitic rocks form the upper part of the continental crust in a layer with an average thickness of perhaps 10

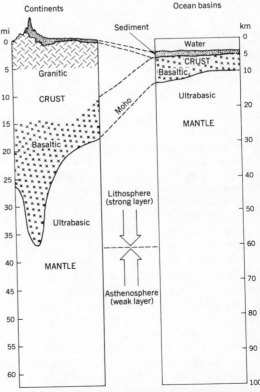

Figure 7.8. Schematic diagram of composition and thickness of crust and mantle under continents and ocean basins.

mi (16 km). The lower part of the crust is probably largely of basaltic rock, down to an average depth of 25 mi (40 km), at which there is an abrupt change to a denser mantle rock, which we interpret to be ultramafic rock with a composition resembling peridotite.

The surface of abrupt change is known as the *moho,* this word being the first part of the long name of a Yugoslav scientist who discovered the discontinuity on the basis of earthquake studies. A more elegant term for moho is *M-discontinuity.* Actually, the only evidence concerning the supposed change of rock composition or physical state comes from abrupt changes in speeds of earthquake waves. As yet no rock samples have been obtained from such depths.

## DISTRIBUTION OF RADIOGENIC HEAT

Heat flows continuously upward from depths of the earth toward the surface. The increase in temperature with depth, or *geothermal gradient,* is well known from observations in deep mines and in bore holes and has a value of about 1 F° per 50 ft (3 C° per 100 m). The flow of heat because of this thermal gradient averages about 1.4 microcalories cm²/sec (0.0000014 cal/cm²/sec). This same figure applies rather well to both continents and ocean basins.

At this rate, the total heat flow in 1 yr is about 50 cal/cm², enough to melt an ice layer 0.2 in. (6 mm) thick. Notice particularly that this quantity of heat is extremely small compared with that received by 1 cm² of the earth's surface from solar radiation (see Chapter 1). Therefore, the earth's heat flow from depth is of no significance in the earth's heat balance or in powering the atmospheric and oceanic circulation systems.

Referring back to the temperature-depth graph in Figure 2.18, you will notice that the rate of temperature increase with depth falls off very rapidly after the first 100 mi or so. The flattening of the temperature curve in the lower

mantle and core expresses the very low thermal gradient that is postulated to exist within the deep interior. If the thermal gradient decreases rapidly with depth, a logical interpretation is that the rate of production of radiogenic heat is greatest near the earth's surface and decreases rapidly with depth. It has been concluded that the concentration of radioactive isotopes is greatest in the rocks of the crust but falls off rapidly in the mantle rocks and is very small in the lower mantle and core.

Table 7.3 shows both the concentrations and rates of heat production of the radioactive isotopes of uranium, thorium, and potassium in each of the three classes of igneous rocks. These rates are based upon chemical analyses of samples of igneous rocks collected at the earth's surface. If we project these figures to the assumed corresponding rocks of the crust and mantle, as shown in Figure 7.8, it is seen that the most rapid production of radiogenic heat is by granitic rocks of the upper zone of the continental crust. The ultrabasic mantle rock produces very little heat per unit of weight. It has been estimated that about one-half of all radiogenic heat is produced above a depth of 22 mi (35 km) in the continental crust.

Some support for the conclusion that the iron core of the earth produces almost no radiogenic heat is found in the analysis of iron meteorites. These fragments of matter are thought to represent the disrupted cores of planetary objects of similar origin to the earth (see Chapter 12). Radioactive minerals are present in only very small quantities in iron meteorites.

## EARLY THERMAL HISTORY OF THE EARTH

Modern hypotheses of the earth's origin, discussed in Chapter 12, tend to favor the process of accretion of the earth and other planets through the coming together of cold clouds of dispersed gases and dusts under gravitational attraction. Once formed, such solid masses

Table 7.3.  CONCENTRATIONS AND HEAT-PRODUCTION RATES OF RADIOACTIVE ISOTOPES

| | Concentrations | | | Heat Production (cal/gm/yr) | | | |
|---|---|---|---|---|---|---|---|
| | U (ppm) | Th (ppm) | K (%) | U | Th | K | Total |
| Granitic | 4 | 14 | 3.5 | 3 | 3 | 1 | 7 |
| Basaltic | 0.6 | 2 | 1.0 | 1.5 | 1.5 | 0.5 | 3.5 |
| Ultrabasic | 0.015 | — | 0.011 | 0.01 | 0.01 | <0.001 | 0.02 |

Source: Based on data of B. Mason (1966), *Principles of Geochemistry,* 3rd ed., New York, Wiley, Table 11.1; and P. J. Hurley (1959), *How Old Is the Earth?* New York, Doubleday, p. 64.

would grow by the infall of solid bodies of many sizes. It is generally supposed that at the time accretion was largely complete the earth's interior temperature had not risen to the melting point, although local areas may have become molten from the energy of impacts. Modern thinking is thus along quite different lines from that of early speculators, such as Laplace, who postulated an earth formed from high-temperature gases and passing from the gaseous state to the molten state in its initial development.

It is interesting to recall that Lord Kelvin, the distinguished nineteenth-century English physicist, had calculated the age of the earth using the premise that the earth cooled from a molten state and that the cooling rate followed simple laws of radiative and conductive heat loss. On this basis he concluded that the earth could not be more than 100 million years (m.y.) old and that an age of 20 to 40 m.y. was a reasonable figure. Present estimates are on the order of 4.6 b.y. for the completion of the accretion process. We can excuse Lord Kelvin's gross miscalculation in view of the fact that the phenomenon of radioactivity was not then known.

The discovery of natural radioactivity by Henri Becquerel in 1896, followed by the isolation of radium by Marie and Pierre Curie in 1898, radically altered all scientific thinking about the earth's heat. John Joly in 1909 applied the new knowledge of radioactivity to recalculations of the earth's thermal history. Moreover, Joly brought forward the underlying principle that radiogenic heat provides the prime energy source for vulcanism, intrusion, and deformation of the earth's crust into mountain belts and perhaps also great horizontal movements of the crust and upper mantle.

It is considered most unlikely that the earth, at the time of its formation as a planet about 4.5 b.y. ago, contained the same quantity and distribution of radioactive isotopes that we find today. Primarily, there is the consideration that radioactive decay progressively reduces the available supply of radioactive isotopes. Hence we conclude that the total production of radiogenic heat within the earth was at the maximum level at the time of the earth's formation and has diminished ever since. The relative rates of decay of uranium, thorium, and potassium isotopes are not the same but are well established for each isotope. Figure 7.9 is a

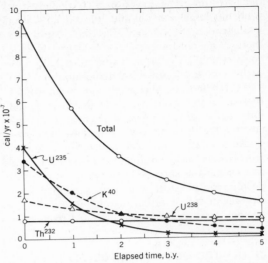

Figure 7.9. Rate of production of radiogenic heat projected back 5 b.y. [Data of A. P. Vinogradov (1961), as shown in B. Mason (1966), *Principles of Geochemistry*, New York, John Wiley & Sons, p. 61, Figure 3.9.]

graph in which time is plotted on the horizontal axis starting at an arbitrary zero point at the assumed time of formation of the earth. Total planetary radiogenic-heat production per year is given on the vertical scale. Curves have been plotted for the major radioactive isotopes of uranium, thorium, and potassium individually, while the total production is shown in a separate curve. Note that uranium-235 and potassium-40 have short half-lives in comparison with those of uranium-238 and thorium-232. Referring to the total curve, we see that it is obvious that total radiogenic-heat production was vastly greater when the earth was first formed than it is at present, roughly by a factor of six. The implications of such a history are of great consequence.

First, assume that at the time of the earth's formation by accretion the radioactive isotopes were uniformly distributed throughout the entire earth. There is no reason to think otherwise. Silicate minerals and free iron were also uniformly mixed. Heat would accumulate at great depths, bringing the primary material to the melting point. Melted rock would have tended to rise toward the surface, bringing up with it the radioactive isotopes. Because these latter elements remain in the liquid state at temperatures lower than the transporting minerals, cooling and crystallization of the surrounding minerals would have been accompanied by a sinking of those mineral crystals (which are denser), leaving the liquid fraction closer to the earth's surface. Although such a process of differentiation is speculative, it offers a mechanism for the selective removal of the radioactive isotopes from the inner earth and their eventual concentration near the surface.

We postulate further that during this same melting process the density layering of the earth came into existence, resulting in the concentration of iron in the core, a less dense ultrabasic rock mantle of olivine above it, and the basaltic crust at the top. During the segregation process the heat-production rate was falling. Consequently, along with redistribution of the heat-generating isotopes, the episodes of melting must have become fewer and eventually ceased. Today the earth is thermally stable, in the sense that melting and movement of magma are limited to an extremely shallow layer in terms of the earth's total diameter. The inner core and much of the mantle are no longer subject to melting through the accumulation of excess heat.

It is fortunate, indeed, that the chemistry of the radioactive elements is such that they would tend to rise toward the earth's surface throughout its history. If, on the other hand, they had tended to sink and collect near the earth's center, the heat produced by their concentrated activity would have repeatedly melted the earth. Under such conditions no planetary stability would have been possible throughout geologic history. As we find conditions today, radiogenic-heat production in the core is negligible, while the rate of surfaceward flow of heat from the upper mantle and crust closely balances the rate of heat production. The mantle remains for the most part at a temperature lower than its melting point. There exists, however, a shallow layer of the mantle in which melting on a large scale is a likely occurrence.

## PLASTIC LAYER OF THE MANTLE

A layer within the upper mantle in the depth range from 40 to 125 mi (60 to 200 km) is of particular interest in connection with the radiogenic-heat system and its geological effects. In this zone, which has very indefinite upper and lower boundaries, the mantle rock is at a temperature very close to its melting point and is, therefore, in a condition of reduced strength. The term *plastic layer,* or *soft layer,* has been applied to this part of the mantle.

Figure 7.10 shows some details of the temperature and strength properties of the plastic layer. At the left is a graph of actual temperature with increasing depth, compared with the curve of melting temperature of the same rock. Notice that the temperature curve swings close to the melting curve in the depth zone between 60 and 180 mi (100 and 300 km). Taking the temperature difference only, and plotting that quantity against depth, gives the curve in the middle graph. The graph at the right shows strength of the rock at corresponding depths. Notice the marked drop to low strength with a minimum about 125 mi (200 km) depth. Apparently, while remaining solid and in a crystalline form, the mantle rock at this depth develops a plastic quality when close to its melting point. A plastic zone here was suspected as far back as 1926, when the seismolo-

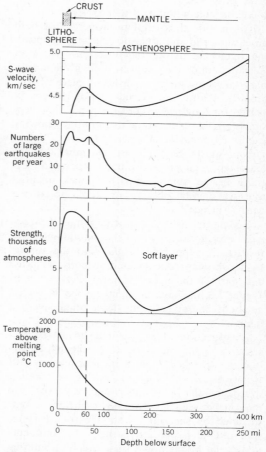

Figure 7.10. Physical properties of the upper mantle. [Based on data of D. L. Anderson (1962), *Scientific American,* July, pp. 58–59.]

gist Beno Gutenberg presented evidence that earthquake waves are slowed in velocity in this zone. Reduction of earthquake velocity can be interpreted as due to a reduction in rigidity of the rock.

The plastic quality of rock in the soft layer makes possible very slow flowage movements when this rock is subjected to unequal stresses. As we will see, flowage of mantle rock plays a vital part in modern hypotheses of crustal changes and mountain-making. At the same time, it is clear that the mantle also behaves as a crystalline solid in response to stresses that are applied suddenly and over short periods of time. Earthquakes, which are generated by intense stresses and rapid movements of rock masses, can originate in the plastic zone. The very fact that one type of earthquake wave, the transverse or shear wave, travels through the mantle shows that the mantle retains the properties of an elastic solid, for such waves cannot travel through a liquid.

The mantle thus exhibits properties of both an elastic solid and a plastic substance, depending upon the nature of the stresses applied. Certain common substances, among them ordinary tar, show such properties. A piece of cold tar will fracture when struck, but if left unsupported for long periods of time it will flow very slowly in a thick stream. Material showing such dual behavior is described as an *elastico-viscous* substance. We must remember that the extremely high pressures and temperatures existing in the mantle impart to rock qualities that we cannot observe or duplicate at the earth's surface.

Geologists have given the name *asthenosphere* to the soft layer of the mantle and have restricted the term *lithosphere* to the strong, rigid overlying zone (including both the crust and part of the upper mantle). As shown in Figure 7.8, the base of the lithosphere is placed at about 38 mi (60 km) as a rough average figure.

Identification of a plastic layer of reduced strength in the mantle leads to the hypothesis that the stronger, more rigid lithospheric shell which overlies it may be capable of rotating independently of stronger mantle below, the motion between the two bodies being accommodated by shearing within the soft asthenosphere. Under such a hypothesis the continents and ocean basins might shift widely in latitude and longitude. It is also possible to conceive of portions of the lithosphere as moving independently of one another as plates over the asthenosphere. In general, such postulated movements come under the heading of *continental drift* and may involve separation of lithospheric plates as well as plates coming together along a common line. These activities result in *orogeny*, the making of mountains by crustal movements.

## ISOSTASY

Existence of a plastic layer in the mantle allows for the possibility that individual segments of the lithosphere may be free to rise or sink in response to unequal stresses. Sinking of the lithosphere will require that the mantle material of the asthenosphere be displaced laterally by slow flowage. Rising of the crust will require that mantle material be brought in from surrounding zones of the asthenosphere. Such accommodations are the basis of the principle of *isostasy*, one of the fundamental doctrines of geology. The word *isostasy* comes from Greek words meaning "equal" and "stand." The concept is that lithospheric elements seek an equilibrium level of stability, just as icebergs float at rest in the ocean.

We shall examine a particular crustal model of isostasy proposed over a century ago by Sir George Airy, Astronomer Royal of England, in an attempt to justify certain observations of variations in the force of gravity in the zone of the Himalaya Mountains in northern India.

Airy's hypothesis is illustrated by a simple model using floating blocks (Figure 7.11). Suppose that we take several blocks, or prisms, of a metal such as copper. Although all prisms have the same dimensions of cross section, they are cut to varying lengths. Because copper is

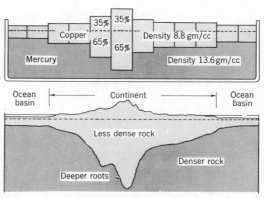

Figure 7.11. The Airy hypothesis of mountain roots is suggested by the equilibrium positions of blocks of the same density.

less dense than mercury, the prisms will float in a dish of that liquid metal. If all blocks are floated side by side in the same orientation, the longest block will float with the greatest amount rising above the level of the mercury surface, and the shortest block has its upper surface lowest. With all blocks now floating at rest, it is obvious that the block rising highest also extends to greatest depth.

Airy supposed that the material of which mountains are composed extends far down into the earth to form roots composed of lighter (less dense) material. This lighter material, which may be granitic rock, protrudes downward into a location normally occupied by denser basaltic or ultrabasic rock. Under a plains region the root of less dense rock will be very shallow, and under the floors of the ocean basins it will be shallowest of all.

Referring back to Figure 7.8, we find that the depth of the M-discontinuity, marking the base of the crust, is greatest under the highest mountain mass. This downward projection of the crust constitutes a *mountain root*. Under the oceans, the M-discontinuity is very shallow under a thin crust. Independent evidence from seismology and gravity measurements has verified this picture and shown that isostatic equilibrium prevails generally over the earth.

## INTRUSION AND GRANITE BATHOLITHS

The formation of pockets of magma in the upper mantle or lower crust is adequate to explain the sources of bodies of igneous rock that the geologist observes as he examines the surface exposures of rocks. While some of these bodies are as extensive as a large state or province, their size is very small in terms of the entire earth's surface (Figure 7.12).

No known igneous rock on earth exceeds an age of about 3.5 b.y. It is generally agreed that the earth achieved its identity as a planet from −4.5 to −5 b.y. Note that this leaves about 1 b.y. or more of earth history unaccounted for by rock records. One must conclude that all known igneous rocks are formed of magma that invaded and completely replaced whatever older crustal rock may have previously existed. We have already seen that the earth's earliest history may have been one of repeated melting and solidification, whether as a whole globe, or in parts, until mineral stratification was completed and the radiogenic isotopes were concentrated near the surface. In the final stages of this segregation process, it is conceivable that

Figure 7.12. Map of Cretaceous batholiths of western North America. The word *batholith* has been omitted from each label. [After C. O. Dunbar and K. M. Waage (1969), *Historical Geology,* 3rd ed., New York, John Wiley & Sons, p. 376, Figure 16-7.]

many small magma pockets were formed, invaded the overlying crust, and replaced preexisting rock. This process seems to have continued into relatively recent geologic periods and may be active today, although we cannot observe what magmas are doing at depth at the present time.

Geologists visualize upward movements of magma in the crust and refer to this process as *intrusion,* although they perhaps do not know as much about the mechanisms as they would like to know. It is understandable that if a rock body is heated until it melts, the magma, being of lower density than its solid equivalent at the same level, will tend to rise. In a sense, ensuing motion is a form of convection powered by heat energy, similar in principle to convective motions of the atmosphere. In exerting upward pressure upon the overlying rock layers, rising magma can incur mechanical changes, such as the bodily lifting and rupturing of the overlying mass.

Blocks of the enclosing solid rock (known as the *country rock* in contrast to the invading magma) can break off and sink into the magma, allowing the magma to rise and occupy the cavity. Such a process of magma rise is termed *stoping,* from the miner's term for mining upward into a ceiling. The finding of unmelted blocks of country rock (*xenoliths*) enclosed by igneous rock attests to stoping as a real process (Figure 7.13).

There is also the possibility that magma can rise by melting the overlying rock and incorporating the molten material into the original magma. The magma is said to *assimilate* the country rock as melting proceeds, and the magma composition may be changed by addition of different mineral components. For example, if a magma of basaltic composition were to assimilate rock rich in free silica and aluminosilicates of potassium and sodium (feldspars) the average composition for the magma would be changed in the direction of the granitic rocks.

Whatever may be the details of the process of magmatic rise and intrusion, the end result can be studied after the process of denudation, described in Chapter 9, has exposed to view rocks that formerly were many miles below the earth's surface. In such exposures we recognize an igneous body known as the *batholith.* Batholiths are mostly of granitic rock in a rather coarsely crystalline state. Granite as a particular rock is a major constituent of batholiths. Batholiths seem to be "bottomless" because their great extent downward does not permit the observation of a lower boundary. Lack of knowledge of conditions at depth is in large measure responsible for uncertainty and extensive debate about the origin of granite batholiths.

Perhaps granite bodies have more than one origin. For the moment, we may rest with the possibility that the magma of a granite batholith came from a deeper parent body of igneous rock of the same composition, which was merely melted, intruded, and recrystallized higher in the crust. Granite of this origin has been designated as *primary.* Under this hypothesis, the magma would originate by melting in the upper (granitic) part of the continental crust, and not within the lower or oceanic (basaltic) crust or within the mantle. One can thus argue that granite magma comes from the melting of previously existing granite, but such a statement only defers the problem of origin of the preexisting granite. For the moment, the question of origin of granite will be deferred, to be taken up again in Chapter 10 in different context.

## RISE OF BASALTS ON THE CONTINENTS

Next to the granites in importance as igneous rocks within the continents are some vast accumulations of basalt. These extrusive rocks represent outpourings of basaltic magma upon the surface of the granitic continental crust. The molten basalt, extremely fluid at high temperatures, has issued from near-vertical cracks, known as *fissures,* and has spread in thin sheets to solidify rapidly in the form of *lava flows* (Figure 7.14).

In certain regions, outpouring of basalts occurred in enormous quantities within fairly short spans of geologic time. The numerous basalt layers can aggregate thicknesses of several thousands of feet, while the areas covered run into the order of 50,000 to 100,000 mi² (130,000 to 260,000 km²). Two notable examples are shown in the maps of Figure 7.15. One is the Columbia Plateau region of Washington, Oregon, and Idaho. A second is the Deccan Plateau of peninsular India.

That plateau basalts originate from very great depths in the crust seems reasonable. Figure 7.16 shows diagrammatically the source of basalt as a pocket of molten basalt from the

Figure 7.13. Xenoliths of various kinds of igneous and metamorphic rocks enclosed in granite. Prescott, Arizona. (Photograph by A. N. Strahler.)

Figure 7.14. Basaltic lava flow from Mauna Loa moving toward the village of Hoopuloa, Hawaii, April, 1926. (U.S. Air Force photograph.)

basaltic rock layer of the lower part of the continental crust. The depth of such a source might lie between 20 and 30 mi (30 and 50 km).

The rise of basaltic magma from a deep source would require that the overlying crust subside to occupy the space vacated by the magma. Fracturing of the subsiding rigid crust into cracks would provide additional planes of weakness through which more magma could rise. Such a statement does not, however, provide insight into the causes of the rise of basalt magma. The extrusion of the basalt in large quantities agrees with the model of a continental crust having a basaltic composition in its lower part, but because the place of origin of the magma is not established by independent evidence, plateau basalts do not prove that the lower crust is basaltic.

As to the basalt of the ocean floors, the supposition was long held that this crust represents a single ancient rock layer that has undergone little subsequent change. This concept has been completely destroyed in recent years by important discoveries concerning its age as revealed in magnetic properties. The new concepts are discussed in Chapter 10.

## VOLCANIC EXTRUSION

The term *vulcanism* (also *volcanism*) is applied generally to the formation of extrusive igneous rocks and includes both the outpourings of basalt lavas in extensive sheets and the more localized accumulations of magma in the

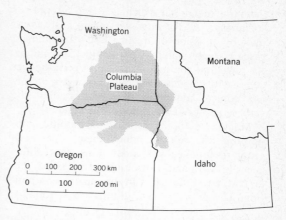

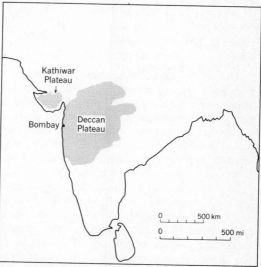

Figure 7.15. Approximate present surface extent of the Columbia Plateau basalts (*above*) and the Deccan Plateau basalts of India (*below*).

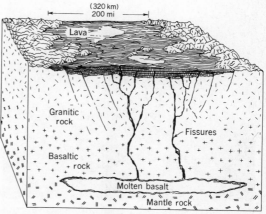

Figure 7.16. Schematic drawing suggesting the relation of plateau basalts to crustal zones beneath.

form of individual volcanoes and groups of volcanoes. By *volcano,* we mean a structure built by emission of magma and its contained gases (largely water) from a pipelike conduit. As eruption continues through time, the accumulated igneous rock must form a more-or-less conical mountain mass surrounding the *vent,* or point of emergence of the conduit.

Magmas of both granitic and basaltic composition, as well as intermediate types, can erupt to produce volcanoes. Important differences in form and distribution of volcanoes can be traced to differences in the magma composition. The principal lava groups are as follows:

| Parent Magma Type | Name of Lava | Classification of Lava |
|---|---|---|
| Granitic | Rhyolite | Acidic |
| Intermediate | Andesite | Intermediate |
| Basic | Basalt | Basic |

The acidic and intermediate lavas have a high viscosity and retain large amounts of gas under pressure. As a result, these lavas tend to give explosive eruptions. Basaltic lavas, as a group, are of low viscosity and the contained gases readily escape. Consequently, large basaltic emissions are typically quiet, as we have seen in the case of the plateau basalts.

Eruption of acidic and intermediate lava typically produces a tall, steep-sided cone which characteristically steepens to the summit, where a small depression (the *crater*) marks the position of the vent. Familiar to all are the graceful profiles of such volcanoes as Mt. Fujiyama in Japan, Mt. Mayon in the Philippines, and Mt. Hood in the Cascade range (Figure 7.17). Cones of this type are

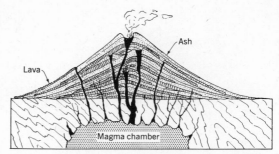

Figure 7.18. Idealized cross section of a composite volcanic cone with feeders from magma chamber beneath.

designated as *composite volcanoes,* or *strato-volcanoes,* because they consist in part of lava flows and in part of volcanic ash. Internal structure of such a volcano is shown in Figure 7.18. By *ash* is meant finely divided igneous rock that results from the explosive emission of magma heavily charged with gases under high pressure. Collectively, this material is described as *pyroclastic rock.* Particles are literally blown out into the air and come to rest at various distances from the vent, depending upon their size. Very fine volcanic dust can travel many miles from the vent, coarser particles fall close to the vent (Figure 7.19). Huge masses of boulder-size (*volcanic bombs*) can be hurled only a short distance from the vent (Figure 7.20). Collectively, these solid particles are termed *ejecta;* they are important in shaping the form of the cone.

Flows of lava are also emitted from the volcano, typically emerging from vents on the flanks of the cone. Thus the cone is constructed of both pyroclastic material and flows, the latter forming an apron around the base of

Figure 7.17. Summit and crater of an active composite volcano in central Java. (Photograph by Luchtvaart-Afdeeling, Ned. Ind. Leger., Bandoeng.)

Figure 7.19. Volcanic ash almost buried this village during the 1914 eruption of Sakurajima, a Japanese volcano. (Photograph by T. Nakasa.)

Figure 7.20. A blocky lava flow advancing slowly over a ground surface littered with volcanic blocks and bombs, Sakurajima, 1914. (Photograph by T. Nakasa.)

the cone. Yet another important form of emission is a cloud of incandescent gases and fine ash, known as a *nuée ardente* (French for "glowing cloud"). This cloud moves rapidly down the side slopes of the cone. A cloud of this type emerged from Mt. Pelée on the island of Martinique in 1902, destroying St. Pierre and killing most of its 30,000 inhabitants.

Basaltic volcanoes are often referred to as being of the *Hawaiian type,* for they are exemplified in the chain of mid-Pacific volcanoes that extends from the Midway Islands to Hawaii, a total distance of almost 2000 mi (3200 km). The Hawaiian type of volcano is often termed a *basaltic dome,* or *shield volcano.* The volcano summit is typically broadly domed, with gentle summit slopes (Figure 7.21). Built up from the deep ocean floor, a single large basaltic dome reaches a total height of 5 mi (8 km) above the sea floor and has a basal diameter of over 100 mi (160 km). Individual basalt flows, of which the domes are built, emerge from fissures on the volcano flanks and travel long distances before solidifying. Characteristic of the active Hawaiian volcanoes is a *central depression,* which is a steepwalled cavity up to 2 mi (3 km) wide and several hundred feet deep. The depression appears to be caused by a subsidence of the summit area of the dome as lava is withdrawn from beneath.

Interpretation of volcanoes in terms of the processes that act in the earth's crust is based upon the patterns and areas of distribution of

Figure 7.21. Hawaii Volcanoes National Park. (*Top*) Aerial view of Mokuaweoweo, the broad central depression on the summit of Mauna Loa, March, 1962. The volcano Mauna Kea is on the distant skyline. (*Middle*) Halemaumau, a pit crater on Mauna Loa, seen in 1952. (*Bottom*) A fire fountain on the floor of Halemaumau during the eruption of July, 1961. (Courtesy of National Park Service, U.S. Dept. of the Interior.)

the three lava types of which the volcanoes are formed. Andesite lavas, of the intermediate classification, form much of the greatest of all volcano chains—the *circum-Pacific ring* (see Figure 10.14). This ring extends from the Andes range of South America (note that the word *andesite* is derived from Andes) through the West Indian archipelago, along the Cascade range of the American Cordillera, thence along the Alaskan coast and out along the Aleutian Islands chain. Continuing through Kamchatka, the Kuriles, and Japan, the andesite ring runs southward in the form of island chains of the western Pacific and passes through New Zealand.

Distinct in location from the andesite lavas are the oceanic basalt lavas that comprise volcanoes of the Pacific Ocean basin and the middle zone of the Atlantic Ocean. These basalts are rich in the mineral olivine. In the Pacific basin, geologists have drawn the *andesite line*, separating andesite lavas from basaltic lavas (see Figure 10.14).

A particularly important chain of andesitic-class volcanoes forms a great arc in the East Indies. We shall see that this *Indonesian chain* is closely related to the circum-Pacific chain.

Of secondary importance on a global basis are the Mediterranean volcanoes, among them Etna, Stromboli, and Vesuvius. Important minor groups also include those of east central Africa.

Interpretation of the great volcano belts and their origin is so closely tied in with the breaking and bending of the crust that it is a subject best deferred for consideration in Chapter 10.

## A SYSTEM IN REVIEW

The radiogenic-heat system obtained its energy supply at the time of the earth's formation and has consumed its own substance ever since. Consequently, it is a decay system that conforms with the negative exponential-decay function. Heat production was initially greater than today by a factor of perhaps six times and must have played the essential role in redistributing the elements and minerals of an originally homogeneous primitive earth. These changes led to the stratified earth we have today, with its segregations of elements and minerals according to their densities. At the present time, the radiogenic-heat system is stable. The quantity of heat produced in the upper mantle and crust is disposed of by continuous upward flow in conduction, as well as by local movements of magma which carry heat to the earth's surface, where it is rapidly dissipated. As we shall see in Chapter 10, there

may exist slow convective movements within the mantle which also bring heat toward the surface.

In addition to the flow of heat within the system, the expenditure of energy takes the form of mechanical work in lifting and deforming solid rock masses of the crust.

The radiogenic-heat system has a time span that is geologic in scope, where significant changes are measurable only in millions of years. Looking ahead billions of years, we can anticipate that the decline in production of radiogenic heat will reduce the intensity and frequency of intrusion and extrusion of molten rock and of crustal changes. The processes of denudation will then be felt more strongly and the persistence of low-lying continental surfaces, partially submerged by ocean waters, will become more general. But, because radioactivity will never entirely cease, igneous activity will persist, though diminished in importance as aeons pass.

## References for further study

Hurley, P. M. (1959), *How Old Is the Earth?* Garden City, N.Y., Anchor Books, Doubleday, 160 pp.

Bullard, F. M. (1962), *Volcanoes, in History, in Theory, in Eruption,* Austin, Univ. of Texas Press, 441 pp.

Spock, L. E. (1962), *Guide to the Study of Rocks,* 2nd ed., New York, Harper & Row, 298 pp., chaps 2–6.

Mason, B. (1966), *Principles of Geochemistry,* 3rd ed., New York, Wiley, 329 pp., chap. 5.

Simpson, B. (1966), *Rocks and Minerals,* New York, Pergamon, 292 pp.

Strahler, A. N. (1971), *The Earth Sciences,* 2nd ed., New York, Harper & Row, 826 pp., chaps. 20, 21, 23, 25.

## Review questions

1. Describe the structure of the atomic nucleus. What is the mass number? the atomic number? Explain what is meant by an isotope.

2. Describe the process of radioactive disintegration. What forms of emission accompany this breakdown? How is heat produced? Describe the chain of daughter products in the decay of uranium-238. What is an exponential-decay function? What is meant by half-life of this process?

3. What is a rock? a mineral? Name in order the eight most abundant elements in rocks of the earth's crust, giving approximate percentage by volume for each. How does this

list compare with that of elements of the earth as a whole? What implication about earth development can be drawn from such a comparison?

4. What are the silicate minerals? Name them and describe their chemical compositions in terms of constituent elements present. In what way do these minerals form a series? In what way do the terms *felsic* and *mafic* apply to the silicate minerals?

5. What is meant by the mineralogical phase rule, and how does it relate to the silicate minerals? Describe a silicate magma. What are volatiles, and what is their importance in a magma?

6. What kinds of reactions occur during crystallization of a silicate magma? Describe the Bowen reaction series. How does it relate to the formation of varieties of igneous rocks? What is meant by the term *magmatic differentiation?*

7. What controls the size of crystals in an igneous rock? Distinguish between plutonic rocks and extrusive rocks (lavas) in terms of physical properties.

8. Describe the granite-gabbro series of igneous rocks. How does this series relate to the Bowen reaction series? Describe each of the principal members of the granite-gabbro series and give the mineral components of each. What are the ultramafic (ultrabasic) rocks? Name two examples.

9. Describe the earth's crust, giving thickness and rock composition. At what depth is the mantle encountered under continents and ocean basins? What is the M-discontinuity? What is the composition of the mantle?

10. Describe the geothermal gradient. How does the quantity of heat reaching the surface compare with heat derived from solar radiation? How does the thermal gradient change with increasing depth? What is the significance of this change?

11. In what earth zones is the production of radiogenic heat concentrated? What evidence do meteorites provide concerning radiogenic heat within the earth's core?

12. How did the discovery of radioactivity affect estimates of the age of the earth? What contributions were made in this field by Becquerel, the Curies, and Joly? Compare the production of radiogenic heat in the geologic past with that of the present. What events in the early history of the earth are postulated to have led to existing conditions of thermal stability?

13. What is the plastic layer (soft layer) of the earth's mantle? Describe the physical conditions within this layer. At what depth does it lie? How does the term *elastico-viscous* apply to the plastic layer? What is the distinction between the asthenosphere and the lithosphere? Why is this distinction of importance in earth processes and history?

14. Explain the concept of isostasy and illustrate with a simple physical model. According to this concept, what is the relationship between depth to the M-discontinuity and surface elevation of the continents? Does isostasy explain the shallow depth of the M-discontinuity beneath the oceanic crust?

15. Is it possible to describe the original rock of the earth's crust? Defend your answer with geologic evidence. Describe the intrusion of magma to form a batholith. What is stoping? What is a xenolith? In what way can a magma influence the country rock which it invades?

16. Describe the rise and extrusion of basalts in large volumes. What may be the source region of this magma? Name two regions of great basaltic-lava accumulations.

17. What is the process of vulcanism? Describe the structure and form of a volcano. Name three groups of lavas and classify them as to mineral affinities. How does lava composition influence viscosity of the magma? How is explosiveness related to composition? What kinds of volcanic structures and ejecta are associated with each type of magma?

18. Name and describe the earth's major belts of volcanoes. What is the andesite line? What general significance can be attached to belts of volcanoes?

19. Review in broad terms the radiogenic-heat system and its activity through geologic time. What is the source of energy of this system, and how long will it last? Does this energy system bear any similarity to that of the sun and other stars?

# chapter 8 exogenetic processes and products: i. rock transformation and sediments

In this chapter two very unlike planetary systems are brought into linkage at the continental surface. The total atmosphere-hydrosphere system of energy flux and matter transport that sustains the global balances of radiation, heat, and water is one. The other is the geologic system of rise of molten rock and other geologic processes of crustal movement and rock metamorphism which create and elevate the continental masses. These internal geological activities, or *endogenetic processes,* furnish the solid earth surface that comes into contact with the external solar-powered planetary activities, or *exogenetic processes,* in which the atmosphere and hydrosphere attack and alter the exposed rock mass. As a result, rock is changed physically and chemically to produce *sediment,* broadly defined as any particulate mineral and organic matter derived directly or indirectly from the disintegration, decomposition, and reprocessing of preexisting rock. Exogenetic processes also transport and redistribute sediment, producing accumulations that constitute a second rock class—the *sedimentary rocks.* These in turn can be acted upon by endogenetic processes of crustal change and heating to be transformed into a third rock class—the *metamorphic rocks*—or melted to form successive generations of igneous rocks. From this analysis of cause and effect there emerges a *rock-transformation cycle,* in which the mineral matter of the earth's crust is continually reprocessed to the accompaniment of enormous expenditures of energy, some of which is supplied by electromagnetic radiation of the sun and some of which is supplied by radiogenic heat inherited from early in the earth's history. The rock-transformation cycle is not in itself an energy system; instead it is the product of other systems of energy transformation and mass transport working in a linkage that uniquely characterizes our planet and sets it apart from other members of the solar system.

This chapter concentrates upon the part of

the rock cycle in which solid rock is transformed into sediment, in turn becoming sedimentary rock. Later chapters will treat remaining phases of the rock cycle, until finally a unified concept of physical geology stands completed.

## WEATHERING AND THE SURFACE ENVIRONMENT

The interface between lithosphere and atmosphere represents a specialized environment as far as minerals and rocks are concerned. This surface environment is one of relatively low temperature and low confining pressure in contrast to the high-temperature and high-pressure environment in which plutonic igneous rocks are formed deep within the earth's crust.

The surface environment is one of instability for the silicate minerals, for they succumb readily to the presence of free oxygen, carbon dioxide, and water. We may like to think that no substance is more enduring than the granite we use in monuments to signify an everlasting tribute, yet in fact granite is one of the most decay-susceptible of mineral assemblages to face the "elements." Much the same statement can be made of most varieties of metamorphic rocks, for they too were produced in an environment of high pressures and temperatures and are not well adapted to endure exposure to atmospheric conditions.

The alteration of minerals in the presence of water, oxygen, and various natural acids is greatly aided by a group of physical forces of disintegration. These forces can break apart and fragment the hard well-knit minerals of igneous and metamorphic rocks, thereby increasing the mineral surface area exposed to chemical reagents. Were it not for the forces of physical disintegration, rock alteration would have proceeded very slowly throughout the geological past, and the course of earth history would have been quite different.

Geologists use the term *weathering* for the total of all processes acting at or near the earth's surface whereby rock undergoes physical disintegration and chemical decomposition.

## BEDROCK AND ITS OVERBURDEN

Examination of a freshly cut cliff, such as that in a new highway excavation or quarry wall, may reveal several kinds of earth materials (Figure 8.1). Solid hard rock that is still in place and relatively unchanged is called *bedrock*. It grades upward into a zone where

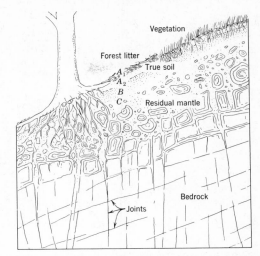

Figure 8.1. Soil and residual overburden overlying bedrock. (© 1960, John Wiley & Sons, New York.)

the rock is partly decayed and has disintegrated into clay and sand particles. This material may be called the *residual overburden,* or *regolith.* At the top is a layer of true *soil,* often called *topsoil* by farmers and gardeners. It is usually less than 3 ft (1 m) thick and in humid regions may be relatively dark in color in comparison with the regolith below. A distinctive feature of the soil is the presence of a layered structure formed of two or three *horizons.* Horizons are designated in Figure 8.1 by the letters $A_1$, $A_2$, *B,* and *C,* Over the soil may be a protective layer of grass, trees, or other vegetation.

In some places the soil and regolith have been stripped off down to the bedrock, which then appears at the surface as an *outcrop* (Figure 8.2). In other places, after cultivation or forest fires, only the true soil is stripped off, exposing the regolith, which is infertile.

The thicknesses of soil and regolith are variable. Although the true soil is rarely more than a few feet thick, the regolith of decayed and fragmented rock may extend down tens or even hundreds of feet. Formation of the regolith is greatly aided by the presence of innumerable cracks, termed *joints,* in the bedrock (Figure 8.1).

The term *overburden* is broad in scope and may refer to any sort of relatively loose or soft mineral particles lying on the bedrock. Thus gravels, sands, or floodplain silts laid down by streams or rubble left by a disappearing glacier are also forms of overburden, but they are unique in having been transported by such

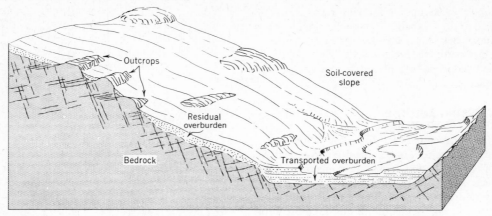

Figure 8.2. Residual and transported overburden. (© 1960, John Wiley & Sons, New York.)

agents as streams, ice, wind, or waves. Such material is called *transported overburden* to distinguish it from regolith, formed in place by decay and disintegration of the bedrock below it. Figure 8.2 shows a deposit of transported overburden of a type known as *alluvium,* covering the bottom of a valley, where it has been left by a stream.

## NATURE OF WEATHERING

The weathering processes may be thought of as leading to the preparation of parent matter of the true soil and, from the geological standpoint, as the preparation of sediment for transportation. One aspect of weathering is the breaking up of hard bedrock, occurring in large masses, into particles ranging down through various size grades to minute chemical ions. As breakdown occurs, the total surface area of the particles in a given bulk volume is enormously increased, facilitating complex chemical changes.

Another aspect of weathering is the change in chemical composition of the rock-forming minerals, through reaction with acids and water, to yield new minerals that will remain indefinitely without further change under the conditions of temperature, pressure, and moisture prevailing at the earth's surface.

A third aspect of weathering is the continual agitation of the soil and weathered overburden as soil-moisture content increases and decreases seasonally and as soil temperatures rise and fall daily and seasonally. Drying and wetting, freezing and thawing, growth and decay of plant roots, and the burrowing and trampling of the soil by animals continually agitate the soil. Such disturbances affect the soil

rhythmically long after the mineral matter has been reduced to minute particles and the principal chemical changes have largely occurred.

Looking at these three aspects of weathering, then, we see that certain one-way, or irreversible, changes have superimposed upon them a pattern of rhythmic fluctuations in physical and chemical state, so that weathering is indeed a most complex natural phenomenon.

## PHYSICAL (MECHANICAL) WEATHERING

Consider, first, the physical processes in which mechanical stresses act upon rock, causing disintegration. These processes constitute the initial, or primary, breakdown of bedrock into fragments whose surfaces are in turn exposed to chemical weathering.

Most bedrock is so fractured by systems of joints that it is rare to find flawless bodies of rock (monoliths) more than a few feet across. Most joints occur in parallel sets, and there are often two or more sets intersecting at a large angle. Consequently, most bedrock is already broken into blocks from a few inches to a few feet across. When stresses are exerted upon jointed rock, the rock comes apart rather readily along these planes (Figure 8.3).

In climates of the middle and high latitudes and at high altitudes, alternate freezing and melting of water in the soil and rock provides a powerful mechanism of rock breakup. Soil water and water that has penetrated the joint planes and other openings of the rock are transformed into ice crystals of needlelike form. Growing masses of such crystals exert great pressures upon the confining rock walls, causing joint blocks and layers to be heaved up and pried free of the parent mass.

Figure 8.3. Jointed sandstone in a cliff. Two sets of vertical joints crossing at nearly right angles, in combination with horizontal bedding planes, yield joint blocks of almost-cubical form. (Photograph by J. R. Stacy, U.S. Geological Survey.)

The results of disintegration of bedrock by freezing water, a process commonly referred to simply as *frost action,* are most conspicuous above the timber line in high mountains and at lower levels in arctic latitudes.

Formation of ice bands and layers in the soil is a widespread occurrence in winter in the colder climates. Where the soil is rich in fine-grade silt and clay, soil water tends to freeze in the form of horizontal ice layers that consist of narrow ice crystals perpendicular to the surface. Therefore, as the ice layer thickens a strong upward pressure is exerted upon the overlying soil layer, thus lifting, or *heaving,* the soil.

In the dry climates of the low and middle latitudes an important agent of rock disintegration is *salt-crystal growth,* a process quite similar physically to ice-crystal growth. Such climates have long drought periods in which evaporation can occur. Water films are drawn surfaceward by capillary-film tension and moisture is steadily evaporated, permitting dissolved salts to be deposited in openings in the rock and soil. Although minute in size and appearing fragile, the growing salt crystals are capable of exerting powerful stresses. Even the hardest rocks (also concrete, mortar, and brick) can be reduced to a sand by continued action of the process. Hence the granular disintegration of rocks in dry climates is often a conspicuous process.

The simple process of wetting and drying soil and rock can result in forces capable of agitating soil and disintegrating rock. Clay con-

sists of *colloids,* extremely tiny flakelike mineral particles having a strong affinity for water. Most clays swell greatly when permitted to absorb water. Rocks containing clay particles tend to disintegrate by moisture absorption on exposed surfaces. Clay-rich soils—swelling when wet, contracting when dry—are continually affected by changes in moisture content. In this manner *soil cracks* and *mud cracks* are formed (Figure 8.4).

Rock distintegration is commonly attributed to temperature changes alone. It is well known that most crystalline solids expand when heated and contract when cooled. It is reasoned that because the heating of rock will cause expansion of the minerals, the rock may be broken. Sudden and intense heating by forest and brush fires causes severe flaking and scaling of exposed rocks. Also, we know that primitive mining methods included the building of fires upon a quarry floor to cause slabs to break free. But it is uncertain that the daily temperature cycle under solar heating and nightly cooling produces sufficiently great stresses to cause fresh hard rock to break apart. Laboratory tests have shown that rocks can stand the equivalent of centuries of daily heating and cooling without showing signs of disintegration. It is at least reasonable to suppose, however, that expansion and contraction through daily temperature changes may assist in breaking up rocks already affected by other stresses and by chemical decay.

Closely related to physical weathering, and commonly included as one of the processes, is the rupturing of otherwise solid bedrock as a

Figure 8.4. Mud cracks. Individual blocks are about 1 ft (0.3 m) across. (Photograph by G. K. Gilbert, U.S. Geological Survey.)

result of the spontaneous volume expansion which the rock undergoes when it is relieved of the confining pressure of overlying and surrounding rock. In quarries of certain massive rocks, including granite, it is a well-known phenomenon that the rock rifts loose in great slabs or sheets, sometimes with explosive violence. When such a slab is cut into a block, the block expands measurably. As a vertical saw cut is made, the cut immediately narrows, and rock expansion continues slowly thereafter for many days.

This evidence shows that most massive rocks, such as the igneous and metamorphic types, are under a state of slight compression when deeply buried, because of confining pressures of overlying rock or because of mountain-building strain that has not been relieved. As the denudation of the landmass proceeds, such rocks are gradually brought nearer the surface. Free of load or of confining rock on the sides, the mass expands. Usually the expansion results in the splitting off of shells of rock up to several feet thick to produce *sheeting structure*. Sheeting in granite of a coastline will result in bedrock slabs sloping seaward everywhere along the shore (Figure 8.5).

Still another physical-weathering process is that of the action of growing plant roots exerting pressure upon the confining walls of soil or rock. This process is of importance in the breakup of rock already affected by other physical and chemical processes.

## CHEMICAL WEATHERING

*Chemical weathering,* essentially synonymous with *mineral alteration,* consists of several important chemical reactions, all of which

Figure 8.5. Sheeting structure in granite, Mt. Desert Island, Maine. (Photograph by A. N. Strahler.)

may occur more-or-less simultaneously. Consider, first, that all surface water—whether it is in the form of raindrops, soil water, ground water, or water in streams, lakes, and the oceans—contains in solution ions of the gases of the atmosphere. Disregarding nitrogen—the major atmospheric component, although a comparatively inactive element—the principal gases of interest are oxygen and carbon dioxide. Oxygen ions in water are readily available for the process of *oxidation,* in which the oxygen ion combines with such metallic ions as may be available. Carbon dioxide in solution in water forms a weak acid capable of reacting with certain susceptible minerals. Other acids of organic origin are also active in the water found in soil and rock. Water itself is capable of dissolving minerals directly, a process we see daily in the solution of table salt (the mineral halite).

All of these chemical processes require water, and the earth's surface is abundantly endowed with water. There is no truly dry environment on the earth's surface. Even the most nearly rainless deserts are easily supplied with water vapor that diffuses through the troposphere. While water is not obviously present much of the time in many deserts, rain does occasionally fall and the processes of mineral alteration do act. If there is any surface environment in which rocks can escape the chemical processes of decay, it is in the perpetually frozen layer found below the surface in arctic and antarctic lands.

Chemical union of water with mineral compounds is termed *hydrolysis.* The process is a true chemical change and is not reversible in the surface environment. It is not merely a form of water absorption, which can be followed by desiccation (drying). Hydrolysis produces a new mineral compound from the original mineral.

The chemistry of mineral alteration is very complex, so that we offer here only a few examples of alteration of common silicate minerals into other minerals.

Potash feldspar, an abundant constituent of granite, takes up water to yield a clay mineral, *kaolinite.* This soft, white mineral becomes plastic and exudes a distinctive clay odor when moistened. It is widely used in the manufacture of chinaware, porcelain, and tile.

Feldspars and muscovite mica are altered to another clay mineral, *illite,* an abundant constituent of sediments. Figure 8.6 shows illite particles highly magnified under the electron

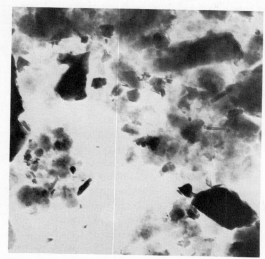

Figure 8.6. Fragments of the clay minerals illite (sharp outlines) and montmorillonite (fuzzy outlines) which have settled from suspension in tidal waters of San Francisco Bay. Enlargement about 20,000 times. (Photograph by Harry Gold. Courtesy of R. B. Krone, San Francisco District Corps of Engineers, U.S. Army.)

microscope. A third important clay mineral is *montmorillonite,* also shown in Figure 8.6; it is derived from the alteration of igneous rocks.

Through hydrolysis plagioclase feldspar is altered to *bauxite,* a mixture of several clay minerals composed largely of aluminum oxide and water. Bauxite occurs in abundance in warm, wet climates and forms important deposits of aluminum ore. The mafic silicate minerals contain iron in abundance, and this element, when released by chemical weathering, combines with oxygen to form very stable oxides in combination with water. An example is *limonite,* an earthy substance of brown to yellowish color, abundant in soil and regolith of warm, wet climates.

An important point about mineral alteration is that it changes very hard igneous and metamorphic rocks into soft substances, thus weakening the bedrock and enabling it to be broken up by mechanical processes. The clay minerals consist of extremely small particles down to the size of colloids, and these are easily suspended in water for long-distance transport. In contrast, the hydrous oxides of iron and aluminum tend to accumulate as hard masses and layers in the soil and regolith. Being almost immune to further change, they resist removal and transportation.

Chemical decay of joint blocks of igneous rock takes two forms. Grain-by-grain disinte-

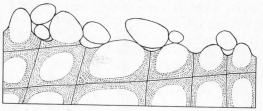

Figure 8.7. Rounded boulders produced by granular disintegration of rectangular joint blocks of granite. (Based on a drawing of W. M. Davis; © 1960, John Wiley & Sons, New York.)

gration, commonly affecting the coarse-grained igneous rocks, tends to produce rounded egg-shaped boulders (Figure 8.7). The products of disintegration, in the form of a coarse sand or gravel of individual mineral crystals, are swept away by rains to become the sediment load of streams. The finer-grained igneous rocks are commonly affected by *spheroidal weathering,* in which the joint blocks are modified into spherical cores surrounded by shells of decayed rock (Figure 8.8).

In the warm humid climates chemical decay of igneous and metamorphic rocks extends to depths as great as 300 ft (90 m) and has produced a thick layer of soft clay-rich rock known as *saprolite.* Examples may be found throughout the Piedmont and Appalachian regions of the southeastern United States.

Generally speaking, the felsic rocks with abundant quartz and potash feldspar are more resistant to alteration than the mafic rocks, rich in plagioclase feldspar, pyroxene, amphibole, and olivine. Olivine in particular decomposes very readily. As a result, where felsic and mafic igneous rock masses are side by side (as where a dike of felsic rock cuts through a mass of

Figure 8.8. Spheroidal weathering of a boulder of gabbro from the Palisades of the Hudson River, New Jersey. (Photograph by Douglas Johnson.)

mafic rock, or vice versa), the felsic rock usually stands out boldly (Figure 8.9).

## WEATHERING AND SOILS

All plant and animal life of the lands is dependent for survival upon the true soil, or *solum,* which is a mineral layer at best only a few feet thick over much of the continental surface. Prolonged action of weathering processes combined with organic activity of plants and animals brings the soil layer into physical and chemical equilibrium with the prevailing climatic factors of heat and moisture. Place-to-place variations in character of the soil are apparent through differences both in chemical composition and physical texture of the soil itself and in the characteristic forms of natural vegetation it bears. At the risk of oversimplification, we shall attempt only to differentiate five *soil-forming regimes.* Figure 8.10 is a schematic representation of soil profiles produced in four of the regimes.

Consider, first, the soil-forming regime of *laterization,* which operates in an environment of prevailingly warm temperatures and abundant precipitation occurring year-round or in a long rainy season. This is the environment of

Figure 8.9. Felsic dike (angular blocks at center) in deeply altered mafic rock, Sangre de Cristo Mountains, New Mexico. (Photograph by A. N. Strahler.)

equatorial lands and of those parts of tropical lands having a monsoon climate. Intensity of bacterial activity, a major factor in soils of moist climates, is determined largely by temperature.

The relations of bacterial activity to temperature are shown diagrammatically in Figure 8.11. On this graph the vertical scale represents the intensity, or rate, at which vegetative matter is either produced or destroyed, and the horizontal scale gives average annual air temperature. One curve shows the activity of the larger plants, or *macroflora,* which produce vegetative matter by photosynthesis. Two other curves show the activity of bacteria, which consume vegetative matter produced by macroflora—one curve for *aerobic bacteria* (those which require oxygen), the other for *anaerobic bacteria* (those which do not require oxygen). The activity of aerobic bacteria, which live in the well-drained and aerated soils, exceeds that of macrofloral growth at an average temperature of about 77° F (25° C), which is equaled or exceeded year-round in the equatorial rain forests. Because the rate of bacterial activity above this temperature exceeds the rate of macrofloral production, the soil is lacking in *humus,* the partially decomposed remains of plants.

The activity of anaerobic bacteria does not exceed macrofloral production until a still higher temperature, well above 95° F (35° C), is reached. Such a high average annual temperature is not found in any climate. Thus in the poorly drained soils of meadows and swamps, where the soil is saturated and oxygen kept out, the humus is not consumed, even in warm climates, and it can accumulate as thick deposits of *peat.*

In humid low latitudes the percolation of great quantities of rainfall through the soil causes silica ($SiO_2$) to be removed, a process termed *desilication* (Figure 8.10*A*). Soluble bases, including such ions as calcium, sodium, and potassium, are also completely removed. What finally remains in these tropical soils is a group of highly stable oxides and hydroxides of iron, manganese, and aluminum. These form such minerals as limonite and bauxite, which are not soluble in the soil water of the warm humid climates. Soils containing these hydroxide minerals in abundance are known generally as *latosols.*

The color of latosols is typically a reddish-brown or chocolate brown. Horizons are not

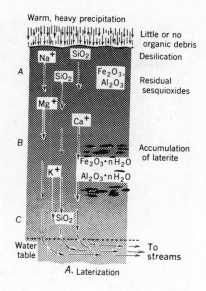

A. Laterization

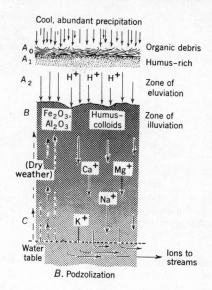

B. Podzolization

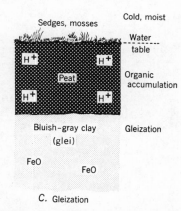

C. Gleization

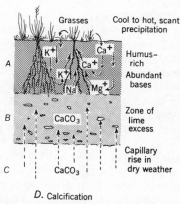

D. Calcification

Figure 8.10. Schematic diagrams of soil development under four pedogenic regimes. (© 1965, John Wiley & Sons, New York.)

apparent. Small irregularly shaped nodules of hydroxides are distributed throughout the soil. The soil is favorable for the growth of a native vegetation consisting of rain forest.

In areas of wet-dry tropical, or monsoon, climate latosols exhibit a remarkable property of becoming hardened to bricklike consistency after the soil has been cut into blocks and exposed to the atmosphere. Such material, called *laterite*, has been widely used as a building material, particularly in Southeast Asia.

Latosols contain valuable mineral deposits where conditions have been favorable to the concentration of layers or lenses of bauxite, limonite, and manganite (manganese hydrox-

ide). These minerals belong to a group termed *residual ores*, which accumulate near the surface because they are not readily dissolved by soil water.

A second pedogenic regime is that of *podzolization*, characteristic of moist climates with long cold winters. Such climates are widespread in latitudes 45° to 65° in North America and Eurasia, and at high altitudes generally throughout the middle latitudes. Referring again to Figure 8.11, we find that at colder mean annual temperatures, the production of plant matter by macroflora exceeds the rate of its destruction by aerobic bacteria. So in cold, moist climates humus accumulates in

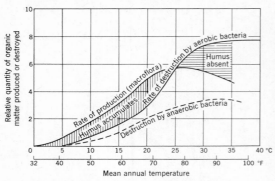

Figure 8.11. Relative rates of production and destruction of plant matter as dependent upon average annual temperature. [After M. W. Senstius (1958), *Amer. Scientist,* vol. 46.]

substantial quantities. Organic acids produced in the decomposition of plant matter pass downward through the soil (Figure 8.10*B*). Hydrogen ions of the acid solution replace ions of the bases, which are leached from the soil and are exported from the region as runoff in streams. Colloidal mineral and humus particles are also carried down from a thin upper layer of the soil, resulting in a characteristic ashengray horizon, labeled $A_2$ in Figure 8.10*B*. These materials accumulate in the underlying zone, forming a dense horizon designated as the *B* horizon. Figure 8.12 is a photograph of a typical *podzol* soil exhibiting the distinctive horizons produced under the regime of podzolization.

Podzols are rated low in fertility for agricultural purposes because strong leaching has removed bases needed for many crops and has resulted in an acid soil. Whereas the coniferous trees and certain broad-leafed evergreens thrive on the podzols, the addition of lime and fertilizers is necessary for successful agricultural production.

A third pedogenic regime is *gleization* (*glei* is pronounced "glay"), operating in cool, moist climates where water drainage is impeded and conditions of saturation prevail much of the time. Bogs and wet meadowlands in middle and high latitudes are favorable to gleization, and much of the wet arctic tundra is affected by this process. As shown in Figure 8.10*C*, gleization is characterized by a thick upper horizon of organic accumulation, which may be peat. Beneath the peat is typically a dense bluish-gray clay known as the *glei horizon*.

A fourth regime is *calcification,* characteristic of soils in regions deficient in soil moisture. Such climates include the semiarid

Figure 8.12. Podzol soil profile developed on sandy granite till in Maine. (Photograph by C. E. Kellogg; courtesy of Soil Conservation Service, U.S. Dept. of Agriculture.)

steppes and deserts, found widely distributed from tropical to middle latitudes. Calcification is found where annual evaporation on the average exceeds annual precipitation. The effects of this moisture imbalance are illustrated in Figure 8.10*D*. During dry periods or dry seasons soil water rises toward the surface and is evaporated, leaving behind calcium carbonate, which forms nodules or lenses in the soil. This zone of carbonate accumulation is designated the *B* horizon. Figure 8.13 shows a profile of one of the major varieties of soils produced under a regime of calcification.

The most widespread type of natural vegetation in a regime of calcification is grasslands. The grasses are deep-rooted and bring up to the surface the bases they require for growth. Thus there is a recycling of the bases, which might otherwise be permanently removed from the soil in periods of excess rainfall. Partial decay of grass roots adds substantial amounts of humus to the uppermost, or *A,* horizon, which is typically brown to black. Soils produced in the regime of calcification are extraordinarily rich in nutrients needed for the cultivation of grains. Major wheat-producing regions of the world lie under this regime.

Calcification may proceed to an advanced state in which accumulation of calcium carbonate assumes the form of a rocklike layer. The material is known variously as *caliche,* *lime-crust,* or *calcrete.*

Fifth among the soil-forming regimes is *salinization,* or accumulation of soluble salts in the soil zone. This process occurs in poorly drained places in desert climates, where water received as stream flow from surrounding highlands is evaporated on the floors of basins. Common salts found in these soils are sulfates and chlorides of calcium and sodium. Soils developed under a regime of salinization can support only a sparse vegetation of salt-tolerant plants and may be totally devoid of vegetation.

## CLASSIFICATION OF THE SEDIMENTARY ROCKS

A classification of the sedimentary rocks follows logically in terms of the possible origins of the sediment constituting the rock. Figure 8.14 attempts to organize sedimentary rocks according to sediments, minerals, and rocks. The first order of classification is into *clastic* and *nonclastic* divisions. The adjective *clastic* comes from the Greek word *klastos,* meaning "broken," and describes a sediment consisting of particles removed individually from a parent-rock source. The clastic rocks are in turn subdivided into those made up of *pyroclastic* sediments (Chapter 7) and those made up of *detrital* sediments. The latter are mineral fragments derived by the weathering of preexisting rocks of any classification.

The nonclastic division itself includes two basic subdivisions, *chemical precipitates* and *organically derived sediments.* Chemical precipitates (hydrogenic sediments) are inorganic compounds representing solid mineral matter precipitated from an aqueous solution in which that matter has been transported. The organically derived (biogenic) sediment consists of both the remains of plants or animals and mineral matter produced by the activities of plants and animals. For example, the shell matter secreted by animals is a crystalline inorganic substance and therefore a true mineral. Separated from the organic matter of these animals, shells constitute an inorganic sediment. On the other hand, accumulating plant remains, consisting of hydrocarbon compounds, form a truly organic sediment. As used here, the adjectives *organic* and *inorganic* agree in meaning with the chemist's classification of compounds as well as with the mineralogist's definition of a mineral. We shall need to be careful to distinguish between organically derived mineral matter and organic sediment (hydrocarbon compounds).

Once the sediments are classified and understood, the essential component minerals can be listed (Figure 8.14). Minerals that have not

Figure 8.13. Profile of a brown soil developed on loess in Colorado. The *B* horizon shows prismatic structure. (Photograph by C. C. Nikiforoff; courtesy of Soil Conservation Service, U.S. Dept. of Agriculture.)

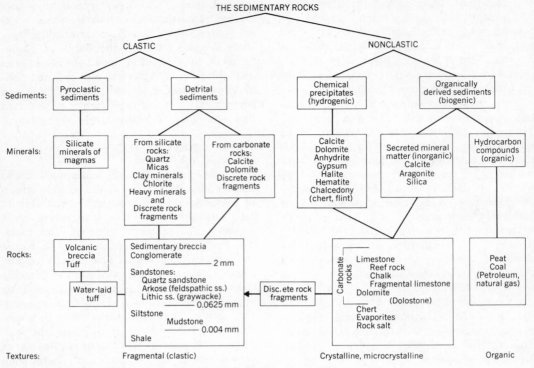

Figure 8.14. Composition and classification of the sedimentary rocks.

been described in the previous chapter can be treated in the discussion of the appropriate sediment group. The naming of a particular sedimentary rock depends not only upon its mineral composition but also upon the size of the component mineral grains. Clastic sediments are named primarily on the basis of the mineral composition of the component fragments. For example, *sandstone* is a detrital rock in which the grains range between 0.0625 mm (⅟₁₆ mm) and 2 mm in diameter.

Sedimentary rocks are usually recognizable through the presence of distinct layers resulting from changes in particle size and composition during the period of deposition. These layers are termed *strata,* or simply *beds.* The planes of separation between layers are *planes of stratification,* or *bedding planes.* The rock is described as being *stratified,* or *bedded* (see Figure 13.1). Bedding planes in their original condition are nearly horizontal, but they may have become steeply tilted (see Figure 8.20) or otherwise distorted into wavelike folds by subsequent movements of the earth's crust.

## THE CLASTIC SEDIMENTS

Of the clastic sediments, the pyroclastic varieties have been discussed in connection with volcanic rocks and the structure of volcanic cones. We shall therefore turn, instead, to the detrital sediments and rocks derived from them.

The most abundant particles of detrital sedimentary rocks consist of (1) quartz, (2) rock fragments, and (3) feldspar. Fragments of unaltered fine-grained parent rocks can easily be identified in coarse sandstones by microscopic examination. Such fragments are typically second in abundance to quartz grains and are the chief component in the coarser grades of detritus. Mica and other minerals generally make up less than 3% of an average sandstone. Clay minerals, principally kaolinite, montmorillonite, and illite, may be abundant in the finer-grained detrital sediments.

There are, in addition to quartz, feldspar, and muscovite, a number of minor minerals, found in the igneous and metamorphic rocks, which are highly resistant to physical abrasion and chemical alteration and which therefore remain intact during transportation. Because of their relatively greater specific gravity, as compared with that of quartz and other felsic minerals, these detrital minerals are referred to as the *heavy minerals.* An example is *magnetite,* an oxide of iron, referred to in Chapter

2 as occurring in a naturally magnetic variety called "lodestone" (Figure 8.15).

Because of their greater relative density, the heavy detrital minerals are easily separated from the less dense quartz and mica by processes of water transportation or by winds. Consequently, these minerals form local concentrations as dark layers in many types of sand accumulations.

Because the naming of clastic rocks depends in part upon the sizes of component mineral grains, it is important to establish a system of size grades. Among geologists the *Wentworth scale* is widely accepted (Table 8.1). The units of length are millimeters.

Table 8.1.  SIZE GRADES OF SEDIMENT PARTICLES

| Grade Name | mm |
|---|---|
| Boulders | Over 256 |
| Cobbles | 64–256 |
| Pebbles | 2–64 |
| Sand | 0.06–2 |
| Silt | 0.004–0.06 |
| Clay | Under 0.004 |

## THE DETRITAL SEDIMENTARY ROCKS

Coarsest of the detrital sedimentary rocks are the *sedimentary breccias,* consisting of large angular blocks in a matrix of finer fragments. These rocks often represent ancient submarine landslides, or terrestrial flows of mud, and are comparatively rare rocks. *Volcanic breccias* are equivalent rocks in the pyroclastic group.

*Conglomerate* consists of pebbles or cobbles, usually quite well rounded in shape, embedded in a fine-grained matrix of sand or silt (Figure 8.16). The principal distinction between a conglomerate and a breccia is that the large fragments in the breccia are angular. Rounding of the conglomerate pebbles is a result of abrasion during transportation in stream beds or along beaches. Essentially, then, conglomerates represent lithified (changed to hard rock) stream gravel bars and gravel beaches.

The *sandstones* are composed of grains in the range from 2 mm to 0.0625 mm ($\frac{1}{16}$ mm). Perhaps the most abundant and familiar form is *quartz sandstone,* in which quartz is the predominant constituent. Beautifully rounded quartz grains, many of spherical form,

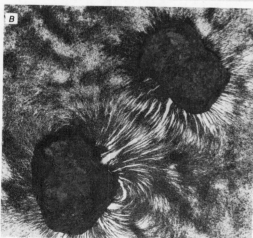

Figure 8.15. (*A*) Octahedral (eight-sided) crystals of magnetite from the Magnet Cove locality, Arkansas. (Courtesy of the American Museum of Natural History.) (*B*) This variety of magnetite, known as lodestone, attracts iron filings much as does a bar magnet. (Courtesy of Ward's Natural Science Establishment, Inc., Rochester, N.Y.)

Figure 8.16. A conglomerate, consisting of well-rounded quartzite pebbles in a matrix of fine sand and silt. (Photograph by A. N. Strahler.)

from a sandstone rock are pictured in Figure 8.17. In this example rounding was perfected by wind transport in ancient sand dunes. Quartz sandstones contain minor amounts of the heavy detrital minerals and frequently small flakes of muscovite mica, some grains of feldspar, and rock fragments. The quartz sandstones are commonly lithified sediment deposits of the shallow oceans bordering a continent or of shallow inland seas. The quartz grains have survived a long distance of travel and finer particles have been sorted out and removed during the transportation process. As implied above, certain quartz sandstones were formed from large deposits of dune sands in deserts on the continents. Also, some quartz sandstones are formed largely of quartz derived from pre-existing sandstones, in which the quartz grains have been recycled.

Lithification of quartz sands to become hard sandstones requires *cementation* by mineral deposition in the interstices between grains. This cementation is accomplished by slowly moving ground water importing the cementing matter as ions in solution. The cementing mineral may be silica ($SiO_2$), in which case the sandstone is called a *sedimentary quartzite* and is an extremely hard rock with great resistance to weathering and erosion. If the cementing material consists of calcium carbonate ($CaCO_3$), a less durable rock results.

The compaction and cementation of layers of silt gives a compact fine-grained rock known as *siltstone* when largely free of clay particles.

Siltstone has the feel of very fine sandpaper and is closely related to fine-grained sandstone, with which there is a complete intergradation. A mixture of silt and clay with water is termed a *mud,* and the sedimentary rock indurated from such a mixture is a *mudstone* (Figure 8.18). Most mudstones also contain minor amounts of sand grains. The compaction and consolidation of clay layers leads to the formation of *claystone.*

Many sedimentary rocks of mud and clay composition are laminated in such a way that they break up easily into small flakes and plates. A rock that breaks apart in this way is described as *fissile* and is generally called a *shale.* Shale is fissile because clay particles lie in parallel orientation with the bedding to form natural surfaces of parting.

The bulk of the claystone and clay shale consists of the clay minerals derived from the alteration of the silicate minerals. Kaolinite, illite, and montmorillonite are the most common of these minerals. Compaction of clay sediments into rock is largely a process of exclusion of water under pressure of the overlying sediments. Because the clay minerals consist of minute flakes and scales, the proportion of water held in the initial sediment is very

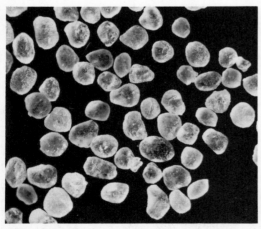

Figure 8.17. Well-rounded quartz grains from the St. Peter sandstone of Ordovician age. The grains shown here average about 1 mm (0.04 in.) in diameter. (Photograph by A. McIntyre, Columbia University.)

Figure 8.18. Horizontal strata, largely unconsolidated muds and clays, of Cenozoic age, near Price, Oregon. (U.S. Geological Survey.)

large. Once thoroughly compacted, claystone and clay shale do not soften appreciably when exposed to water, but under impact they break apart easily.

Shales of mud and clay composition make up the largest proportion of all sedimentary rocks. They can be subdivided by color into *red shales* and those of gray to black color. The red shales, owing their color to finely disseminated hematite (oxide of iron) are associated with red siltstones and red sandstones in enormously thick accumulations. Collectively known as *red beds,* these strata are interpreted as having been deposited in an environment of abundantly available oxygen, such as would be found on river floodplains and deltas of arid climates. The gray and black shales, also found in great thicknesses, are interpreted as deposited in a marine environment in which oxygen is deficient. The dark color is due to disseminated carbon compounds of organic nature, possibly produced by anaerobic bacteria. Dead organisms produced in shallow water above would rain down to the bottom, furnishing organic matter that would not readily decompose and would be added to the sediment. Petroleum is generally believed to have originated in this way.

## THE NONCLASTIC SEDIMENTARY ROCKS

The nonclastic rocks are formed from sediment that may be either directly precipitated from solution (hence inorganic in origin) or secreted by the activity of plants and animals (hence organically derived). Inorganic precipitates have been designated as *hydrogenic sediments* to distinguish them from the second type, or organically derived sediments, which can be designated as *biogenic sediments* (Figure 8.14).

Perhaps the most important class of minerals of the nonclastic sediments are the *carbonates,* compounds of the calcium ion or magnesium ion, or both, with the carbonate ion. Calcium carbonate ($CaCO_3$) is the composition of one of the most abundant and widespread of minerals, *calcite* (Figure 8.19). A related mineral of the same composition is *aragonite,* secreted by some invertebrate animals as shell matter. Another important hydrogenic mineral is *dolomite,* a carbonate of both magnesium and calcium. Also important as hydrogenic minerals are two sulfate compounds of calcium: *anhydrite* and *gypsum.* Another class of hydrogenic minerals is the *evaporites.* These are

Figure 8.19. Rhombohedral cleavage pieces of calcite of a clear variety known as Iceland spar. About half natural size. (Courtesy of Ward's Natural Science Establishment, Inc., Rochester, N.Y.)

highly soluble salts deposited from ocean water and the water of salt lakes when evaporation is sustained under an arid climate. We are all familiar with *halite,* or rock salt, one of the commonest of the evaporites.

Two other common minerals are important in sedimentary rocks. These are *hematite,* an oxide of iron, and *chalcedony,* a form of silica lacking obvious crystalline structure. Chalcedony occurs abundantly as nodules and layers in sedimentary rocks and is referred to as *chert.*

The nonclastic sedimentary rocks fall largely into two major groups: the *carbonate rocks,* and the *evaporites* (Figure 8.14). Chert forms a sedimentary rock in a class by itself.

## THE CARBONATE ROCKS

Of the carbonate rocks the most important is *limestone,* broadly defined as a sedimentary rock in which calcite is the predominant mineral. Because either clay minerals or silica (as quartz grains or chert) can be present in considerable proportions, limestones show a wide variation in chemical and physical properties. Limestones range in color from white through gray to black, in texture from obviously granular to very dense.

The most abundant limestones are of marine origin and are formed by inorganic precipitation, or as the by-product of respiration and photosynthesis of organisms, or by the release of clay-size particles of aragonite upon decay of green algae. These marine limestones show well-developed bedding and may contain abundant fossils. Dark color may be due to finely divided carbon. A representative exposure of limestones is seen in Figure 8.20. Many limestones have abundant nodules and inclusions of chert and are described as *cherty limestones*.

Important accumulations of limestone consist of the densely compacted skeletons of corals and the secretions of associated algae— they are seen forming today as coral reefs along the coasts of warm oceans. Rocks formed of these deposits are referred to as *reef limestones*. These limestones are in part fragmental, since the action of waves breaks up the coral formations into small fragments that accumulate among the coral masses or in nearby locations. Limestones composed of broken carbonate particles are recognized in Figure 8.14 as *fragmental limestone*.

*Dolomite* is a rock composed largely of the mineral of the same name. Dolomite rock poses a problem of origin, since the mineral is not excreted by organisms as shell material. Direct precipitation from solution in sea water is not considered adequate to explain the great thicknesses of dolomite rock that are found in the geologic record. The most widely held explanation of the formation of dolomite rock is that it has resulted from the alteration of limestone by a replacement process in which magnesium ions of sea water are substituted for a part of the calcium ions. It is not known whether the replacement, referred to as *dolomitization,* occurs immediately after deposition, or over long periods by the slow movement of salt water through the rock after the limestone has accumulated in thick sequences.

Carbonate rocks are particularly susceptible to a form of chemical weathering known as *carbonation,* in which carbonic acid present in weak solutions in rainwater and water present in soil and rock reacts with the carbonate mineral.

When carbon dioxide gas is dissolved in water, *carbonic acid* is produced:

$$2H_2O + 2CO_2 \rightleftharpoons 2H_2CO_3$$
Water    Carbon    Carbonic
dioxide    acid

In the chemical reaction between carbonic acid and mineral calcite the acid is written as consisting of two hydrogen ions and two bicarbonate ions. The hydrogen ion acts upon the carbonate ion in the calcite to yield carbon dioxide and water. The calcium ion joins the two bicarbonate ions to become calcium bicarbonate, which is a highly soluble salt:

$$CaCO_3 + 2H^+ + 2(HCO_3)^- \rightleftharpoons$$
Calcite    Hydro-  Bicarbonate
gen    ion
ion

Carbonic acid

$$Ca^{2+} + 2(HCO_3)^- + H_2O + CO_2$$
Calcium    Bicarbonate    Water    Carbon
ion    ion    dioxide

Calcium bicarbonate

Although the normal solution of atmospheric carbon dioxide in rainwater constitutes a weak acid, the carbon dioxide produced in the humus layer of soil by plant decay gives to soil water a much higher concentration of carbonic acid. It is believed that much of the solution of limestone in humid regions can be attributed to acid produced in the soil layer and in the layer of raw humus that overlies it.

Carbonation is responsible for the formation of caverns in limestone strata as ground water moves slowly through joints and bedding planes. Calcium ions are then discharged by ground-water seepage into streams and eventually reach the sea.

The carbonic acid reaction is reversible, so that under favorable conditions that permit some of the dissolved carbon dioxide in the solution to escape into the air as a gas, calcite is precipitated as a mineral deposit:

$$H_2CO_3 + Ca^{2+} + 2(HCO_3)^- \rightarrow$$
Carbonic    Calcium bicarbonate
acid    in solution

$$2CO_2 + 2H_2O + CaCO_3$$
Carbon    Water    Calcite
dioxide    precipitate
gas

Figure 8.20. Dipping limestone strata of the Manlius and Rondout formations, New York State. (Photograph by A. K. Lobeck.)

Precipitated calcium carbonate accumulates as ornamental deposits in caverns above the water table in a mineral form known as *travertine.* More important geologically is the precipitation of calcium carbonate in lakes and shallow seas as limestone strata.

## THE EVAPORITES

The great bulk of evaporite rocks consists of the sulfates of calcium as gypsum and anhydrite and of sodium chloride as halite. Evaporites occur in association with one another in sedimentary strata, usually with marine sandstones and shales, but in some instances with chemically precipitated limestones and dolomites. Although details differ, most hypotheses of origin of thick sequences of the evaporites of the geologic record require a special set of environmental conditions. First, an arid climate is assumed in which evaporation on the average exceeds precipitation. Such climates are widespread in tropical latitudes today and can be presumed to have been present in the geologic past. Second, a shallow evaporating basin is required, and this may have been a large shallow bay or lagoon cut off from the open sea by a barrier bar. A narrow inlet, through which ocean water could enter to replace water lost by evaporation, is necessary to account for thick beds of evaporites. A slow subsidence of the area of deposition is required to accommodate the accumulating beds.

Huge accumulations of halite have formed at several points in geologic time. A good example is the salt beds and associated layers of red shales and sandstones, gypsum, and anhydrite of the *Permian basin* of Kansas, Oklahoma, and parts of northern Texas and southeastern New Mexico. In the Permian Period (see Chapter 13) dozens of halite beds were deposited here, many being of great thickness. A few individual salt beds 300 to 400 ft (90 to 120 m) in thickness are known. Thick anhydrite beds also occur in the series— one bed over 1300 ft (400 m) is on record. Important salt beds of other geologic ages occur beneath Michigan, Ohio, and western New York.

## HYDROCARBON COMPOUNDS IN SEDIMENTARY ROCKS

Hydrocarbon compounds of organic origin make up the last class of sedimentary rocks shown in Figure 8.14, although only coal qualifies for designation as a rock. The solid forms of hydrocarbon compounds—peat and coal—remain in the place of original accumulation, whereas the liquid and gaseous forms— petroleum and natural gas—can migrate far from the places of origin to become concentrated in distant rock reservoirs.

In a swamp or bog environment where water saturation persists, plant remains accumulate faster than they can be destroyed by bacterial activity. Only partial decomposition occurs because oxygen is deficient in the stagnant water and the organic acids released by the decay process inhibit further bacterial activity. The product of this environment is *peat,* a soft fibrous material ranging in color from brown to black.

Under the load of accumulating sediments, layers of peat have become compacted into *lignite,* or "brown coal," a low-grade fuel intermediate between peat and coal. Lignite has a woody texture.

Upon further compaction, lignite is transformed into *bituminous coal,* or "soft coal," and this in turn has been in places transformed into *anthracite,* or "hard coal," where the strata were subjected to intense pressures of folding in the mountain-making process.

Lignite and coal are composed largely of carbon, hydrogen, and oxygen with minor amounts of ash and sulfur. For convenience in analysis and emphasis upon heat efficiency as a fuel, composition of coal is given in terms of three variable constituents: fixed carbon, volatiles, and water. (Ash and sulfur remain fairly constant.) Figure 8.21 shows the relative proportions of the three variable constituents for

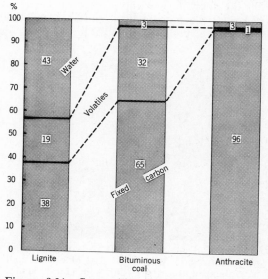

Figure 8.21. Composition of representative examples of coals.

representative examples of lignite, bituminous coal, and anthracite. A complete series of intergradations is known. Notice that water is largely driven off in the transition from lignite to bituminous coal. Although the proportion of volatiles undergoes a relative rise from lignite to bituminous coal, they are almost entirely driven off when anthracite is formed.

Coal occurs in layers, known as *seams,* interbedded with sedimentary strata, which are usually thinly bedded shales, sandstones, and limestones (Figure 8.22). Collectively, such accumulations are known as *coal measures.* Individual coal seams range in thickness from a fraction of an inch to several tens of feet. Coal measures are described in more detail in Chapter 13.

*Petroleum,* or "crude oil," is a mixture of several fluid hydrocarbon compounds of organic origin found in localized concentrations in certain sedimentary strata. In composition, a typical crude oil might run about as follows: carbon, 82%; hydrogen, 15%; oxygen and nitrogen, 3%. Petroleum is neither a mineral nor a rock, but its close association with the clastic sedimentary rocks justifies inclusion. Natural gas, which is closely linked in origin and occurrence with petroleum, is a mixture of gases, principally *methane* (*marsh gas;* $CH_4$), and small amounts of other hydrocarbons. In addition, there are small amounts of carbon dioxide, nitrogen, oxygen, and sometimes helium.

As found in commercially exploitable accumulations, known as "oil pools," petroleum fills the interconnected pore spaces of a *reservoir rock,* which is usually a sand or sandstone,

limestone, or dolomite formation. Natural gas accumulates above the oil, while water saturates the zone beneath the oil. It is essential that the reservoir rock be overlain by an impervious cap rock, typically a shale formation, that prevents the upward movement of the petroleum. A favorable structural arrangement of sedimentary rocks is achieved by a number of configurations. The simplest of these is an up-arching of strata in either a *dome* or an *anticline* (Figure 8.23). Various other favorable arrangements of rock units exist and are referred to as *petroleum traps.*

It is generally agreed that petroleum and natural gas are of organic origin. A major hypothesis of oil origin attributes the oil to microscopic plant forms—for example, diatoms—living in vast numbers in the seas. Upon death of the diatom a minute particle of oil was released on the ocean floor, becoming incorporated into accumulating sediment. Where this was a dark mud the sediment eventually became a shale formation. Today we find petroleum disseminated through *oil shales,* which can be processed to derived petroleum. Eventually, the petroleum must have been forced to migrate from the source rock to the reservoir rock.

Coal, petroleum, and natural gas are referred to collectively as *fossil fuels.* Throughout the development of our modern civilization the fossil fuels have provided the major share of energy consumed in heating, mechanical power, and other industrial processes. Problems relating to the limited world supplies of fossil fuels are discussed in the Epilogue.

## ENVIRONMENTS OF SEDIMENT DEPOSITION

Sediment is transported and deposited by fluid agents: streams, waves and associated

Figure 8.22. Outcrop of an 8-ft (2.4-m) coal seam, Dawson County, Montana. Large blocks of coal have slumped to the base of the cliff (foreground). (Photograph by M. R. Campbell, U.S. Geological Survey.)

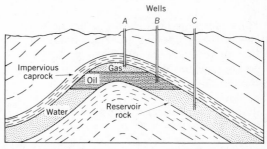

Figure 8.23. Idealized cross section of an oil pool on an anticline or a dome structure in sedimentary strata. Well *A* will draw gas; well *B* will draw oil; and well *C* will draw water. The caprock is shale; the reservoir rock is sandstone.

coastal currents, winds, and glaciers. We shall examine these geological processes in the next chapter. Under favorable conditions substantial accumulations of sediment are transformed into sedimentary rocks, a process referred to as *diagenesis*. Included in this process are compaction and hardening of the sediment into rock through application of pressure of overlying layers (as in the case of claystone and shale) or by cementation (as in the case of sandstone). Diagnesis may also include recrystallization under pressure, as in the case of certain limestones, and the replacement of ions by action of chemical solutions, as in the case of dolomites.

Considering the variety of processes of transportation there can obviously be a corresponding variety of environments of sediment accumulation. These same environments are also occupied by plant and animal life. We have seen that organisms are in themselves important contributors of sediment, classed as biogenic in origin. In the geologic past plants and animals have become incorporated into sediment, and their remains constitute *fossils,* which are an integral part of sedimentary rocks. Fossils are very useful in interpreting the environments of sediment deposition, as explained more fully in Chapters 12, 13, and 14. Geologists who interpret the history of sedimentary strata have set up a system of environments of sediment deposition that corresponds closely with existing environments of animal and plant life. Figure 8.24 is a schematic diagram to illustrate the classification of environments.

The *terrestrial environment* includes all land surfaces lying above high-tide level. The *marine environment* includes all ocean water and bottom lying below the level of low tide. The *littoral environment* lies in the *intertidal zone* between high- and low-tide levels and is thus alternately exposed to the atmosphere and covered by sea water.

Terrestrial environments are of a wide variety of types. First, there are *aquatic* environments, consisting of lakes and ponds (*lacustrine* environment), streams (*fluvial* environment), and fresh-water marshes and swamps. Many forms of stream deposits are aqueous environments only at the time of deposition but are exposed to the atmosphere most of the time—for example, floodplains and parts of deltas. Nonaquatic environments of sediment deposition are defined in terms of processes of transportation other than flowing water. These include the subglacial zone of deposition and surfaces of accumulation of wind-transported sand and silt.

The marine environment is further broken down into the mass of water itself (*pelagic* body) and the bottom (*benthic* layer). Obviously, sediments do not accumulate in the pelagic body, but it is the living space of floating organisms (plankton) and swimming animals (nekton), which settle to the bottom to become part of the sediment. In terms of the pelagic body, or water mass, there are two environmental divisions: the *neritic zone*, shallower than 600 ft (180 m), and the *oceanic zone*, deeper than that level.

The benthic layer, which is the site of sediment accumulation, as well as the home of organisms dwelling on the bottom (*benthos*), is subdivided into depth zones as follows (Figure 8.24):

**Littoral:** Intertidal zone (littoral environment).

**Sublittoral:** Low tide to −600 ft (−180 m); continental shelf and shallow epicontinental sea.

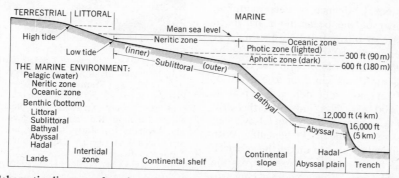

Figure 8.24. Schematic diagram of environmental zones, not to scale. [Based on J. W. Hedgpeth (1957), Geol. Soc. Amer., Memoir 67, pp. 17–27.]

**Bathyal:** Continental slope and continental rise from −600 ft (−180 m) to about −12,-000 ft (−4 km).

**Abyssal:** Abyssal plains and abyssal hills in the range from −12,000 ft (−4 km) to −16,-000 ft (−5 km).

**Hadal:** Trenches below −16,000 ft (−5 km).

As labeled at the top of Figure 8.24, depositional environments of the continents are *terrestrial, littoral,* and *sublittoral.* The sublittoral zone extends to the outer limit of the *continental shelves* at a depth of about 600 ft (180 m). Sediments and sedimentary rocks thus far described are largely of the continental environments and constitute the bulk of the geologic record. Ocean-basin environments include the *bathyal, abyssal,* and *hadal* zones. It is to the sediments of the deep-sea floors that we turn next.

## SEDIMENTS OF THE OCEAN FLOOR

Beginning with the voyage of H.M.S. *Challenger,* in the 1870s, oceanographers have systematically taken samples of materials of the ocean floors. At first this could be done only by means of dredges that scraped off a thin layer and brought it to the surface for examination.

By the 1930s information about the sediment layer itself began to be obtained by the process of *coring,* which is simply vertical penetration by a long section of pipe that cuts a cylindrical sample, or *core.* Brought to the surface, the core is extruded, giving a complete cross section of the layer. Tube lengths were gradually increased until cores over 50 ft (15 m) were readily obtained (Figure 8.25). The cores are cut in half longitudinally, revealing the bedded structure and permitting small interior samples to be taken for microscopic examination and chemical and physical analysis.

The most recent advance in deep sampling of the sediment of the ocean floor has been through the use of oil-well drilling methods. A specially designed 10,000-ton vessel, the *Glomar Challenger,* was built with the capability of drilling into the ocean floor to a depth of 2500 ft (750 m) in water depths as great as 25,000 ft (7600 m). Not only can the drill pass through a sediment layer, but also it can obtain cores of the bedrock beneath. With teams of scientists aboard to direct the research the vessel has made many traverses across the ocean basins. In terms of new findings concern-

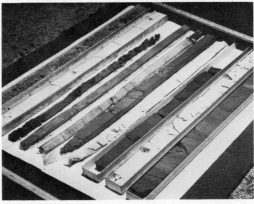

Figure 8.25. Obtaining deep-sea cores aboard the Research vessel *Vema.* (*Top*) Piston coring tube with its heavy driving weight is prepared for lowering. (*Middle*) Members of the ship's company bring a 50-ft (15-m) core aboard. (*Bottom*) Cores that have been extruded into plastic tubes, then sliced through the center to reveal composition and layering for study. Core segments shown here are about 3 ft (1 m) long. (Courtesy of Lamont-Doherty Geological Observatory of Columbia University, and National Academy of Sciences, IGY.)

ing the sediment and bedrock of the ocean floors, this cruise has been hailed as the most successful oceanographic mission of all time.

Setting aside the thick accumulations of marine sediments found at shallow depths on the continental margins and obviously derived from the continents through direct transportation by streams, waves, and currents, consider the possible terrestrial sources of sediment on the deep ocean floors far from land.

Atmospheric circulation provides an important transport mechanism for the movement of extremely fine particles from lands to the oceans. Mineral particles are raised high into the atmosphere by dust storms of the tropical deserts. Tropical easterlies carry these particles far westward over the adjacent oceans, where they may settle to the ocean surface or may be carried down in raindrops. Other important sources of atmospheric dusts are volcanic eruptions, emitting minute shards of volcanic glass, and the vaporization of meteors in the upper atmosphere.

Transport by surface ocean currents is an obvious means for the wide distribution of very fine suspended particles derived from sources close to the continental margins.

A related mechanism is transport by icebergs, which float far out to sea and melt, dropping mineral fragments of many sizes. By this means even huge boulders may reach positions hundreds of miles from the nearest land.

The great bulk of the thick sediment layers found beneath abyssal plains and in trenches requires transport mechanisms of far greater capability than those described in the paragraphs above. Bottom currents capable of moving large quantities of sediment close to the ocean bed are thought to be of major importance.

Finally, the action of turbidity currents in transporting sediment from relatively high positions of accumulation to the deepest parts of the ocean floor is now recognized as probably responsible for most thick accumulations of sediment consisting of silts and fine sands as well as of finer particles.

A *turbidity current* is a tonguelike flow of highly turbid water—a mixture of sediments with sea water—originating in soft sediments deposited in fairly shallow water. The current flows downslope under the force of gravity because the mixture is denser than the surrounding sea water. Upon reaching the deep

ocean floor the tongue spreads into a vast sheet and the sediment settles out in a thin layer.

Total thickness of sediments of turbidity-current origin varies greatly from place to place on the ocean-basin floor. Thickest accumulations are on the sides of basins and within reach of the continental shelves from which the sediment is derived.

There are four main classes of deep-sea sediments. The *biogenic-pelagic* sediments consist principally of calcareous or siliceous mineral matter secreted by organisms The word *pelagic* (from the Greek *pelagikos,* for "sea") simply means "originating in, or derived from, the ocean." The pelagic organisms of most importance in furnishing deep-sea sediment are *plankton,* the very small floating plants and animals growing in vast numbers in the shallow well-oxygenated surface layer of the ocean. These organisms secrete hard structures, referred to as *tests.* Upon death of the organism the organic matter is destroyed, but the tests sink down to great depths and, if not dissolved in passage, reach the ocean floor.

Accumulated sediment rich in tests is referred to as *ooze.* Inorganic clays are also present in substantial quantities. One variety of ooze is calcareous and is composed of the tests of *foraminifera* (one-celled animals) and other organisms (Figure 8.26). Another variety is siliceous and is composed of tests of *diatoms* (one-celled plants) and *radiolaria* (microscopic animals), which secrete ornate tests of silica (Figure 8.27). Rate of accumulation of oozes is extremely slow—perhaps from 0.4 to 2 in. (1 to 5 cm) per 1000 years.

A second class of sediments, designated as *pelagic-detrital,* consists of nonbiogenic particles that have settled to the bottom from the near-surface layer above. Carried by winds or ocean currents, this sediment forms *brown clay,* a soft, plastic material consisting mostly of clay minerals referred to earlier in this chapter (illite, montmorillonite, kaolinite). Rate of accumulation of brown clay is only from 0.004 to 0.04 in. (0.1 to 1 mm) per 1000 yr. Also included in the pelagic-detrital class are *glacial-marine sediments* carried out to sea and dropped into deep water by icebergs. Volcanic ash carried in the atmosphere and settling into the ocean also forms detrital sediment layers on the deep ocean floor.

The third class, designated as *bottom-transported,* includes sediments carried as turbidity

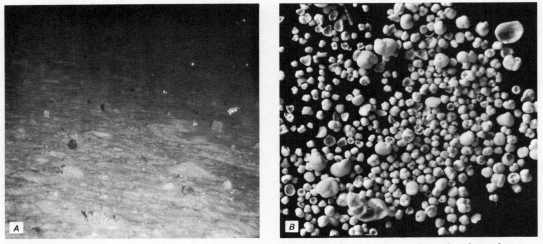

Figure 8.26. Calcareous ooze of the ocean floor. (*A*) Photograph of the deep-sea floor showing calcareous ooze at a depth of 15,000 ft (4510 m) in the east equatorial Pacific Ocean. The photograph shows an area of about 50 ft² (5 m²). The small mounds in the right foreground are probably formed by the burrowing action of worms. Several spongelike animals and small echinoids are visible. (Photograph by Carl J. Shipek, U.S. Navy Electronics Laboratory, San Diego, California.) (*B*) Calcareous shells and shell fragments separated by sieving a sample of Globigerina ooze, the bulk of which is composed of fine clay material. This sample is from a core obtained by scientists of the Research vessel *Vema* from a depth of 10,000 ft (3000 m) in the South Atlantic Ocean. Enlargement about 12 times. (Photograph by A. McIntyre, courtesy of Lamont-Doherty Geological Observatory of Columbia University.)

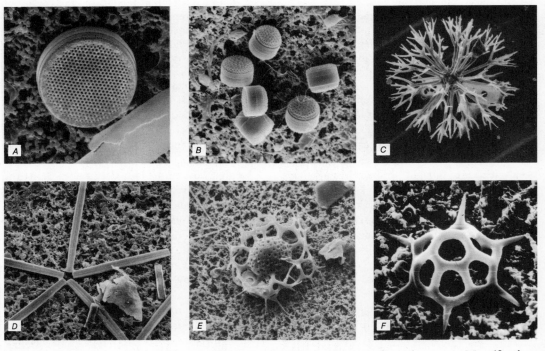

Figure 8.27. Plankton seen in high magnification under the electron scanning microscope. Magnifications indicated on individual photographs. These specimens were collected in plankton nets from within the uppermost 650 ft (200 m) in the western North Atlantic Ocean. (*A*, *B*, and *D*) Diatoms. (*C* and *E*) Radiolaria. (*F*) Silicoflagellate. (Photographs by courtesy of Allan W. H. Bé, Lamont-Doherty Geological Observatory of Columbia University.)

flows and called *turbidites.* Sediment is also carried by bottom currents, which bring fine muds from continental margins into deep water; these are called *terrigenous muds.*

Finally, there are *hydrogenic sediments,* consisting of minerals formed by alteration in place or reformed from other minerals. Both basaltic rock and volcanic ash are subject to such alteration. A great deal of interest centers around the finding of abundant nodules of hydrous manganese and iron oxides exposed on the surface of the deep ocean floors in many places. Referred to as *manganese nodules,* these objects often prove to be thick mineral coatings surrounding nuclei of volcanic rock (Figure 8.28). Manganese nodules are believed to be formed from manganese and iron derived either from detrital sediments of continental origin or from volcanic rocks of the ocean floor.

The deep-sea sediments described here are of great importance for the interpretation of global environmental conditions. Cores of these deposits show alternations of various types of sediment, each reflecting certain physical and chemical conditions of the ocean waters or a certain set of climatic conditions prevailing in the atmosphere. For example, a thick accumulation of turbidities reflects a glacial stage in

which vast amounts of sediment were being brought to the brink of the continental shelf. Particular species of foraminifera are associated with water temperature of a given range. By studying species variations in layers of calcareous ooze a record of changing atmospheric temperatures can be derived.

## SEDIMENTS THROUGH GEOLOGIC TIME

Production of sediment and the sedimentary rocks has gone on throughout at least 3.5 billion years of geologic time. It is thought that much of the enormous bulk of sedimentary rock produced during this time has been remelted to form new igneous rock. We shall want to inquire further into this process at the close of the next chapter, which explores in detail the processes of erosion and transportation operating on the continents. In this chapter we have traced a part of the rock-transformation cycle, in which exogenetic agents and forces have altered exposed rock and reduced it to sediment, yielding the sedimentary rocks. The cycle will be taken up again in Chapter 10, which reviews the endogenetic processes of mountain-making acting upon the sedimentary rocks to produce metamorphic rocks and new igneous rocks.

### References for further study

Dunbar, C. O., and J. Rodgers (1957), *Principles of Stratigraphy,* New York, Wiley, 356 pp.

Spock, L. E. (1962), *Guide to the Study of Rocks,* 2nd ed., New York, Harper & Row, 298 pp., chap. 8.

Shepard, F. P. (1963), *Submarine Geology,* 2nd ed., New York, Harper & Row, 557 pp., chaps. 14–17.

Simpson, B. (1966), *Rocks and Minerals,* New York, Pergamon, 292 pp., chaps. 15–20.

Turekian, K. K. (1968), *Oceans,* Englewood Cliffs, N.J., Prentice-Hall, 120 pp., chaps. 1–3.

Strahler, A. N. (1969), *Physical Geography,* 3rd ed., New York, Wiley, 733 pp., chaps. 18, 19.

Thornbury, W. D. (1969), *Principles of Geomorphology,* 2nd ed., New York, Wiley, 594 pp., chaps. 3, 4.

Figure 8.28. A manganese nodule, about 4 in. (11 cm) high, dredged from the floor of the Atlantic Ocean. Cross section reveals a nucleus of volcanic rock (light color) surrounded by a layer of manganese and iron oxides. (Karl K. Turekian, *Oceans,* © 1968. By permission of the author and Prentice-Hall, Inc.)

### Review questions

1. Evaluate the earth's surface environment in terms of chemical stability of minerals and rocks. What is mineral alteration? Define weathering. Comment on the geological importance of weathering.

2. Describe the earth materials normally found in an exposure cut into the solid earth.

What kinds of overburden can be recognized? What is the nature of the true soil (topsoil)? What is regolith? alluvium?

3. Describe the three aspects of weathering. Which of these would be classed as reversible change? which as irreversible change? List the important processes of physical (mechanical) weathering and explain how each operates. How does climate play a role in effectiveness of physical weathering processes? Where would you expect to find examples of sheeting structure?

4. What are the principal chemical reactions involved in chemical weathering (mineral alteration)? Describe hydrolysis of feldspars and name the principal alteration products. What are some of the physical effects and manifestations of chemical weathering?

5. Describe each of the five soil-forming regimes, referring each to a characteristic climate or world region. Explain the relationships between temperature and the activity of macroflora and microflora. Use this relationship to explain laterization and podzolization. Define the following terms: laterite, humus, podzol, glei, caliche, calcrete.

6. Describe a classification of sedimentary rocks based upon sediments and minerals. What are the subdivisions within the clastic and nonclastic groups? Describe the various forms of chemical precipitates and explain how they differ from the organically derived sediments.

7. How is grain size used in the classification of clastic sediments and rocks? Describe the appearance of sedimentary strata as seen in exposures. What terms are applied to the various layered structures?

8. What are the most abundant consituents of the detrital sedimentary rocks? Describe the heavy minerals occurring in sedimentary rocks. What grade scale is in general use to describe dimensions of sedimentary particles?

9. Name the common detrital sedimentary rocks in order of texture from coarse to fine. Describe the appearance and physical properties of each type. How are sediments lithified? What clay minerals are common in claystone and shale? What is the environmental significance of red beds?

10. Distinguish hydrogenic sediments from biogenic sediments. Describe the minerals making up carbonates and evaporites.

11. Describe limestone and dolomite. Where do these rocks originate? How do coral reefs contribute to formation of limestones? What is meant by dolomitization?

12. Describe the chemical reactions in which carbonic acid is formed and in which this acid acts upon calcium carbonate. What geological role has the process of carbonation? Describe the reverse process of precipitation of calcium carbonate. Where may such precipitation take place?

13. Under what conditions do evaporites accumulate in large quantities? What role do evaporites play in the geologic record?

14. What are hydrocarbon compounds? In what forms do hydrocarbons occur in sedimentary rocks? What is the composition of lignite? of bituminous coal? of anthracite? Under what conditions is anthracite formed?

15. What is the composition of petroleum? of natural gas? In what rocks and structures do petroleum and natural gas accumulate? What is the origin of petroleum?

16. Describe the process of diagenesis. How do fossils reveal information about the environments of sediment deposition? Classify environments of sediment deposition and describe the processes associated with each. Define these adjectives: pelagic, benthic, terrestrial, littoral, sublittoral, bathyal, abyssal, hadal.

17. Describe the procedure for obtaining sediment cores from the deep ocean floor. How is drilling carried out in these same regions?

18. Explain how sediment can reach the deep ocean floors, far from continents. Do currents act upon sediments of the deep ocean floors? What is a turbidity current? Where do such currents act? What kind of sedimentary accumulations do they produce?

19. What are the four main classes of deep-sea sediments? What are plankton? What kinds of sediment do plankton produce? What types of detrital sediment accumulate on the deep ocean floors? How are hydrogenic sediments produced on the ocean floor? What are manganese nodules? What is the scientific value of the deep-sea sediments in interpretation of global environments of the geologic past?

20. How do the atmosphere and hydrosphere play important roles in geologic processes? Explain how two unlike planetary systems are linked in the chemical and physical activities affecting rock and soil exposed at the continental surface. What are the endogenetic processes, and how do they differ from the exogenetic processes? How do these two groups of processes differ in terms of energy sources?

# chapter 9 exogenetic processes and products: ii. continental denudation and its landforms

Besides the alteration of minerals and rocks and the resulting production of sediments, there is a closely related geologic function of the exogenetic processes acting upon an exposed lithosphere. Weathering of rock is accompanied by erosion and transportation by the fluid agents: running water, glacial ice, waves and associated coastal currents, and wind. The role of these agents in reducing the elevation of the continents is encompassed by a single term: *denudation*. The character of the agents of denudation as parts of energy systems of atmospheric circulation and the secondary systems of gravity flow of water on the lands has been analyzed in Chapters 4 and 6. In this chapter we turn to the geologic role of these exogenetic processes in shaping the surface of the lands.

Man and all other forms of terrestrial life evolved upon continental surfaces of denudation. These surfaces are extremely varied from place to place in terms of physical environ-

mental qualities. In combination with climatic factors of availability of heat and water, the nature of a given type of land surface strongly influences the capacity of that surface to support life. Since denudation never ceases on the lithospheric surface, there has been a continual change in terrestrial environments through geologic time. The importance of these long-term environmental changes will become evident in the discussion of organic evolution in Chapters 13 and 14.

## GEOMORPHIC PROCESSES

The study of the origin and evolution of the relief features of the landscape, or *landforms*, constitutes a branch of the earth sciences known as *geomorphology*, closely affiliated with physical geology and hydrology. In the study of landforms the various landscape features are sorted out according to processes of origin—the *geomorphic processes*.

In the broadest sense all landforms fall into

two great classes, the products of two great classes of geomorphic processes. The *endogenetic processes,* internally powered, include tectonic activities that dislocate the crust and volcanic processes that construct new landforms by extrusions of magma (Chapter 7). New relief features thus created can be designated as *initial landforms* (Figure 9.1). The initial landforms are acted upon by the *exogenetic processes,* powered by external sources of energy, largely solar. These processes, or agents of landmass denudation, yield the *sequential landforms.*

The sequential landforms can in turn be subdivided into two varieties: *erosional* and *depositional.* Erosional landforms are those resulting from the progressive removal of earth materials, and depositional landforms are those resulting from the accumulation of the products of erosion. In the example shown in Figure 9.1, erosion by runoff on slopes and in streams has carved a host of erosional landforms, consisting of canyons and the intervening divides and peaks. Deposition of sediment by streams has at the same time been forming a type of depositional landform known as an *alluvial fan.* Each agent of erosion produces a characteristic assemblage of erosional and depositional landforms.

In summarizing this introduction to geomorphology, it might be said that all landscapes of the continents reflect the existing stage in an unending conflict between endogenetic and exogenetic processes. Where endogenetic processes

have been recently active, through orogeny and vulcanism, there exist rugged alpine mountain chains and high plateaus. Where exogenetic processes have been given opportunity to operate with little disturbance for vast spans of time, the landmasses have been reduced to low plains.

In many periods of the geologic past continental relief was generally low, and the subsidence of continental crust allowed shallow seas to spread far inland. At such times the exogenetic processes dominated. The continents today are, in contrast, generally high in elevation and rugged in relief, suggesting that we live at a time when the endogenetic processes have temporarily gained the upper hand on a world-wide scope. The possible importance of high-standing continents in the rapid evolution of mammals, including Man, is taken up again in Chapter 14.

## AGENTS OF DENUDATION

Almost all sequential landforms are shaped or greatly modified by the *active agents* of landform development: flowing water (overland flow and channel flow), waves and associated coastal currents, glacial ice, and wind. All these active agents consist of fluids (in the broad sense) and are acting directly or indirectly under the force of gravity or the atmospheric pressure-gradient force. The fluid agents are engaged in *erosion,* which is the effect of the flow of water, ice, or air over the solid land surface to dislodge in one way or another particles of soil, overburden, or bedrock. The particles are then carried as sediment to progressively lower and more distant locations.

There are also *passive agents* of denudation. The *weathering processes*—including all forms of mechanical disintegration and chemical decomposition of mineral matter discussed in Chapter 8—act continuously on all soil, overburden, and bedrock lying close to the surface where atmospheric influences are felt. The products of weathering tend to remain in place where formed unless they are moved under the force of gravity or by fluid agents. The *mass-wasting processes* include all forms of downslope movement of soil, overburden, or bedrock under the direct influence of gravity, but without the action of a fluid agent, as in the erosion processes. Mass wasting represents the spontaneous yielding of earth materials when gravitational force exceeds the internal strength

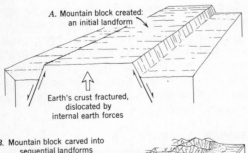

A. Mountain block created: an initial landform

Earth's crust fractured, dislocated by internal earth forces

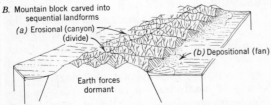

B. Mountain block carved into sequential landforms
(a) Erosional (canyon)
(divide)
(b) Depositional (fan)

Earth forces dormant

Figure 9.1. Two great classes of landforms. (*A*) Initial. (*B*) Sequential. (© 1960, John Wiley & Sons, New York.)

of the material. Therefore, mass wasting involves the sliding, rolling, and flowage of masses of soil, overburden, and bedrock to lower positions, but it is regarded as a passive agent because it provides no means of transport to distant places.

Denudation thus consists of the combined agents of erosion, weathering, and mass wasting.

## DYNAMICS OF DENUDATION SYSTEMS

The approach to denudation must be a dynamic one, stressing the action of forces to dislocate and transport masses. Force acting through distance constitutes work in the mechanical sense. Energy must be transformed when work is done. Therefore landscape development can be resolved into systems of energy transformation and mass transport.

The endogenetic processes powered by internal (radiogenic) heat are responsible for raising large masses of rock above sea level. In so doing, they furnish every particle of the elevated mass with a supply of potential energy. Work is required to achieve the mechanical and chemical breakdown of this rock into soil and sediment. As individual sediment particles move from high to low levels, the potential energy of position is transformed into kinetic energy of motion, which in turn is dissipated through friction and is transformed into heat. Such is the nature of the geologic aspect of denudation.

The exogenetic processes operate on solar energy. Some of this energy is utilized directly when solar heating and evaporation occur under direct impact of the sun's rays. But most of the exogenetic processes are powered indirectly through motions of the atmosphere and oceans and attendant processes of condensation. Thus streams and glaciers depend upon precipitation to deposit water at high elevations on land, which gives the water an initial store of potential energy to be expended in flow to lower levels. Wind is a fluid flow induced by pressure-gradient forces. Kinetic energy of moving air powers two active agents of erosion and transportation. First, the direct frictional drag of air over the ground surface, called *wind action,* results in certain forms of erosion and deposition. Second, winds blowing over ocean surfaces generate waves. Energy transferred to waves ultimately is transported to the shores of the continents, where it is absorbed in erosion and transportation of mineral matter.

To sum up, the exogenetic processes fall into three groups: (a) those which are sustained by direct input of solar radiation, (b) those which are simple gravity-flow systems (mass wasting, streams, and glaciers), and (c) those which derive energy from atmospheric motion (wind action and wave action).

## MASS WASTING

Although the force of gravity acts constantly upon all soil, overburden, and bedrock, the internal strength of these materials is ordinarily sufficient to keep them in place, thus we rarely see soil or rock moving spontaneously except when carried by an active agent of erosion. Wherever the ground has a measurable slope with respect to the horizontal, a proportion of the acceleration of gravity is directed downslope parallel with the surface. Every particle has at least some tendency to roll or slide downhill and will do so whenever the downslope force exceeds the resistive forces of friction and cohesion that tend to bind the particle to the rest of the mass.

The downslope force increases as the sine of the angle of the slope measured from the horizontal. Thus on a slope of 30° the force acting on a unit of mass is just half the total gravitational force, but on a slope of 60° it is about 87%. Hence, as everyone knows, the tendency to slide is greater on steeper slopes, but it is not often appreciated that the tendency increases most rapidly in the lower range of angles, from 0° to 45° or so, and thereafter less rapidly. Above 70° the slope behaves almost as if it were perpendicular.

From these facts we might reason that precipitous slopes will be rare in nature simply because they waste away so rapidly that, when formed by any geologic agent, they do not endure for long. The percentage of the total area of land slopes steeper than 45° is very small indeed, although it is the few steep mountain slopes that are readily visible from afar and therefore attract our attention. By far the greatest proportion of the earth's land surface is in slope less than 5°, and on such subdued relief the effects of mass wasting are rarely noticed.

The forms of mass wasting range from the great catastrophic slides in alpine mountains, involving millions of cubic yards of rock and capable of wiping out a whole town, down to the small flows of saturated soil seen commonly along the highways in early spring. But extremely slow movement of soil, imperceptible from one year to the next, also acts on almost every hillside.

## SLOPE EROSION BY OVERLAND FLOW

Of the denudation processes we shall take up first those described as *fluvial,* meaning that the process involves water flowing over the surfaces of the ground (overland flow) and in stream channels (channel flow). The flow of a sheet of water over the soil surface exerts a *shearing stress,* or *drag,* upon the mineral grains. If this stress is sufficient to overcome the cohesive forces binding a grain to the parent mass, the grain is *entrained* into the flowing layer and is rolled, dragged, or carried downslope. The progressive removal of grains in this manner is described as *slope erosion.* As used here, *slope* means an element of ground surface.

Greatly aiding the process of erosion on barren soil surfaces is *splash erosion,* the dislodgment and movement of soil particles under the impact of falling raindrops (Figure 9.2). Contained in the geyserlike spray of droplets are particles of clay and silt, which may be lifted to heights of 2 ft (0.6 m). Within a single violent rainstorm drop impacts can cause the disturbance of as much as 100 tons of soil per acre (225 metric tons per hectare). On a sloping surface particles thus agitated creep gradually downhill. Splash erosion is an important process on rounded divides and hill summits where overland flow is not normally effective. Moreover, openings of the soil surface tend to become clogged by splash action, causing a reduction of infiltration capacity and a consequent increase in rate of runoff.

Of considerable interest to geologists and soil scientists are the factors that govern the intensity of soil erosion by overland flow. In Chapter 6 it was pointed out that the smaller the infiltration capacity of the soil and the longer the ground slope, the greater the flow over a given patch of ground. We can reason that the less the infiltration capacity of a soil surface, the more rapid will be the rate of erosion. Another factor is the resistance of the surface to the entrainment of particles. A good vegetative cover, particularly a grass sod, breaks the force of falling raindrops and absorbs the energy of the overland flow, thus tending to reduce the rate of erosion. Hence even under heavy and prolonged rains a thickly vegetated slope may yield very small quantities of min-

Figure 9.2. The fall of a large raindrop upon a wet soil surface produces a miniature crater and throws grains of silt and clay high into the air. (Official U.S. Navy photograph.)

eral solids, whereas the barren surface of a desert landscape or the unprotected surface of a cultivated field will produce large quantities of sediment with each rainstorm.

Finally, the factor of *slope angle,* or inclination of the ground surface from the horizontal, is important in slope erosion. It is easy to see that as the ground surface steepens, the force of gravity acting parallel with the surface is increased, and that hence the velocity of the flow is increased and the eroding stress becomes greater. In general, then, the rate of erosion increases with the steepness of the slope. On the other hand, the steeper the slope angle, the less is the quantity of rainfall intercepted by a unit of ground surface, until on a vertical surface no vertically falling rain can be caught at all. Combining the two effects, we find that the most intense erosion may be expected on surfaces having an inclination of about 40° from the horizontal. Rate of erosion increases most rapidly in the range from horizontal up to 30° or so.

These principles of slope erosion are put to use in the Epilogue to assess the consequences of Man's disturbance of the land to produce greatly accelerated rates of soil erosion. From the geologic standpoint, slope erosion is an essential part of the total process of fluvial denudation, for it is one mechanism by means of which solid matter is supplied to channels for transport to lower levels and eventually to the oceans.

## WORK OF STREAMS

Streams perform three closely interrelated forms of geologic work: erosion, transportation, and deposition. *Stream erosion* is defined as the progressive removal of mineral matter from the surfaces of a stream channel, whether the exposed material consists of bedrock, residual or transported overburden, or soil. *Stream transportation* is the movement of eroded particles in chemical solution, in turbulent suspension, or by rolling and dragging along the bed. Particles in stream transport constitute the *stream load*. *Stream deposition* consists of the accumulation of any transported particles on the stream bed, on the adjoining floodplain, or on the floor of a body of standing water into which the stream empties. The material of such deposits is known as *alluvium*. These phases of geologic work cannot be separated one from the other, because where erosion occurs there must be at least some transportation, and eventually the transported particles must come to rest.

The nature of stream erosion depends upon the materials of which the channel is composed and the means of erosion available to the stream. One simple form of erosion is by *hydraulic action,* the effect of pressure and shearing force of flowing water exerted upon grains projecting from the bed and banks. Weakly consolidated bedrock and various forms of uncemented transported and residual overburden are readily worn away by hydraulic action alone, but the process has little effect on strongly bonded bedrock.

Mechanical wear, termed *abrasion,* occurs through the impact of rock particles carried in the current striking against the exposed bedrock of the channel surfaces. Small particles are further reduced by crushing and grinding when caught between larger cobbles and boulders. Chemical reactions between ions, carried in solution in stream water, and the exposed mineral surfaces result in a form of erosion

referred to as *corrosion,* which is essentially the same as chemical rock weathering described in Chapter 8.

Hydraulic action is the dominant process of stream erosion in weak deposits of floodplains. In flood stage the swift, highly turbulent flow on the outside of stream bends undermines the channel wall, causing masses of sand, gravel, silt, or clay to slump and slide into the channel, an activity described as *bank caving.* Huge volumes of sediment are thus incorporated into the stream flow in times of high stage, and the channel may shift laterally by many yards in a single flood.

Three forms of stream transportation of mineral matter can be distinguished. First, chemical reactions yield ions that may travel downstream indefinitely. Such matter, referred to by hydraulic engineers as constituting the *dissolved solids,* does not appreciably affect the mechanical behavior of the stream.

Second, particles of clay, silt, and sometimes fine sand are carried in *suspension,* a form of transport in which the upward currents in eddies of turbulent flow are capable of holding the particles indefinitely in the body of the stream. Material carried in suspension is referred to as the *suspended load* and constitutes a large share of the total load of most streams. The more intense the turbulence of the stream, the greater the total quantity and the larger the particles that can be held in suspension. Clay particles, once lifted into suspension, are so readily carried that they travel long distances. Silts settle rapidly when turbulence subsides. Sands are rarely transported in suspension except in the highly turbulent flow of floods. As a result, suspension provides a means of separating solid particles of various size grades and carrying each size fraction to a different location, a process known as *sorting.* (Other sorting mechanisms exist.)

Third of the modes of transportation is that of rolling or sliding of grains along the stream bed, a motion that can be conveniently included in the term *traction.* Particles thus in motion are referred to collectively as the *bed load* of the stream (Figure 9.3). Traction results both from the direct pressure of the water flow against the upstream face of a grain and from the dragging action of the water as it flows over the grain surface. In bed-load movement, individual particles roll, slide, or take low leaps downstream, then come to rest among other grains.

Figure 9.3. Bouldery channel materials in the bottom of a steep-walled canyon. The coarse, poorly rounded fragments are moved down-valley in times of intense, short-lived desert floods. Gonzales Pass Canyon, Arizona. (Photograph by Mark A. Melton.)

## SOLID LOAD OF STREAMS

The solid load of a stream can be stated in units of weight of sediment moved past a fixed cross section in a unit of time, for example, *tons per day*. At certain of the stream-gauging stations operated by the U.S. Geological Survey measurements are regularly made of the quantities of load being moved in both suspension and traction.

It is well known that the suspended load increases very rapidly as the discharge increases. Figure 9.4 is a graph relating suspended load to discharge in the Powder River, Wyoming. Likewise, bed load increases greatly with increasing discharge. From Figure 9.4 it can be seen that a 10-fold increase in discharge brings about almost a 100-fold increase in suspended load. Obviously, the great bulk of sediment is moved at relatively high stream stages, whereas relatively little is moved at low stages, when the water of the stream becomes quite clear.

Rivers differ greatly in their typical suspended loads, depending upon the environment of the watershed. The Missouri River, for example, derives much suspended load from badlands and other barren surfaces of soft clays and shales of the semiarid Great Plains region, whereas the eastern tributaries to the Mississippi—such as the Ohio and the Tennessee, with forested watersheds in a humid climate—contribute a much smaller proportion of suspended load. The Hwang Ho (Yellow River) of China drains an arid region of silts and can receive vast quantities of suspended matters to give an extraordinarily high concentration.

The ratio of suspended load to bed load in a stream will range from predominantly suspended load in streams of humid climates (the Mississippi carries about 90% of its total load in suspension) to perhaps an equal amount of both forms of transport in streams of semiarid and arid regions. The latter streams tend to have broad shallow channels of relatively steep gradients well adapted to moving coarse materials in traction (Figure 9.3), whereas the streams of humid climates tend to be relatively narrow and deep, with lesser gradients, a combination better suited to carrying more fine material in suspension.

## CONCEPT OF THE GRADED STREAM

A fully developed stream system with its contributing valley-side slopes, as described in

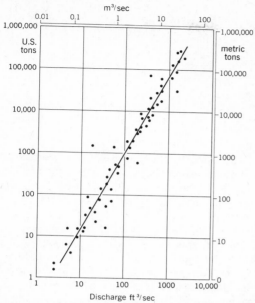

Figure 9.4. Graph of the relation of suspended load to discharge for the Powder River at Arvada, Wyoming. The dots suggest individual observations. The sloping line shows the average trend of all observations. [Modified from L. B. Leopold and T. Maddock (1953), *U.S. Geol. Survey Professional Paper 252*, p. 20, Figure 13.]

Chapter 6, is adjusted to dispose of not only surplus water but the load with which it is supplied. A purely hydraulic system might need little gradient. On the other hand, the transport of bed load requires appreciable slope. By appropriate adjustments of channel slope throughout the parts of the converging channel system, the stream evolves in such a way as to transport the load continuously downstream to the mouth, where it enters standing water and becomes a delta deposit or is swept seaward by marine currents.

To understand the adjustment of a stream it is helpful to consider the case of a stream that is at first poorly adjusted and gradually improves its operation. Suppose the crustal movements have recently and rapidly brought above sea level a new mass of land. We can assume an irregular, steplike land surface with various down-sagged portions (Figure 9.5). The surface does, however, descend to the sea despite these irregularities, from a crudely delimited divide far inland. Assume a region in which average annual rainfall exceeds losses by

evaporation. The surplus water proceeds by overland flow from high to low places. Any natural troughlike configuration of the ground serves to concentrate the flow of water. Here erosion is intensified and a channel forms. Depressions in the landscape fill with water to form lakes; these overflow at their lowest points. Soon a continuous chain of flow is established leading to the sea, and a trunk stream is formed. Let us examine the profile of this channel from its upper end to the sea (Figure 9.5). Note the variety of channel gradients and the contrast in flat surfaces of the ponded sections with the rapids and falls that connect them.

The rate of expenditure of energy per unit of horizontal distance traveled from one point to another along the irregular profile is highly nonuniform. It may seem intuitively obvious that a series of changes will take place leading to a more uniform profile in which energy expenditure is uniformly carried out. Mechanically, the necessity for such changes is obvious. As the gradient of a stream steepens in passing over a rapid or fall, the velocity increases. Erosion is intensified at the point of increasing velocity. Where the stream gradient lessens, in approaching a flat reach or lake, the velocity is diminishing. Here erosion is greatly reduced or may not occur at all. Consequently, falls and rapids are quickly cut away. The bed load derived from erosion will accumulate in the lakes and they will quickly fill, giving way to flood plain and new channel. Uniform descent of the profile throughout its length has now replaced the irregular descent. Energy transformations are roughly uniform throughout. Rate of expenditure of energy per unit volume has been equalized to the maximum extent throughout.

But an observation of many river profiles will show that truly uniform descent is not the rule. Instead, almost all river profiles are upwardly concave, with the slope diminishing downstream (Figure 9.6). The cause of upconcavity is of great interest in analyzing the river as part of an open system. We first assume that the trunk river and its branches in time achieve the condition of *grade*. A *graded stream* is one which, averaged over a period of many years, is delicately adjusted in gradient and cross-sectional form so that, with its available discharge, it will transport through the system exactly the average quantity of load supplied to it from the contributing watershed. When graded, the channel is neither built up

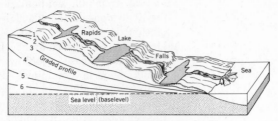

Figure 9.5. Gradation of a stream profile.

nor cut down, because the energy transformed in flow of water and in movement of bed load is neither too little nor too great.

Assuming that the graded condition exists, why is the profile up-concave? Why does channel slope lessen in the downstream direction? This last question is particularly interesting in the light of knowledge that reduced channel slope tends to reduce velocity (Chapter 6) and hence to reduce the power of a stream to transport load. Yet, as a river is traced downstream, it is receiving increasing load (and water discharge) from tributaries.

The answer lies, at least in large part, in the efficiency of a large stream compared with a small one. For streams of identical cross-sectional form, the one with larger cross-sectional area is more efficient because the line of contact of cross section with channel (the *wetted perimeter*) is proportionately less in ratio to its area than for the smaller stream. The larger stream expends relatively less energy in boundary friction, hence it can maintain its transporting activity with a lower gradient. The stream which we observe has already adjusted its gradient to compensate for its increasing efficiency.

This explanation for the downstream decrease in gradient of a stream was set forth in 1877 by the distinguished American geologist Grove Karl Gilbert. The downstream decrease in gradient thus explained by increasing efficiency is often referred to as *Gilbert's law of declivities*.

Additional proof of the law of declivities lies in a detail of the actual form of stream profiles (Figure 9.7). If the graded profile of a single channel is plotted from one of the fingertip ends (point *A*) downstream to the mouth (point *D*), the profile will show abrupt changes in profile at each point where a tributary channel of roughly equal magnitude makes its junction. The profile is thus actually *segmented*. Where two streams segments of equal dis-

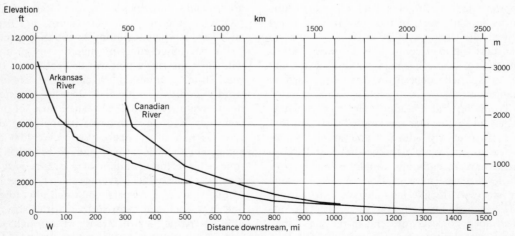

Figure 9.6. Longitudinal profiles of the Arkansas and Canadian rivers. Poorly graded upper portions reflect effects of glaciation and rock inequalities. (© 1969, John Wiley & Sons, New York. Data of Gannett, U.S. Geological Survey.)

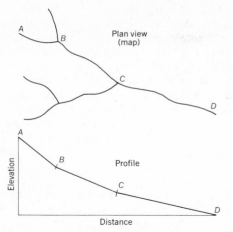

Figure 9.7. Stream junctions and a segmented stream profile.

gradients must lessen. A continual, but very slow adjustment of the profile must occur.

## ALLUVIAL RIVERS

Many of the world's graded rivers occupy broad floodplain belts over which the depth of alluvium equals or exceeds the depth to which scour takes place in time of flood. Designated *alluvial rivers* by hydraulic engineers, these streams flow on very low gradients and have extremely sinuous bends known as *alluvial meanders* (Figure 9.8).

Meanders originate from the enlargement of bends in the path of flow of the stream. For example, the growth of a sand bar along the side of a straight channel will deflect the lines of flow toward the opposite bank, where undercutting takes place and a bend begins to form (Figure 9.9*A*). Material from the undercut bank is carried a short distance down-channel, forming another bar, which in turn deflects the flow to the opposite side to develop a second bend. Once a bend is produced, centrifugal force continues to thrust the flow toward the outside of the bend, resulting in continued undermining and the enlargement of the bend until a meander loop is formed.

On the inside of the bend a series of arcuate sand and gravel bars accumulates to produce a *point-bar deposit* (Figure 9.9*B*). Ideally, we might expect a uniform series of meander bends to reach an optimum size suited to the

charge join (points *B* and *C*), discharge and load are roughly doubled. Correspondingly, the efficiency takes a sudden jump (quantum jump) and the channel gradient abruptly lessens.

We shall see below that a graded stream can be considered an open system in steady state for only limited spans of time. Quite apart from the short-term variations in load and discharge that always affect a stream system, there is the further consideration that, as matter is taken from the drainage basin, the basin surface itself is lowered. As lowering occurs,

Figure 9.8. Air view of meanders, oxbow lakes and marshes, and bar-and-swale topography. Mudjalik River, northern Saskatchewan. (Canadian Armed Forces official photograph, No. A1814-27.)

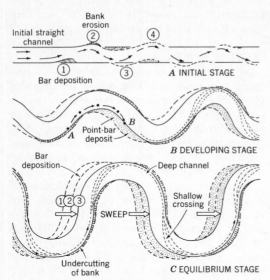

Figure 9.9. Development of simple alluvial meanders from an initially straight reach of a stream. [After G. H. Matthes (1941), *Transactions Amer. Geophys. Union,* vol. 22.]

magnitude of the stream and thereafter to cease growth. A down-valley shift, or *sweep,* of the entire system of bends would continue because of the inclination of the alluvial valley in the direction of the stream's mouth (Figure 9.9*C*). But because of inequalities of erodibility in the materials constituting the floodplain deposits, a meander may become constricted, creating a narrow *meander neck,* and the neck may be cut through by bank-caving or by overflow in time of flood, permitting the stream to bypass the bend and thereby to produce a *cutoff.* The cutoff meander bend is quickly sealed off from the main stream by silt deposits and becomes an *oxbow lake* (Figure 9.8). Gradual filling of the lake results in an oxbow swamp or marsh.

In the discussion of floods (Chapter 6) it was noted that many alluvial rivers of humid climates have a yearly flood of such proportions that the water can no longer be contained within the channel and spreads out upon the floodplain. Such overbank flooding permits fine-grained sediment (silts and clays) to be deposited from suspension in the relatively slowly moving water covering the floodplain. The sediment is laid down in layers, which may be called *overbank deposits.*

Adjacent to the main channel, in which flow is relatively swift because of greater depth, the coarsest sediment—sand and coarse silt—is de-

posited in two bordering belts. After many floods there are thus built up lateral zones of somewhat higher ground, termed *natural levees.* The highest points on the levees lie close to the river bank. There is a gentle slope away from the river down to the low-lying marshy areas of floodplain some distance from the river. Figure 9.10 is a greatly exaggerated cross section of the Mississippi River showing its flanking levees. Levee height is generally 12 to 15 ft (3.5 to 4.5 m) above the surrounding floodplain, and slopes are on the order of 3 to 4 ft/mi (0.5 to 0.7 m/km) away from the river. In times of overbank flood the channel of an alluvial river is often clearly delineated by a double line of trees growing on the levees and projecting above the flood waters.

## AGGRADING STREAMS; ALLUVIAL FANS

When rock waste, particularly the coarse material carried as bed load, is supplied to a stream by its tributaries and by runoff from adjacent slopes in greater quantity than the stream is capable of transporting, the excess load is spread along the channel floor, raising the level of the entire channel. Such up-building is termed *aggradation,* in contrast to *degradation,* which is the process of down-cutting carried on by a stream capable of transporting more load than it is supplied with.

A stream channel in which aggradation is in progress is typically broad and shallow. Aggradation takes the form of deposition of long narrows bars of sand and gravel, which tend to divide the flow into two or more lines (Figure 9.3). The flow thus subdivides and rejoins in a manner suggesting complexly braided cords, giving rise to the descriptive term *braided stream,* in contrast to the typical single-channel form of streams whose sinous meander loops have already been described. As channel aggradation proceeds, the stream is shifted laterally to flow in lower adjacent ground and will thus move widely from side to side wherever there are no confining valley walls.

Perhaps the most common cause of aggradation in stream channels is the combination of arid climate and mountainous relief, as in the southwestern United States. Barren, steep mountain slopes shed large quantities of coarse debris when eroded by runoff of torrential rains. Floods in the mountain valleys are thus characterized by a large proportion of coarse bed load carried down-valley on steep gradients. Where a canyon emerges upon a pied-

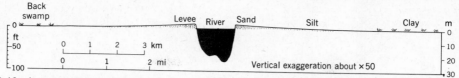

Figure 9.10. A transverse profile, greatly exaggerated, showing relation of natural levee to river channel.

mont valley floor of gentle slope, aggradation occurs because the stream is not able to transport its load on a sharply reduced gradient. Moreover, stream discharge may diminish rapidly in the lowland region because of influent seepage and evaporation. Free to shift from side to side as aggradation occurs, the stream spreads its excess load in the form of an *alluvial fan* (Figure 9.11).

The alluvial fan takes the form of a sector of an upwardly concave low cone steepening in gradient toward an apex situated at the canyon mouth. At its outer edge the fan slope grades imperceptibly into the flatter plain. As one might suspect, the diameter of particles constituting the fan is greatest near the apex, where much bouldery material may be found, and grades to progressively finer particles toward the periphery. Large fans of mountainous deserts may be several miles in radius from apex to outer edge.

From the standpoint of ground water, alluvial fans are of extremely great importance in arid climates because they act as ground-water reservoirs. Water enters near the fan apex by influent seepage and moves downward and outward along the layers of sorted gravels and sands, filling the interstices. Wells driven into the alluvium of the lower slopes of the fan will often prove to have artesian flow, because sloping impermeable mud layers interbedded with the permeable gravels form aquicludes, which confine the water under pressure.

## DELTAS

A stream reaching a body of standing water, whether a lake or the ocean, builds a deposit, the *delta,* composed of the stream's load. The growth of a simple delta can be followed in stages, shown in Figure 9.12. For simplicity we imagine that the water body is not appreciably affected by waves and tides. The stream enters the standing-water body as a jet whose velocity is rapidly checked. Sediment is deposited in lateral embankments in zones of less turbulence on either side of the jet, thus extending the stream channel into the open water. The stream repeatedly breaks through the embankments to occupy different radii and in time produces a deposit of semicircular form, closely analogous to the alluvial fan (which is in a sense a terrestrial delta).

In cross section the simple delta consists largely of steeply sloping layers of sands (Figure 9.13), which grade outward into thin layers of silt and clay. As the delta grows, the stream will aggrade slightly and spread new layers of alluvium. An important factor in

Figure 9.11. An alluvial fan at the margin of Death Valley, California. Shoreline of pluvial Lake Manly follows the outer fan margin. (Photograph by Mark A. Melton.)

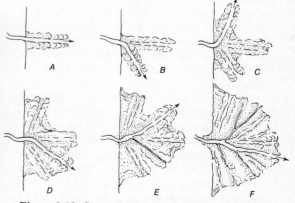

Figure 9.12. Stages in the development of a simple delta built into a lake in which wave action is slight. (© 1960, John Wiley & Sons, New York. Based on data of G. K. Gilbert.)

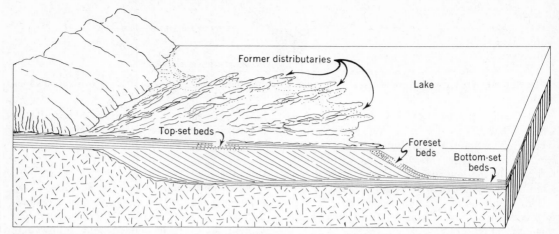

Figure 9.13. Internal structure of a simple delta built into a lake. (© 1960, John Wiley & Sons, New York.)

causing the finer suspended particles to settle close to the stream mouth is the presence in sea water of dissolved salts, which act to cause the particles to clot together, or *flocculate,* into aggregates of such size that they readily sink to the bottom.

### CONCEPT OF THE DENUDATION SYSTEM

That part of the continental crust lying above sea level, which is the base level for reduction by streams, constitutes the *available landmass* subject to denudation and to ultimate removal. However, to this landmass as it exists at any one moment must be added the crustal mass that will rise under isostasy to replace in part any rock mass that is removed in the denudation process. Estimates vary as to what factor to allow for isostatic replacement, but ratios on the order of 3 to 4 or 4 to 5 are considered realistic. Using the second of these ratios, the removal of 5000 ft of rock would be accompanied by uplift of 4000 ft and would result in a net lowering of the land surface only 1000 ft. Thus the available landmass includes the crustal mass furnished by isostatic replacement.

We have already seen that the available landmass upon which denudation acts is provided by endogenetic systems of mass transfer, but the reduction of the landmass is achieved by exogenetic systems expending solar energy. The two systems come into accidental linkages at various times and places over the earth. An alpine-mountain system is raised by orogenic and volcanic processes at a time and place that depends upon large-scale crustal tectonic processes totally unrelated to world patterns of in-

coming solar radiation, atmospheric circulation, precipitation, and evaporation (as witness the eruptions of volcanoes in almost any latitude on the globe). The global patterns of mountain-building and vulcanism are completely unrelated in any systematic way to the basic planetary systems of atmospheric circulation. So it is in an almost accidental manner that the great mountain chains transgress the flow paths of the easterlies and westerlies, disrupting what would otherwise be a rather simple system of global climates. The climatic differences, in turn, influence denudation processes and rates from place to place over the globe. Geologic and climatic controls together act in many combinations to regulate the denudation process.

### RATES OF OROGENIC UPLIFT AND DENUDATION

A model system of denudation must take into account rates of both crustal uplift and of denudation, since it is the balance of the two that determines the elevation at which the land surface stands with respect to sea level.

Using various methods for calculation, including direct surveys of crustal rise in historic time, it has been estimated that maximum uplift rates during orogeny may be on the order of 25 ft (7.5 m) per 1000 yr. At this rate, a mountain summit could rise from sea level to an elevation of 20,000 ft (6 km) in 800,000 yr, assuming none of its mass to be removed by denudation processes, and even the towering Himalaya range might well have been raised through a large part of its height in 2 million years (m.y.).

Denudation rates appear, by contrast, to be very much slower than uplift rates. Estimates are based upon the quantity of solid load and dissolved load passing oceanward through the mouths of major rivers, as well as upon records of sediment accumulating in man-made reservoirs.

The denudation rate, which can be expressed in terms of depth of removal of rock per 1000 yr, varies greatly with average elevation of the contributing surface and with nature of the vegetative cover of that surface. For a continental surface of moderate to low average elevation, well-forested, and under a humid climate, the rate runs 0.13 to 0.20 ft (6.8 to 6.1 cm) per 1000 yr. For a region of mountains and high plateaus under an arid climate with little effective plant cover, the rate is much higher—up to 0.5 ft (15 cm) per 1000 yr. Measurements made in some small mountainous watersheds have shown that rates of 3 to 5 ft (1 to 1.5 m) per 1000 yr are about the maximum that can be expected for high mountain masses. Compared with maximum crustal uplift of 25 ft (7.5 m) per 1000 yr, maximum denudation rates are probably not more than one-fifth to one-tenth as great, and we can conclude that orogeny can easily raise a mountain mass to high elevations before a significant portion can be removed by denudation. Existence of great alpine ranges such as the Himalayas, Alps, and Andes which are very young, geologically speaking, prove this point even without using calculated rates of uplift and denudation.

## A MODEL DENUDATION SYSTEM

Using certain reasonable assumptions, we can devise a model of the denudation process and from it perhaps obtain some idea of the order of magnitude of time spans involved in reduction of a mountain mass to a low plain.

First, it is assumed that during orogeny a substantial crustal mass is arched up (Figure 9.14). Arbitrarily, we assign a width of 100 mi (160 km) to the uplifted mass, for this is about the order of magnitude of width of a number of present-day ranges. Length of the uplift is not important in this analysis—a segment some tens of miles long will do. The uplifted mass is bordered by low areas, at or below sea level, which can serve as receptors of detritus. An initial surface of reference, close to sea level, is raised to a summit elevation of, say, 20,000 ft (6 km). In Figure 9.14 a dashed line shows

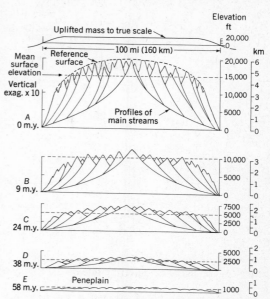

Figure 9.14. Schematic diagram of denudation of a landmass following orogenic uplift.

how this reference surface has been deformed by the orogenic uplift. In Figure 9.15, a graph on which elevation is plotted against time, orogeny is shown by the steeply rising dashed line. Orogeny is given a span of 5 m.y., but most of the rise in elevation occurs within 2 m.y. Uplift tapers off in rate and becomes zero at zero reference time.

Denudation has been in progress during the uplift, increasing in intensity as elevation increases. The elevated mass has been carved into a maze of steep-walled gorges organized into a fluvial system of steep-gradient streams. The profile of the rugged mountain mass and the main stream system are suggested in greatly exaggerated scale in stage *A* of Figure 9.14. Let it be assumed that at time-zero the average elevation of the eroded surface lies at 15,000 ft (4.6 km). Thus some 5000 ft (1.5 km) of rock has been removed during orogenic uplift.

Starting at time-zero, a denudation rate of 3.5 ft (1.05 m) per 1000 yr is assumed for the entire surface. However, with decreasing elevation the rate of denudation itself diminishes in such a constant ratio that one-half of the available landmass is removed in each 15-m.y. period. We may call this time unit the *half-life* of the available mass. An additional assumption is that isostatic restoration occurs constantly in the ratio of 4 to 5. The initial rate of net lowering of the surface will be only one-

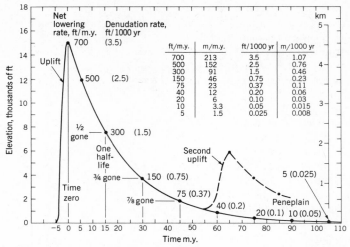

Figure 9.15. Graph of elevation change with time during landmass denudation, assuming a half-life of 15 m.y. and an initial net lowering rate of 700 ft/m.y. (213 m/m.y.).

fifth of the denudation rate, or 0.7 ft (21 cm) per 1000 yr. In m.y. units, this net lowering rate is 700 ft/m.y. (213 m/m.y.) at time-zero. As shown by labels on the descending curve of Figure 9.15, when the elevation is reduced to 7500 ft (2.3 km) at the end of 15 m.y., the net rate of lowering will have fallen to about 300 ft/m.y. (91 m/m.y.).

What we are describing here is a negative exponential-decay process not unlike the mass rate of decay of radioactive isotopes (Chapter 7). The curve of elevation flattens with the passage of time. Rates of denudation comparable with those observed today in the central and eastern United States are attained when the average elevation is about 1000 ft (0.3 km) after a lapse of some 60 m.y. Thereafter further decline in elevation is extremely gradual.

Any one of a large number of arbitrary initial values of elevation and net lowering rates might be substituted. The particular values selected for illustration seem to be commensurate with what is known about denudation rates.

Figure 9.14 shows a succession of imagined profiles of the landmass, as it is lowered. The gradients of the streams are shown as declining with time, while the valley-side slopes become less steep. The overall ruggedness of the landscape therefore decreases with time and gradually assumes a more subdued aspect (Figures 9.16 and 9.17). When the average elevation is reduced to 1000 ft (0.3 km) and less, the land surface may be considered to represent a *peneplain*. The word *peneplain* was coined by a

Figure 9.16. The San Gabriel Mountains, near Montrose and Altadena, California. (Photograph by A. N. Strahler.)

geomorphologist, W. M. Davis, from two words: *penultimate* and *plain*. It is evident from the nature of the exponential-decay curve that zero elevation can never be reached. Instead, elevation approaches zero as time approaches infinity. Thus our model of denuda-

Figure 9.17. The Blue Ridge Upland in North Carolina. (Photograph by Frank J. Wright.)

tion has no ultimate stage. In this context, the word *peneplain* is appropriate. Attainment of a peneplain in an uninterrupted denudation span of 40 to 70 m.y. is not an unreasonable guess, considering that most of the geologic periods are about of that order of duration. Continuous sedimentation throughout a single geologic period can thus be roughly equated to the contemporaneous denudation of an adjacent mountain mass produced by orogeny at the start of the period.

The denudation process can be interrupted at any point by renewal of orogenic uplift. A new curve of denudation then follows the cessation of uplift (Figure 9.15). Interruption can occur early in the denudation process, when elevations are high and relief is strong, or it may occur in the peneplain stage, when relief is low and even a minor crustal uplift can have radical effects.

In the model of landmass denudation illustrated in Figure 9.14 both channel slopes and valley-wall slopes are shown to be steepest in the early stage of denudation, when average elevations are highest. Erosion rates are most rapid at this time, and, consequently, within the total system the most rapid rates of energy transformation are found at this time. However, as the net lowering of land surfaces continues the potential energy of the system is steadily reduced, with the result that erosion rates diminish. A reduction in rate of downcutting of stream channels (because average elevation drop in the given horizontal distance is reduced) reduces also the rate at which valley walls are subjected to undermining. Under the attack of weathering, mass wasting, and overland flow the valley walls can now be reduced to lower angles of inclination. Reduction in angle tends also to reduce the rates of slope wasting and hence to reduce the rate of production of debris, as well as to reduce the average size of the particles. In response, stream channels become graded to lower slopes.

Evidence of peneplains of the geologic past is given in Chapter 13 by examples from the inner gorge of Grand Canyon. There we can reconstruct a multiple history of peneplanation followed by orogeny (see Figure 13.7).

## THE ROLE OF FLUVIAL DENUDATION THROUGHOUT GEOLOGIC TIME

The principal geologic role of the continental denudation process, as presented in Chapter 8, has been that of producing sediment, part of which becomes consolidated sedimentary rock of the continents and part of which enters the deep ocean basins. Estimates have been made of the yearly rate of total mass transport from continents to ocean basins. The figure comes to about 10 million metric tons per year. Although the calculations are subject to some uncertainty in view of the lack of sufficient basic information, they show clearly that streams contribute almost all of the total mineral matter entering the oceans. Furthermore, since most of the sediment accumulates in water depths of less than 10,000 ft (3 km), much of it remains near the continental margins.

Let us now consider the production and accumulation of sediment in terms of geologic time, using the annual rate of 10 million ($10^{10}$) metric tons. It has been estimated that the total existing world mass of sediments, including the sedimentary rocks, is $1.7 \times 10^{18}$ metric tons, which is about 200 million times the annual increment. Consequently, all of the known sediment of the earth could have been furnished by continental denudation in about 200 m.y. (or since late Triassic time). However, sedimentary rocks (now metamorphosed) have been dated as 3 billion years (b.y.) old, or even older, thus it is certain that many times over the mass of sedimentary material has been produced than now exists. What became of this enormous mass of sediment? The answer lies in the rock-transformation cycle. While some sedimentary strata became metamorphic rocks without undergoing melting, it seems inescapable that most of the sediment eventually was melted to produce magmas deep within orogenic belts. These magmas intruded higher parts of the crust to become batholiths of plutonic igneous rock, largely of granitic composition. Vast areas of such granitic igneous rock must have been exposed over the continental shields for long spans of geologic time. Therefore the same mineral matter must have been recycled repeatedly, passing through the sequence of denudation, sedimentation, metamorphism and remelting, intrusion, crustal uplift, and again release by denudation to begin the next cycle.

The rock-transformation cycle and the production of metamorphic rock are taken up again in the next chapter, where we return to the endogenetic processes as agents of crustal bending and breaking.

## GLACIER EROSION, TRANSPORTATION, AND DEPOSITION

Just as in the case of streams of water, glaciers represent to the geologist much more than gravity systems of water flow within the hydrologic cycle, as described in Chapter 6. Glaciers cause erosion, transportation, and deposition of mineral matter and are thus contributors to the total process of continental denudation.

In valley-glacier systems rock fragments are incorporated into glacial ice from the subglacial rock floor and walls (Figure 9.18). Close to the headwall of the *cirque,* or collecting basin, meltwater pouring down from snowbanks above the glacier enters the joint fractures in the headwall rock, where it freezes into seams of ice. Joint blocks are thus pried loose, in the freeze-thaw process described in Chapter 8, to become incorporated into the upper end of the glacier. Beneath the glacier, ice may flow plastically around joint blocks, then drag them loose when a sudden blockslip movement occurs, an activity termed *glacial plucking.* Blocks of rock being carried within the glacial ice are scraped and dragged along the rock floor, gouging and grooving the bedrock and chipping out fragments of rock, a process of abrasion termed simply *grinding.*

Still another source of glacier load is the rolling and sliding of rock fragments down the steep sides of the cirque and the valley walls adjacent to the ice stream. At the glacier margin the fragments are dragged along by the moving ice. These marginal embankments of debris are termed *lateral moraines* and can be seen in Figure 9.19. After the glacier has disappeared, these embankments form ridges parallel with the valley walls (Figure 9.20). Where two ice streams join, the debris of the inner lateral moraines is dragged out into the middle of the combined ice streams to form a long line of debris termed a *medial moraine*

(Figure 9.19). Debris supplied from marginal slopes remains largely on the glacier surface.

In the zone of ablation, wasting of the glacier surface, combined with down-valley flowage, brings lower layers of ice progressively nearer to the surface. Here any rock fragments that were incorporated into the ice by plucking and grinding now emerge at the surface, giving the ice a dirt-covered appearance.

Near the terminus the proportion of solid load to ice increases greatly, until at the very end there is more solid debris than ice (Figure 9.21). This residual mass of rock debris constitutes the *end moraine* of the glacier and may take the form of a bouldery embankment curved convexly down-valley (Figure 9.20). The end moraine commonly extends up-valley on either side as a lateral moraine. Because glacial recession leaves the end and lateral moraines largely intact, they serve to document the earlier glacial history of the area and will show the maximum limits of ice advance.

In observing the huge boulders composing glacial moraines, we may not realize that much rock is also ground by the glacier into extremely fine particles—of fine silt and clay size—constituting glacial *rock flour.* This material in suspension gives to meltwater streams issuing from a glacier a characteristic milky appearance. Settling out in lakes beyond the glacier limit, the rock flour forms layers of silt and clay. Should we examine such sediments under a microscope, we would find that the particles are freshly broken, angular, mineral grains of numerous types rather than being composed of the clay minerals which characterize the clay sediments derived by chemical decay of rock.

At times during the Pleistocene Epoch, or "Ice Age," which began about $-2$ m.y. and ended only very recently, almost every stream-carved valley at high elevation within a mountain system was occupied by a valley glacier.

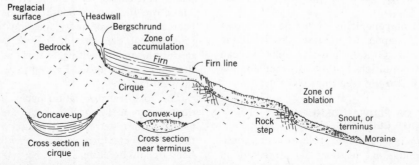

Figure 9.18. Idealized longitudinal and transverse sections of a simple alpine glacier.

Figure 9.19. Oblique air view of a glacier of the Swiss Alps, Mer de Glace, famed as the subject of early glaciological observations. (Swissair Photo.)

Figure 9.20. Lateral and end moraines forming continuous loops and marking the sides and end of a former valley glacier in two positions. (© 1960, John Wiley & Sons, New York. After a sketch by W. M. Davis.)

Continued glacial erosion greatly altered the topography of these mountain areas. As you can see in the background of Figure 19.19, the enlargement and deepening of cirques has consumed the rock masses between them, so that there remain knife-edged ridge crests and sharply pointed peaks.

The body of the glacier deepens and widens the valley it occupies, converting it into a *glacial trough* of U-shaped cross-profile (Figure 9.22A). After the ice has disappeared there remains a trough-shaped valley (Figure 9.22B). Floors of cirques and glacial troughs normally contain a series of basins, and these are subsequently occupied by lakes. Where a glacial trough was carved to depths well below sea level, and has been subsequently invaded by sea water, the result is a *fiord* (Figure 9.22C). Partial filling of the trough by stream-deposited sediments has in many cases produced a flat valley floor within the trough (Figure 9.22D).

The erosive action and depositional forms of

continental ice sheets differ in some important respects from those of valley glaciers, since an ice sheet covers the land surface completely and overrides all preexisting landforms. Unevenly distributed sites and depths of bedrock erosion in areas well back from the ice front result in a terrain of many shallow lakes and marshes exemplified over wide areas of the Canadian Shield (Figure 9.23).

Near the marginal zones of Pleistocene ice

Figure 9.21. Shrunken remnant of the Black Glacier, almost buried in its own morainal debris. Bishop range, Selkirk Mountains, British Columbia. Talus cones have been built from the valley walls. (Photograph by H. Palmer, Geological Survey of Canada.)

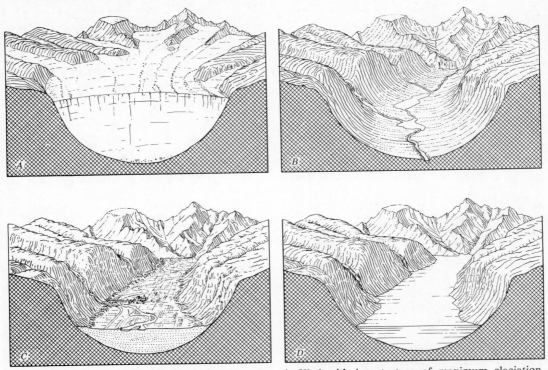

Figure 9.22. Glacial-trough development. (*A*) Trough filled with ice at stage of maximum glaciation. (*B*) Trough free of ice; U-shaped cross-profile. (*C*) Trough floor partly filled with alluvial deposits. (*D*) Trough partly submerged; a fiord. (© 1960, John Wiley & Sons, New York. Based on drawings by Erwin Raisz.)

Figure 9.23. This esker, near Boyd Lake in Canada, crosses irregular hills of glacially eroded bedrock and rock basin lakes. (Photograph by Canada Department of Mines, Geological Survey.)

sheets large accumulations of debris, known collectively as *glacial drift,* were built by the ice itself and by streams of meltwater issuing from stagnant ice (Figure 9.24). Debris of widely assorted sizes, including a large proportion of boulders, dragged forward by ice motion or released directly from the ice during melting, produced *till,* which accumulated at the ice margin as a *terminal moraine.* Most moraines show a surface of innumerable deep depressions (*kettles*) left by melting out of isolated ice blocks, and intervening knobs, giving a terrain described as *knob-and-kettle* (Figure 9.25). In front of the stagnant ice, streams build an accumulation of well-washed sands and gravels, known as *outwash,* which are spread in a plain sloping away from the ice front. Ice blocks remaining from earlier advances of the ice sheet are surrounded by outwash and later melt away to produce pits which may contain ponds (Figure 9.25).

Because the last of the Pleistocene ice sheets underwent repeated minor readvances and recession periods during the long period of final disappearance, moraines occur in multiple arrangements and show convexities of outline wherever the ice moved ahead more rapidly in *lobes* (Figure 9.26).

Unlike fluvial denudation, which has acted over most of the continental surfaces throughout all of recorded geologic time, glacial denudation has been active only in brief and sporadic periods in the past. Because glacial action has been of major importance in the last 1 to 2 m.y. and continues to be prominent today, we should not be misled into holding a distorted view of the glacial role in geologic history—it is a very minor role when viewed in the perspective of geologic time.

As we inquire in Chapter 14 into the many and varied events of the Pleistocene Epoch, it will become more evident that the terrestrial environment in which Man evolved and lives today is exceptional in many ways to the prevailing tenor of most of recorded geologic time.

## WAVE ACTION AS A GEOLOGIC AGENT

Both waves and wind act upon the continents in the geologic role of denudation agents, but totally unlike the gravity-flow systems of streams and glaciers, their energy source is through direct kinetic coupling of wind with the surfaces of oceans and lands. The shores of all continents and islands and of all inland lakes are shaped by the unceasing work of waves. Energy derived from winds is carried forward by deep-water waves, and as they reach the shallow waters of a coastline their energy of orbital motion is transformed into currents and surges possessing great ability to erode rock and to transport sediment.

As an ocean wave nearing shore passes across a progressively shallower bottom, the wave becomes steeper until it collapses as a *breaker.* The orbital motion present in deep water is thus transformed into the forward surge of a water mass, which is carried landward up the sloping beach or rock platform as the *swash* (or *uprush*). Forward motion of the swash is quickly brought to a halt by frictional resistance. The water then flows back down the beach slope under the force of gravity, becoming the *backwash* (or *backrush*). The effect is that of an alternating water current, capable of dragging particles of rock in alternate landward and seaward motions.

Where great storm waves are breaking on a shore, the swash can be a powerful agent of erosion. The landward thrust may be spent against a cliff, causing undermining and cliff recession. This form of marine erosion is not only an agent of continental denudation, but it is also the source of sediment that is carried seaward to form marine sediments of the conti-

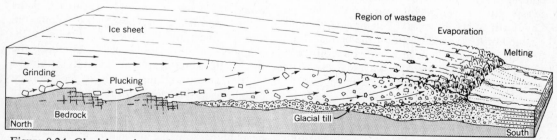

Figure 9.24. Glacial erosion and transportation in the marginal zone of an ice sheet. (From A. N. Strahler, *A Geologist's View of Cape Cod.* © 1966 by A. N. Strahler. Reproduced by permission of Doubleday & Co., Inc.)

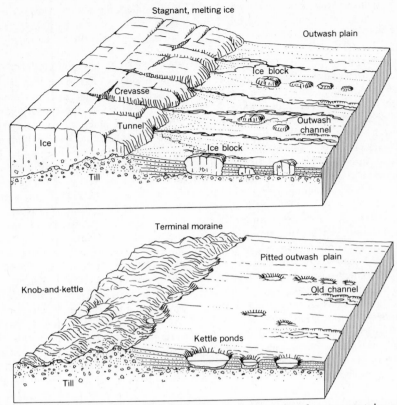

Figure 9.25. (*Above*) Building of outwash deposits along the margin of a stagnant ice sheet. (*Below*) Landforms remaining after disappearance of ice (From A. N. Strahler, *A Geologist's View of Cape Cod*. © 1966 by A. N. Strahler. Reproduced by permission of Doubleday & Co., Inc.)

nental shelves. Many shorelines of the continents today are characterized by a *marine cliff* of wave erosion and a broad *abrasion platform* extending seaward from the base of the cliff (Figure 9.27).

Where sediment of sand and gravel sizes has accumulated in substantial quantities in the zone of breaking waves, a *beach* is formed. Some details of a typical sand beach are shown in Figure 9.28. Sand carried shoreward by the bottom drag of incoming waves is built by the swash into a benchlike feature, the *berm*. Landward of the berm is a belt of dunes built by wind of loose sand swept off the berms. One or more sand ridges, or *bars,* will commonly be found in the zone of breaking waves.

In certain respects beaches are analogous to the alluvial deposits of a floodplain, particularly to the point-bar deposits of meandering rivers or to alluvial fans. In all these cases moving water shapes excess quantities of detritus into sorted and layered deposits. For both river and beach deposits the accumulation is closely

associated with a condition of grade, or equilibrium, in that the deposition represents an attempt by the fluid agent to restore and maintain an equilibrium profile despite a continuous series of disturbances tending to upset the equilibrium.

In the foregoing discussion we have assumed that the wave crests are parallel with the water line and that each wave breaks at the same instant along its entire length. If such were the case, sediment moved by swash and backwash would travel landward and seaward in paths exactly normal to the beach—i.e., along the line of the profile shown in Figure 9.28. Actually, on most beaches waves approach the shore with some degree of obliquity at almost all times, causing the swash to be directed obliquely up the foreshore, as shown in Figure 9.29. As a result, particles carried in the swash ride obliquely up the beach face but tend to be brought back in the normal downslope direction by the backwash. With each cycle of such movement the particles are moved along the

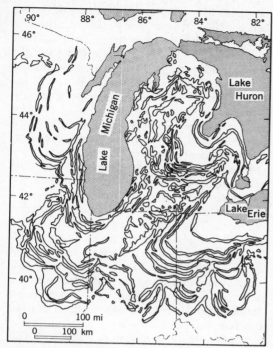

Figure 9.26. Moraines of the north central United States. (© 1965, John Wiley & Sons, New York. Based on *Glacial Map of North America,* by R. F. Flint and others.)

Figure 9.27. Abrasion platform at low tide. A pocket beach is at lower left. Pacific coast, south of Cape Flattery, Washington. (Photographer not known.)

beach by an increment of distance that may amount to several feet. Multiplied by countless repetitions, this lateral movement, termed *beach drift,* accounts for transport of vast quantities of sediment and is of primary importance in development of various kinds of beach deposits along a coast.

Still another mechanism causes lateral sediment movement in the offshore zone. When waves approach the shoreline at an angle water can flow parallel with the shore as a *longshore current* with sufficient velocity to move sediment. Longshore currents are most strongly felt in the breaker zone. Sediment movement by this process is termed *longshore drift.*

Both beach drift and longshore drift operate at the same time and in the same direction. Their combined effect in moving sediment may be called *littoral drift.*

Along a straight coast littoral drift will carry sediment continuously along the beach, often for many tens of miles, much as bed load is carried by a river (Figure 9.30). However, if the coastline undergoes an abrupt change in direction, as where a bay is encountered, sediment is carried out into open water to form a *sandspit,* a fingerlike extension of the beach. Bending of waves around the end of the spit causes the end to curve landward in a characteristic spiral of lessening radius and the spit is described as *recurved.* In pursuing our analogy of surf zone to stream, the spit may be thought of as analogous to a stream's delta, for it is a growing deposit of sediment built into open water.

The case of an embayed coast is also shown in Figure 9.30. Strong action of waves and breakers against the promontories result in erosion of an abrasion platform and a marine cliff.

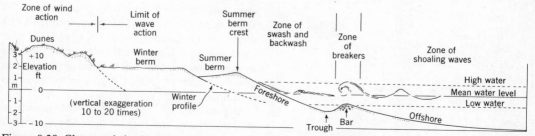

Figure 9.28. Characteristic elements and zones of the profile of a sand beach.

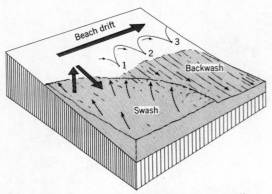

Figure 9.29. Beach drift of sand, caused by oblique approach of swash. (© 1960, John Wiley & Sons, New York.)

Detritus thus produced moves by littoral drift along the sides of the bays, where wave approach is oblique. Sediment movement is directed along both sides of the bay toward the bayhead and accumulates there, producing a crescentic *pocket beach*.

We can readily deduce the trend in evolution of an embayed coastline by imagining that the promontories are progressively eroded back while the bayheads are being filled by a widening beach. In due time the result will be a straight shoreline formed of sections of wave-

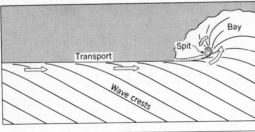

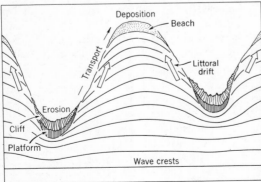

Figure 9.30. Littoral drift along a straight section of coastline, ending in a bay (*above*); along an embayed coast (*below*).

cut cliff alternating with sections of broad beach. Thus a fundamental law of shoreline evolution is that any shoreline of irregular plan tends to be reduced in time to a simple straight (or broadly curving) shoreline along which the drift of sediment is continuously in one direction for any given direction of wave approach. Removal of irregularities in shoreline plan by wave processes is analogous in some ways to the removal of falls and rapids by a stream to reach the condition of grade.

It is conceivable that, given sufficient time and stability of the crust, wave action in the surf zone might ultimately plane off an entire continent, reducing it to a shallow submarine platform. This process can be called *marine planation*. The supply of wave energy is practically limitless, since it depends upon wind stress, rather than upon the gravity-flow mechanism required by streams. Moreover, the deep ocean basins provide a sink for almost limitless quantities of detrital material derived from continental denudation.

The possibility of marine planation as a real event in the geologic past becomes somewhat more likely when we consider that fluvial denudation would be active under the same set of stable conditions. Reduction of the landmass to a peneplain would minimize the volume of rock that wave action would need to remove. Even so, the process of marine planation would be extremely slow, since the equilibrium profile of the shore is adjusted to dissipate most of the wave energy in frictional resistance.

## TIDAL FLATS AND SALT MARSHES

The growth of sandspits typically seals off a bay from the open sea, leaving only a narrow inlet for inflow and outflow of tidal currents. Bays and lagoons of any origin shut off from the open ocean are gradually filled by layers of clay and silt brought into the quiet water by streams draining the land. In this littoral environment sediment is distributed over the bay by ebb and flood tidal currents. Clays of the type illustrated in Figure 8.6 upon reaching the saline water of the bay or lagoon flocculate and settle to the bottom, where they adhere and form sediment layers. Sediment of this type has a very large proportion of water-filled voids and is capable of a high degree of compaction if drained of water.

Organic matter, both that carried in suspension in streams and that produced by growth of plants and animals on the bottom, may constitute a substantial proportion of the sediment. Gradually, the sediment is built upward until the upper surface is approximately at the level of low tide. The result is a mud flat, or *tidal flat,* exposed at low water but covered at high water (Figure 9.31).

Ebb and flood currents maintain a branching system of *tidal streams* scoured by flow in alternating directions. A completed tidal-channel network consists of trunk streams joined by tributaries of smaller dimensions and discharges, just as for ordinary fluvial systems on the land. There are, however, many interconnections among the smaller channels. Highly sinuous meanders are characteristic of tidal streams.

Upon the tidal mud flats a salt-tolerant vegetation takes hold, eventually forming a resistant mat of plant roots. More sediment is trapped by plant stems, and the level of the deposit is built up to the mean level of high tide. The resulting surface is described as a *tidal marsh,* or *salt marsh* (Figure 9.32). Tidal flats and tidal marshes encroach in succession upon the open water until the entire bay or lagoon is filled, except for the system of tidal channels. Where sea-level rise has been gradual, salt-marsh vegetation has maintained its growth at tide level by building newer layers

Figure 9.32. Tidal creek with sinuous meanders in coastal salt marsh, Rock Creek, Orleans, Massachusetts. (Photograph by Harold L. R. Cooper, Cape Cod Photos, Orleans, Mass.)

upon old. In this manner layers of *peat* are produced (not to be confused with peat formed in fresh-water bogs; see Chapter 8).

Tidal flats and salt marshes, together with their channels, constitute a highly complex life environment for both plants and animals. Production of organic matter goes on at a very high rate, with plant matter providing food for a great variety of marine animals, including shellfish and finfish.

## WIND ACTION AS A GEOLOGIC AGENT

Wind is a fourth agent of active erosion and deposition capable of producing distinctive landforms. In all probability, an analysis of the world's landscapes would show that landforms produced by wind action are of relatively minor importance compared with those produced by running water, glacial ice, and waves. Nevertheless, in certain favored localities, particularly in the world's deserts and steppes, wind produces depositional features that locally dominate the landscape. Along many of the world's coasts, including those in humid climates, belts of sand dunes are conspicuous landscape elements. From the geologic past enormous accumulations of dune sands have been preserved in the stratigraphic record. Layers of wind-transported silt are widespread over parts of the middle-latitude continents and make up the parent matter of fertile soils of greatest importance to Man.

The flow of air over a solid or liquid surface exerts a drag force, or *shearing stress,* against that surface. Air moving over a solid mineral surface, such as bedrock or hardened clay, is quite ineffectual in causing any appreciable change, so greatly does the cohesive strength of

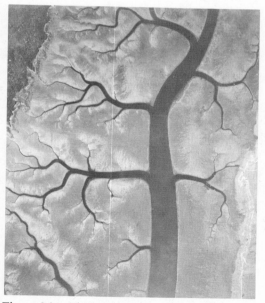

Figure 9.31. Tidal mudflats and tidal channels at low water near Yarmouth, Nova Scotia. This vertical air photograph covers an area about 1 mi (1.6 km) wide. (Canadian Armed Forces official photograph, No. KA51-15.)

the material exceed the stresses exerted by the wind. Only where mineral grains of relatively small size are lying loose upon an exposed surface can wind exploit its full powers of erosion and transportation.

One form of wind erosion is *sand-blast action,* in which hard mineral grains (usually of quartz) of sand sizes are driven against exposed rock surfaces projecting above a plain. Because sand grains travel close to the ground, their erosive action is limited to surfaces lying within a few feet of the flat ground over which the sand is being driven. Sand-blast action probably does not erode resistant bedrock to depths of more than a few inches and is responsible only for minor features such as notches and hollows at the base of a cliff or a boulder.

A second form of wind erosion is *deflation,* the lifting and entrainment of loose particles of clay and silt sizes, collectively referred to as *dust,** by turbulent eddies in the wind structure. The process is much like that of suspension of fine sediment in stream flow. Grains are carried up by vertical currents exceeding the settling velocities of the grains in still air. The dust is diffused upward into the atmosphere to heights ranging from a few feet to several miles, depending upon intensity of wind turbulence, duration of the wind, and fineness of the particles.

Deflation occurs where clays and silts in a thoroughly dried state are exposed on barren land surfaces. Such conditions exist in steppes and deserts generally and locally in desiccated floodplains, tidal flats, and lake beds. Even upon actively forming glacial outwash plains, deflation is active in times of cold, dry weather.

Winds of high intensity and turbulence, blowing over plains and plateaus at times when the soil is dry, lift great quantities of dust into suspension in the atmosphere, giving rise to a *dust storm* (Figure 9.33). The smaller particles may quickly diffuse to heights of thousands of feet and will travel for hundreds of miles before settling to earth in less turbulent air.

In the United States the passage of a rapidly moving cold front, bringing a turbulent mass of colder air southward over the Great Plains region, is a common cause of a severe dust storm. As the front approaches, a dark dust

* Dust carried in suspension by wind is finer than 0.01 mm (10 microns) in diameter—i.e., a silt of medium grade. Dust includes clay particles, 0.004 mm (4 microns) in diameter and finer.

Figure 9.33. This rapidly moving cloud is the leading edge of a dust storm. The dust is suspended within turbulent air of a cold front. Coconino Plateau, Arizona. (Photograph by D. L. Babenroth.)

cloud, representing the leading edge of the front, moves over the plain. When the cloud strikes it may bring semidarkness and reduce visibility to only a few yards. The fine dust penetrating into all open spaces makes breathing difficult.

The quantity of dust suspended in a great dust storm has been estimated at values up to 4000 tons/mi³ of air (875 metric tons/km³). Thus a storm 300 to 400 mi (500 to 650 km) across might be transporting at one time more than 100 million tons (90 million metric tons) of dust, or enough to produce a mound 100 ft (30 m) high and 2 mi (3 km) across. Repeated many times each year and prolonged over many centuries, dust storms have geologic importance as a method of sediment transport, but their relative importance is difficult to evaluate. Probably the present rates of removal and accumulation by dust storms are a very small fraction of the rates attributable to overland flow and stream flow in the same area.

The importance of air-borne dusts in contributing to pelagic detrital sediment of the deep ocean floors has been discussed in Chapter 8.

That thick deposits of wind-transported dust can accumulate under favorable conditions is amply demonstrated by the widespread occurrence in the middle latitudes of surficial layers of *loess,* a porous, friable, yellowish sediment of finely divided mineral fragments mostly in the size range of silt, 0.06 to 0.004 mm (62 to 4 microns) in diameter.

The grain size and mineral composition of

loess of the middle latitudes in the United States and Europe are best explained by the hypothesis that loess is wind-blown dust of Pleistocene age carried from alluvial valleys and outwash plains lying south of the limits of the ice sheets and from glacial deposits uncovered by glacial retreat.

Most American loess is found in a blanket over the north central states, with an important extension southward along the east side of the Mississippi alluvial valley and with patches over the high plains of Oklahoma and Texas. Thicknesses of 50 to 100 ft (15 to 30 m) occur locally (Figure 9.34). Most of this area lies within and immediately adjacent to the glaciated region.

In northern China, loess reaches thicknesses commonly over 100 ft (30 m), and in some places as much as 300 ft (90 m).

Removal of dust in suspension by wind from a mixture of grades, such as an alluvial deposit or beach, leaves the sand and gravel sizes behind. The sand grains travel downwind, staying close to the surface, in a manner described below, and are gradually separated from the gravel particles, which are too heavy to be moved very far by wind. Thus there comes into existence a distinctive body of sediment which we may designate as *eolian sand,* or *dune sand,* most of whose grains are from 0.004 to 0.04 in. (0.1 to 1 mm) in diameter. Wind is thus a most effective sediment-sorting agent.

Sand grains travel over a loose sand surface by a process known as *saltation,* in which individual grains make forward leaps, rebounding repeatedly off other grains. Most grains in saltation travel in a layer only a few inches in depth. There is an accompanying slow forward motion of surface sand grains under impact of leaping grains. Rate of sand transport by wind increases disproportionately with increasing wind speed.

Where wind is free to act upon large supplies of loose sand, distinctive depositional landforms result, which may take the form of fixed accumulations (*drifts*) and moundlike structures capable of downwind movement (*dunes*). Many varieties of sand dunes exist, each associated with a particular set of climatic and topographic conditions. Figure 9.35 illustrates a large area of vegetation-free dunes in a desert environment. Where the sand is in the form of a thick continuous cover, dunes take the form of transverse waves. Where the sand cover is discontinuous, individual dunes of crescent shape, known as *barchans,* are formed.

Where sparse vegetation is able to retain a hold upon masses of sand, dunes grow with irregular shapes. Locally, vegetation yields to deflation and deep hollows (*blowouts*) are formed. In the coastal dunes sketched in Figure 9.36, blowouts are bordered by high sand ridges of horseshoe shape, and those have been classified as *parabolic dunes.*

Although the intensive work of wind is limited to those specific places where unattached mineral particles are available in quantity, the wind's activities of erosion and

Figure 9.34. This nearly vertical road cut in thick loess, south of Vicksburg, Mississippi, illustrates the remarkable stability of the undisturbed material. (Photograph by Orlo Childs.)

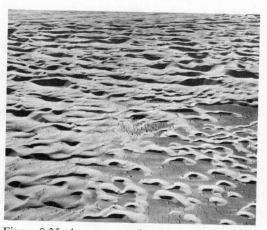

Figure 9.35. A great sea of transverse dunes, bordered by a field of barchan dunes (*lower right*). Imperial County between Calexio, California, and Yuma, Arizona. (Copyrighted Spence Air Photos.)

each mechanism of erosion most effective? Distinguish between abrasion and corrosion. What is bank-caving? How is intensity of stream erosion related to stage of stream flow?

7. What are the three forms of stream transportation? In which form of transport is fluid turbulence essential? Define stream load. How does sorting take place in stream transportation? What sizes of particles travel as bed load?

8. How does the solid load of a stream vary with relation to stream discharge? What is the factor of increase involved? How do rivers differ in concentrations of suspended load, depending upon watershed characteristics? How do streams with large quantities of coarse bed load adapt their channels to transport that load?

9. What is the concept of the graded stream? What functional needs does the condition of grade satisfy? Show how grade is achieved from an initial profile having many irregularities of form. How is the expenditure of energy distributed in a graded stream? Does the condition of grade exist in fact at any given instant? Consider changes in discharge and their effects in preparing an answer.

10. Why does the gradient (channel slope) of a graded stream decrease in the downstream direction? Use the principle of efficiency as related to cross-sectional area. Derive a statement of the law of declivities. How does segmentation of the graded profile conform with that law? Will a graded stream undergo a profile change with the passage of time? Explain.

11. What is meant by an alluvial river? Describe the form of meanders and explain their development and growth. In your answer use the following terms: sweep, meander neck, cutoff, oxbow lake. Of what material are overbank deposits formed? How are natural levees built?

12. Explain stream aggradation and degradation. What conditions are responsible for these activities? Describe an aggrading stream. Why is the channel braided? Describe an alluvial fan and explain its construction. Of what material is a fan built, and how does it function as a storage medium of ground water?

13. What is a delta? How is it related to the functions of a stream? What role does flocculation play in delta formation in salt water? In what ways is a delta analogous in function and form with an alluvial fan?

14. Explain the concept of available land-

mass in the denudation process. How is the principle of isostasy involved in this concept? What is the significance of high alpine mountain ranges in terms of relative effects of endogenetic and exogenetic processes?

15. Explain the concept of available landmass in the denudation process. How is the principle of isostasy involved in this concept? What is the significance of high alpine mountain ranges in terms of relative effects of endogenetic and exogenetic processes?

16. Discuss rates of orogenic uplift in comparison with rates of denudation. How do denudation rates vary with average elevation of the land surface? Upon what kinds of evidence are estimated rates of uplift and denudation based?

17. Describe a model denudation system, and show how elevation and denudation rates must decline with passage of time. Compare this decay system with that of radioactive isotopes (Chapter 7). How would the term *half-life* fit into this denudation model?

18. What is a peneplain? In what sense is a peneplain the "penultimate" surface of denudation? Give a general figure for the time required to produce a peneplain under conditions of crustal stability. How will valley-wall slopes change in angle throughout denudation? Describe the land surface of a peneplain.

19. Place the continental denudation process in its geologic role. Compare estimates of total estimated sediment production throughout geologic time with estimates of total existing crustal sedimentary rock. Explain the discrepancy, and comment on its geological significance.

20. Describe the process of glacier erosion. What is a cirque? Describe the moraines formed by a valley glacier. What is rock flour? Describe glacial troughs and fiords.

21. What are the various forms of glacial-drift accumulations of a continental ice sheet? What role do blocks of stagnant ice play in forming surface relief features? What is outwash?

22. Describe the action of breaking waves on a beach. What forms of deposition and erosion result from wave action? Relate the condition of equilibrium of a beach to that of grade of a stream.

23. Explain how the action of waves and currents transports detritus along the shore. What processes are combined in littoral drift? What is a sandspit, and how is it formed? What

is the fundamental law of form evolution of an embayed coastline? How important is marine planation?

24. Under what conditions do tidal mud flats and salt marshes accumulate? What is the environmental importance of these coastal zones for life forms?

25. How does wind act as a geologic agent? Where is wind action most important? Describe the processes of wind erosion and transportation. Describe a dust storm. What is loess? How do dunes form? What is saltation? Describe one or more common dune forms.

26. Review the major concepts of continental denudation as a geologic process, using the model of an exponential-decay system and analyzing energy sources. What is the importance of denudation processes and the resulting landforms in the environment of Man?

# chapter 10
# geologic systems:
# ii. radiogenic heat
# and diastrophism

This chapter continues an inquiry into the geologic system of radiogenic heat and its effects. We shall postulate that extremely slow convectional movements exist within the mantle. It is conceivable that such currents are set in motion and sustained by inequalities in the production and concentration of radiogenic heat within the mantle. Convection systems involve vertical motions of rising and sinking, as well as horizontal motions paralleling the earth's surface. The overlying lithospheric shell can thus be subjected to various sets of forces, depending upon location with respect to the convection currents. One product of such forces is *diastrophism*, or crustal breaking and bending. Where lithospheric plates are brought together, the crust and its veneer of sediments is compressed and caused to buckle and fracture in long, narrow uplift belts, located close to continental margins. Where the lithospheric plates are pulled apart, the crust is rifted in fracture zones located largely in mid-oceanic areas.

Along crustal zones of both compression and rifting, rise of molten rock, explained in Chapter 7, has taken place. Along mountain belts of compression there has occurred the rise of felsic (granitic) magma to form batholiths. Along mid-oceanic fracture belts there has been a rise of basaltic magma, spreading out upon the ocean floor. Volcanoes have appeared in large numbers along these same belts. Earthquakes are generated in large numbers by sudden slippage along fractures in active crustal belts; these represent yet another form of energy release.

As a working hypothesis we view all of these varieties of crustal activity as forms of energy transformation and work done as accumulated radiogenic heat makes it escape to the earth's surface and eventually into outer space. Moreover, there is evidence that the continents themselves are the accumulated end products of the varied processes of diastrophism, vulcanism, and intrusion and have evolved and expanded throughout geologic time, rather than being originally present at the time the layered earth structure evolved.

## ISLAND ARCS AND TRENCHES

Present-day crustal activity in the form of earthquakes, vulcanism, uplift of high mountain chains, and down-sinking in deep trenches is principally concentrated in long, narrow, broadly curving zones known as the *primary arcs.* As seen on a world map (Figure 10.1), these arcs fall into two chains. First is the *circum-Pacific belt,* already referred to in Chapter 7 as the locus of much volcanic activity. Throughout North and South America, arcs of the circum-Pacific belt lie along the western continental margins, except for the West Indies Arc, which is oceanic. Starting with the Aleutian Arc, and continuing south along the western side of the Pacific, the primary arcs are in oceanic positions at some distance from the Asiatic shoreline. In large part, these arcs are represented by chains of volcanic islands. Second of the chains of primary arcs is the *Eurasian-Melanesian belt,* extending from the Mediterranean region, eastward through southern Asia, and terminating in the Indonesian Arc, which appears to intersect the circum-Pacific belt in a T-junction. Notice that the primary arcs are convexly bowed outward from the continental centers, a

form that must be highly significant in terms of the mechanics of their origin.

The primary arcs contain the world's great mountain ranges, which are commonly described as belonging to the *alpine system.* Exemplary are the Alps of Europe, the Himalayas of southern Asia, the Andes of South America, and the Cordilleran ranges of western North America. Comparative recency of the uplift of these ranges is well established by identification and dating of fossils of marine origin among the summit rocks. Because mountain-making is an active process in the primary arcs, they are also known as *orogenic belts,* after the word *orogeny* (from the Greek *oros,* mountain, and *geneia,* origin) applied to mountain-making by bending and breaking of the crust, as distinguished from magma extrusions in vulcanism.

Of equal interest to the alpine ranges are deep *trenches,* or *foredeeps,* typically located adjacent to the mountain chains on their oceanic sides. Trenches of the western Pacific Ocean are particularly striking (Figure 10.2). These oceanic trenches represent narrow zones of extreme crustal sinking (as opposed to zones of excavation of rock). They have bottom depths on the order of 24,000 to 30,000 ft (7.5 to 10 km) below sea level. Equally impressive is the Peru-Chile Trench (Figure 10.3). Because sources of sediment are quite limited in

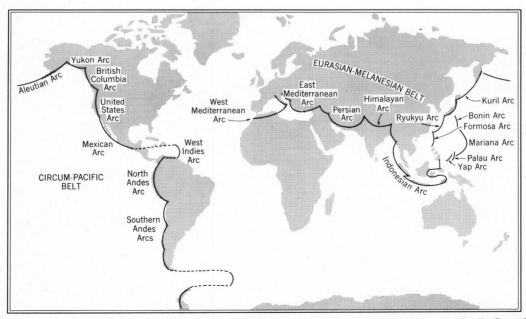

Figure 10.1. Generalized world map of the primary arcs. [After a map by J. A. Jacobs, R. D. Russell, and J. T. Wilson (1959), *Physics and Geology,* New York, McGraw-Hill, p. 291, Figure 14-1.]

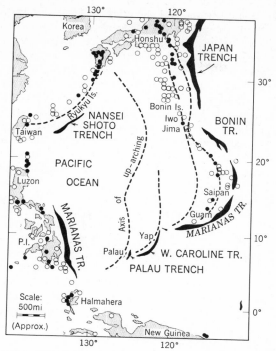

Figure 10.2. Map of the western Pacific Ocean showing trenches (black), island arcs (dashed lines), active volcanoes (black dots), and epicenters of deep-focus earthquakes (open circles). (© 1960, John Wiley & Sons, New York. Based on a map by H. H. Hess.)

the vicinity of an oceanic trench, these depressions are only partly filled with sediment. On the other hand, comparable belts of crustal depression adjacent to mountain ranges on the continents are filled with sediment derived by stream erosion and transportation from the mountains. An example is the Indo-Gangetic plain of northern India and Pakistan, which is filled to a depth of thousands of feet by sediment derived from the Himalayan range.

In summary, each primary arc consists basically of an elevated mountain chain bordered by a deeply depressed trench located on the oceanic side of the arc. These superficial characteristics must be explained by orogeny involving deep-seated crustal processes.

## EARTHQUAKES AND FAULTING

We are all familiar with the outward phenomena of the *earthquake*, whether by direct experience or from first-hand accounts. In a severe earthquake the ground is sensibly moved, often with destructive violence. It is evident that the earthquake is a form of instantaneous release of mechanical energy. Sudden motion of one segment of the earth's crust against another is associated with the earthquake. *Faulting*, the geologist's term for the displacement between rock masses in contact,

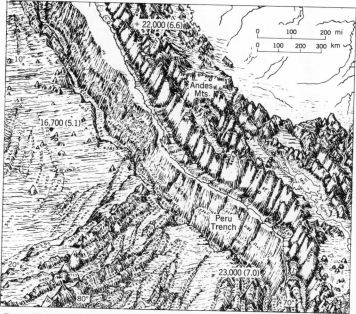

Figure 10.3. The Peru-Chile Trench, off the west coast of South America. [Portion of *Physiographic Diagram of the South Atlantic Ocean* (1961). By B. C. Heezen and M. Tharp, Boulder, Colo., Geol. Soc. Amer., reproduced by permission.]

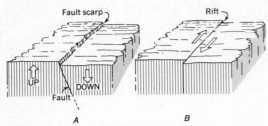

Figure 10.4. (*A*) Normal fault. (*B*) Transcurrent, or strike-slip fault.

is the immediate cause of most earthquakes. We may think of faulting as a sudden slippage along a more or less planelike surface of separation. Motion may be largely in the vertical direction (*normal fault*) or in the horizontal direction (*transcurrent fault*), as illustrated in Figure 10.4.

Faulting is a type of structural failure typical of brittle solids, which can accommodate a certain degree of stress with only a very small elastic deformation, but which fail by sudden rupture when a limit of strength is exceeded. *Elastic strain,* which precedes the rupture, is essentially a bending of the solid. When the stress is removed, the solid unbends, returning to the original form. Mechanical energy is stored within a solid that is in a state of being elastically strained. When the limit of strength is reached, the occurrence of a rupture instantly releases the stored strain. The result is the formation of wave motions that are propagated throughout the surrounding substance, gradually distributing the energy and transforming it through friction into heat as resistance is encountered in the traveling waves.

A simple laboratory model of an earthquake is shown in Figure 10.5. A steel saw blade is flexed between two firm end supports, one of

which is moved past the other. Energy is stored in the flexing of the blade, then suddenly released as the blade snaps. We are aware of the energy release through a train of sound waves sent out from the broken ends of the blade. The same model can be applied on a more realistic basis to a common form of earthquake, illustrated in Figure 10.6. Here we are looking down upon a small square of the earth, perhaps one mile on a side. Imagine that in prehistoric time a line (*A–B*) has been drawn on the surface and that lateral forces acting in opposite directions along the two sides of the block have gradually bent the rock in such a way as to deform the straight line into an S-shaped bend, as shown in the second block. In modern times a railroad or fence is built straight across the deformed area, the presence of strain being unknown. In the third block the fault movement has occurred, releasing the elastic strain and causing the fence to be broken and its ends to assume a bent plan (Figure 10.7). The original reference line, *A–B*, is again restored to straightness.

The earthquake model outlined above is known as the *elastic-rebound theory.* Precision ground measurements taken repeatedly over many years on both sides of a known earthquake fault line, as well as observations of the offsetting and bending of reference lines, such as fences, have established beyond a doubt the correctness of the elastic-rebound theory as applied to the great San Francisco earthquake

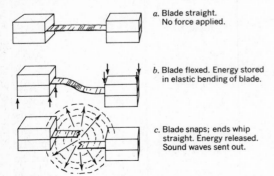

*a.* Blade straight. No force applied.

*b.* Blade flexed. Energy stored in elastic bending of blade.

*c.* Blade snaps; ends whip straight. Energy released. Sound waves sent out.

Figure 10.5. A steel blade, bent until it snaps, illustrates certain basic features of the earthquake mechanism.

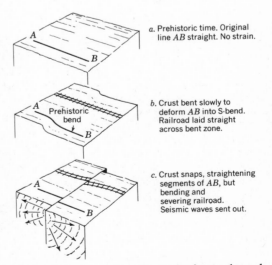

*a.* Prehistoric time. Original line *AB* straight. No strain.

*b.* Crust bent slowly to deform *AB* into S-bend. Railroad laid straight across bent zone.

*c.* Crust snaps, straightening segments of *AB*, but bending and severing railroad. Seismic waves sent out.

Figure 10.6. An earthquake results from the sudden release of elastic strain that has been accumulated in rock over a long period of time.

Figure 10.7. This road in the Santa Cruz Mountains of California was offset by fault movement during the San Francisco earthquake of April 18, 1906. Lateral displacement was about 4 ft (1.2 m). [Sketched from a photograph by E. P. Carey (1906), *Jour. of Geography,* vol. 5, no. 7, p. 292.]

of 1906 along the San Andreas fault, a major transcurrent fault, in northern California (Figure 10.8). Here it was ascertained that the maximum fault movement was 20 ft (6.4 m). The slow bending preceding the earthquake had probably been going on for hundreds of years. In the period from 1851 to 1906 geodetic surveys actually measured a significant deformation of the rock preceding the slippage.

The elastic-rebound theory may not apply to all major earthquakes, particularly to those at great depth where conditions of pressure and temperature are unlike those at the earth's surface. Nevertheless, the general principle of the sudden release of stored energy of rock strain appears to be behind all major earthquakes.

Earthquakes are generated in the earth's crust and outer mantle down to depths as great as 400 mi (640 km). The point of slippage is known as the *focus,* while the ground-surface point directly above the focus is the *epicenter.* Energy is dispersed from the focus in the form of *seismic waves,* of which there are three major varieties. *Surface waves,* resembling simple ocean waves in physical behavior, travel over the earth's surface in ever-widening concentric circles, much as do the waves generated when a pebble is thrown into a quiet pond. *Primary waves* (*P-waves*), which travel through the entire earth, are waves of compression and rarefaction, in which all motion is forward and backward in the direction of the path of wave motion. *Secondary waves* (*S-waves*), which travel only through the solid crust and mantle, but not through the liquid iron core, consist of sidewise motions of particles, transverse to the direction of wave travel.

Figure 10.8. The San Andreas rift zone in the Temblor range of central California takes the form of a straight valley. View southeast through Palo Prieto Pass with Grant Lake in foreground. (Copyrighted Spence Air Photos.)

From measurement of the elapsed time of arrival of the three wave forms, as well as the amplitude of those waves, the earthquake focus can be located and its intensity can be determined. Depth of the focus can also be determined from the seismogram, along with a great deal of information concerning the physical properties of the mantle and core. Our concern here is with the intensity of earthquakes as energy-release mechanisms, as well as with the distribution of the earthquake *foci* (plural of *focus*) as indicators of the processes of crustal deformation.

Foci of earthquakes, while not strictly points, have such small dimensions as to be shown as points on a cross-sectional diagram or map. According to depth, three classes of earthquakes are recognized. Shallow-focus quakes are centered within 35 mi (55 km) of the surface; intermediate-focus quakes from 35 to 150 mi (55 to 240 km); deep-focus quakes from 185 to 400 mi (300 to 650 km). Below a depth of about 400 mi (640 km) the properties of the mantle are such that unequal stresses cause continuous slow yielding of the plastic rock, so that sufficient elastic strain cannot be stored to produce an earthquake. As noted in Chapter 7, mantle rock in the asthenosphere at depths below about 40 mi (60 km) is also capable of very slow flowage in response to stresses applied continuously over long periods of time. Thus rock in the zones of intermediate- and deep-focus earthquakes is capable of both sudden rupture by faulting and slow flowage, depending upon the nature of the stresses that are applied.

### EARTHQUAKE ENERGY AND INTENSITY

Interpretation of seismograms has made possible a calculation of the quantities of energy released as wave motion by earthquakes of various magnitudes. In 1935 a leading seismologist, Charles F. Richter, brought forth a scale of earthquake magnitudes describing the quantity of energy released at the earthquake focus. The *Richter scale* consists of numbers ranging from 0 to 8.6. The scale is logarithmic, which is to say that the energy of the shock increases by powers of 10 in relation to Richter magnitude numbers. Some data concerning various magnitudes is given below:

| Magnitude (Richter scale) | |
|---|---|
| 0 | Smallest detectable quake. Energy release $6.3 \times 10^5$ ergs. |
| 2.5–3 | Quake can be felt if it is nearby. About 100,000 shallow quakes of this magnitude per year. |
| 4.5 | Can cause local damage. |
| 5 | Energy release about equal to first atomic bomb, Alamagordo, New Mexico, 1945. |
| 6 | Destructive in a limited area. About 100 shallow quakes per year of this magnitude. |
| 7 | Rated a major earthquake above this magnitude. Quake can be recorded over whole earth. About 14 per year this great or greater. |
| 7.8 | San Francisco earthquake of 1906. Energy release $3.3 \times 10^{24}$ ergs. |
| 8.4 | Close to maximum known. Energy release $2 \times 10^{25}$ ergs. Examples: Honshu, 1933; Assam, 1950; Alaska, 1964. |
| 8.6 | Maximum observed between 1900 and and 1950. Three million times as much energy released as in first atomic bomb. |

Total annual energy release by earthquakes is roughly on the order of $10 \times 10^{26}$ ergs, most of it being from a very few quakes of magnitude greater than 7.

The actual destructiveness of an earthquake also depends upon factors other than the energy release given by Richter magnitude—for example, closeness to the epicenter and nature of the subsurface earth materials. *Intensity scales* designed to measure observed earth-shaking effects are important in engineering aspects of seismology.

An intensity scale used extensively in the United States is the *modified Mercalli scale* as prepared by Richter in 1956. This scale recognizes 12 levels of intensity, designated by Roman numerals I through XII. Each intensity is described in terms of phenomena that any person might experience. For example, at intensity IV hanging objects swing, a vibration like that of a passing truck is felt, standing automobiles rock, and windows and dishes rattle. Damage to various classes of masonry is used to establish criteria in the higher numbers of the scale. At an intensity of XII, damage to man-made structures is nearly total and large masses of rock are displaced (Figure 10.9). A detailed listing of phenomena associated with each intensity level is beyond the scope of this discussion.

Many of the destructive effects of a severe earthquake are secondary, in the sense that the earthquake movements set off gravity movements of bodies of rock, soil, and alluvial overburden. An example is the Good Friday earthquake of March 27, 1964, centered about 75 mi (120 km) from the city of Anchorage, Alaska. Magnitude on the Richter scale was 8.4 to 8.6, which is close to the maximum known. Intensity on the Mercalli scale was probably VII to VIII in Anchorage, but as most buildings were of frame construction, damage was largely through secondary effects. Of these the most important were landslides of

Figure 10.9. Severe masonry damage produced by the San Francisco earthquake and fire of 1906. View is southwest from the corner of Geary and Mason streets. (Photograph by W. C. Mendenhall, U.S. Geological Survey.)

great masses of gravel overlying layers of unstable clay (Figure 10.10). Major snowslides were set off in the adjacent mountains.

Throughout the region of the Alaskan earthquake sudden changes of land level, both up and down, took place at points as far distant as 300 mi (480 km) from the epicenter and covered a total area of about 80,000 mi$^2$ (200,000 km$^2$). A belt of uplift reaching a maximum of 30 ft (10 m) ran parallel with the coast and largely offshore, while a broad zone of shallow subsidence, reaching amounts somewhat more than −6 ft (−2 m), lay along the landward side of the uplift zone (Figure 10.11). The epicenter lay between these zones. Sudden rise of the sea floor produced a train of seismic sea waves, a phenomenon described in following paragraphs.

The supposed fault along which slippage occurred to generate the Alaska earthquake is not exposed on land, but presumably lies at depth in the offshore zone in a position between the zone of subsidence and the zone of uplift. The entire zone of seismic activity occupies a position between the volcanic Aleutian Arc on the northwest and the deep submarine Aleutian Trench on the southeast. The significance of these larger crustal structures is discussed later in this chapter.

## SEISMIC SEA WAVES, OR TSUNAMIS

An extraordinary kind of ocean wave not related to wind or tide is the *seismic sea wave,* or *tsunami,* produced by a sudden displacement of the sea floor. The displacement may be caused by a submarine landslide set off by faulting, a sudden rising or sinking of a rock mass when faulting occurs, or a submarine volcanic eruption. The effect is very much like that of dropping a stone into a very shallow, quiet pond. A series of simple oscillatory progressive waves is sent outward in concentric rings (Figure 10.12).

Seismic sea waves are of enormous length, some 60 to 120 mi (100 to 200 km), whereas the wave height may be only 1 to 2 ft (0.3 to 0.6 m). Such low waves cannot be felt by persons on a ship on the open sea. Seismic sea waves have periods of 10 to 30 min. A typical wave might travel at a speed of 300 mph (480 km/hr).

Seismic sea waves are very long in comparison with the depth of water in which they travel. For example, a 100-mi wavelength is roughly 33 times as great as an ocean depth of 3 mi. In such comparatively shallow water the velocity of travel of the simple oscillatory wave varies as the square root of the water depth. Therefore, if we know the time at which the wave was sent out (this information is available from earthquake records) and the time at which the wave arrived at a distant coast, we may calculate roughly the depth of ocean water lying between. Just such a procedure was used in 1856 to estimate the average depth of the Pacific Ocean, long before soundings were available to give direct measurements.

On the other hand, seismologists now issue

Figure 10.10. Slumping and flowage of unconsolidated sediments, resulting in property destruction at Anchorage, Alaska, Good Friday earthquake of March 27, 1964. (U.S. Army Corps of Engineers photograph.)

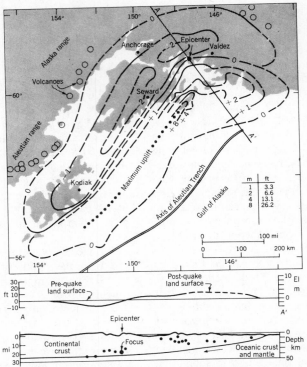

Figure 10.11. Map of south-central Alaska showing crustal uplift and subsidence associated with the Good Friday earthquake of March 27, 1964. Contours in meters. Profile and structure section below are drawn through the epicenter along a NW–SE line (*AA'*). [Redrawn and simplified from G. Plafker (1965), *Science*, vol. 148, p. 1677, Figure 2, and p.1681, Figure 6.]

warnings of possible destructive seismic sea waves, using the known depths of the ocean and the known instant of the earthquakes as a basis for computing the time the first waves will reach a given coast (Figure 10.12).

Upon reaching a distant shore the individual wave crest takes the form of a slow rise in water level over a period of 10 to 15 min. Superimposed on this are ordinary wind waves. These waves break close to shore, producing a destructive surf. Several great catastrophes in recorded history have been wrought by seismic sea waves. For example, flooding of the Japanese coast in 1703, with a loss of more than 100,000 lives, may have been of this cause. One should not confuse the seismic sea waves with coastal flooding caused by storm surges (see Chapter 5).

## EARTHQUAKE DISTRIBUTION

A world map showing the plotted epicenters of many large shallow earthquakes can reveal much about crustal activity (Figure 10.13). The picture is essentially the same for earthquakes of lower magnitudes and for different

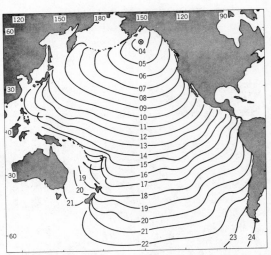

Figure 10.12. Map of the Pacific Ocean showing the location of a tsunami wave front at 2-hr intervals, GMT. The wave originated in the Gulf of Alaska as a result of the Good Friday earthquake of March 27, 1964. [After B. W. Wilson and A. Torum (1968), U.S. Army Corps of Engineers, *Tech Memorandum No. 25,* Washington, D.C., Coastal Engineering Research Center, p. 38, Figure 27.]

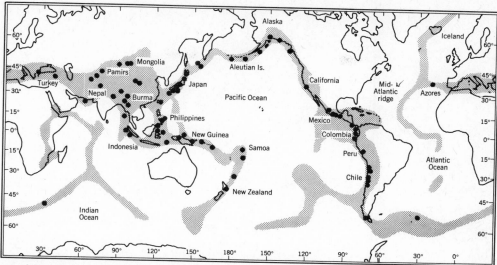

Figure 10.13. World distribution of shallow-focus earthquakes. Black dots show epicenters of major earthquakes (7.9 or over on the Richter scale); shaded zones are principal areas of abundant earthquakes. [Generalized from data of C. F. Richter (1958), *Elementary Seismology*, San Francisco, W. H. Freeman and Co., Figures 25-3 and 25-4; 26-3 through 26-15.]

spans of time. Notice particularly the great concentration in the circum-Pacific belt of primary mountain and island arcs and their related trenches. It is estimated that earthquakes of this belt account for about 80% of the total world earthquake energy release. Of further interest is the fact that large earthquakes are much more numerous on the western (Asiatic) side of the Pacific, where island arcs dominate, than on the eastern (American) side, where mountain arcs lie on the continental margins. Earthquakes also correspond with the Eurasian-Melanesian belt of primary arcs but are somewhat fewer and more dispersed than in the circum-Pacific belt. This belt accounts for about 15% of the total energy release.

Yet another location of frequent earthquakes is in mid-ocean in the Atlantic Ocean, Indian Ocean, and southern Pacific Ocean. We will later see that this seismic zone coincides with the Mid-Oceanic Ridge system. Although no areas of the world are entirely free of earthquakes, large parts of the continental interiors have very few, a fact of importance in considering the origin and history of these sections of the granitic continental crust.

## DEEP-FOCUS EARTHQUAKES AND THRUST FAULTING

Deep-focus and intermediate-focus earthquakes occur in far fewer numbers than the shallow-focus quakes and account for far less

of the total world earthquake energy release; the energy percentages are approximately as follows: shallow, 85%; intermediate, 12%; deep, 3%.

What is of great importance in interpreting the crustal movements that produce primary arcs is the relative location of the foci of shallow, intermediate, and deep earthquakes. Figure 10.14 is a map of the Pacific Ocean and its bordering lands, showing schematically the three depth classes of earthquakes. The nature of the pattern is clear: shallow-focus earthquakes lie adjacent to the ocean basin; deep-focus earthquakes lie nearest the continental interiors; and intermediate-focus earthquakes lie between.

To analyze this pattern further, examine Figure 10.15, a block diagram showing parts of the Kuril and Japan arcs. Earthquakes appear to originate upon a sloping surface starting at the surface along the Japan Trench and reaching a depth of over 400 mi (650 km) under the Asiatic coastal mainland. Earthquakes apparently originate by local slippages along a great fault plane descending under the continental margin. Essentially the same pattern is seen in the Andean Arc of South America, but with the fault sloping down to the east under the continent.

On the assumption that the crust below the fault plane is moving downward, toward the continent, while the crust above the plane is

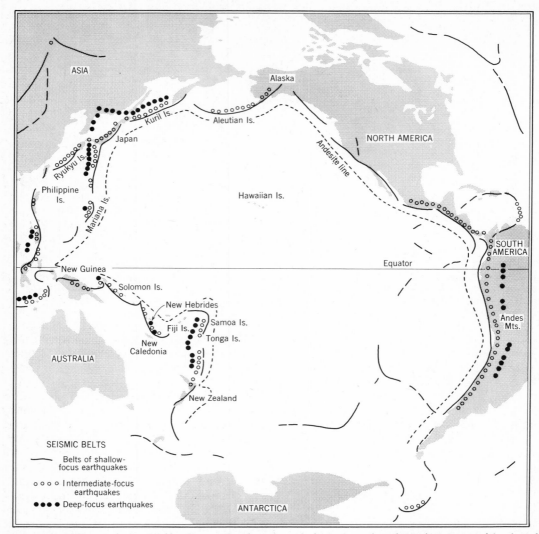

Figure 10.14. Map of the Pacific Ocean showing the relation of earthquake epicenters to island and mountain arcs. [After B. Gutenberg and C. F. Richter (1949), *Seismicity of the Earth,* Princeton, N.J., Princeton Univ. Press.]

being pushed upward toward the ocean basin, the fault belongs to a type known as a *thrust fault*. From the geometry of the blocks and their relative motion, it is clear that a thrust fault is associated with a major compressional movement in the lithosphere. Obviously, surface points lying on two sides of the fault are being brought close together as a result of such fault movement.

Independent evidence exists for the hypothesis that the deep trenches are the edges of lithospheric plates being forced down by compression. When a precision survey of the earth's gravity is made along a line crossing the

trench and island arc, it will be seen that the value of gravity is considerably less than expected over the trench, as shown by the graph in the upper part of Figure 10.15. Such a deficiency in the expected value of gravity is known as an *isostatic gravity anomaly*. The condition of isostasy explained in Chapter 7 is not present where such an anomaly exists. In this case, the anomaly has a negative sign and may be interpreted as meaning that the crust beneath the trench is being forcibly held in a depressed position (Figure 10.16). Powerful forces of lithospheric compression are implied by the existence of the negative gravity anom-

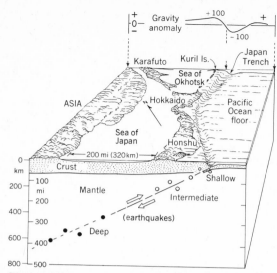

Figure 10.15. Block diagram of the Japan-Kuril Arc showing how earthquake foci are distributed in the crust and mantle beneath. [Based on data of B. Gutenberg and C. F. Richter (1949), *Seismicity of the Earth,* Princeton, N.J., Princeton Univ. Press.]

aly. Over the adjacent mountain arc, the gravity is unexpectedly high in value (a *positive* gravity anomaly) and may be interpreted as representing a part of the crust forcibly raised along the upper edge of the rising fault block.

Closely tied in with the seismic activity of the circum-Pacific belt is the presence of chains of active volcanoes composed of andesitic lavas (see Chapter 7). This volcanic belt surrounds the huge central region of oceanic basalts and isolated basaltic volcanoes of the Pacific Ocean basin. A line was drawn in the southwest Pacific to mark the division between andesitic and basaltic rocks. The *andesite line,* as this boundary is known, is often taken as marking the outer limit of the Pacific Ocean basin as a

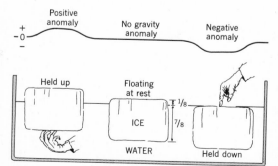

Figure 10.16. The principle of an isostatic gravity anomaly can be illustrated by a floating cake of ice.

geologic unit (see Figure 10.14). Although large ocean areas—such as the Philippine Sea, Sea of Japan, Sea of Okhotsk, and Bering Sea—lie between the andesite line and the Asiatic mainland, those seas with their island arcs and trenches are considered as lying within the continental margins. Along the eastern side of the Pacific, the andesite line is drawn close to the continents. Here island arcs are missing. Consequently, there is a fundamental difference in this respect between the two sides of the Pacific Ocean basin.

From the existence of andesite lavas we infer that local melting occurs at great depth close to the sloping fault plane. Basaltic rock of the oceanic crust, carried down with the sinking edge of the lithospheric plate, would be entering regions of progressively higher temperatures. Perhaps local melting occurs and the new magma is differentiated into two fractions: a felsic magma that rises toward the surface and an ultrabasic magma that remains behind. This process is illustrated in Figure 10.32, where andesitic magmas are shown to be rising in bubblelike masses to reach the upper crust in the island arc.

## GEOSYNCLINES AND OROGENY

Orogenic belts have appeared at many times throughout the earth's past 3.5 billion years (b.y.) of recorded geologic history. A typical orogeny, or period of mountain-making, has passed through a series of evolutionary stages, seen today in various parts of the primary arcs of the alpine system and in the remains of older belts long since deeply eroded and exposed to examination.

Perhaps the earliest stages of orogeny are represented by island arcs and trenches, such as those of the western Pacific. The upper block diagram of Figure 10.17 shows an island arc and its adjacent trench, together with the slanting underthrust fault passing beneath it. Between the mainland and the island arc, which consists of andesitic volcanoes and lavas, is a shallow sea underlain by continental crust with an upper granitic layer.

Erosion of the rapidly forming volcanic islands produces large quantities of clastic sediment derived by weathering and erosion of the volcanic rock. This sediment is carried by streams into the adjacent coastal areas. Spread over the floor of the shallow sea by tidal and bottom currents, this sediment accumulates in extensive layers, later becoming consolidated

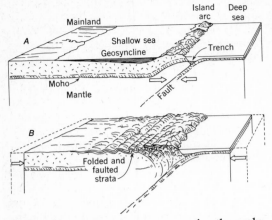

Figure 10.17. Block diagrams suggesting the evolution of a volcanic island arc into a belt of intensely deformed rocks of the continental crust.

into sedimentary rock strata. These processes of erosion and sedimentation have been described in the previous chapter.

The accumulated sedimentary strata of the shallow sea constitute a *geosyncline,* labeled in the upper block diagram of Figure 10.17. As sediment layers continue to accumulate, the geosyncline thickens and may reach a total accumulation of as much as 50,000 ft (15 km) in the central part. Under the weight of the accumulating sediment, the crust beneath the geosyncline sags into the shape of a shallow trough.

It should be pointed out that not all geosynclines are adjacent to island and mountain arcs in orogenic belts. Belts of thick sediment accumulation are also found along stable continental margins which lack young mountains and active volcanoes. For example, along the

Gulf coast of the United States there is a thick wedge of geologically young sedimentary rock derived from streams that drain the continental interior. A similar type of geosyncline exists along the continental shelf of the eastern United States.

Judging by past geologic history as interpreted from the rocks themselves, the period of geosynclinal sediment deposition comes to an end after several tens of millions of years. Intense crustal compression sets in, crumpling the geosyncline and throwing the rock layers into wavelike folds, suggested in the lower block diagram of Figure 10.17. Some further details of the ensuing changes are shown in Figure 10.18. The belt of volcanic rocks remains active adjacent to the trench. Between this belt and the undisturbed rocks of the mainland the sedimentary strata of the geosyncline are intensely crumpled. Numerous thrust faults have divided the rock mass into slices, each one riding over the slice beneath it. Crustal shortening is thereby produced.

Under high pressures and temperatures, the shearing action of compression taking place deep in the zone of intense folding has altered much of the sedimentary rock to produce metamorphic rock. As shown in Figure 10.18, the deeply buried metamorphic rock and andesite lavas in the zone of maximum compression have melted through accumulated radiogenic heat. The resulting body of magma makes its way upward by melting, dissolving, and stoping the overlying rock. Upon cooling, this magma body has become a granite batholith.

Closer to the continent, the thin layer of sedimentary strata has been thrown into a belt of open, wavelike folds, but this is a compara-

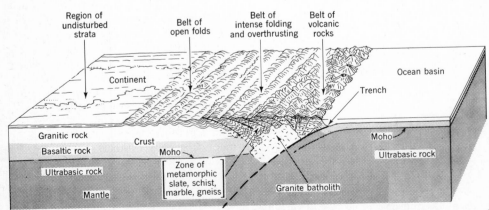

Figure 10.18. Schematic block diagram of an orogenic belt after folding and intrusion have occurred.

tively superficial action compared with the metamorphism and intrusion taking place deep within the belt of intense orogency.

## ROCK METAMORPHISM

Consideration of the third major class of rocks, the metamorphic rocks, has been deferred to this point in order that some understanding might first be gained of the nature of the orogenic process. The metamorphic rocks are by-products of orogeny and intrusion.

Metamorphism may affect rocks of both igneous and sedimentary origins. Changes may be affected by application of unequal stresses during the orogenic process under conditions of high confining pressure and high temperature. Such changes constitute *dynamothermal metamorphism* and most often take place deep within thick sedimentary strata of geosynclines. The effect of dynamothermal metamorphism is felt in two ways. First, original minerals recrystallize and new minerals are formed. Second, a new set of structures is imposed on the rock and may replace or obliterate original bedding structures. Dynamothermal metamorphism has affected enormous bodies of rock within the root zones of mountain chains of the alpine type. Consequently, the effects are seen over large areas and are often described as *regional metamorphism.*

Application of high temperatures alone can also cause metamorphism. Such effects are often conspicuous in country rock close to an igneous intrusion. The changes are essentially those of baking in a high-temperature oven. A shale rock close to an igneous contact may experience a hardening and color change not unlike that caused by baking of brick or tile. However, most large igneous intrusions cause *contact metamorphism* by emanations of hot watery solutions containing ions of many kinds. These are highly active solutions and cause mineral alteration of the country rock. The process of mineral replacement is known as *metasomatism* and may leave original structures, such as bedding in sedimentary rocks, essentially intact.

Metamorphism is a change of mineral state in response to a change in environment. Minerals unsuited to the environment of deformation under stress at high pressures and high temperatures will be altered to form minerals capable of attaining equilibrium under those environments. There will often be changes in grain size and shape as well.

Many of the most common and abundant minerals of metamorphic rocks are also abundant constituents of igneous and sedimentary rocks and have been discussed in Chapters 7 and 8. Among these are quartz, the feldspars, hornblende, olivine, biotite and muscovite micas, calcite, and dolomite. Others are newly formed aluminosilicates. As a group, these are hard minerals with specific gravities comparable to those of the mafic minerals.

## METAMORPHIC ROCKS

It has been a common practice to subdivide the metamorphic rocks into two groups. First are rocks with obvious parallel structures which appear as lines on the rock surface— these structures are *foliation,* a crude layering along which the rock easily separates, and *banding,* a layered arrangement of strongly knit crystals forming a massive rock. Second are metamorphic rocks lacking in obvious parallel structures and characterized by granular texture.

*Slate* is a very fine-grained rock that splits readily into smooth-surfaced sheets along cleavage surfaces. Slate is largely derived from fine-grained, clay-rich marine clastic sediments (shale). The cleavage of slate is a new structure imposed by metamorphism and usually cuts across the original bedding. Slate colors range from gray to green to red.

*Schist* is a foliated rock and comes in many varieties. Foliation results from the parallel alignment of easily cleavable minerals such as mica. The reflecting surfaces of these minerals give a characteristic glistening sheen to the foliation surfaces (Figure 10.19). Schists have

Figure 10.19. Mica schist. This fragment, about 6 in. (15 cm) long, shows a glistening, undulating surface of natural parting (*above*). An edgewise view (*below*) shows the thin foliation planes. (Photograph by A. N. Strahler.)

undergone a high degree of metamorphism and their origin is not always clear. Most schists are interpreted as altered clastic sedimentary strata rich in aluminosilicate minerals. It is commonly inferred that slates represent an intermediate grade of metamorphism between shale and schist, and this sequence is borne out in various localities by tracing the changes continuously from one region to another.

Basaltic lava flows subjected to dynamothermal metamorphism yield a foliated rock of dark greenish color that has long been known to geologists as *greenstone*. It is perhaps more properly referred to as *greenschist*.

*Gneiss,* a general term for a metamorphic rock showing banding or lineation, requires subdivision into gneisses of different origins. Certain granite bodies show an elongation of crystals into streaklike or pencillike forms, suggestive of flowage of the granite in its final stages of solidification or later under orogenic stresses. Such a rock is often termed a *granite gneiss.*

Certain banded gneisses consist of alternate layers of foliated rock and granular rock. The latter may be granitic or composed of quartz and feldspar (Figure 10.20). Where the rock clearly consists both of schist layers and igneouslike layers, the rock is presumed to have resulted from the injection of igneous components by solutions penetrating the schist layers. Such rocks are described as *injection gneisses.* The bands may be contorted into small folds.

Figure 10.20. Outcrop of banded gneiss of Precambrian age, east coast of Hudson Bay, south of Povungnituk, Quebec. (Photograph G.S.C. No. 125221 by F. C. Taylor, Geological Survey of Canada, Ottawa.)

Injection gneisses can often be traced into masses of pure granite, suggesting that the invading granite magma has *assimilated* the country rock. Thus there arises the possibility that granite magmas and the batholiths that result from them are derived by melting of metamorphosed sedimentary rocks. The process is known as *granitization*. Controversy has been intense between those who consider granite to have its origin as a true igneous magma differentiated from a primary magma of more basaltic composition and those who espouse granitization.

Of the granular metamorphic rocks, the most widespread are metamorphosed from sedimentary rocks. Pure quartz sandstone undergoes minor physical change and virtually no chemical change when subjected to the same orogenic process that produces slates and schists. Under extreme pressure, the quartz grains are crushed and forced into closer contact. Strongly cemented by silica, this process results in a *metaquartzite,* one of the hardest and most durable rocks known.

Limestone and dolomite are metamorphosed into *marble,* which is typically a light-colored granular rock exhibiting a sugary texture on a freshly broken surface. Although white when pure, marbles come in many colors, depending upon the presence of impurities.

Metamorphic rocks are found today over wide areas of the continental crust. They represent the root structures of intensely folded geosynclines from which many thousands of feet of overlying rock have been uncovered. Lineation and foliation of these rocks, along with the orientation of folds within them, can be interpreted to delineate ancient orogenic belts and thus give a means for reconstructing the growth of the continents.

## THE CYCLE OF ROCK TRANSFORMATIONS

This is a good place to summarize the relationships among the three major rock classes in terms of a *cycle of rock transformations,* because that entire cycle can be seen in perspective in the evolution of orogenic belts.

Figure 10.21 is a triangular diagram showing that any one of the three major rock classes—igneous, sedimentary, and metamorphic—can be derived from either of the other two classes. Sequences of changes already examined in this and earlier chapters are labeled on the sides of the triangle and need no further explanation here.

Let us relate the rock cycle to the contrast-

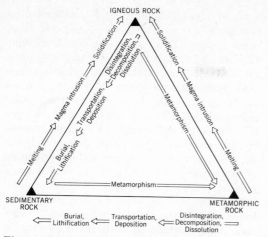

Figure 10.21. The three major rock classes.

ing physical-chemical environments found at depth within the earth and at the earth's surface (Figure 10.22). The modified diagram now represents a schematic vertical cross section of the crust, say to a depth of about 20 mi (30 km). Throughout the rock cycle, large masses must be moved from the deep environment of high temperatures and pressures to the surface environment of low temperatures and pressures. We see that this change of environment can be accomplished by two processes. (1) Rise of magma brings igneous rock to various intermediate positions, where it solidifies into plutonic rock bodies, or by extrusion it may reach the surface to form volcanic rocks. (2) Rock formed at depth can appear at the surface of the earth by uncovering as a result of the combined processes of crustal uplift and

denudation. Thus large bodies of igneous, metamorphic, or sedimentary rock can migrate upward from the deep environment to the surface environment.

Transition from the surface environment to the deep environment can be accomplished by burial and down-sinking of the earth's crust. Both sedimentary strata and extrusive volcanic rocks can eventually reach the deep environment where either metamorphism or partial melting can take place.

Operation of the rock-transformation cycle requires the expenditure of large quantities of energy. The cycle is not, however, an energy system in itself. It is the product of both the geologic system of radiogenic heat and the system of solar radiational energy acting through exogenetic processes of the atmosphere and hydrosphere. This linkage of two great and unlike systems has been pointed out in Chapter 8 and deserves to be repeated here, for it is the key to understanding of the earth's unique physical environment.

## TECTONIC EVENTS IN THE SCALE OF GEOLOGIC TIME

We have arrived at a point in this study of the earth's crustal processes where a geologic time scale in the sense of epoch is required. It becomes necessary to refer the events of intrusion, extrusion, folding, faulting, and sedimentation to an established time scale to synchronize the history of these events from place to place over the earth.

The search for a means by which to establish the *absolute age* in years of an event in the

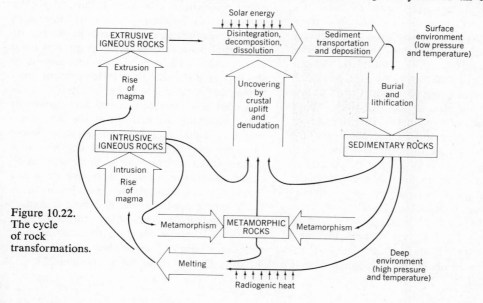

Figure 10.22.
The cycle
of rock
transformations.

earth's past history was for decades frustrating and, in retrospect, misleading. Geological estimates were based upon two lines of calculation —salinity of the oceans and thickness of accumulated sediments. It was thought that the total amount of salt in the oceans, a figure subject to rather close estimate, could be divided by the annual increment of salt to give the age of the oceans. The annual increment of salt was estimated from chemical analyses of stream waters and estimated annual stream discharges. Toward the end of the nineteenth century the calculation was made that the total weight of sodium in the oceans is about $1.6 \times 10^{16}$ tons and that the annual increment of sodium is about $1.6 \times 10^8$ tons. Division yields a figure of roughly 100 million ($10^8$) years (m.y.). Two major sources of error come immediately to mind. We know now that the salts of the ocean enter sediments and that a given element has a certain residence time, that of sodium being 230 m.y. (see Table 11.4). As a result, the salinity of the oceans has probably remained close to its present value for a large part of geologic time. Proof that enormous quantities of sodium have been removed from the oceans lies in the known occurrence of thick salt beds among marine sedimentary strata of several of the geologic periods. A second major source of error lies in the extrapolation of present rates of sodium contribution far into the past. We have good reason to believe that continents stand high today, in comparison with average elevations in much of the past, so that present rates are probably much too high.

The second approach was to total the measured thicknesses of sedimentary strata, taking the thickest known deposit of each age unit of the geologic column. These thicknesses totaled about 100 mi, or 500,000 ft. Using a value of 1 ft per 200 yr as an average rate of accumulation, an age of about 100 m.y. was obtained for the start of sedimentation. Allowing for periods of nondeposition by introducing a correction factor of 15 times, the age would come to 1.5 b.y. Between uncertainties as to rates of deposition and lengths of periods of nondeposition, this method is scarcely better than a blind guess. A dozen or more estimates made between 1860 and 1909 range from roughly 20 m.y. to 1.5 b.y.

Recall that Lord Kelvin, late in the nineteenth century, had made a calculation of the earth's age based upon rates of cooling of both earth and sun (Chapter 7). Kelvin's estimate was for a time span of 20 to 40 m.y. for all of earth history. This figure was disappointingly short to the geologists and also to Darwin and his followers, whose theory of organic evolution by natural selection seemed to require much longer spans of time. Darwin originally estimated that 300 m.y. were needed for only the later stages of evolution. Kelvin had moved his estimate far in the wrong direction, but it was difficult to find any flaw in his application of what were believed to be correct laws of physics.

Dramatically, the dilemma over the age of the earth and the duration of periods of geologic time was solved with the discovery of radioactivity, an event we referred to in Chapter 7. Using these principles, the first reliable age determinations of rocks were made in 1907 by B. B. Boltwood, a chemist. His figures have required only minor adjustments to the present day. The oldest rock age found by Boltwood was about 1.6 b.y.

## RADIOMETRIC AGE DETERMINATION

Basic principles of radioactivity and production of heat by spontaneous decay of radioactive isotopes are discussed in Chapter 7. These principles provide us with the basis of a method of determining the age in years of an igneous rock, a procedure of science known as *geochronometry*. Ages thus determined are referred to as *radiometric* ages.

At the time of solidification of an igneous rock from its liquid state, minute amounts of minerals containing radioactive isotopes are entrapped within the crystal lattices of the common rock-forming minerals, in some cases forming distinctive radioactive minerals. At this initial point in time there are present none of the stable daughter products that constitute the end of the decay series. However, as time passes the stable end member of each series is produced at a constant rate and accumulates in place. Knowing the half-life of the decay system (see Table 7.1), we can estimate closely the time elapsed since mineral crystallization occurred. An accurate chemical determination of the ratio between the radioactive isotope and the stable daughter product must be made. A fairly simple mathematical equation is used to derive the age in years of the mineral under analysis. Take, for example, the uranium-lead series $U^{238}$–$Pb^{206}$, which has a half-life of 4.5 b.y. Quantities of both uranium-238 and lead-206 are measured from a sample of uranium-bearing minerals (e.g., *uraninite,* or *pitchblende*) or from a common mineral (*zircon*) enclosing the radioactive isotopes. The instrument used for such determinations is the *mass spectrometer.* The ratio of lead to uranium is then entered into the following equation:

$$\text{Age (m.y.)} = \frac{6.50 \times 10^9}{\text{logarithm } (1 + Pb^{206}/U^{238})}$$

(The "logarithm" referred to in the equation is the *natural logarithm* of the number within the parentheses and may be found in a set of mathematical tables.)

Similar age determinations can be made using the series $U^{235}$–$Pb^{207}$. Because both series of uranium-lead isotopes are normally present in the same mineral sample, analysis of one series can serve as a cross-check upon the other. Accuracy of the method depends upon the accuracy with which the half-life of the series is known. In this case, accuracy of the half-life of the $U^{238}$–$Pb^{206}$ series is known to within 1% and that of the $U^{235}$–$Pb^{207}$ series to within 2%. It is therefore possible to determine the absolute age of a sample of uranium-bearing mineral to within about 2% of the true value, and in some cases to within 1%. But this level of accuracy also assumes that none of the components in the decay series have been lost from the sample. Use of the uranium-lead systems for age determination can be applied to the oldest rocks known, as well as to meteorites. As noted in Chapter 11, age of meteorites is close to 4.6 b.y., about 1 b.y. older than the oldest rocks of the earth's crust that have thus far been dated.

It may be mentioned in passing that the radioactive thorium-lead decay series, $Th^{232}$–$Pb^{207}$, listed in Table 7.1 as an important heat-producing system, is in disfavor for age determination because loss of the lead tends to occur and to give erroneously low ages.

Of great importance in age determination is the potassium-argon series $K^{40}$–$Ar^{40}$, with a half-life of 1.3 b.y. It is particularly adaptable to use with the micas, specifically muscovite and biotite, and hornblende, all of which are widely present in igneous rocks. The potassium-argon series gives reliable minimum ages for fine-grained volcanic rocks (lavas) which cannot be dated by other methods. Moreover, the method can be used for relatively young rocks (as young as 1 m.y.), as well as for the most

ancient rocks. It has been a highly important tool for the geologist, particularly in deciding which of two rock groups is the older.

The Rubidium-strontium decay series, $Rb^{87}$–$Sr^{87}$, with an extremely long half-life of 47 b.y., is of great value in dating both individual minerals and whole rock samples. It has proved successful in dating metamorphic rocks and thus in dating the orogenies that produced the metamorphism.

Ideally, the above three dating systems—uranium to lead, potassium to argon, and strontium to rubidium—should serve as cross-checks upon one another when all three are applied to mineral samples from the same rock body. In some instances the ages check out as closely similar, but there are instances in which moderate discrepancies are evident. Despite existing uncertainties, the radiometric ages given for various events in the timetable of the earth's history are now accepted by geologists as valid within small percentages of error. Success of the radiometric age determinations of rocks stands as a striking scientific achievement based upon the application of principles of physical chemistry to geology.

Radiometric ages are assigned to the divisions of a scale of geologic time in Table 13.1. Geologic events for which rocks have been found, but older than about 600 m.y. before present, are referred to *Precambrian time.* This vast and obscure block of time, about 3 b.y. in duration, holds the history of evolution of the continental crust.

## EVOLUTION OF THE CONTINENTAL CRUST

Origin of the continents has long been a major problem of geology. Most modern thought on this problem favors the supposition that the continental crust was not present when the accretion of the earth was completed, some $-4.6$ b.y. Instead, the continents were formed later of rock of felsic mineral composition gradually segregated from an original crustal rock of mafic composition, perhaps similar to basalt of the present oceanic and subcontinental crust. Some support for this inference lies in the fact that among the oldest known rocks of the continental crust there is found an abundance of greenstone, already described as metamorphosed volcanic rock of basaltic composition.

A mechanism of segregation of felsic mineral matter from rock of average mafic composition perhaps can be found in the pro-

cesses of igneous mineral alteration by hydrolysis, yielding silica and aluminosilicate clay
minerals which were then deposited as geosynclinal sediments and subsequently melted into
granitic magmas during orogeny. There are, of
course, various problems and uncertainties
connected with the selective removal of mafic
components—iron, magnesium, and calcium.

Another mechanism that might be invoked is
that of magmatic segregation described in
Chapter 7. A rising magma of mafic composition could, after fractionation of the earlier-
crystallizing mafic minerals, yield a granitic
magma, which would solidify as a batholith in
the upper part of the crust. Again, we are
brought back to the problem of origin of
granites and granite magmas. In any case, the
hypothesis of continental evolution requires
that initially small elevated masses of granitic
rock were added to by repetitions of the sedi-
mentation-orogeny sequence described in
earlier paragraphs.

## CONTINENTAL SHIELDS

If the hypothesis of gradual continental
accretion is valid we should find the continental interiors to be composed largely of
metamorphic and intrusive igneous rocks of
great geologic age, representing the roots of
mountain ranges produced in a succession of
orogenies. The continental interiors are of such
composition and are known as *shields.* Figure
10.23 shows the distribution of shields in the
Northern Hemisphere. These are areas largely
of rock of Precambrian age. Younger strata
form thin covers over large areas of the shields,
but these can be regarded as superficial.
Younger orogenic belts typically surround the
shields along the continental margins. It is the
marginal position of these younger orogenic
belts, together with the bordering primary arcs
of present-day orogeny, that suggest that new
material was added to the continental crust by
successive orogenies.

If the continents developed by growth
throughout Precambrian time, we should look
to the distributions of rock ages in the continental shields. A pattern suggestive of growth
stages emerges. The oldest rocks of the shields,
older than about 2.5 b.y., make up relatively
small patches of shield and are designated as
*continental nuclei.*

Figure 13.10 shows the world distribution of
continental nuclei. These areas have yielded
rocks with radiometric ages older than 2.7 b.y.,
although most determinations are in the somewhat younger range of 2.3 to 2.7 b.y. In
addition to the areas shown on the map, there
is an area of very old rock, dated in the 2.3–2.7
b.y. range, in the region of the Baltic Sea. This
*Baltic Shield* may also be considered a continental nucleus.

The continental nuclei are surrounded by or
are contiguous to larger areas of shield rock
with maximum ages falling in middle and
upper Precambrian time, suggesting the validity
of the hypothesis of continental evolution by
accretion.

## THE OCEANIC CRUST

Origin of the huge ocean basins with their
sustained great depths has been a geological
problem as intriguing as that of the origin of
the continents. These basins occupy two-thirds
of the area of the globe. Referring back to
Figure 7.8, recall that the oceanic crust is relatively thin (3 to 5 mi; 5 to 8 km), so that the
M-discontinuity is encountered about 6 to 8 mi
(10 to 13 km) below sea level. Water depth
averages about 2.8 mi (4.5 km). A layer of
unconsolidated sediment, averaging about 0.3
mi (0.5 km), but highly variable in thickness,
overlies the rock floor.

Figure 10.24 is a rather detailed cross section of the western half of the North Atlantic
Ocean basin. Notice first that the soft sediments bury many irregularities in the rock
floor, producing in places a smooth *abyssal
plain.* Toward the east, as the Mid-Atlantic
Ridge is approached, sediments occur only as
isolated fillings in low places. The crust is
divided into two layers. An upper layer, the
*basement,* is probably composed of basalt
(basalt samples have been taken from it) but
might in places consist of densely consolidated
sediments. The lower layer, or *oceanic layer,* is
considered from evidence of seismology almost
certainly to consist of basalt. Notice the uniformity in depth to the M-discontinuity beneath the oceanic layer.

Perhaps the most striking fact about the
oceanic basalts thus far brought to the surface
is that their ages are all very much younger
than the rocks of the continental shields. The
oldest known oceanic basalts are only 50 m.y.
old and we have no reason as yet to suspect
that any of the basalt is older than 150 m.y.
The oldest sediments thus far brought up in
deep-sea drill cores are in the range of 125 to
150 m.y. In contrast, the continental shield

Figure 10.23. Continental shields of the Northern Hemisphere and their bordering mountain arcs. (© 1960, John Wiley & Sons, New York. Based on a map by A. J. Eardley.)

rocks range from 1 to 3.5 b.y. Do these facts mean that the ocean crust is a very much younger feature than the continental crust? Such an interpretation may seem difficult to accept along with the hypotheses of slow continental accretion. But consider that the basalts which have been dredged from the sea floor may represent lava flows that have spread over much older oceanic crust, concealing it from direct observation. Consider also that processes of denudation are almost nil upon rocks exposed on the deep ocean floors. On the continents denudation uncovers the oldest rocks, whereas submarine extrusion of lava and

deposition of sediment tend to bury and conceal the oldest rocks of the oceanic crust.

### THE MID-OCEANIC RIDGE SYSTEM

Of all the many and varied relief features of the ocean floor, none is so filled with scientific importance as a belt of rugged submarine topography running approximately down the middle of the Atlantic Ocean basin, continuing into the Indian Ocean basin, and then across the southern Pacific basin (Figure 10.25). Flanking this *Mid-Oceanic Ridge* are broad zones of relatively flat ocean floor. Figure 10.26 shows a profile across the Mid-Oceanic

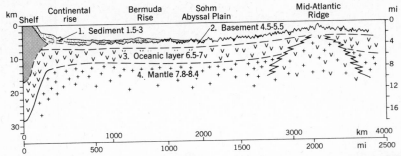

Figure 10.24. Generalized west-to-east cross section of the oceanic crust of the western North Atlantic. Figures after layer names give P-wave velocities in km/sec. [After J. Ewing (1969), in *The Earth's Crust and Upper Mantle,* Geophysical Monograph 13, Washington, D.C., Amer. Geophys. Union, p. 221, Figure 1.]

Ridge and flanking areas in the North Atlantic. The ridge consists of a high central axial zone, at the crest of which there is typically a narrow, steep-sided trenchlike depression termed a *rift valley.* On either flank the topography descends in rugged steplike sections to the level of the deep ocean floor.

The Mid-Oceanic Ridge has been mapped over a continuous total length of about 40,000 mi (64,000 km). In the Indian Ocean, a branch of the ridge runs north and has extensions into the African continent forming the Red Sea rift depression and rift valleys of eastern Africa. In the eastern Pacific Ocean,

the Mid-Oceanic Ridge runs north to project into the Gulf of California and may be extended in rift valleys and related fault features of the western United States, including the San Andreas fault of California.

Accessory to the central rift line of the Mid-Oceanic Ridge are great cross faults (Figure 10.25). These appear to be of the transcurrent variety (see Figure 10.4), with extensive horizontal movement of one crustal mass past the other. Movement along these cross faults has offset the axial rift valley by distances up to many tens of miles.

Interpretations of the Mid-Oceanic Ridge

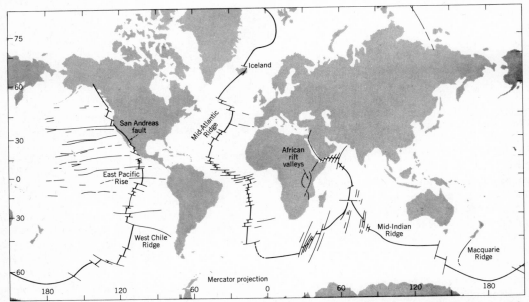

Figure 10.25. Mid-Oceanic Ridge system (heavy lines) and related fracture zones (light lines). [After L. R. Sykes (1969), in *The Earth's Crust and Upper Mantle,* Geophysical Monograph 13, Washington, D.C., Amer. Geophys. Union, p. 149, Figure 1. Based on data of B. C. Heezen, M. Tharp, H. W. Menard, and other sources.]

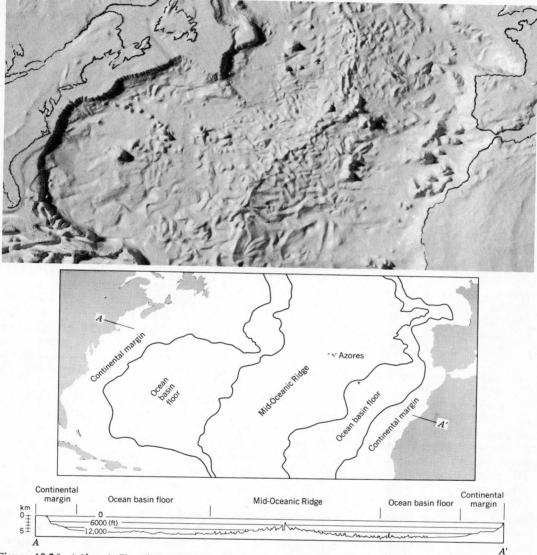

Figure 10.26. (*Above*) Terrain model of the North Atlantic Ocean basin. Vertical exaggeration about 25 times. (Official U.S. Navy photograph, courtesy of U.S. Naval Training Device Center.) (*Below*) Outline map of the major divisions of the North Atlantic Ocean basin, with representative profile from New England to the Sahara coast of Africa. Vertical exaggeration about 40 times. [After B. C. Heezen, M. Tharp, and M. Ewing (1959), *The Floors of the Oceans*, Geol. Soc. Amer. Spec. Paper 65, p. 16, Figure 9.]

now seem in general agreement that this feature represents a great global line of lithospheric separation, along which the oceanic crust is being pulled apart. Instead of a huge trenchlike gap appearing along this line, there has been an up-welling of molten mantle rock to fill the breach. This up-welling has caused the rift zone to be elevated to a relatively high position. Accompanying the pulling apart of

the crust there has been an almost continuous extrusion of basalt lavas from fissures close to the ridge axis. The Mid-Oceanic Ridge system is the site of many earthquakes, attesting to the crustal activity that exists along its length. Locally, as in the Azores Islands and Iceland in the North Atlantic, the crest of the Mid-Oceanic Ridge appears above sea level as islands. These islands are constructed of basaltic lavas, and, as in Iceland, they are the sites of modern volcanic eruption.

Important lines of evidence, leading to the conclusion that crustal spreading and separation have occurred along the Mid-Oceanic Ridge axis, have been found in the determinations of ages of both sediments and lavas on the flanks of the ridge. The soft pelagic sediments lying upon the lavas have accumulated from the settling of minute particles through the ocean water and are undisturbed in their positions of accumulation. If the crust is being spread apart along the Mid-Oceanic Ridge axis, with new rock of fresh lava flows up-welling along the line of separation, we should find that the soft sediments accumulating close to the axis are of only very young age, while progressively older sediment will be found resting on basalt at increasing distance from the axis. Results have been obtained that agree with this pattern. Direct dates of basalt rock samples, while not completely consistent, suggest that the youngest basalt flows lie close to the axial rift valley of the ridge; those of greater age lie in flanking zones.

## PALEOMAGNETISM AND REVERSALS OF THE EARTH'S MAGNETIC FIELD

We will now put to use basic information about the earth's magnetism, developed in Chapter 2. Basaltic lavas contain, in addition to the silicate minerals named in Chapter 7, minor amounts of oxides of iron and titanium. Magnetite, the mineral of which lodestone is a naturally magnetic variety, is an example (Figure 8.15). At the high temperatures of the magma, these minerals have no natural magnetism. However, as cooling sets in each crystallized mineral passes a critical temperature known as the *Curie point*, below which the mineral is magnetized by lines of force of the earth's field. At first, this magnetization is not permanent, but rather of the type known as *soft* magnetization, similar to that acquired by soft iron. With further cooling, however, the soft magnetism abruptly becomes permanent, a state known as *hard* magnetism, resembling the permanent magnetic condition of the alnico magnet. In this way a permanent record of the earth's magnetic field is locked into the solidified lava.

In the study of rock magnetism a sample of rock is removed from the surrounding bedrock. Orientation of the specimen is carefully documented in terms of geographic north and horizontality. The specimen is then placed in a sensitive instrument, the *magnetometer,* which measures the direction and intensity of the permanent magnetism within the rock. As with the magnetic needle, the angles of declination and dip are determined. After a number of samples have been obtained from a single lava flow and the magnetic parameters compared for consistency and averaged, the direction and inclination of the relict magnetism (*paleomagnetism*) can be compared with present conditions and with the magnetic field at other locations and in different times in the geologic past.

As early as 1906, Bernard Brunhes, a French physicist, had observed that the magnetic polarity of some samples of lavas is exactly the reverse of present conditions. He concluded that the earth's magnetic polarity must have been reversed at the time the lava solidified. One might wish to propose as an alternative hypothesis that the rock magnetism itself has undergone a change in polarity, but in recent years there has been general agreement among members of the scientific community that the rock magnetism is permanent and a reliable indicator of the former states of the earth's magnetic field.

In addition to the magnetic data of the lava, there is needed a radiometric determination of the age of the rock, giving the date of solidification of the magma. Extensive determinations of both magnetic parameters and rock age have revealed that there have been at least nine reversals of the earth's magnetic field in the last 3.5 m.y. of geologic time. Figure 10.27 shows the timetable of magnetic events. Polarity such as that existing today is referred to as a *normal epoch;* opposite polarity as a *reversed epoch.* Each epoch is named for an individual or a locality. For example, the pioneer work of Bernard Brunhes is recognized in the present normal epoch which began about −700,000 yr. An epoch of reversal, named for the Japanese scientist Motonori Matuyama, extends to 2.5 m.y. before present and includes two shorter periods of normal polarity classified as *events.* A still older normal epoch, named in honor of the mathematician Karl Gauss (1777–1855), carries back the paleomagnetic record to about 3.5 m.y. and contains one brief reversed event. Oldest of the reversed epochs thus far dated is named after Sir William Gilbert, whose early work on terrestrial magnetism was discussed in Chapter 2.

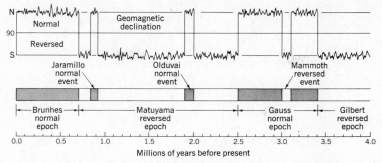

Figure 10.27. Time scale of magnetic polarity reversals. The graph of geomagnetic declination fluctuations is schematic. [After A. Cox, R. R. Doell, and G. B. Dalrymple (1964), *Science,* vol. 144, p. 1541, Figure 3, and other sources.]

## ROCK MAGNETISM AND CRUSTAL SPREADING

We are now prepared to return to the subject of crustal spreading along the Mid-Oceanic Ridge. If the axial rift valley is a line of up-welling of basaltic lavas, and if crustal spreading is a continuing process, the lava flows that have poured out in the vicinity of the axial rift will be slowly moved away from the rift. Lavas of a given geologic age will thus divide into two narrow strips, one on each side of the rift. As time passes these strips will increase in distance of separation, as shown in Figure 10.28. When lavas are identified and classified in terms of the epochs of normal and reversed magnetic field, these epochs will be represented by symmetrical strip patterns, as shown in Figure 10.29.

Confirmation of the symmetrical magnetic strips has been found in the interpretation of magnetic information gained in the course of oceanographic surveys. We cannot take oriented core samples of lavas from the ocean floors. However, it is possible to operate a

sensitive magnetometer during a ship's traverse across the Mid-Oceanic Ridge. When this is done, it is found that the value of magnetic inclination fluctuates with a range of about 1000 gammas (Figure 10.29). (Refer to Chapter 2 for explanation of terms.) These departures from a constant normal value are referred to as *magnetic anomalies*. When several parallel cross lines of magnetometer surveys have been run across the Mid-Oceanic Ridge, the magnetic anomalies can be resolved into a pattern, such as that shown in Figure 10.30. Notice the mirror symmetry of the striped pattern with respect to the axial line. From a study of the anomaly pattern, it is possible to identify the normal and reversed epochs, as done in Figure 10.28.

Recently, it has been found possible to identify the normal and reversed magnetic epochs in core samples of soft sediment obtained from the ocean floor by piston-coring devices. Here, the epochs are encountered in sequence from top to bottom within the core. Some 15 older epochs have been discovered, extending back to 20 m.y. (middle Miocene Epoch).

It is apparent that the evidence of rock magnetism not only makes a virtual certainty of crustal spreading, but also allows the rates and total distances to be estimated as well. Take, for example, the case of the anomaly pattern shown in Figure 10.30, which is part of the Mid-Atlantic Ridge south of Iceland in the North Atlantic. Here the width of the anomaly zone is 750 mi (1200 km), which represents the total distance of crustal separation in about 4 m.y. The average rate of horizontal motion of the crust during this time has been about 0.4 in./yr (1 cm/yr), which means that the rate of separation is double this value, or 0.8 in./yr (2 cm/yr). Elsewhere the rates of spreading are

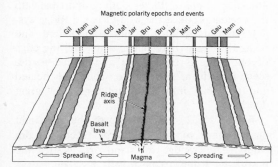

Figure 10.28. Schematic diagram of development of symmetrical pattern of magnetic polarity belts in oceanic basalts during crustal spreading. (See Figure 10.27 for time scale.)

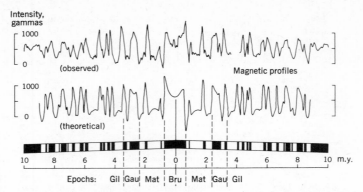

Figure 10.29. Observed profile of magnetic intensity (*above*) along a traverse of the Mid-Oceanic Ridge at about latitude 60° S in the South Pacific. Theoretical magnetic profile and time scale of magnetic polarity reversals are shown (*below*). [After W. C. Pitman and J. R. Heirtzler (1966), *Science,* vol. 154, p. 1166, Figure 3.]

found to be higher, up to 1.8 in./yr (4.5 cm/yr).

## PLATE THEORY OF GLOBAL TECTONICS

Rapid advances in our knowledge of the oceanic crust, and in particular of the wide extent of crustal spreading in the Mid-Oceanic Ridge, have led to a general hypothesis of *global tectonics* meeting with rather widespread acceptance among geologists and geophysicists as an effective working model. (The noun *tectonics* means the study of structural features of the earth's crust and their origin. The adjective *tectonic* refers to large-scale movements of

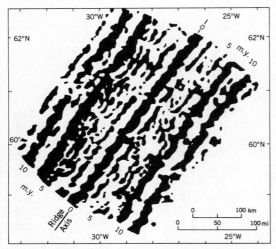

Figure 10.30. Magnetic anomaly pattern for Reykjanes Ridge, located on the Mid-Atlantic Ridge southwest of Iceland, with approximate rock ages in millions of years. [After J. R. Heirtzler, X. Le Pichon, and J. G. Baron (1966), *Deep-Sea Research,* vol. 13, p. 427.]

the crust and mantle.) The term *plate tectonics* has been applied to the hypothesis, which features the largely horizontal movements of platelike elements of the strong, brittle lithosphere over a readily yielding asthenosphere having essentially no strength. The model of plate tectonics reflects the collective efforts of many individuals and integrates an enormous accumulation of information gathered by many research programs and institutions.

Six principal rigid plates are defined in the total system of global tectonics. Each plate moves horizontally as a unit and may also rotate as it moves over the asthenosphere. Obviously, two major possibilities are that adjacent plates may move apart, creating a widening gap between them, or they may move together, causing crustal rupture of the edges of the plates. A third possibility is that they may slide along each other.

Figure 10.31 is a three-dimensional schematic diagram showing relationships among lithospheric plates. Plates pulling apart beneath the oceans produce the Mid-Oceanic Ridge system with its axial rift and transcurrent and related faults. Where plates converge, the edge of one plate is bent down and forced to descend into the asthenosphere, where it is heated and absorbed into the mantle rock at great depth.

Figure 10.32 shows details of the crust and mantle in a hypothetical cross section from Mid-Oceanic Ridge to island arc. Notice the postulated rising of the mantle rock under the Mid-Oceanic Ridge to provide new oceanic crust as spreading occurs. Rising motions tend to elevate the axis of the Mid-Oceanic Ridge.

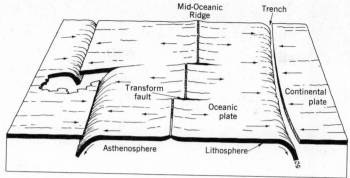

Figure 10.31. Schematic block diagram of plate tectonics. Earth-curvature removed. (Based on data of X. Le Pichon, L. R. Sykes, B. Isacks, and others.)

Ultrabasic rock of the mantle must be differentiated into basaltic magma, and it is inferred here that the denser magma fractions sink back into the mantle. Notice that isolated basaltic volcanoes form over the oceanic crust by eruption through the plate. Where the plate descends into the mantle, oceanic sediments are crumpled and accumulated against the adjacent plate. Melting of the descending crust produces magmas, which are differentiated to yield andesitic magma, leaving behind ultrabasic magma. Rising andesitic magmas produce volcanoes and thus build the island arc. As a result, the crust thickens and becomes felsic in composition, taking on characteristics of the continental crust.

Let us return to the global plan of plate tectonics. It has been postulated that there are six

enormous plates (Figure 10.33). The *America plate* includes North American and South American continental crust and all of the oceanic crust of the western Atlantic extending eastward to the Mid-Atlantic Ridge. This America plate has a relative westward motion as a single unit and, consequently, there is no important tectonic activity along the eastern margins of the American continents. The western edge of the America plate lies along the western continental margins.

The *Pacific plate,* the only unit bearing only oceanic crust, occupies all of the Pacific region west of the East Pacific Rise. It is forced down under the America plate along the compressional zone of the Alaskan–British Columbia coastal region. The *Antarctica plate* occupies the globe south of the Mid-Oceanic Ridge sys-

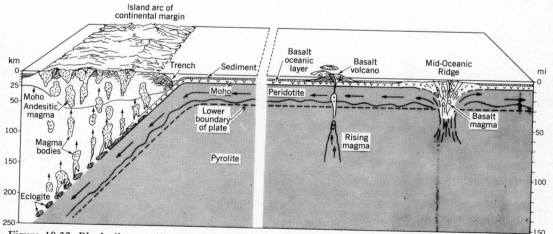

Figure 10.32. Block diagram illustrating hypothetical details of plate tectonics at island-arc or continental margin. [Modified from H. H. Hess's 1962 model, as given by A. E. Ringwood (1969), in *The Earth's Crust and Upper Mantle,* Geophysical Monograph 13, Washington, D.C., Amer. Geophys. Union, p. 12, Figure 5.]

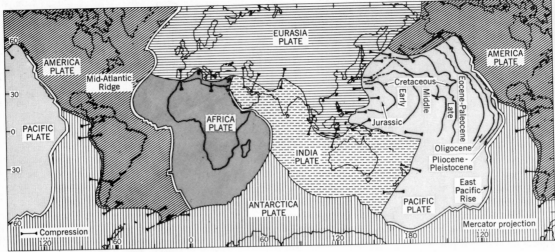

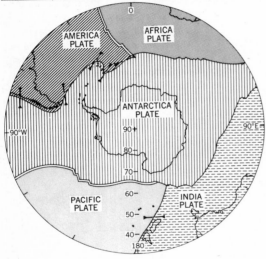

Figure 10.33. World and polar maps of a system of six lithospheric plates. Double-line plate boundary shows Mid-Oceanic Ridge rift zone on which spreading is active. Other plate boundaries in solid lines. Double arrow symbol shows zones of active compression. [Modified and simplified from a map by X. Le Pichon (1968), *Jour. Geophys. Research*, vol. 73, p. 3675, Figure 6. Pacific plate ages from A. G. Fischer, B. C. Heezen, and others (1970), *Science*, vol. 168, p. 1211, Figure 1.]

tem. An extension of this plate, lying between the East Pacific Rise and South America, moves eastward against the west margin of South America, meeting in the compressional zone of the Peru-Chile Trench and the Andes range. The *Africa plate* consists of the African continental crust and a zone of surrounding oceanic crust limited by the Mid-Oceanic Ridge.

A single *Eurasia plate,* which consists largely of continental crust, is bounded on the east and south by compressional zones of the great alpine mountain chains and island arcs but also extends into the North Atlantic as oceanic crust lying east of the Mid-Atlantic ridge. An *India plate,* consisting of continental crust of India and Australia as well as of oceanic crust of the Indian Ocean and a part of the south-western Pacific, is separated from the Pacific

plate by a compressional belt passing through New Zealand. Other smaller lithospheric blocks may be required to complete the picture.

Because of its vast extent the Pacific plate can be expected to possess, in its westernmost portion, the oldest oceanic crust on earth. Deep-sea cores obtained in 1970 provided confirmation of this inference. Sediments as old as 125 to 150 m.y. (early Cretaceous or upper Jurassic) were identified in cores in the vicinity of longitude 156° to 158° E. Figure 10.33 includes a sketch-map of age zones of the Pacific plate. (See Tables 13.1 and 14.1 for geologic periods and epochs.)

While the six-plate hypothesis of global tectonics appears to offer a unifying explanation of most of the major crustal phenomena, discrepancies are known. We may anticipate modifications of the model from time to time as new data are brought to light.

## CONTINENTAL DRIFT

If we accept the evidence of plate separation on a vast scale throughout more than 150 m.y. there is no escape from the conclusion that continents were formerly situated much closer together than they are today and may even have been joined together. The idea is not a new one—it was proposed as early as the end of the nineteenth century that a single continent once existed. (See Figure 13.10.) A scientist who renewed the hypothesis in 1910 named this single continent *Pangaea* and postulated that it began to split apart about −200 m.y. (Triassic Period). Separation of the fragments of Pangaea is known as *continental drift*. Long discredited by geologists, the reality of continental drift has now been accepted by a majority segment of the community of research geologists and geophysicists. We shall document this remarkable process with additional evidence in Chapters 12 and 13.

## CONVECTION CURRENTS IN THE MANTLE

Crustal spreading and plate tectonics require a driving mechanism. Little is known of actual mass movements within the mantle, but most models of global tectonics have been referred to systems of very slow mantle circulation under the general heading of *convection currents*.

Figure 10.34*A* shows a model of convection involving the entire thickness of the mantle. Rising of less-dense mantle rock under the Mid-Oceanic Ridge and corresponding sinking beneath the compressional zones of the trenches and island arcs are key activities within the convection system. Dominantly horizontal motion under the lithospheric plate would exert a drag, causing the plate to move away from the Mid-Oceanic Ridge and toward the compressional belt. Rates of flow of mantle rock were originally postulated to be on the order of magnitude of 0.04 in./yr (1 mm/yr) throughout most of the system, but this rate is only one-tenth that required by crustal spreading.

More recently, a model has been proposed in which convection occurs within a very shallow zone of the upper mantle (Figure 10.34*B*). All motion takes place within the asthenosphere, or soft layer. The lithosphere is moved by drag force of the flow beneath. Advocates of the plate theory of tectonics have devised a totally

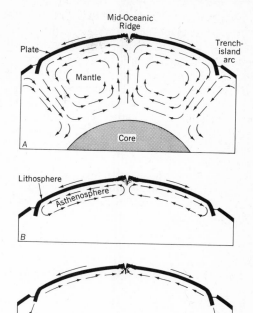

Figure 10.34. Schematic diagrams of convection hypotheses. (*A*) Large, deep convection cells. (*B*) Shallow convection layer. (*C*) Opposite flow beneath lithospheric plate.

different model, in which the asthenosphere moves in the opposite direction to the lithospheric plate (Figure 10.34*C*). In this case the drag force would tend to oppose the plate motion, and we would have to look for some other force to cause the plate to move. It has been suggested that the sinking of the downturning edge of the plate is capable of exerting a pull on the rest of the plate and that the movement is by a simple gravity mechanism in which the elevated plate near the rift axis tends to move downgrade toward the lower, downturning edge. Objections have been voiced against all of the above models of lithosphere-moving mechanisms, while at the same time other models of quite different sorts have been proposed.

The energy source for convectional or other large-scale motions of the mantle may lie in the uneven accumulation of radiogenic heat, or it may consist of kinetic energy of motions persisting from much earlier time in the earth's history. Earth rotation has been invoked as a driving mechanism. Another hypothesis requires energy input from an asteroid impact. The most recently proposed energy source is that of earth tides (see Chapter 3).

## A GEOLOGIC SYSTEM IN REVIEW

In this chapter and Chapter 7 the entire scope of physical geology has been encompassed by a single unifying concept, namely, that of a single great energy system powered by radiogenic heat inherited from the time of the earth's formation. In the first billion years of the earth's life, this radiogenic-heat source became concentrated near the earth's surface, allowing the mantle and core to become stable and free of further melting or overturning on a vast scale. Nevertheless, despite greatly reduced heat production, many processes of energy release continue to operate in the earth's upper mantle and crust. Diastrophism continues, in the form of rifting and crustal spreading in certain locations and in the form of crustal compression and orogeny in other locations. Locally, excess heat causes melting of rock and the upward migration of magmas to form volcanoes, basaltic lava flows, and batholiths. As the rigid crust yields by sudden slippages, energy is released in the form of earthquake shocks.

The geologic system powered by internal heat sources is also affected by and interrelated with the solar radiation and gravity-flow systems that operate geologically as exogenetic processes at the earth's solid surface. Denudation of the continents and sediment production profoundly affect the development of continents. Not only are continental shields leveled and mountain roots exposed, but the sedimentary deposits of geosynclines provide the raw material for production of new mountain ranges with their reconstituted metamorphic and igneous roots. The rock-transformation cycle summarizes the effects of interaction between the two great systems of wholly unlike nature.

What remains to be added to the list of processes that have shaped the face of our planet? The next chapter describes a wholly different process from those covered so far and requires us to examine the surfaces of the moon and inner planets.

### References for further study

Richter, C. F. (1958), *Elementary Seismology,* San Francisco, Freeman, 768 pp.

Spock, L. E. (1962), *Guide to the Study of Rocks,* 2nd ed., New York, Harper & Row, 298 pp., chap. 9.

Shepard, F. P. (1963), *Submarine Geology,* 2nd ed., New York, Harper & Row, 557 pp., chaps. 13, 15.

Hodgson, J. H. (1964), *Earthquakes and Earth Structure,* Englewood Cliffs, N.J., Prentice-Hall, 166 pp.

Eicher, D. L. (1968), *Geologic Time,* Englewood Cliffs, N.J., Prentice-Hall, 149 pp., chaps. 1, 4, 6.

Phinney, R. A., ed. (1968), *The History of the Earth's Crust: A Symposium,* Princeton, N.J., Princeton Univ. Press, 244 pp.

### Review questions

1. What is diastrophism? How does it differ from vulcanism and intrusion? Name and describe the primary arcs (orogenic belts). How are trenches (foredeeps) related to the arcs?

2. What is an earthquake? How are earthquakes associated with faults? What kinds of faults have surface expression? Describe the elastic strain observed to precede earthquakes. What is the elastic-rebound theory of earthquakes, and how was it demonstrated to apply to the San Francisco earthquake of 1906?

3. What is the focus of an earthquake? the epicenter? Describe the major varieties of earthquake waves. How are they recorded? What kinds of information can be derived from study of seismograms? In terms of depth, what are the three classes of earthquakes? Give approximate depth range for each.

4. Describe the Richter scale of earthquake magnitudes. How does it tell quantity of energy released? From what magnitude of earthquakes is most of the total annual energy release derived? How does the modified Mercalli scale differ in purpose and definitions from the Richter scale?

5. Describe the destructive effects of major earthquakes. What crustal changes of level accompanied the Good Friday earthquake of 1964 in Alaska? How do these changes relate to larger features of the crust?

6. Describe the seismic sea wave (tsunami) in terms of origin, dimensions, and manner of propagation. What factor controls speed of this type of wave? What is the environmental importance of the seismic sea wave?

7. Compare the world distribution of earthquake epicenters with that of major orogenic features. What is the significance of the world distribution in terms of crustal processes?

8. Describe the relationship of foci of shallow-focus, intermediate-focus, and deep-focus earthquakes when these are plotted on a map and in a vertical cross section. What structure and type of movement within the crust and mantle are suggested by the observed relationship?

9. What is an isostatic gravity anomaly? Describe gravity anomalies associated with island arcs and adjacent trenches. What meaning can be attached to such anomalies?

10. What is the andesite line? Where is it located? How is the andesite line related to the circum-Pacific belt of island and mountain arcs? Compare western and eastern sides of the Pacific Ocean basin with respect to location of andesite line and arcs. Where does andesitic magma come from?

11. Review the general sequence of events in the evolution of an orogenic belt, starting with early stages of orogeny and sedimentation and ending in a high alpine mountain range. What is a geosyncline? What happens to sedimentary strata of a geosyncline during orogeny?

12. What is rock metamorphism? How do the adjectives *dynamothermal* and *regional* apply to this process? How does contact metamorphism occur? What is metasomatism? Compare minerals of metamorphic rocks with those of igneous rocks.

13. What two groups of metamorphic rocks are recognized in terms of structure? Describe slate, schist, metaquartzite, and marble. From what rocks are they derived? What varieties of gneiss are found, and what is the significance of each? What is granitization?

14. Describe the complete cycle of rock transformations and illustrate by means of a triangular diagram. Which of the rock types represents the original crustal rock? Relate rock types to environments of temperature and pressure and to energy sources.

15. Describe and criticize earlier methods and estimates of the earth's age based upon ocean salinity and thickness of sedimentary strata. In what way was Kelvin's estimate of the earth's age incompatible with Darwin's theory of organic evolution?

16. How is absolute age of a rock determined? Describe the methods of geochronometry. How is half-life of a radioactive isotope used in determining radiometric age? What isotopes and minerals are most useful in age determination? What age in billions of years before the present is spanned by Precambrian time?

17. How and when did the continental crust originate? What problems are involved in explaining continental evolution? What are the continental shields? Describe the continental nuclei. How do ages and arrangements of shield rocks suggest the pattern of continental evolution?

18. Compare the oceanic crust with that of the continents. How do crustal thicknesses and depths to the M-discontinuity compare in the two types? How do ages of oceanic basalts compare with ages of continental shield rocks? Explain.

19. What is the Mid-Oceanic Ridge system? Describe its position and surface form. How far does it extend? What is the significance of the axial rift valley in the Mid-Oceanic Ridge? of faults cutting across the Ridge? How are earthquakes related to the Ridge?

20. What crustal and igneous activity is associated with the Mid-Oceanic Ridge? What lines of evidence point to crustal spreading away from the Ridge axis?

21. Describe the natural magnetism of basaltic lavas. How is this magnetism studied, and what interpretations can be made from the data? What is meant by magnetic polarity reversal? How are magnetic epochs and events classified and designated?

22. How are magnetic anomaly patterns used to demonstrate crustal spreading and to measure the rates of that spreading?

23. Describe the plate theory of global tectonics. How is the earth's lithosphere divided into major plates? Describe the major plates and their boundaries. What kinds of boundaries exist between adjacent plates?

24. Review the hypothesis of continental drift and relate it to plate tectonics. What was Pangaea? When did it exist? Describe two or three models of convection systems within the mantle that have been proposed to explain movement of lithospheric plates. What is the energy source for convection currents?

25. Describe in broad terms the energy system powered by radiogenic heat and its interaction with the system of solar energy and exogenetic processes. Work these concepts into a unified theory of evolution of the continental and oceanic crusts of the earth.

# chapter 11
# impact system, space to earth and moon: the geology of planetary space

Closely linked with the system of planets and satellites in orbital motion is a system of energy transformation so different in action as to be the antithesis of ceaseless orderly motion. This system is one of impacts: head-on collisions between rapidly moving objects in the solar system. The abrupt cessation of forward linear motion of a smaller mass as it impacts a much larger mass results in the almost instantaneous transformation of kinetic energy of motion into heat. In the process, solids are ruptured and matter is dislocated. The cold space missile becomes at once highly heated, perhaps vaporizing and generating an enormous explosion. The receiving body gains in mass but suffers a lasting scar, which may be of minor or major proportions.

At the present time, the Earth* receives a rain of solid objects from space. For the most

* In this chapter, as in Chapter 3, Earth, Moon, and Sun are capitalized as proper names, to be consistent with the names of the other planets.

part, these are extremely tiny particles that fail to pass through the atmosphere, but a few objects are many tons in mass and impact the lithosphere. Earth's far-reaching gravitational field draws toward it and entraps small masses that by chance pass nearby. Literally, the planets are sweeping up debris from the solar system. It takes only a moment's reflection to make us aware that the quantity of space debris must have been vastly greater at earlier stages of the planetary history, unless space objects are somehow being produced as fast as they are entrapped. Such reasoning leads to the hypothesis that the planets and their satellites grew to their present dimensions by the infall of objects of many sizes. If so, what is today a relatively trivial energy-transformation process was once the process of paramount importance in the solar system.

On Earth, processes of weathering, erosion, and sedimentation quickly erase an impact scar. Few can be found. But on the Moon such features are preserved in abundance and invite study. Paradoxically, we can learn much about the history of Earth from studying its satellite companion. Perhaps we need to rephrase the prophetic line "Speak to the Earth and it shall teach thee" to read "Reach to the Moon and she shall teach thee." Investigation of the Moon is understandably at the forefront of physical-science research today.

## ASTEROIDS

Among the minor objects in heliocentric orbit, the asteroids occupy an intermediate size range between the major planets and the tiny particles of meteoroids and comets. It was long suspected that a planet might exist between the orbits of Mars and Jupiter, for a definite space gap exists there. The discovery in 1801 of a small planetary object in this region was followed in quick succession by the discovery of three more. In order of discovery these objects were named *Ceres, Pallas, Juno,* and *Vesta.* A fifth object was found 40 years later. Then, as observational astronomy improved, many smaller ones were identified. Collectively, they are known as *asteroids.* It is said that as many as 40,000 asteroids can be identified on photographs; the total number is suspected to include many more.

The four largest asteroids have diameters ranging from 480 mi (770 km) for Ceres, to 120 mi (193 km) for Juno. Most are much smaller and appear only as points of light. The total mass of all asteroids combined is estimated to be from 1/500 to 1/1000 that of Earth. Most asteroids have orbits that remain well within the space between the orbits of Mars and Jupiter. However, a few have highly eccentric orbits which bring them within the Earth's orbit and quite close to the Sun (Figure 11.1). The hair-raising prospect of a collision of an asteroid with Earth at some future time cannot be dismissed, although it is an event of very small probability.

The asteroid *Icarus* came within about 4 million mi (6.5 million km) of Earth on June 14, 1968. Observations showed that Icarus is irregular in shape, less than a mile in width, and may be composed of iron. A somewhat larger asteroid, *Eros,* comes as close as 13.5 million mi (21 million km) to Earth on occasion. It is about 15 mi (24 km) long and irregularly shaped. The asteroids arouse considerable interest among astronomers because of their significance in the formation of the

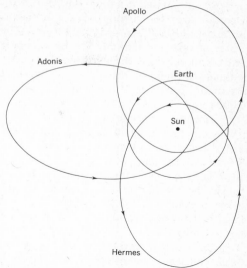

Figure 11.1. Orbits of the asteroids Apollo, Adonis, and Hermes. [After R. A. Lyttleton (1956), *The Modern Universe,* New York, Harper & Row.]

solar system. They may represent fragments of a disrupted planet, or of a primitive, planetlike body.

## METEOROIDS

*Meteoroids* are particles that enter the Earth's upper atmosphere, becoming visible as *meteors* when they are heated to incandescence and produce a thin trail of light (Figure 11.2). The entering velocities of meteoroids range

Figure 11.2. This meteor trail showed a sudden increase in brightness as it traveled toward the lower right. (Yerkes Observatory.)

from 15 to 50 mi/sec (25 to 80 km/sec). Most meteoroids are extremely tiny specks of matter, with masses of less than 1/30 oz (1 gm). The number of such particles that silently strike the Earth's atmosphere each day probably runs to thousands of millions. The daily mass infall of meteoroids has been estimated at 1000 to 10,000 tons.

Occasionally, a very large meteoroid (which may be, in fact, a small asteroid) enters the Earth's atmosphere. Though highly heated by friction and partially vaporized, it may have had a sufficient mass that portions of it have reached the Earth's surface. Such exotic rock objects are then called *meteorites*. We shall take up the interpretation of meteorites in a later paragraph.

Tiny meteoroids travel in *swarms,* and each swarm follows a highly elliptical orbit about the sun. An example is the Leonid meteoroid swarm, whose orbit is shown in Figure 11.3. A few meteoroids are scattered about the entire elliptical orbit of the swarm. Eight swarms have been identified and their orbits established. As Figure 9.3 shows, the Earth's orbit can intersect the meteoroid swarm orbit once each year, at which time meteors are particularly frequent and constitute a *meteor shower.*

## COMETS

*Comets* are luminous masses in highly eccentric orbits about the Sun. Typically, the comet has a brightly luminous head (the *coma*) and a duffuse *tail* that is directed away from the Sun (Figure 11.4). The matter is so diffuse that stars can be clearly seen through the comet. Because comet orbits are extremely elliptical, the velocities at perihelion, when the comet is close to the Sun, are extremely high in

Figure 11.4. Halley's comet photographed on May 12 and 15, 1910, at Honolulu, Hawaii. The shorter tail (*right*) covers 30° of arc, the longer tail (*left*) 40°. (The Hale Observatories.)

comparison with velocities in aphelion, when the comet is far out near the limits of the solar system. As a result, comets are seen for only brief periods. Most have orbital periods of tens of thousands of years and are seen once in the span of recorded history. However, some comets, among them Halley's comet, reappear in time spans of 3 yr to 200 yr (Figure 11.5). About 100 such periodic comets are known.

A particular comet group, known as the *Jupiter family,* or *Jovian comets,* about 40 in all, have orbits that pass close to Jupiter. It is believed that the gravitational attraction of Jupiter entrapped these comets into their relatively small orbits. Their periods range from 3.3 yr (Encke's comet) to 8.6 yr.

Analysis of the composition of comets, based upon use of the spectroscope, shows that the denser coma, which often contains a bright starlike nucleus, is composed largely of methane, ammonia, carbon dioxide, and water. This mixture is extremely cold, and the gases exist in the frozen state as particles. During close approach to the Sun some of the gas is vaporized and ionized under the intense heat of the

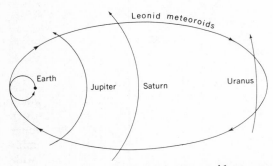

Figure 11.3. Orbit of the Leonid meteoroid swarm. The plane of the meteoroid orbit is inclined 17° to the plane of the ecliptic. [After E. A. Fath (1934), *Elements of Astronomy,* New York, McGraw-Hill.]

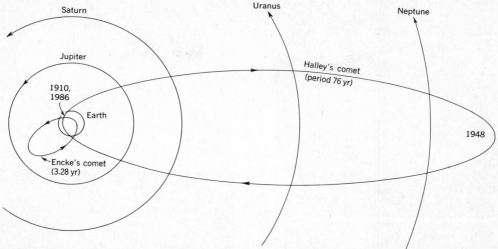

Figure 11.5. The orbits of Halley's and Encke's comets. The orbital plane of Halley's comet is inclined 18° to the ecliptic, that of Encke's comet 12°. [After R. A. Lyttleton (1956), *The Modern Universe*, New York, Harper & Row.]

Sun's rays, diffusing outward to form the tail. Under pressure of the solar wind (see Chapter 2) the tail is pushed away from the Sun. As a result of passage close to the Sun, a comet may lose a part of its mass or be completely disrupted. It is thought that the diffuse dust particles of disintegrated comets may constitute the meteoroid swarms. This possibility is strengthened by noting that the highly eccentric orbits of both meteor swarms and comets are much alike. Several cases are known in which the orbit of a meteoroid swarm is identical with the orbit of a previously known comet.

The source of matter for comets and meteoroids is a topic of speculation. The Dutch astronomer Jan H. Öort suggested that the comets originate in a vast cloud, or "reservoir," containing the substance of millions of comets and located between 50,000 and 150,000 astronomical units from the Sun. The matter in such a belt would be at a temperature close to absolute zero and would have been formed early in the history of the solar system (see Chapter 12).

## TESTIMONY OF THE METEORITES

We cannot take samples of the matter making up the Earth's mantle and core, although the MOHOLE drilling project raised hopes of obtaining sample material directly from the upper mantle. However, for what it is worth in allowing controlled inferences, the evidence supplied by meteorites has been exploited with interesting results, as to both the composition of the Earth's interior and the age of the members of the solar system.

Unlike the silent atmospheric penetration of the meteor, which leaves only a passing streak of light, the fall of a meteorite is accompanied by a brilliant flash of light, to which the term *fireball* is given, and by sounds resembling thunder or cannon fire. Frictional resistance with the atmosphere causes the outer surface of the object to be intensely heated. However, this heat does not penetrate to the interior of a meteorite, which reaches the Earth with its original composition and structure unchanged. The single mass may explode before the impact, showering fragments over a wide area. The observed arrival of a meteorite and subsequent collection of the fragments is designated as a *fall*. Collection of a meteorite whose fall was not observed is designated as a *find*. Examples of large meteorites are shown in Figure 11.6.

Meteorites have been intensively studied, not only as to chemical composition and structure, but also as to age. They fall into three classes. (1) The *irons* (*siderites*)* are composed almost entirely of a nickel-iron alloy, in which the nickel content ranges from 4% to 20%. (2) At the other end of the series are the *stones* (*aerolites*), consisting largely of silicate minerals, mostly olivine and pyroxene, and with only 20% or less nickel-iron. Plagioclase feldspar may also be present. (3) An intermediate

---

* Terms in parentheses are now considered obsolete but will be encountered in readings on the subject.

Figure 11.6. Two varieties of meteorites. (*A*) This stony meteorite, weighing 745 lb (338 kg), is the largest single stony meteorite of which the fall has been observed. It struck the ground at Paragould, Arkansas, on February 17, 1930, forming a huge fireball visible over thousands of square miles. Height of the meteorite is about 2 ft (0.6 m). (Yerkes Observatory.) (*B*) The Willamette meteorite, an iron meteorite, weighs 15½ tons (14 metric tons) and is over 10 ft (3 m) long. The huge cavities were produced by rapid oxidation of the iron during fall through the atmosphere. (Courtesy of American Museum of Natural History—Hayden Planetarium.)

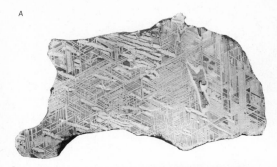

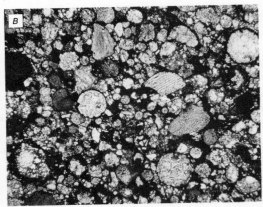

Figure 11.7. (*A*) Widmanstätten figures etched into an iron meteorite. (Smithsonian Astrophysical Observatory photograph, courtesy of J. A. Wood.) (*B*) Microscopic photograph of a thin slice of a chondrite meteorite, showing an area about 0.4 in. (1 cm) across. [From John A. Wood (1968), *Meteorites and the Origin of Planets,* New York, McGraw-Hill, p. 18, Figure 2–3. Used with permission of the publisher.]

class of meteorites consists of the *stony irons* (*siderolites*), in which silicate minerals and nickel-iron occur in about equal proportions. The nickel-iron may form a continuous medium in which spherical bodies of silicate minerals are enclosed.

Structures of the meteorites have aroused much interest in their similarities to and differences from terrestrial rocks. The nickel-iron of an iron meteorite typically shows crystalline structure. When a polished surface is etched, there appear distinctive line patterns known as *Widmanstätten figures* (Figure 11.7*A*), unknown in terrestrial iron, from which the interpretation can be made that the alloy has cooled very slowly from a high tem-

perature. This evidence suggests that the iron meteorites are disrupted fragments of larger original masses, such as might be found in the cores of planets.

One class of stony meteorites, the *chondrites,* possess an internal structure never observed in rocks of Earth. Olivine or pyroxene crystals occur in small rounded bodies (*chondrules*) on the order of 0.04 in. (1 mm) in diameter (Figure 11.7*B*). This structure is certainly important in the origin of the stony meteorites, but the significance is not known. However, another group of stony meteorites (*achondrites*) possesses a coarse-grained structure that resembles the structure of Earth's plutonic igneous rocks. We can infer that meteorites with such structure solidified from a magma.

When the meteorites of observed falls are catalogued, their relative abundance turns out to be about as follows: stones, 94%; irons, 4.5%; stony irons, 1.5%. The stony meteorites are thus preponderant in bulk, and most of these are chondrites possessing the unique structure noted above as not found in terrestrial rocks. These facts suggest as a working hypothesis that the chondrites represent distributed fragments of the earliest planetary bodies to be formed in the solar system. The nickel-iron meteorites can be interpreted as cores of these planetary bodies in which the process of differentiation had taken place. Stony meteorites having textures resembling terrestrial igneous rocks point to the possibility that melting and recrystallization had taken place to some degree in these original planetary bodies.

Age determinations of meteorites have been made, using the uranium-lead, potassium-argon, and rubidium-strontium methods described in Chapter 10. There is a high degree of agreement in the results pointing to the time of formation of all types of meteorites at 4.5 billion years (b.y.) before present. It has already been noted that this age is about 1 b.y. greater than that of the oldest known crustal rocks on Earth.

We conclude from the study of meteorites that the first large solid objects of the solar system were formed rapidly by aggregation of iron-magnesium silicates and nickel-iron (and of many less abundant elements) and that this event took place about 4.5 b.y. ago. These first large bodies have been named *planetoids,* which simply means "bodies resembling the planets." Within the larger planetoids some melting and recrystallization evidently took place, accompanied by differentiation of the nickel-iron into core material. Melting by radiogenic heat and differentiation of silicates from nickel-iron calls for a planetoid as large as Earth or Venus. Disruption of such a planetoid into fragments, which became the asteroids and meteoroids, obviously took place at a subsequent time. The effect of exposure to cosmic rays provides evidence of the age of disruptive collisions in which meteorites were reduced to fragments on the order of 3 ft (1 m) in diameter. Typically, this age is on the order of 0.5 b.y. for irons and 20 million years (m.y.) for stones.

The assumption that the terrestrial planets were created out of the same substance as the disrupted planetoids led to the accepted hypothesis that the Earth's core is composed of nickel-iron and the mantle of iron-magnesium silicates. This conclusion is greatly strengthened by independent evidence of the density and related physical properties of the Earth's interior derived from the study of earthquake waves (Chapter 2).

## IMPACT FEATURES ON EARTH

Have meteorites of great size struck the Earth's surface to produce recognizable impact features? The largest known single meteorite is the Hoba iron, found in southwest Africa; it weighs about 66 tons (60 metric tons) and measures $9 \times 9 \times 3$ ft ($3 \times 3 \times 1$ m). The next five in order of size are irons weighing roughly half as much as the Hoba meteorite. However, no stony meteorites have been found whose weight is over 1 ton. The largest single stony meteorite observed to fall, pictured in Figure 11.6, weighs one-third of a ton.

Rarely has an observed meteorite fall produced craters of measurable dimension. One of them was the Siberian Sikhote Alin fall of February 12, 1947, witnessed by many persons. The largest iron fragment recovered weighed 2 tons (1800 kg). Funnel-shaped craters as large as 92 ft (26 m) in diameter were produced by the larger iron fragments. Soviet scientists deduced from the observed trajectory of the meteoroid trail that it was a small asteroid traveling at a speed of 25 mi/sec (40 km/sec).

We therefore turn to prehistoric impacts of enormous meteorites capable of producing rimmed craters with diameters of 500 to 5000 ft (150 to 1500 m) and larger. Several fine examples of almost perfectly circular large craters with sharply defined rims have been found and examined over the continental surfaces of Earth (see Figure 11.8). In addition, there are many more circular rock structures which prove upon examination to show intense disturbance and alteration of the rock in which they occur. Altogether, perhaps fewer than 12 large, rimmed craters and about 50 circular structures are known. The widespread availability of air photographs, combined with satellite photography, has brought the discovery of many structures of possible meteoritic impact origin. We are, of course, excluding from this discussion all known volcanic craters constructed of lava and volcanic ash, as well as obvious *calderas,* the large craters produced by explosive demolition of a preexisting volcanic cone.

At the outset, we must recognize that there exists a wide range of opinion as to the origin of circular structures and of certain sharp-rimmed deep craters as well. Because we are treating these features under a discussion of meteorite impacts, that origin may seem to be implied to be the favored hypothesis. However, a substantial number of geologists who have given intensive study to circular structures hold that they may have been formed by internal earth processes—for example, by uplift under pressure of rising magma, followed by collapse. Explosion by volcanic gases is also postulated as a cratering mechanism and has had many adherents, who refer to the circular forms as *crypto-volcanic structures*. Those who hold that the circular structures are extraterrestrial in origin, resulting from impact of large objects from space, refer to the same forms as *astroblemes* (freely translated as "starwounds"). While originally possessing sharp-rimmed craters, the astroblemes today represent only the deeply eroded basal parts of the original impact structures.

Perhaps the finest example of a large circular-rimmed crater of almost certain meteoritic impact origin is the Barringer Crater (formerly known as Meteor Crater) in Arizona (Figure 11.8). The diameter of this crater is 4000 ft (1200 m) and its depth almost 600 ft (180 m). The rim rises about 150 ft (46 m) above the surrounding plateau surface, which consists of almost horizontal limestone strata. Rock fragments have been found scattered over a radius of 6 mi (10 km) from the crater center, while meteoritic iron fragments numbering in the thousands have been collected from the immediate area. Other evidence of severe shock forces and high temperatures comes from the finding of closely fractured rock, silica glass, and a unique silica mineral known as *coesite*. The latter was produced by severe shock pressures from a pure sandstone formation underlying the limestone of the plateau. Although boreholes and shafts were put down in the bottom of the crater in an attempt to locate a large iron body, none was found. It has been calculated that an impacting meteorite capable of producing such a crater would have disintegrated and partially vaporized during impact, leaving no single large mass intact. Carefully derived estimates of the impacting object specify that it was a 63,000-ton ($56 \times 10^6$ kg) iron meteorite about 100 ft (30 m) in long dimension and that it was traveling at about 34,000 mph (15 km/sec) when impact occurred.

Figure 11.9 shows inferred steps in the formation of a simple meteorite crater of moderate size, such as the Barringer Crater. Kinetic energy estimated to be on the order of $10^{21}$ to $10^{28}$ ergs is almost instantly transferred to the ground by a shock wave, which intensely fractures and disintegrates the rock around the point of impact. As the shock wave is reflected back to the meteorite body, it is fragmented into thousands of pieces and partly vaporized as well. Large amounts of fragmental debris

Figure 11.8. Oblique air view of the Barringer Crater in northern Arizona. (Yerkes Observatory.)

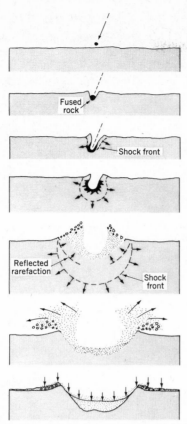

Figure 11.9. Hypothetical stages in the formation of a meteorite impact crater. [Modified from E. Anders (1965), *Scientific American,* October, 1965, p. 34. Data of E. M. Shoemaker and U.S. Geological Survey.]

are then thrown out, while the solid bedrock is forced upward and outward to create the crater rim. A great deal of rock material falls back into the crater, filling the bottom, where melted rock may be concealed.

A number of other craters of generally accepted meteoritic origin deserve mention. Comparatively small but abundantly endowed with nickel-iron fragments are the Odessa craters in Texas, evidently formed by two large impacting fragments. A group of smaller craters in Argentina, the Campo del Cielo swarm, are associated with meteoritic iron fragments and silica glass. Within Australia, four outstanding crater localities are known, all with meteoritic iron. One of these, the Wolf Creek Crater, is remarkably perfect in form, the rim being 2800 ft (850 m) in diameter (Figure 11.10). In Estonia, the Kaalijarv Crater is accepted as being of meteoritic origin,

as is the Aouelloul Crater in Mauretania. Altogether, the list consists of only eight craters (or crater groups) with which meteoritic iron is associated.

Of those well-formed large craters whose origin is disputed, and which have not revealed meteoritic iron, the New Quebec Crater of Canada is perhaps the most outstanding (Figure 11.11). It is exceptionally large: 2 mi (3.4 km) in diameter and 1300 ft (400 m) deep. The rim rises 300 to 500 ft (90 to 150 m) above the surrounding land surface. The bedrock, which consists of gneiss and granite of the Canadian Shield, is intensely fractured. Similar in some respects is the Ashanti Crater of Ghana, which contains a lake over 6 mi (10 km) in diameter. This crater also lies in ancient shield rocks.

Large circular structures lacking a rim or crater, presumably because of erosional removal, run to much larger diameters than the craters listed above. About a dozen such structures have been found in the Canadian Shield. Typically, they are represented by circular depressions containing lakes (Figure 11.12). If these structures are astroblemes, as some investigators claim, they represent extremely ancient impacts, perhaps dating back as far as 200 to 300 m.y., when the Canadian Shield had been reduced to a low continental platform.

From a review of craters and circular structures of our Earth, we can draw the conclusion that impacts by large meteorites have been extremely rare events in recent geologic time. Perhaps the number has been on the order of half a dozen occurrences in 1 m.y. Moreover, possible meteorite impact features of greater age are widely scattered and the number of impacts appears to have been small over the past 0.5 b.y. But these frequencies are what we might expect, on the assumption that meteorites are not being produced in the modern solar system. If they represent space debris that continues to be swept up by planets and satellites, the frequency of impacts should be small in later geologic eras compared with a high frequency in the early stages of planetary formation. We must therefore look to a celestial body on which impact features would have been preserved with little or no erosion for the entire 4.5 b.y. since Earth and the other planets formed. Two such bodies are available for study. They are our Moon and the planet

Figure 11.10. Olique air view of Wolf Creek Crater, Western Australia. The crater is about 0.5 mi (0.8 km) in diameter, and the rim rises about 200 ft (60 m) above the flat sediment-filled floor. (Photograph by courtesy of R. M. L. Elliott, West Australian Petroleum Pty. Limited.)

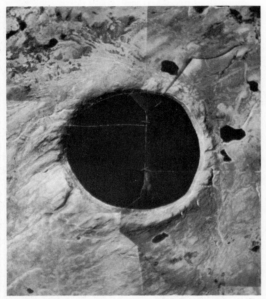

Figure 11.11. Vertical air view of New Quebec Crater (Chubb Crater), located at about latitude 61° N, longitude 73½° W in northern Quebec. The depression, 2 mi (3.2 km) wide and 1300 ft (400 m) deep, is formed in gneisses of Precambrian age. (Mosaic air photograph by courtesy of K. L. Currie, Geological Survey of Canada, Dept. of Energy, Mines & Resources.)

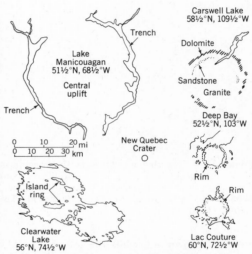

Figure 11.12. Large circular structures of the Canadian Shield. Solid lines are lake shorelines. New Quebec Crater, shown for scale comparison, is pictured in Figure 11.11. [After M. R. Dence (1965), *Annals New York Acad. Sci.,* vol. 123, p. 943, Figure 2.]

Mars. Perhaps in the future Mercury will also provide a third body for study.

### TEKTITES

Among the most puzzling and controversial natural mineral objects found on Earth's surface are small pieces of glass ranging in size from a sand grain to individual pieces weighing as much as 2 lb (1 kg). These glass objects are named *tektites.* The collection and scientific study of tektites spans the past 200 years, yet evidence as to their age and mode of origin is largely a product of intensive research through use of modern tools and disciplines of science applied within the past decade or two.

One of the most interesting and unique features of tektites relates to their shapes. Usually smoothly rounded in contour, they take the symmetrical forms of buttons, dumbbells, teardrops, disks, winged bodies, and rods (Figure 11.13). The glass is colored green, brown, or

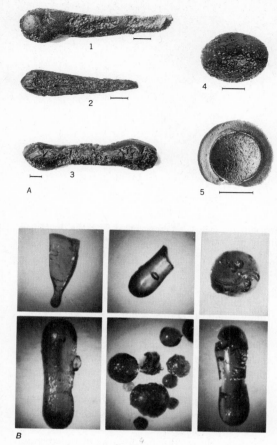

area of the Indian Ocean, as shown in Figure 11.14, and constitute a part of the single Australasia strewnfield. A second strewnfield is that of the Ivory Coast. Microtektites have also been recovered from deep-sea sediments off this coast. A third locality is in Czechoslovakia. Here tektites occur in small areas in Moravia and Bohemia. The name *moldavites* has been locally applied to these tektites. A fourth strewnfield is in the southern United States, where tektites have been found at two localities, one in Texas and one in Georgia. A fifth strewnfield is in the Libyan desert.

The age of tektites, representing the time at which they last solidified from a molten state, has been measured through the potassium-argon age-determination method. Within each strewnfield the age is the same for all specimens, but ages differ greatly from one strewnfield to another. The results are:

| | |
|---|---|
| Australasia field | 700,000 yr |
| Ivory Coast field | 1.1  m.y. |
| Czechoslovakia field | 15   m.y. |
| United States field | 34   m.y. |
| Libya field | 34   m.y. |

Microtektites of the Indian Ocean are found in sediments deposited near the close of the Matuyama geomagnetic reversal, an event dated at 700,000 yr, and hence in agreement with the geochemical date for tektites on land in the Australasian strewnfield.

Facts concerning the chemical composition of tektites must also be taken into account in hypotheses of their origin. All are glasses high in silica, which ranges from 70% $SiO_2$ in the Australasian tektites to as high as 97.6% $SiO_2$ for those of the Libyan strewnfield. Aluminum oxide is the second-ranking constituent, forming about 13% of the Australasian tektite glass. Iron, magnesium, and calcium are important lesser constituents. Tektite glass is unique in having a very high melting point (higher than that of Pyrex glass) and a low coefficient of expansion. Chemically, then, tektite glass with its high silica content is not the same as any glass that might be produced by melting of a stony meteorite.

The shapes of tektites show clearly that they solidified from droplets free to adjust their outlines to surface tension. Moreover, many show markings, such as grooves, that suggest the effects of attrition by air resistance during their fall. All opinion seems to be in agreement that

Figure 11.13. (*A*) Tektites: 1 and 2, teardrop forms, Lang Bien, South Vietnam; 3, dumbbell, Tan Hai Island, China; 4, spherical form, Philippine Islands; 5, flanged button form, Australia. Length of bar: 1 cm. (Photographs by Virgil E. Barnes, Director of Tektite Research, Bureau of Economic Geology, University of Texas at Austin.) (*B*) Microtektites from deep-sea cores off the Ivory Coast. All are less than 0.05 in. (1.3 mm) in size. (Courtesy of Billy P. Glass, Lamont-Doherty Geological Observatory of Columbia University.)

amber. In the past they have been collected for use as ornaments and were even shaped by Stone Age man into weapon points.

Facts concerning the areas of concentration of tektite finds are quite well understood and free of controversy. There appear to be five world localities of occurrence, designated as *strewnfields* (Figure 11.14). Largest of the strewnfields is the Australasia field, which includes southern Australia, the Philippine Islands, Indonesia, and parts of Indochina and China. Recently, extremely minute tektites, known as *microtektites* (Figure 11.13), have been found in deep-sea sediments from a broad

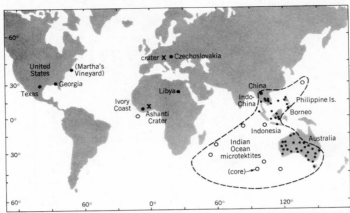

Figure 11.14. World distribution of tektites. Black dots show generalized positions of tektite localities. Open circles show locations of deep-sea cores in which microtektites have been found. [Data from V. Barnes (1961), *Scientific American*, November, 1961; and W. Gentner *et al.* (1970), *Science*, vol. 1968, p. 359, Figure 1.]

tektites solidified from liquid drops falling through the atmosphere.

Until about a decade ago, the most commonly held hypotheses of tektite origin invoked an extraterrestrial source. One such hypothesis is that a disrupted planetoid provided tektites as well as the more generally recognized forms of meteorites. Under this hypothesis, tektites are classed as one variety of meteorite, along with stones and irons.

If the tektite material was derived from a disrupted planetoid, the high-silica rock must have been already segregated from more basic rock within the planetoid before its disruption. Layers or pools of glassy silicate have been postulated as forming upon the surface of the planetoid, providing a source of tektite glass.

Another extraterrestrial hypothesis holds that tektite glass is derived from comets. Melted by intense heat from passage near the Sun, the silicate remains of the comet were intercepted by the Earth and provided the molten matter for a shower of tektites.

A still different extraterrestrial hypothesis, defended by John A. O'Keefe and others, suggests that huge meteoritic masses, impacting the surface of the Moon, forced lunar surface matter into space orbits and that some of these chunks of lunar materials reached the Earth. This hypothesis faces the difficulty of explaining how high-silica rocks came to exist on the Moon's surface. Lunar rocks thus far analyzed are mafic in composition, a fact that might appear to rule out a lunar origin for tektites. However, glassy matter in lunar-rock samples

chemically resembles some tektites, so that a lunar origin of tektites is not ruled out.

The lunar hypothesis has been modified to suggest that large solid masses, thrown from the Moon by an impacting meteorite, came into eliptical orbit as Earth satellites. Finally, these objects entered the Earth's atmosphere at low grazing angles. Intensely heated by atmospheric friction, the surfaces of these satellites were fused and gave off droplets which solidified into tektites during downward fall through the atmosphere. This hypothesis explains the broad pattern of tektite distribution over vast strewnfields.

A different group of hypotheses regards tektite glass as being of terrestrial origin, derived from melting of rocks of the Earth's surface. Melting occurred through the impact of large meteorites, producing craters from which surface material was thrown upward into the atmosphere in a molten state. The tektites were formed as these melted particles fell back through the atmosphere. One line of evidence has recently been brought forward to support the terrestrial hypothesis. If the tektite glass was derived from surface rocks of the Earth, the age of the mineral matter prior to its melting should agree with the age of rocks in the supposed area of impact of the meteorite.

Based upon the ratio of isotopes of strontium and rubidium, it has been possible to derive the age of the original rock material from which the glass of tektites was formed. When this is done, the age of the Australasian, Czechoslovakian, and United States tektite materials proves to be similar, about 300 to 400 m.y. In the Czechoslovakia area, crystalline rocks of the tektite region are also of 300-m.y. age, and it can be reasoned that these rocks provided the source of those tektites. Upon similar age analysis, tektite material of the Ivory Coast field yields an original age of 2 b.y., which is the same as for shield rocks exposed in an area of Ghana about 200 mi (300 km) east of the tektite field; moreover, a possible meteorite crater, today containing Lake Bosumtwi, can be postulated as the point of impact of the meteorite that produced these tektites.

Diversity of hypotheses of tektite origin is extreme. The various lines of evidence seem uncompromisingly at odds. Perhaps the only area of complete agreement among carefully considered hypotheses of tektite origin is that the showers of droplets were generated in some manner by collisions of extraterrestrial masses with Earth or Moon. Further sampling of the Moon's surface may ultimately decide whether the tektite glass could be of lunar material, although evidence found thus far is indecisive on this question. In the meantime, intensive researches by scientists in many disciplines—among them geochemistry, geology, astronomy, planetary science, and lunar science—are sure to bring new evidence to bear upon this most puzzling problem of the small glass objects.

## THE LUNAR ENVIRONMENT

If we are to interpret correctly the physical features of the Moon's surface, it will first be necessary to consider the surface environment of that satellite. Environmental factors include the Moon's gravity field, lack of both atmosphere and hydrosphere, intensity of incoming and outgoing radiation, and surface temperatures. All of these factors show striking differences when compared with the environment of Earth.

Gravity* on the Moon's surface is about one-sixth as great as on Earth. Therefore, an object that weighs 6 lb on Earth will weigh only 1 lb on the Moon. This relatively small gravity is of great importance in interpreting the Moon's surface and history. For example, rock of the same strength as rock on Earth could stand without collapse in much higher cliffs and

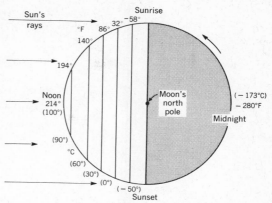

Figure 11.15. Surface temperatures to be expected on the Moon at various times of the lunar day and night. [After F. L. Whipple (1968), *Earth, Moon, and Planets,* 3rd ed., Cambridge, Mass., Harvard Univ. Press, p. 135, Figure 99.]

peaks on the Moon than on Earth. Objects thrown upward at an angle from the Moon (as when the Moon is struck by a large meteoroid) will travel much higher and farther than under the same impetus on Earth. Lack of sufficient gravity has cost the Moon the loss of any atmosphere that it may have once possessed, since the escape velocities of the gas molecules will be comparatively low.* Lack of a lunar atmosphere is shown by the fact that the rays from a star are instantaneously cut off as the Moon's edge passes over the star. Were a gaseous envelope present on the Moon, those rays would be bent, causing the light to be cut off over a definite span of time and a slight alteration by refraction of the star's apparent position.

Lacking an atmosphere, the Moon's surface intercepts the Sun's radiation on a perpendicular surface with the full value of 2 ly/min. The Moon's albedo (percentage of reflected energy) is small (only about 7%), thus most incoming solar energy is absorbed by the Moon's surface. The effect is to cause intense surface heating during the long lunar day of about two weeks' duration (Figure 11.15). With the Sun's rays striking at a high angle for several days continuously, surface temperatures at lunar noon reach 214° F (101° C). Correspondingly, conditions on the dark side of the Moon reach opposite extremes of cold during the long lunar night. With no atmosphere to return longwave

---

* Gravity is defined as the attraction which Earth or Moon exerts upon a very small mass located at its surface.

* Earth's escape velocity is 7 mi/sec (11.2 km/sec), in comparison with a value of only 1½ mi/sec (2½ km/sec) for the Moon.

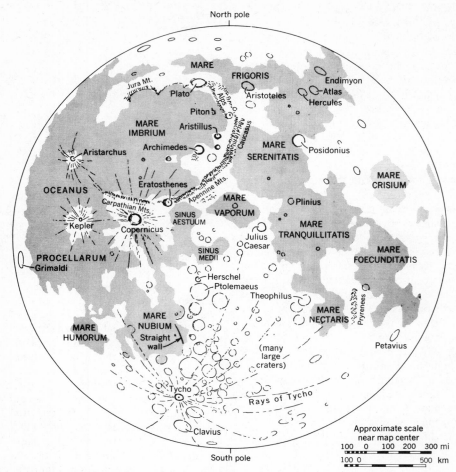

North pole

MARE
FRIGORIS
Jura Mt.
Plato
Aristoteles
Endimyon
Atlas
Hercules
Piton
MARE
IMBRIUM
Aristillus
Archimedes
MARE
SERENITATIS
Posidonius
Aristarchus
Eratosthenes
MARE
CRISIUM
OCEANUS
Carpathian Mts.
Apennine Mts.
MARE
VAPORUM
Plinius
Kepler
Copernicus
SINUS
AESTUUM
MARE
TRANQUILLITATIS
Julius
Caesar
PROCELLARUM
Grimaldi
SINUS
MEDII
MARE
FOECUNDITATIS
Herschel
Ptolemaeus
Theophilus
MARE
NUBIUM
Straight
wall
MARE
NECTARIS
Pyrenees
MARE
HUMORUM
(many
large
craters)
Petavius
Tycho
Rays of Tycho
Clavius

South pole

Approximate scale
near map center
100   0   100   200   300 mi
100  0                     500 km

Figure 11.16. Sketch-map of the major relief features of the moon. This diagram may be used as an aid in identifying areas and subjects in the lunar photographs of this chapter. The Moon is shown here as it appears to the unaided eye or through binoculars, whereas most astronomical telescopes invert the image.

radiation, surface temperatures drop to values estimated at below −280° F (−173° C).

Of particular interest is the sudden drop in lunar-surface temperature when sunlight is abruptly cut off by a lunar eclipse. In one such instance the surface temperature fell from 160° F (71° C) to −110° F (−79° C) in only 1 hr. This drop of 270 F° (150 C°) is vastly greater than any natural temperature drop on the Earth's surface in a comparable period of time and may be a significant mechanism in causing the rupture of exposed rocks.

From the scientific standpoint, such huge temperature ranges are of interest because of the possible effect upon minerals exposed at the Moon's surface. The expansion and contraction that crystalline minerals undergo when heated and cooled can bring about the disinte-

gration of solid rock into small particles. These variations can also cause loose particles to creep gradually to lower levels on a sloping ground surface. These effects may be unusually important on the Moon, because without an atmosphere and running water ordinary terrestrial processes of weathering, erosion, and transportation cannot act upon the Moon.

The Moon's surface contains no bodies of standing water, hence there are no features of wave and current erosion. Without streams and water bodies, the Moon has no mechanisms or receiving areas for accumulation of water-laid sedimentary strata.

## THE LUNAR SURFACE

Astronomers and geologists have for decades been documenting the Moon's relief features, a

Figure 11.17. The Moon as it would appear if its whole disk could be simultaneously illuminated from a source at the same altitude. (Yerkes Observatory.)

field of study that has been called *selenography*. As the advent of the great telescopes permitted more and more details to be revealed, progress was made in mapping and interpreting details of the lunar surface. Information on magnitude of the relief features came from measurement of the shadows they cast under the Sun's rays at a low angle. But it was not until the successful use of space vehicles equipped with cameras that minute details were revealed and experimental investigations of the surface directly performed.

In 1963 and 1964, three United States *Ranger* spacecraft impacted the lunar surface, sending back some 17,000 pictures from a wide range of elevations. Photographs made from distances as close as 1000 ft (300 m) revealed

features as small as 18 in. (45 cm) across. There followed landings by *Surveyor* spacecraft, making direct physical and chemical tests of lunar-surface materials as well as photographs of the ground immediately surrounding the vehicle. By 1968, five *Lunar Orbiter* vehicles had completed their missions of photographing the lunar surface from heights as low as 35 mi (56 km). A total of almost 2000 vertical photographs, at least 10 times sharper than the best taken by telescopes from Earth, were obtained from the nearside of the Moon, as well as almost complete coverage of the previously unknown farside. Scientific analysis of this plethora of information will require years for full exploitation.

In 1969 and 1970 manned space vehicles of

*Apollo 9, 10, 11,* and *12* missions circled the Moon at low levels and descended to the lunar surface, permitting photographic negatives in color to be brought back to Earth. Extremely high resolution photographs were thus obtained (see Figure 11.20).

As anyone can easily see by use of a small telescope or binoculars, the first major subdivision of the Moon's surface is into light-colored areas and dark-colored areas (Figures 11.16 and 11.17). The former constitute the relatively higher surfaces, or highland (upland) areas, and can be collectively termed the *terrae.* This Latin word reflects the earliest interpretations of Galileo—that these areas were dry lands. The dark-colored areas, the low-lying smooth lunar plains, are named the *maria,* plural of the Latin word *mare* for "sea"; Galileo applied this term to what he believed to be true seas of liquid. Of the nearside of the Moon, about 60% is terrae and about 40% maria.

Lunar highland areas, or terrae, exhibit a wide range of relief features. Most outstanding are the great mountain ranges, of which there are 20 major groups on the nearside. Perhaps the most spectacular of these are the Appenines rimming the Mare Imbrium on the southwest side (Figure 11.18). Several peaks within the Appenines rise to heights of 12,000 to 16,000 ft (4 to 5 km) above the nearby mare surface. The highest and most massive mountains are those of the Leibnitz range, near the lunar south pole, which have peaks rising to heights of 35,000 ft (11 km). Elsewhere, the highland terrain consists of gently rolling surfaces with slopes less than 10° from the horizontal and of rough areas with slopes exceeding 10°.

Lunar maria of the nearside are divided into 10 major named areas, in addition to a single vast area, Oceanus Procellarum (Figure 11.16). Although maria outlines are in places highly irregular, with many bays, it is noteworthy that a circular outline is persistent for several, and particularly striking for Mare Imbrium.

Most spectacular of the Moon's surface features are the *craters.* Even under the low magnification of a small telescope the large craters form an awe-inspiring sight when seen in a partial phase of the Moon. Craters are abundant over both the terrae and the maria surfaces. Using telescopes alone, some 30,000 craters have been counted on the nearside with

diameters down to 2 mi (3 km). This number has been increased to an estimated 200,000 with space-vehicle photography and includes recognizable craters as small as 2 ft (0.6 m) across. On the lunar nearside there are 150 craters of diameter larger than 50 mi (80 km). Largest of these is *Clavius,* 146 mi (235 km) in diameter and surrounded by a rim rising 20,000 ft (6 km) above its floor. (See south polar area in Figure 11.16.) *Tycho* and *Copernicus* are among the most striking of the large craters (Figure 11.19).

The forms of large craters fall into several types. In some the floor is flat and smooth, and the rim is sharply defined and abrupt. In others, such as Copernicus, the floor is saucer-shaped, while the rim consists of multiple concentric ridges. Of particular interest are systems of *rays* of lighter-colored surface radiating from certain of the larger craters—for example, Copernicus (Figure 11.19). In several of the large craters there is a sharply defined *central peak,* which must be taken into account in interpreting the origin of craters. That of Eratosthenes shows up particularly well in Figure 11.19.

Small lunar craters, down to the limits of resolution, are almost perfectly circular and have a cup-shaped interior and a prominent rim (Figure 11.20). However, these well-defined forms grade into less distinct craters with low slopes and into shallow depressions. The impact origin for almost all of these smaller craters is generally accepted. A few are fresh in appearance, with a litter of boulders on the rim and within the crater itself. The supposedly newer craters are frequently lighter in color than the surrounding surface. The more subdued craters appear to be older and have lost their sharpness through slow processes of mass wasting (Figure 11.21). These grade into the oldest forms, which have lost their rims and show only a shallow depression. A few small craters are elliptical in outline and may represent the secondary fall of masses dislodged by much larger impacts.

It has been shown that the number of lunar craters per unit of area is inversely proportional to the square root of the crater diameter. Consequently, the number of large craters is small and that of very small craters is legion.

Yet another class of distinctive lunar-surface features are the *rilles.* Some are remarkably straight, taking the form of a narrow trench up to 150 mi (240 km) long. Others are irregular

Figure 11.18. Mare Imbrium, with its bordering mountains, the Jura, Alps, Caucasus, Apennines, and Carpathians; and the great craters Plato, Aristillus, Archimedes, and Eratosthenes. Note the spinelike peak, Piton. Identify these features with the aid of Figure 11.16. (The Hale Observatories.)

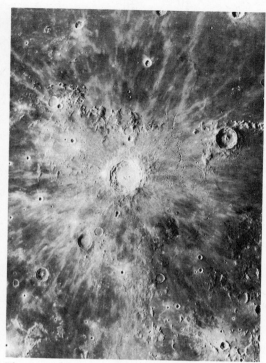

Figure 11.19. Copernicus, the great lunar crater lying south of Mare Imbrium (see Figure 11.16). Note the rays—radial streaks of lighter-colored material. The conspicuous crater lying east-northeast of Copernicus is Eratosthenes. (The Hale Observatories.)

in plan, and a few are sinuous, suggestive of terrestrial meandering rivers (Figure 11.22). It has been suggested that the sinuous rilles were formed over lines of vents from which volcanic gases were emitted under high pressure. Most of the straight rilles are interpreted as fracture features in brittle rock of the lunar crust. Related features are the straight cliffs, or *walls,* which may be fault escarpments. A particularly striking example is the Straight Wall in Mare Nubium (Figure 11.16), which is 800 ft (240 m) high and may represent a fault that broke the mare surface.

Study of *Ranger* and *Lunar Orbiter* photographs has revealed many classes of minor details that are as yet little understood. Particularly prevalent in areas of rough terrain are minute systems of parallel ridges and troughs. Many of the steep slopes exhibit steplike terraces near the base.

The farside of the Moon has now been photographed in detail by *Lunar Orbiter* spacecraft and by astronauts of *Apollo* spacecraft, the first human beings to see that side of the

Figure 11.20. Censorinus (*arrow*), one of the freshest craters on the Moon's nearside, shows a sharp rim and surrounding zone of light-colored soil surface. Crater rim is about 4 mi (7 km) in diameter. (*Apollo 10* photograph by NASA.)

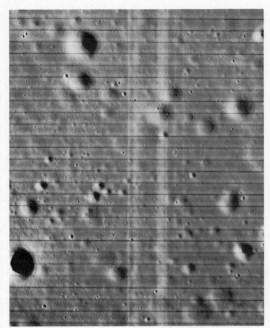

Figure 11.21. Subdued old craters in the southeastern part of Mare Tranquillitatis contrast with sharply defined craters of much smaller size and younger age. Area shown is about 3 × 4 mi (5 × 6½ km). (*Lunar Orbiter III* photograph by NASA.)

Moon. The lunar farside is heavily cratered and generally lacking in extensive maria (Figure 11.23).

## ORIGIN OF THE GREAT CRATERS AND MARIA

Origin of the great craters and the circular-rimmed maria cannot be discussed without placing the subject in the general context of the Moon's total constitution. Two widely divergent hypotheses have found supporters throughout the long history of *lunar geology,* or *selenology,* the science analogous to terrestrial geology. One extreme view holds that the lunar craters and maria are largely of volcanic origin. This hypothesis implies a long history of intrusion and extrusion of molten rock from the Moon's interior. Source of the heat may be radiogenic, as in the Earth. Circular depressions of the great craters are explained by the collapse of volcanoes as magma is removed from below. The maria are interpreted as vast lava fields produced by extrusion of basalt magma from deep sources. The volcanic interpretation encounters difficulty on a number of points. True volcanic cones, such as those

Figure 11.22. Hadley's Rille, a sinuous canyonlike feature, crosses a cratered plain and ends in a highland area. North is at the bottom of this *Lunar Orbiter V* photograph, spanning an area about 30 mi (50 km) wide. Location: 2°27′ E, 24°47′ N. (NASA photograph.)

found in abundance on Earth, are not present, and photographs rarely show features that can be interpreted as lava flows. Moreover, if the Moon's interior is sufficiently heated to produce plutonic rocks, there should also be found orogenic belts of folding and faulting such as characterize the Earth. Except for fracture lines, which are numerous, mountain-making forms of crustal uplift and compression seem to be totally lacking. The high lunar mountain ranges seem, instead, to constitute rims of circular maria or of large craters.

The second major hypothesis of the Moon's geology may be described as the *meteoritic* (or *impact*) *hypothesis* and includes the assumption that the Moon is a cold body without internal rock melting and volcanic action. One of the strong advocates of the meteoritic theory was the distinguished American geologist Grove Karl Gilbert, who published his explanation in 1893. Among the modern group of scientists who have contributed details to the impact hypothesis is Harold C. Urey. His modified explanation is often referred to as the

Figure 11.23. Photographed by *Lunar Orbiter IV* spacecraft from a distance of 1850 mi (3000 km), the eastern limb of the Moon cuts the sphere from top to bottom in a vertical line. The heavily cratered lunar farside lies to the left. The lunar equator is represented by a horizontal line crossing the center of the photograph. (NASA photograph.)

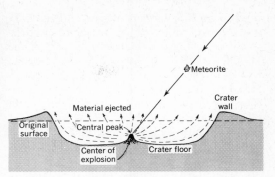

Figure 11.24. Cross section of a lunar crater, according to the meteorite-impact hypothesis of origin. The vertical scale is greatly exaggerated. [After R. A. Lyttleton (1956), *The Modern Universe,* New York, Harper & Row, p. 70, Figure 28.]

Urey-Gilbert hypothesis. According to Gilbert, the great craters were produced by large meteorites, in the manner which we have previously discussed in connection with terrestrial meteorite craters. However, the lunar craters are much larger than those on Earth and require explanation of the characteristic central peak. It has been suggested that the central peak lay directly beneath the center of impact-explosion and that since the shock wave was directed downward, the underlying rock remained intact while that surrounding it was blown outward (Figure 11.24). The rays which emanate from several large craters are explained as debris deposits thrown out over long distances from the explosion centers (Figure 11.19).

Under the Urey-Gilbert hypothesis, the rimmed maria, of which there are at least five on the lunar nearside, are the old impact scars of enormous masses, probably asteroids. The case of Mare Imbrium is particularly striking (Figure 11.18), as Gilbert pointed out. Urey also reconstructed the Imbrium collision, considering it as involving impact of an object about 125 mi (200 km) in diameter approach-

ing from a low angle. The impact raised a great wave of rock that spread outward, coming to rest in a great arc of mountain ridges. Gilbert had proposed that the heat of impact melted a vast quantity of lunar rock that subsequently solidified as the mare surface.

Recently, new evidence has come to light concerning inequalities of mass distribution within the Moon and bears on the Urey-Gilbert hypothesis of maria origin. If each rimmed mare represents the impact of an enormous mass, such as an asteroid, we might expect a deficiency of mass under the mare, because a body impacting at asteroid velocities of 10 km/sec would cause throwout of much more than its own mass. Evidence seems to be to the contrary. *Lunar Orbiter* satellites have recorded the Moon's gravity field in great detail. The resulting map shows definite concentrations of mass, known as *mascons,* under the centers of the ringed maria of the lunar nearside. These concentrations are particularly strong under Mare Imbrium and Mare Serenitatis.

### THE MARTIAN SURFACE

Do the surfaces of planets, other than Earth, show the scars of impacts? The outer planets, with their great distance and dense atmospheres, reveal nothing of this nature. Venus, though close to Earth, conceals her surface beneath a very dense atmosphere. Mercury, without an atmosphere, is a likely candidate for showing a heavily scarred surface, but because of its distance from the Earth and nearness to the Sun, observations have not yet been made.

Mars, another near neighbor, was photographed by U.S. *Mariner 4* spacecraft in 1965 and by *Mariner 6* and *7* spacecraft in 1969. Series of photographs showed that part of the Martian surface is heavily cratered in the southern hemisphere (Figure 11.25). The sizes and numbers of craters per unit of area on Mars are quite similar to corresponding data for the lunar uplands.

It has been noted, however, that the craters of Mars are shallower and have lower rims and flatter floors than lunar craters of the same size. That some forms of erosion or blanketing processes, albeit much less effective than those on Earth, operate on Mars is suggested by the subdued crater forms. The atmosphere of Mars, consisting largely of carbon dioxide, is highly rarefied, with a surface pressure of only about 5 mb, compared with 1000 mb for Earth. There is no suggestion of the action of running water on Mars, but rock weathering and wind action could be effective.

*Mariner 6* and *7* photographs revealed two important types of terrain, in addition to the cratered surfaces. One of these is described as *chaotic terrain,* in which relief features are irregular, suggesting to interpreters that the Martian surface has in places undergone collapse, as if material had been withdrawn from beneath. A third type of surface described as *featureless terrain* appears as a smooth, light-colored plain.

The dark-colored, heavily cratered terrain of

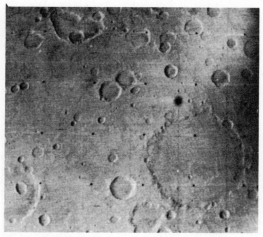

Figure 11.25. Cratered surface of Mars photographed by *Mariner 6* spacecraft at a distance of about 2150 mi (3460 km). The area shown spans about 425 × 375 mi (700 × 610 km). The largest crater visible (*lower right*) is about 160 mi (260 km) in diameter. North is down. Location: longitude 15° E, latitude 16° S. (NASA photograph.)

Mars is interpreted as original, or primeval, Martian surface, comparable with the lunar uplands, and presumed to date from the time of formation of the planet some −4.5 b.y. The chaotic terrain seems to have been affected by some unknown crustal processes at a later time in the planet's history. The featureless terrain is also considered younger than the cratered surface. Although processes of erosion and blanketing seem to have been at work on the Martian surface, photo interpreters have as yet not found any tectonic or topographic forms comparable to those known on Earth.

Thus we can tentatively conclude that there can have been little or no tectonic activity on Mars. We see no indications of the processes of orogeny or vulcanism that have characterized Earth's geologic history. Without the internal melting of rock and the resulting rise of magma to the Martian surface, the processes of outgassing* would necessarily have been very slow. Perhaps therein lies part of the explanation of the extreme thinness of the Martian atmosphere.

Carrying this discussion further to include Venus, the very high density of that planet's atmosphere suggests that outgassing may have occurred in large quantities and that therefore the crust of Venus has been subjected to intensive tectonic activity, along with much vulcanism and intrusion of magma arising from great depth. If so, the surface of Venus, like that of Earth, may preserve few if any impact features of great age, such as have been found on Mars. We might therefore anticipate the discovery of orogenic mountain ranges and many volcanoes on Venus.

## LUNAR SURFACE MATERIALS AND ROCKS

The first samples of lunar soil and rock were obtained in July, 1969, by astronauts of the *Apollo 11* mission from Mare Tranquillitatis. The surface materials here consist of unsorted fragmental debris ranging from dust to blocks almost 3 ft (1 m) across. On the rim and floor of a nearby crater some 100 ft (30 m) deep were found blocks as large as 16 ft (5 m) across. The layer of loose material, which can be termed *regolith,* has been estimated to have a depth of 10 to 20 ft (3 to 6 m) between craters. The larger rock fragments of which

* Outgassing means the emanation of volatile elements from within the planet, resulting in the formation of an atmosphere. This subject is discussed in detail in Chapter 12.

samples were taken are considered to be derived locally from bedrock by the force of impacting meteorites. However, a few small fragments may have come great distances from great craters such as Theophilus and Tycho.

The uppermost few inches of fine-grained surface material at Tranquillity Base has been described as brownish- to medium-gray cohesive soil consisting of grains in the size range of silt to fine sand. The material is easily penetrated. Upon compaction it becomes stronger and shows cohesion, as illustrated by the clear footprints of the astronauts (Figure 11.26).

Rock samples collected from Tranquillity Base are all of igneous mineral composition and fall into three classes. First is a fine-grained crystalline igneous rock with vesicular texture. *Vesicular* refers to presence of *vesicles,* small spheroidal cavities assumed to have been formed by gas bubbles, as in scoriaceous lavas. A second rock type is medium-grained crystalline igneous rock, containing larger irregular cavities (*vugs*) (Figure 11.27). A third rock type is breccia, consisting of mixtures of fragments of mineral grains or igneous rocks mostly smaller than 0.2 in. (0.5 cm) in diameter. The finer particles of the breccia consist largely of glass, in either rounded or angular grains.

A particularly interesting feature of the rock samples is the presence of surface pits lined with glass. These pits average less than 0.04 in. (1 mm) across. The pits, the rounding of gross shape of the fragments, and a lighter-colored surface than the inside rock suggest that some process of erosion has been in operation, pos-

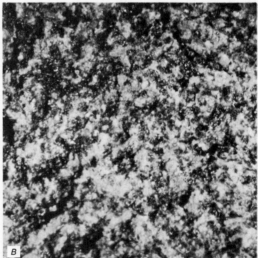

Figure 11.27. Lunar rocks collected by astronauts of the *Apollo 11* mission at Tranquillity Base. (*A*) Holocrystalline rock of granular texture, showing glass-lined surface cavities. Specimen is about 8 in. (20 cm) high. (*B*) Close-up photograph of a vuggy, somewhat shattered, coarsely crystalline rock without glassy pits. Area shown is about 0.8 in. (2 cm) across. (NASA photographs.)

Figure 11.26. Astronaut's footprint in the lunar soil. Notice the many miniature craters in the surrounding surface. (*Apollo 11* photograph by NASA.)

sibly of the nature of impacts by small particles.

All of the crystalline rocks are interpreted as volcanic, formed at or close to the lunar surface by solidification of magma. Rocks of the first type described above consist of about one-half pyroxene, about one-quarter calcic plagioclase feldspar, and considerable ilmenite. Also present is some olivine and a number of other minerals in smaller amounts. The second type of crystalline rock proved to be of very similar mineral composition to the first. In short, they are basic (mafic) igneous rocks and may be considered analogous to terrestrial basalts. There are, however, certain important differences between the lunar rocks and the terrestrial basalts. First, the abundance of pyroxene in the lunar rocks is considerably greater relative to plagioclase feldspar. Second, the abundance of ilmenite, an oxide of titanium and iron ($FeTiO_3$), is strikingly high. The lunar rocks are almost totally lacking in water and in the ferric form of iron. This composition suggests that the rock crystallized in an oxygen-poor and water-poor environment. In view of the high titanium and iron content of the lunar rocks, they cannot be matched to any of the common terrestrial basalts and must have had a quite different geochemical evolution.

The lunar regolith and breccias, taken together, are interpreted as produced by intense shock and partial melting, which can be described as a form of *impact metamorphism*. Melting is indicated by the presence of glass. Particularly interesting are the glass spherules (Figure 11.28), which are interpreted as "splash" phenomena—that is to say, minute droplets which cooled quickly into spheroidal shapes. In view of the great abundance of impact craters of all sizes on the lunar surface,

Figure 11.28. Glass spherules from the lunar regolith. Largest spherule is 0.016 in. (0.4 mm) in diameter. Spherules rest on an aluminum dish with a striated surface. (*Apollo 11* photograph by NASA.)

the presence of a large amount of regolith and breccia of impact origin is to be expected. Craters as small as 0.8 in. (2 cm) in diameter were observed at Tranquillity Base.

Analyses of lunar material showed extremely minute quantities of organic matter, and these can be accounted for by contamination during the processes of collecting and returning the samples to Earth. It is concluded that organic matter is present in lunar rocks in less than one part per million. The presence of life, present or past, seems to have been completely ruled out of the lunar-surface environment.

Age determinations yielded figures of −3.3 to −3.7 b.y. for basaltic crystalline rocks of the Tranquillity Base. This figure is quite close to the age of the oldest terrestrial rocks. A figure of −4.6 b.y. was obtained for breccia and lunar regolith. A single rock fragment unlike other rocks of Tranquillity Base yielded an age of −4.4 b.y. This fragment may have come from possibly older rock of the lunar highlands. If breccia and lunar regolith are representative of the original lunar crust, the Moon must have originated at about the same time as the Earth, namely, about −4.6 to −4.7 b.y.

One interpretation of an age of about −3.6 b.y. for crystalline igneous rock of the Tranquillity Base is that an important event in lunar history occurred at this time. The event was one of melting and may possibly have been of more than local occurrence. The cause of such a *thermal episode* can be referred to one of two sources—massive bombardment of the lunar surface by meteorites, or internal heating from radiogenic sources.

Late in 1969 the *Apollo 12* spacecraft landed at a point in the Ocean of Storms on the western side of the lunar nearside. A radiometric age of −3.4 b.y. has been determined for igneous rock from that locality, an age about the same as for rocks at Tranquillity Base.

One small rock specimen from the *Apollo 12* site has yielded an age of −4.6 b.y., equal to that of meteorites and equivalent to the inferred age of accretion of the Moon and planets. The specimen is of unusual chemical composition with respect to both meteorites and terrestrial rocks in that it contains unusually high concentrations of radioactive thorium, potassium, and uranium.

An interesting discovery was made during analysis of tiny rock fragments from a sample of regolith from Tranquillity Base. These particles represent a sample of the lunar bedrock that has been crushed, dispersed, and repeatedly mixed by successive meteorite impacts. The fragments must have traveled varying distances from the points of origin, some coming from great distances along crater rays. It was found that while most rock fragments are of basaltic composition, similar to that of the large rock specimens, about 6% proved to be of the composition of *anorthosite,* a terrestrial igneous rock consisting largely of calcic plagioclase feldspar.

On the reasonable assumption that a small percentage of the tiny rock fragments could easily have come from the lunar highlands, lying some 30 mi (50 km) south of Tranquillity Base, it was suggested that the highlands are underlain by a crust of anorthosite rock, derived by differentiation of a magma produced by partial melting of the outer layer of the Moon during a brief episode of intense heating. If so, the Moon has a crustal structure analogous in some respects to the Earth's arrangement of a high-standing felsic continental crust and a low-lying basaltic oceanic crust.

Astronauts of *Apollo 15* mission in 1971 brought back from Hadley/Apennine Base a large white rock specimen which Astronaut David R. Scott dubbed the "Genesis Rock." Upon subsequent analysis it proved to be anorthosite, with plagioclase feldspar making up almost all of the volume of the specimen. An age of at least −4.15 b.y., determined by the potassium-argon method, shows it to be one of the oldest of lunar rock types and supports the hypothesis of an ancient anorthosite crust.

## ORIGIN OF THE MOON

Finally, we turn to consider the origin of the Moon as the smaller member of that "binary planet," the Earth-Moon pair. We shall accept the hypothesis of a cold Moon whose surface was severely scarred by infall of huge bodies, probably asteroids, during the final stages of its formation. Those events probably took place rapidly. Infall of objects continued through the remainder of geologic time, producing the craters, large and small, and causing local melting upon impact. But what of the formation of the Moon as a spherical body?

Four basic hypotheses, or groups of hypotheses, of the Moon's origin have been given serious consideration by astronomers and geophysicists, although only three of these are now

credited with a substantial degree of plausibility.

1. The *binary-system hypothesis* supposes that both Moon and Earth grew as independent bodies by gradual accumulation from diffuse cold gases and dust. It is postulated that the Moon was close to Earth during the growth of both bodies, so that there was a binary planet from the outset. A major weakness of this hypothesis is that the Moon has a low density and lacks an iron core. It is difficult to explain the accretion of large amounts of iron by the Earth, but not by the Moon. Further difficulties exist in explaining how the two bodies were prevented from falling together, or falling apart. For these reasons the binary-system hypothesis is not now given serious consideration.

2. The *capture hypothesis* states that the Moon originated independently at some distant position in the solar system; then the Moon entered Earth's gravity field with a retrograde orbit. The Moon spiraled in toward Earth, underwent a reversal of orbit, and spiraled out in direct motion. In a variation of the capture hypothesis it is proposed that the Moon approached Earth in a hyperbolic orbit of direct motion. The capture hypotheses can explain the lower density of the Moon by reason of different conditions prevailing during accretion far from Earth, although those special conditions are difficult to justify.

3. The *fission hypothesis,* touched upon in Chapter 3, requires that the Moon represent a mass which broke away from a fast-spinning Earth. Recall that Sir George Darwin described the process of *rotational fission,* which he arrived at by looking back toward a point in time at which the Earth's speed of rotation was much faster than it is now. The centrifugal force of rotation, together with the Sun's tide-raising force, induced a tidal bulge in Earth. The bulge then separated and moved away from Earth, forming the Moon.

The strongest argument urged against Darwin's hypothesis, and one which caused it to be shelved for a long period of time, was that the total energy and angular momentum of Earth at the time of its fission would have had to be greater than the present quantities within the Earth-Moon pair by a large factor. The present energy is only about 6% of that original required value, and the angular momentum is only about 27%. Although some energy is dissipated in tidal flexing (refer to

Chapter 3), the loss would not be nearly sufficient to account for the difference.

In a recent revival of the fission hypothesis, the suggestion has been made that the high rate of spinning needed to throw off the Moon developed as the Earth's metallic core was separated from the silicate mantle rock and brought a great mass closer to the Earth's center. When the rate of spin increased to the point that the period of rotation was 2.65 hr, centrifugal force in the equatorial belt would have balanced gravitational attraction, allowing the development of the bulge and its fission. Figure 11.29 shows stages in fission.

In a somewhat different version of this hypothesis it has been suggested that the fission process, instead of taking place in the plastic manner shown in Figure 11.29, occurred suddenly by the throwing off of small fragments of the Earth near its equator and that these fragments then accumulated into the Moon.

There has been one strong point of evidence in favor of the fission hypothesis. The Moon's average density is known to be 3.34 gm/cm³, about the same as Earth's mantle rock averages (3.3 to 3.9 gm/cm³). The Earth material which would have broken free would have

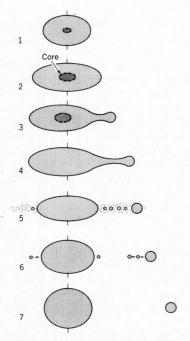

Figure 11.29. Stages in fission of the Earth-Moon body to produce the Moon. [After D. U. Wise (1963), *Jour. Geophys. Research*, vol. 68, p. 1547, Figure 1.]

been composed largely of mantle rock. Thus the low density of the Moon is explained, along with its lack of any substantial quantity of free iron.

Not surprisingly, Darwin and others speculated that the lunar material came from the present area of the Pacific Ocean basin. We do not need to entertain this idea, in view of our knowledge of the processes of crustal separation and continental growth, but it was an intriguing possibility at the time it was put forward.

As stated in earlier paragraphs, rock samples brought to the Earth by *Apollo 11* and *12* missions have proved to be mineralogically quite unlike the terrestrial basalts of the oceanic crust. This evidence seems on the face of it highly unfavorable to the fission hypothesis, although the lunar-rock samples come from only two localities, both in maria. It should also be remembered that the surface zone of the oceanic crust is comparatively very young, perhaps 130 m.y. or less, whereas the lunar igneous rocks have been dated as −4.6 and −3.6 b.y., which prevents any meaningful comparison.

4. The *coagulation* (or *many-moon*) *hypothesis* has in common with the binary-system hypothesis the postulate that Moon and Earth grew at the same time in close proximity. However, the many-moon hypothesis proposes that the lunar matter was dispersed into smaller fragments in a ring about the Earth. There were originally several small moons of various sizes in orbit around the Earth. The largest moon, with a mass about one-quarter to one-third that of the present Moon, orbited closest to the Earth. As it spiraled outward, this largest moon collided with and captured the other smaller moons in succession. A great advantage of the many-moon hypothesis is that the dispersal of the present lunar mass into several small masses greatly reduces the tide-raising effect that a single moon close to Earth would exert. The many-moon hypothesis faces the problem of explaining how the small satellites were originally formed or captured and why they lacked free iron in the same proportions found in Earth.

### REVIEW OF A SYSTEM

We have examined abundant and varied evidence that the collision of objects traveling at high speed in interplanetary space has been a process of great importance in the early history of the planetary bodies. Such collisions continue today. Seen in the collective view, these collisions constitute a physical system in which the inherited kinetic energy of masses in motion is abruptly transformed by impact into high-energy shock waves which produce severe physical rupture of the receiving body. Ultimately, the converted energy is dissipated in the form of heat and leaves the solar system by longwave radiation. The total process is therefore one involving the gradual decline in the total energy of the solar system. As we shall find in the next chapter, the system of collisions apparently plays a major role in the formation of the large bodies of the solar system, since by gravitational attraction of larger bodies for smaller ones the growth of planets by accretion is a reasonable mechanism. There is also reason to suppose that the opposite result—that of fragmentation into small particles—has resulted from a related disruptive process, as in the case of the fragmentation of asteroids and of comets passing close to the Sun.

Robert Jastrow has aptly noted that "the Moon is a Rosetta Stone of the planets."* Because processes of rock disintegration and transport act with extreme slowness on the lunar surface (except under meteoritic impacts), and because her crust is cold and motionless, our close satellite carries the entire record of 4.5 b.y. of solar-system history on her intensely illuminated surface. We have only to decipher the sharply etched lunar markings to read a history that on Earth has been largely erased by the continuum of atmospheric processes and a succession of crustal upheavals, intrusions, and volcanic outbursts.

### References for further study

Glasstone, S. (1968), *The Book of Mars*, NASA SP-179, Washington, D.C., U.S. Govt. Printing Office, 315 pp.

Bates, D. R. (1964), *The Planet Earth*, 2nd ed., Oxford, Pergamon, 370 pp., chap. 15.

Lyttleton, R. A. (1968), *Mysteries of the Solar System*, Oxford, Clarendon, 261 pp., chaps. 3–6.

Whipple, F. L. (1968), *Earth, Moon, and Planets*, Cambridge, Mass., Harvard Univ. Press, 297 pp., chaps. 8, 9, 13.

Wood, J. A. (1968), *Meteorites and the Origin of Planets*, New York, McGraw-Hill, 117 pp.

Mason, B., and W. G. Melson (1970), *The Lunar Rocks*, New York, Wiley–Interscience, 179 pp.

Mutch, T. A. (1970), *Geology of the Moon: A Stratigraphic View*, Princeton, N.J., Princeton Univ. Press, 324 pp.

### Review questions

1. Describe the asteroids in terms of orbits, size, numbers, and composition. How close to Earth do they pass? What is known of the shapes of larger asteroids? What is their origin?

2. Distinguish between meteoroids, meteors, and meteorites. Describe meteors. What is a meteoroid swarm? a meteor shower?

3. Describe a typical comet. What is the coma? the tail? What is known of the composition of comets? What is the nature of their orbits? What are the Jovian comets (Jupiter family), and how did they gain their orbits? What effect has the solar wind on a comet? Where does the substance of comets originate?

4. Describe the fall of a large meteorite. Distinguish between a fall and a find. What are the three classes of meteorites? Describe the composition and relative abundance of each. What are Widmanstätten figures? What is their significance? How do chondrites differ from terrestrial igneous rocks? What is the age of meteorites? Discuss the origin of meteorites. Relate meteorite composition to composition of the Earth's core.

5. Describe the impact of a large meteorite in historic time. What kinds of circular structures are found in bedrock of the earth's surface? What is an astrobleme? Describe the Barringer Crater and interpret the events in its formation. With how many craters is meteoritic iron associated? Why are impact craters rare on the Earth's surface?

6. What are tektites? Describe their forms. What are strewnfields? Where are they located? What are microtektites, and how are they related to tektites? Compare ages of tektites among the several strewnfields. Describe and interpret the chemical composition of tektites. Discuss and criticize the various hypotheses of origin of tektites.

7. Describe the lunar-surface environment in terms of gravity, atmosphere, solar radiation, surface temperatures and temperature ranges, and length of day and night. Does the Moon's surface have a supply of free water? What exogenetic processes operate on the Moon's surface? What geological processes are not active?

8. Review the history of lunar exploration

* R. Jastrow (1967), *Red Giants and White Dwarfs*, New York, Harper & Row, see p. 73.

by spacecraft. Into what two major terrain types is the Moon's surface subdivided? How did Galileo interpret each of these types? Describe other relief features on the Moon's surface, including mountains, craters, rays, rilles, and walls. What forms of craters are present and in what relative numbers? Compare the lunar farside with the lunar nearside in terms of surface features.

9. Compare volcanic and meteoritic hypotheses of crater origin. What evidence supports the presence of volcanic activity? What evidence is opposed? Describe the Urey-Gilbert interpretation of the rimmed maria. What are mascons? How does their presence relate to origin of the maria?

10. Compare the surface of Mars with that of the Moon. What three forms of terrain are identified on the Martian surface? Compare Mars with Earth in terms of volcanic action and orogeny. Do the same for Venus.

11. Describe the terrain and surface in the vicinity of Tranquillity Base. What is the nature of the lunar regolith? What is the source of rock fragments found at the lunar surface? Describe the texture and composition of lunar rocks, stressing the differences with respect to equivalent rocks of the Earth. What is the origin of the lunar regolith and breccias? What ages have been measured for lunar rocks? Interpret these ages. What is the significance of the finding of anorthosite fragments in the lunar regolith?

12. What are the four basic hypotheses, or groups of hypotheses, of origin of the Moon? Describe each and criticize each in terms of available evidence.

13. Give an evaluation of the scientific importance of lunar exploration. What degree of priority should be attached to future lunar and planetary exploration in terms of expenditure of human effort and resources?

14. Describe in broad terms the energy system of impacts of objects in space and compare it with the kinetic-energy system of masses in orbital motion in space. When was the impact system of greatest importance during the evolution of the solar system?

# chapter 12
# geologic systems through time:
# i. origin and early history of the earth

In this chapter we attempt to piece together a tentative sequence of events that constitute the origin of the solar system and the early geologic history of planet Earth. Awareness that evidence is fragmentary and sometimes misleading, and that highly divergent and often contradictory hypotheses continue to be discussed and modified by the best qualified scientists of our time, should not prevent us from trying to set up a tentative calendar of possible events.

This chapter relates a history of great changes in the evolution and operation of natural systems. Changes that occurred throughout early history of the earth stand in marked contrast to the orderly and uniform operation of natural systems within the past 0.5 to 1 billion years (b.y.). Whereas this late geologic history is dominated by repetitious cycles of processes and forms within the limits of overall uniformity, the early history is a progression from one profoundly unique state to another in an irreversible order of change. Early history also differs in character from late history in the time scale used. Whereas early history is described in billion-year units of time, late geologic time is discussed in million-year (m.y.) units of time—a thousandfold difference in the magnitude of time units. If we were to pick out any single 100-m.y. time interval in the earth's early history, we should perhaps find that no significant changes in operation of natural systems could be discerned from the beginning to the end of that period. It is only when we encompass the total time range of perhaps 5 b.y. that the radical nature of the changes is striking.

This chapter therefore deals with profound and sweeping changes in the states and structural arrangements of matter within the solar system and, more particularly, within and upon planet Earth.

## CONDITIONS THAT A SOLAR-SYSTEM HYPOTHESIS MUST SATISFY

Any hypothesis of solar-system origin and planetary development must provide an explanation or solution for several basic facts. Certain of these points have been discussed in previous chapters.

1. The hypothesis must account for the uniformity of direction of revolution and rotation of most of the planets and their satellites, as well as the fact that the orbital planes of almost all of these bodies are in approximate parallelism.

2. An explanation must be given for the fact that whereas the sun contains most of the mass of the solar system, its rate of rotation is very slow and most of the angular momentum of the system is concentrated in the planets, especially in the outer planets. (See Chapter 3, Table 3.2.)

3. It will need to account for the fact that although the chemical composition of the sun is very similar to the average composition of the entire solar system, the composition of the earth is strikingly different from either of these. These differences are discussed in detail in later paragraphs of this chapter. There is also a significant difference in chemical composition between the four inner, or terrestrial, planets as a group and the four great outer planets as a group.

4. The moon's low specific gravity and probable lack of a dense iron core must be explained. (See Chapter 11.)

## CHEMICAL COMPOSITIONS OF SUN, SOLAR SYSTEM, AND EARTH COMPARED

Let us compare the chemical composition of our sun with the average composition of the entire solar system and contrast these compositions with that of our earth. We shall then compare the average composition of the four inner planets with that of the four great outer planets. The differences and similarities are highly significant in terms of origin of the solar system.

The chemical composition of the sun's atmosphere is determined by spectroscopic analysis of solar rays. No information is directly available for the sun's interior, and it must be assumed that the solar atmospheric analysis applies equally to the entire sun. Of the 92 naturally occurring elements, 66 have been recognized on the sun. All remaining elements may exist there as well, some in quantities too small to permit identification. Table 12.1 gives the abundances of the 20 most abundant elements in the sun's atmosphere, as determined by spectroscopic analysis, in order of decreasing quantity. The numbers given are ratios of atoms of each element relative to the abundance of the silicon atom. (Note that the number for silicon is unity.) Although neither neon nor argon has been spectroscopically identified on the sun, both are probably present in important quantities—the quantity of neon is thought to be about equal to that of nitrogen, and argon may have an abundance about equal to that of sulfur or iron. Changes are to be expected in the quantities and orders listed as more accurate analyses are made.

Hydrogen and helium together account for practically all of the sun's mass. These elements, with atomic weights of 1 and 4, respectively, are the lightest of the elements and the most volatile. Following far behind in abundance are oxygen and carbon, in roughly equal amounts. A third group of elements consists of nitrogen, silicon, magnesium, and sulfur. Neon and argon would also fall into this group. The remaining 12 elements are metals, most of which occur in mere traces in comparison with hydrogen and helium.

Average composition of the solar system is given in the second column of Table 12.1. Abundances of elements have been estimated from a combination of sources, including the solar spectrum, solar cosmic rays, and meteorites of the chondrite type. Abundances of the 26 most abundant elements are given in the table. As in the sun's atmosphere, hydrogen and helium are the preponderant elements, in roughly the same proportions as in the sun. Oxygen comes third, in about the same amount as in the sun, while the abundances of carbon, nitrogen, magnesium, silicon, iron, and sulfur are much the same as in the sun. Values assigned to neon and argon give them important places in the ranking scale. Altogether, the elemental abundances in the sun's atmosphere are very much like those of the entire solar system.

Next examine the table of abundances of elements of the entire earth (Table 12.2). Because the units used here are those of percentage by weight, this table cannot be combined with the first. The most striking difference is in the order of the elements themselves. Hydrogen and helium do not even appear among the first 15 elements on earth. Iron is most abundant, making up about one-third of the weight of the earth, whereas it constitutes only $\frac{1}{80}$ of 1% of

Table 12.1.  ABUNDANCES OF ELEMENTS IN SUN AND SOLAR SYSTEM

| Sun's Atmosphere | | | | Solar System | | | |
|---|---|---|---|---|---|---|---|
| Rank | Element | Symbol | Abundance (atoms per atom of Si) | Rank | Element | Symbol | Abundance (atoms per atom of Si) |
| 1 | Hydrogen | H | 32,000 | 1 | Hydrogen | H | 26,000 |
| 2 | Helium | He | 5,000 | 2 | Helium | He | 2,100 |
| 3 | Oxygen | O | 29 | 3 | Oxygen | O | 23.6 |
| 4 | Carbon | C | 17 | 4 | Carbon | C | 13.5 |
| 5 | Nitrogen | N | 3 | 5 | Nitrogen | N | 2.44 |
| (6) | (Neon) | (Ne) | — | 6 | Neon | Ne | 2.36 |
| 7 | Silicon | Si | 1.00 | 7 | Magnesium | Mg | 1.05 |
| 8 | Magnesium | Mg | 0.79 | 8 | Silicon | Si | 1.00 |
| 9 | Sulfur | S | 0.63 | 9 | Iron | Fe | 0.89 |
| 10 | Iron | Fe | 0.12 | 10 | Sulfur | S | 0.56 |
| (11) | (Argon) | (Ar) | — | 11 | Argon | Ar | 0.23 |
| 12 | Sodium | Na | 0.063 | 12 | Aluminum | Al | 0.85 |
| 13 | Aluminum | Al | 0.050 | 13 | Calcium | Ca | 0.074 |
| 14 | Calcium | Ca | 0.045 | 14 | Sodium | Na | 0.063 |
| 15 | Nickel | Ni | 0.026 | 15 | Nickel | Ni | 0.046 |
| 16 | Copper | Cu | 0.0035 | 16 | Phosphorus | P | 0.013 |
| 17 | Chromium | Cr | 0.0033 | 17 | Chromium | Cr | 0.012 |
| 18 | Manganese | Mn | 0.0025 | 18 | Manganese | Mn | 0.0088 |
| 19 | Potassium | K | 0.0016 | 19 | Fluorine | F | 0.0036 |
| 20 | Titanium | Ti | 0.0015 | 20 | Potassium | K | 0.0032 |
| 21 | Cobalt | Co | 0.0014 | 21 | Titanium | Ti | 0.0023 |
| 22 | Zinc | Zn | 0.0008 | 22 | Cobalt | Co | 0.0023 |
| | | | | 23 | Chlorine | Cl | 0.0020 |
| | | | | 24 | Zinc | Zn | 0.0015 |
| | | | | 25 | Copper | Cu | 0.00092 |
| | | | | 26 | Vanadium | V | 0.00090 |

Sources: Sun's atmosphere—after Aller (1961). Solar system—from A. G. W. Cameron (1968), in *Origin and Distribution of the Elements*, L. H. Ahrens, ed., Pergamon, New York. See p. 127.

the sun's mass. Oxygen, about 30% in the earth, is third-ranking in both sun and solar system. Amounts of silicon and magnesium are about equal in the earth, together with iron and oxygen making up 92% of the earth's mass. The remainder of elements on the list are essentially those found in a comparable ranking in the sun. It should be emphasized that the composition of the earth as shown in Table 12.2 is not established with a high degree of certainty, and the figures should be treated as estimates only.

In summary, the virtual absence in the earth of the highly volatile light gases hydrogen and helium, as well as of neon and argon, forms a glaring contrast with the abundances of those elements in the sun and solar system. Clearly, any hypothesis of solar-system origin must account for this contrast in abundances of elements.

## CHEMICAL COMPOSITIONS OF THE INNER AND OUTER PLANETS COMPARED

The four inner, or terrestrial, planets (Mercury, Venus, Earth, and Mars) form a closely related group with respect to both their small size and high average density. The four great outer planets (Jupiter, Saturn, Uranus, and Neptune) form a group related by their large size and low average density. Table 12.3 gives comparative figures on mass and density.

High densities of the inner planets suggest that all are composed largely of silicate minerals with abundant iron. Whether iron cores and silicate mantles exist in all four planets is not known. In terms of chemical composition, all four of these planets probably have abundances of elements similar to that of the earth, as given in Table 12.2.

The four great outer planets (Pluto is largely an unknown planet) have low densities—not greatly different from the density of water at the earth's surface (Table 12.3). It is likely that Jupiter and Saturn, the larger pair of the four, have compositions quite like that of the sun (Table 12.1), about ¾ of the mass being hydrogen and about ¼ helium. Most of the remainder (about 2% of the mass) consists of the elements carbon, nitrogen, and oxygen, which are thought to be in the form of the

Table 12.2.  COMPOSITION OF THE EARTH AND CHONDRITE METEORITES

| Rank | Element | Symbol | Earth Average (% by wt) | Average of Chondrites (% by wt) |
|---|---|---|---|---|
| 1 | Iron | Fe | 34.6 ⎫ | 27.2 ⎫ |
| 2 | Oxygen | O | 29.5 ⎪ 92.0 | 33.2 ⎪ 91.8 |
| 3 | Silicon | Si | 15.2 ⎬ | 17.1 ⎬ |
| 4 | Magne-sium | Mg | 12.7 ⎭ | 14.3 ⎭ |
| 5 | Nickel | Ni | 2.4 | 1.6 |
| 6 | Sulfur | S | 1.9 | 1.9 |
| 7 | Calcium | Ca | 1.1 | 1.3 |
| 8 | Alumi-num | Al | 1.1 | 1.2 |
| 9 | Sodium | Na | 0.57 | 0.64 |
| 10 | Chro-mium | Cr | 0.26 | 0.29 |
| 11 | Manga-nese | Mn | 0.22 | 0.25 |
| 12 | Cobalt | Co | 0.13 | 0.09 |
| 13 | Phospho-rus | P | 0.10 | 0.11 |
| 14 | Potas-sium | K | 0.07 | 0.08 |
| 15 | Titanium | Ti | 0.05 | 0.06 |

Source: Data from B. Mason (1966), *Principles of Geochemistry,* 3rd ed., New York, Wiley, Tables 3.7 and 2.4.

compounds methane ($CH_4$), ammonia ($NH_3$), and water ($H_2O$). Rock-forming elements, such as iron, silicon, and magnesium, which with oxygen constitute the bulk of the inner planets, may constitute only a very small fraction of the masses of the outer planets.

It has been suggested recently that Jupiter has no rocky or metallic iron core but has, instead, a core of extremely dense gases, largely hydrogen and helium. Under enormous gravitational pressures—in excess of 7000

Table 12.3.  MASSES AND DENSITIES OF THE PLANETS

| | Mass (relative to earth) | Mean Density (gm/cm³) |
|---|---|---|
| Inner Planets (Terrestrial) | | |
| Mercury | 0.06 | 5.4 |
| Venus | 0.81 | 5.2 |
| Earth | 1.00 | 5.5 |
| Mars | 1.08 | 3.9 |
| Outer Planets | | |
| Jupiter | 318 | 1.3 |
| Saturn | 95 | 0.7 |
| Uranus | 15 | 1.7 |
| Neptune | 17 | 1.6 |
| (Pluto) | 0.9 | ? |

tons/in.² (10,000 kg/mm²)—these gases would attain densities more than 30 times that of water and would behave physically like metallic solids.

Uranus and Neptune, the smaller pair of the four outer planets, are thought to have very much less free (molecular) hydrogen than Jupiter and Saturn. Most of the volatiles consist of water, methane, and ammonia. Of these, water as ice may constitute about half of each planet's mass.

Comparatively low atmospheric temperatures, combined with the extremely powerful gravitational attraction that the great planetary masses exert, seem to have effectively prevented the escape of the dominant volatile elements into outer space. Uranus and Neptune may have originally possessed much larger proportions of hydrogen and helium, but if so these gases have been greatly depleted in comparison with Jupiter and Saturn.

Using the reasonable assumption that the original substance of all planets was of a composition essentially similar to that of the sun, any hypothesis of solar-system origin must explain how the inner planets lost or were separated from most of the hydrogen, helium, and other highly volatile elements originally present.

## EARLY HYPOTHESES OF SOLAR-SYSTEM ORIGIN

Seen in broad-scale historical review, hypotheses of the origin of the solar system have fallen into two major divisions, or schools of thought. One school attempted to find an explanation of the planets through an external force acting upon the sun to cause that star to yield forth the substance from which the planets and all other objects of the solar system are derived. Typically, the external force evoked was either a direct impact or a tidal force exerted by another stellar object in close proximity to the sun. The second school postulates an ancestral *nebula,* which is simply a cloud of gas containing highly dispersed small particles, from which, by some process of condensation or agglomeration, the discrete bodies of the solar system were ultimately formed. While the first-named category of explanations requires a single catastrophic event of short duration, the second, or nebular, category postulates a continuum of changes over a vast span of time.

We shall review the early hypotheses in

chronological order of their statement. In 1749, the French philosopher Buffon proposed that during a collision with a passing comet the substance of the planets was torn from the sun. Only a few years later (1755) the German philosopher Immanuel Kant, following an earlier proposal by Descartes, suggested that the solar system originated as a cloud of gas and dust, with a high concentration in the central region, which eventually became the sun. Thus the two major schools of thought were born and came into direct conflict.

Kant's suggestion was taken up by the French astronomer Laplace, who in 1796 published the *nebular hypothesis,* according to which the sun was thought to be originally a hot rotating mass of gas and dust larger than the largest of the present planetary orbits. The nebula through its own gravitational attraction contracted into a smaller volume and at the same time greatly increased the velocity of its rotation. At a certain critical point the centrifugal force of rotation at the equator of the nebula exactly balanced the gravitational force. Then, as the nebula continued to contract, the matter in the equatorial belt was left behind in the form of a ring, which split off, providing the substance out of which the outermost planet was formed (Figure 12.1). The same process, repeated, produced nebular rings for each planet, the entire system thus superficially resembling Saturn and its rings. Laplace supposed that the diffuse matter in each ring then condensed to form a single planet and, more-

over, that the planet in turn shrank and left behind rings which became its satellites.

The nebular hypothesis enjoyed widespread popularity for more than a century, but serious objections to it were presented by astronomers and geologists at the beginning of the twentieth century, with the result that the hypothesis was quickly discarded as impossible. One serious objection, raised many years earlier by the Scottish physicist Clerk Maxwell and discussed in Chapter 3, relates to the distribution of angular momentum in the solar system. It was argued that if the nebular hypothesis of Laplace were correct, the sun should have enormously greater angular momentum than it does and should rotate about 200 times faster than it now does. As a further objection to the nebular hypothesis it was difficult to find any reason for the intermittent contraction of the sun to produce rings, rather than a continuous contraction into a single mass. Also, if the rings were composed of highly heated gases, the gas molecules would readily escape the sun's gravitational field and the rings would disintegrate.

In the period from 1900 to 1940 a number of hypotheses of the external-force classification were put forward by leading astronomers and geologists. Two of these hypotheses involved the close passage of a second star, exerting enormous gravitational attraction upon the two bodies and causing gaseous matter from the sun to be drawn out in armlike or filamentlike masses that later condensed to

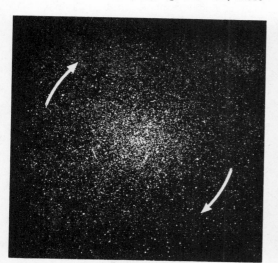
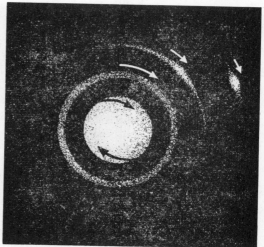

Figure 12.1. Diagrammatic representation of Laplace's nebular hypothesis of origin of the solar system. On the left is a rotating nebula of hot gas. On the right the nebula is shrinking and leaving behind rings of gas that will condense to form the planets. (Yerkes Observatory.)

form the planets and their satellites. A third hypothesis postulated that originally the sun had a companion and the two constituted a binary system. Explosion of one star of the pair produced a large quantity of dispersed matter from which the planets condensed.

Hypotheses involving disruption are vulnerable to serious criticisms. One criticism is that gases as highly heated as those called for by the disruptive process would readily escape into space because of their high molecular velocities.

New chemical evidence has now virtually ruled out the possibility that the planets were derived of matter from the sun's interior. Thermonuclear reactions within the sun's interior would have destroyed all *deuterium* (heavy hydrogen—an isotope of hydrogen) at an early stage in its history as a star. Hence, our earth and meteorites would not now possess deuterium in their compositions. On the contrary, deuterium is found in the gases enclosed in meteorites as well as in earth matter. This finding provides proof that planetary matter originated outside of the limits of a dense high-temperature stellar interior, whether it be that of the sun or of a companion star or passing star.

## CONDENSATION HYPOTHESES

In recent years, scholarly thought about the origin of the solar system has returned in one respect to the basic concept of Kant and Laplace, that the solar system developed in an orderly series of stages beginning with a primeval cloud of gas and dust—the solar nebula—which contracted to a rotating disk-like body with the sun occupying a central position. Through a condensation process the substance of the nebula ultimately formed into the existing solid bodies of the solar system. Strikingly different from Laplace's nebular hypothesis, however, is the newer postulate that the original cloud of gas and dust was very cold, rather than highly heated, as Laplace imagined it to be.

The newer concepts of evolution of a solar nebula we shall group together for convenience under the general heading of *condensation hypotheses*. Any modern condensation hypothesis must conform with an acceptable model of evolution of the sun as a star (see Chapter 15). Stars begin their development from large clouds of cold interstellar gas composed mostly of hydrogen. When such a cloud is compressed to a density of about 1000 hydrogen atoms/cm³ it begins to collapse under gravitational attraction. As a result of compression, the contracting mass ultimately becomes highly heated and a series of internal thermonuclear reactions begins. During a highly luminous phase that lasts about 10 m.y. the star shrinks in size. When this early contraction phase is complete, the star joins the main sequence of stars and thereafter remains essentially constant in diameter and temperature for a very long time.

At some stage during our sun's contraction phase, the planets and other objects of the solar system were formed. It is precisely with this rather trivial event (as judged from the standpoint of the total evolutionary history of a star) that the various versions of the condensation hypotheses are concerned. In their larger perspective, the planets are as insignificant to the origin of the sun as are tiny spattered droplets of molten metal produced in the pouring of an ingot.

An early version of the condensation hypothesis of planetary formation was introduced about 1944 by the German astronomer Karl von Weizsäcker. In reviving Kant's suggestion, von Weizsäcker proposed that as the sun was formed it was surrounded by a cloud of gas and dust having a mass about one-tenth that of the sun. The cloud was of approximately cosmic composition, which is essentially similar to the composition of the sun as well. Gradually the cloud of gas and dust became concentrated into a greatly flattened disk in what is now the plane of the ecliptic. Composed largely of hydrogen and helium, the cloud was in a complex state of motion, with regular eddies (vortices) of various sizes (Figure 12.2). The eddies, arranged in concentric zones of increasing size outward within the cloud, were regarded by von Weizsäcker as providing a mechanism whereby angular momentum could be transferred from the sun outward into the material of the disk, at the same time slowing the sun's rate of rotation.

According to von Weizsäcker, local increases in density of spacing of the particles would have occurred in the zones between adjacent eddies, causing aggregation to begin by mutual gravitational attraction. Small solid objects would have formed and grown by accretion and collision into larger bodies, eventually forming the planets.

Under von Weizsäcker's hypothesis, temperatures within the disk of gas and dust would have been very high close to the sun, but

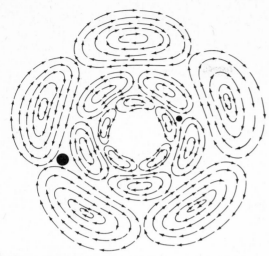

Figure 12.2. Schematic diagram of the formation of planetary bodies (black disks) in zones between eddies in a nebula of dust and gas, as conceived by von Weizsäcker. Denser concentration of matter at the center of the nebula is not shown.

decreasing rapidly toward the outer periphery. Under high temperatures in the inner zone only the least volatile elements would have been able to condense into a solid state, and the rate of planetary accumulation was slow. At the same time, the volatiles, including almost all hydrogen and helium, would have been driven out and lost. Thus the small size and silicate-iron composition of the inner planets is explained. Because of the low temperatures in the outer zone of the disk the volatile elements were easily and quickly condensed, along with the less volatile elements, resulting in the growth of the great planets with their thick shells of ice, ammonia, and methane, and their atmospheres of hydrogen and helium.

In 1951, Gerald P. Kuiper, an astronomer then at the University of Chicago, proposed modifications in von Weizsäcker's hypothesis. Instead of regular eddies arranged in concentric zones, he postulated a highly irregular, or chaotic, type of turbulent motion within the nebular disk. Where local concentrations of matter were sufficiently dense, condensation by gravitational attraction occurred, producing bodies which Kuiper referred to as *protoplanets*. Composition of the protoplanet was essentially the same as that of the sun. In addition to one large protoplanet for each major planet, there were many smaller protoplanets. While the centers of the protoplanets were relatively dense, the outer zones were composed of the volatile gases extending to contacts with adjacent protoplanets.

At about this point in time, after the protoplanets had swept up most of the material in the nebular disk in complete darkness and at very low temperatures, contraction of the central mass formed the sun. As soon as the sun began to shine, its radiation heated the atmospheres of the nearer protoplanets and drove off most of the lighter gases, leaving only the very small fraction of the original mass in the condensed core of heavier elements to become the planets as we know them today. The outer planets were too far from the sun to be strongly heated and were thus able to retain a much larger fraction of their gaseous constituents. Eventually the excess gases, largely hydrogen and helium, were dissipated into space, leaving only the condensed protoplanet cores.

## UREY'S HYPOTHESIS

At about the same time that Kuiper was presenting his version of planetary development, the distinguished chemist and Nobel laureate Harold C. Urey was applying principles of chemistry to problems of the solar system, particularly through the investigation of the compositions of meteorites. These studies led Urey to attempt to formulate a unified hypothesis of origin of the planets, moon, asteroids, and meteorites to account for the observed chemical and physical phenomena. The following paragraphs are based largely on Urey's interpretations of events in the evolution of the solar system.

As contraction of the solar nebula began, any original turbulent motions which its various parts might have had were smoothed out by internal friction and transformed into a slow rotation of the entire mass. With contraction continuing, the conservation of angular momentum caused the angular velocity to increase as the diameter of the nebula became smaller.

Transfer of angular momentum from the central region, or solar mass, to the outer parts of the nebula that later formed the planets posed a vexing problem. It was then suggested that angular momentum might have been transferred outward through the nebula through the action of magnetic fields. This process has now achieved wide acceptance in the scientific community.

As contraction of the nebula continued and its rotational rate increased, the nebula took the form of a greatly flattened ellipsoid. The degree of flattening progressed until the nebula came to resemble a rather thin platelike disk, with a solar mass concentrated at the center (Figure 12.3). It is estimated that about one-third of the nebular mass was in the disk, about two-thirds in the central condensation.

During contraction those particles near the periphery whose centripetal acceleration exactly matched the gravitational acceleration of the total nebular mass were left behind in orbits of fixed size in the equatorial plane of the nebula. There was thus formed a thin nebular disk outside of the contracting mass. This disk comprised the matter from which planets were later formed.

In a manner not fully explained or understood, the cold gas and dust of the nebular disk apparently became separated into gravitationally bound bodies. Perhaps this clustering resulted from chance groupings of the particles. The resulting bodies would have been subjected to the disruptive tidal forces of the sun, hence they would necessarily have had to be of sufficient mass that the mutual forces of gravitational attraction holding the particles together would have exceeded the disruptive tidal forces. Because of the large quantities of hydrogen and helium then present in the solar nebula, the mass of a body that could retain its identity would have been large enough that, after most of the hydrogen and helium had escaped, the remaining heavier elements would have a mass roughly equal to the present mass of the moon. This would imply that the initial condensation would have had a mass 300 to 400 times that of the moon today. Thus the term *lunar-sized body* was applied by Urey to describe the individual nebular bodies.

The cold, finely divided substance of the lunar-sized nebular bodies accumulated by collisions to form solid objects roughly on the order of size of the moon. Such bodies, called *protoplanets* by Urey, would have been too small to hold atmospheres of hydrogen and helium, which largely escaped into space. Many of the protoplanets became unstable as they grew, ultimately exploding into vast numbers of minute solid particles. Protoplanets and

vast swarms of smaller particles were now moving about the sun in planetary orbits. Collisions of these objects occurred in great number, so that in about 10 m.y. time they formed by accretion into the planets as we know them.

Smaller particles falling into the earth lost their excess energy into a primitive atmosphere and reacted chemically with it. Larger objects —the meteorites—arrived at the ground surface only slightly warmed. Still larger masses tens or hundreds of miles in diameter and moving at high speeds penetrated the earth's atmosphere without appreciable loss of energy and were largely volatilized on impact. It may be that such impacts caused local melting of the rock to produce lava pools, but for the earth as a whole the temperature remained below the melting point. The rate of accumulation of a planet would have increased as the planet's mass increased because of its stronger gravitational field and larger intercepting cross section. Periods of rotation of the planets were determined during the process of growth. When completed, the terrestrial planets consisted largely of a mixture of iron and silicates throughout. In earth, separation of these substances into a core and a mantle are considered to have occurred throughout ensuing geologic time by internal processes. The great planets were able to hold the methane, ammonia, hydrogen, and water, which they now possess in abundance, because of their strong gravitational fields and their colder temperatures.

In recent years, the transfer of angular momentum from sun to planets and a consequent slowing of the sun's rotation have been attributed in part to the action of the solar wind (see Chapter 2). Matter streaming from the sun and intercepted by the planets is considered to be a process adequate to remove angular momentum from the sun to the extent observed. It is estimated that in the last 5 b.y. rotation of the sun has been slowed by about 50% through action of the solar wind.

## LOSS OF VOLATILES FROM EARTH

We have placed a great deal of emphasis upon the striking difference between bulk chemical composition of the earth and the

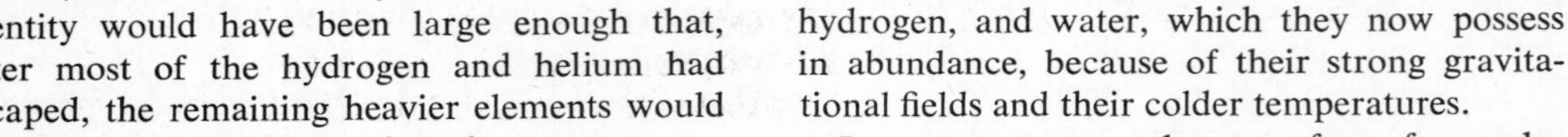

Figure 12.3. According to the modern condensation hypothesis, contraction of the solar nebula produces a thin disk of cold dust and gas that rotates about a central solar mass.

compositions of both sun and solar system (Tables 12.1 and 12.2). Von Weizsäcker's hypothesis of solar-system formation explained the loss of volatiles from the inner planets as related to nearness to the sun and high temperatures during accretion. However, the more recent developments in detailing the condensation hypothesis as developed by Urey and others require that the first condensations into solid lunar-sized bodies (protoplanets) and smaller particles took place at temperatures too low to permit melting of rock material, most of which was silicate and iron. This solid matter was probably in a highly oxidized state—in other words, oxygen existed in combination with other elements. Iron was in an oxide form.

Loss of the highly volatile hydrogen and helium is explained, for these elements remain in the gaseous state at temperatures very close to absolute zero. Argon, neon, krypton, and xenon are also gases of extremely low freezing points and would remain in the gaseous state. Velocities of molecules of hydrogen and helium would have exceeded the escape velocities of the protoplanets. Once the central mass of the nebula had condensed enough to form the sun and it began to radiate, force of the solar wind (Chapter 2) would perhaps have swept large quantities of these gases into interstellar space, beyond the limits of the solar system.

At temperatures far below freezing of water much of the matter of the primeval dust-gas cloud of the nebula was in the solid or liquid state. Water, which would have been ice, with methane and ammonia would have formed a slush of mixed ice and liquid particles. Had the entire nebula at any time been subjected to very high temperatures, these volatiles would have been driven off, whereas they exist today in large quantities in the four great outer planets. Yet these and many other substances were in some way driven off from the inner planets. When and how did this depletion of volatiles occur?

Most qualified scientists who engage in serious discussions of planetary origin agree that no episode of high temperatures and melting of silicates and iron occurred during the nebular phase. Instead, a subsequent high-temperature episode is required. This high-temperature episode also was one of chemical reduction—i.e., the liberation of free oxygen from its chemical bonds with other elements, particularly iron.

Essentially the same process goes on in a blast furnace, causing the oxygen to be driven off from iron-oxide ore to produce free iron in the molten state. It is estimated that the temperatures during the heating episode exceeded 1800° F (1000° C).

The source of heat for a high-temperature episode is readily found in the process of gravitational collapse. As dispersed matter of the nebula became concentrated into discrete masses, gravitational attraction increased. As the matter moved more rapidly toward these centers of gravity, kinetic energy was converted into heat. The larger the mass of the accumulating planet became, the higher its temperature rose.

At a certain point in the episode of heating, methane ($CH_4$), ammonia ($NH_3$), and water ($H_2O$) were vaporized and became gaseous atmospheres surrounding the growing bodies of planetary material. As temperatures rose above 1800° F (1000° C) all of the remaining matter melted. At very high temperatures many of the elements became volatile and were driven off from the melt as gaseous emanations. On the other hand, another group of elements is not volatile at these same temperatures. Table 12.4 lists selected examples of

Table 12.4. VOLATILE AND NON-VOLATILE ELEMENTS UNDER REDUCING CONDITIONS AT HIGH TEMPERATURES

| Volatile (listed in order of cosmic abundance) | | Nonvolatile (listed in order of bulk earth composition) | |
|---|---|---|---|
| Hydrogen | H (as $H_2O$) | Iron | Fe |
| Helium | He | Silicon | Si |
| Neon | Ne | Magnesium | Mg |
| Nitrogen | N (as $N_2$) | Nickel | Ni |
| Carbon | C (as $CO_2$) | Calcium | Ca |
| Sulfur | S | Aluminum | Al |
| Argon | Ar | Chromium | Cr |
| Sodium | Na | Manganese | Mn |
| Chlorine | Cl | Cobalt | Co |
| Potassium | K | Phosphorus | P |
| Zinc | Zn | Titanium | Ti |
| Fluorine | F | Copper | Cu |

Source: Data in part from A. E. Ringwood (1966), in *Advances in Earth Science,* P. M. Hurley, ed., Cambridge, Mass., M.I.T. Press, p. 293, Table 3.

elements in both volatile and nonvolatile categories under a high-temperature reducing environment. Temperatures of 2400° to 2700° F (1300° to 1500° C) are assumed. The elements listed here will be found within the lists of abundances of elements in the sun, solar system, and earth (Tables 12.1 and 12.2).

As temperatures rose in the dense molten bodies during the high-temperature reducing phase of planetary history, a depletion of volatile elements occurred. However, this does not mean that all volatile elements were lost, for we know that important quantities exist today in the earth. Although the chemical environment was one of reduction, vast quantities of oxygen were retained in the melt in combination with silicon. However, much of the iron was reduced to the free metallic state, eventually to become the planetary cores.

Time of occurrence of the high-temperature reducing phase is subject to much discussion and difference of opinion. Under the Urey hypothesis the larger protoplanets underwent a high-temperature stage and may have attained temperatures of about 3600° F (2000° C). Loss of volatiles occurred at that time. The protoplanets then cooled to a temperature near 32° F (0° C). Subsequent breakup of these bodies provided the cold, solid particles from which the planets were formed at low temperatures by accretion. Under this hypothesis, the growth of the earth to its present size involved no large-scale melting, although later melting through accumulation of radiogenic heat remains a possibility, as we noted in Chapter 7.

It has recently been suggested that the early solar wind was possibly far more powerful than it is today and was capable of heating protoplanets to temperatures sufficiently high to melt their interiors. A process of eddy-current heating resulting from interaction of turbulent magnetic fields surrounding the bodies has been suggested as a means of internal heating. Further development of the theory of these processes may lead to an explanation of a high-temperature phase alternative to the hypothesis of heating by gravitational collapse.

More recently (early 1960s), A. E. Ringwood has argued from a minority standpoint that Urey's multi-stage hypothesis is unnecessarily complicated and that a single-stage hypothesis can be defended. Ringwood postulates that the planets grew by accretion of cold, highly oxidized substances of the primordial nebula. As the growing planets became heated by gravitational collapse, ultimately the temperatures reached a level at which the outer layer melted, followed by complete melting of the planet and depletion of the volatiles. The differentiation (separation) of metallic core from silicate mantle within the earth took place

during this process of accretion and heating. When the earth was completely melted the primitive atmosphere was blown off.

As a final observation concerning the chemical evolution of the earth from a primordial nebula of solar composition, the disproportionate increase of iron and nickel as compared with other nonvolatiles on the list is a fact that must be explained by the condensation hypotheses. Referring to Tables 12.1 and 12.2, note that iron rose from 9th place (below magnesium) in the sun's list to take 1st place on the earth's list. Nickel correspondingly rose from 13th place to 5th place. Other nonvolatiles on the list—notably silicon, magnesium, and aluminum—retained their positions relative to each other in both lists, but because of their higher percentages of the total material in the earth and meteorites they moved upward several places in the second tabulation.

It may be informative to look at the average composition of chondrite (stony) meteorites, for which percentages are listed in the second column of Table 12.2. The values are strikingly similar to those for the earth, although reversals of order occur. Again, iron and nickel are high on the list. If, as Urey proposed, these meteorites represent fragments of the protoplanets that were formed in the first stage of accretion, the loss of volatiles and rise in proportion of iron and nickel occurred in those bodies during a high-temperature phase preceding their disruption.

## CAMERON'S HYPOTHESIS

The hypotheses of von Weizsäcker, Kuiper, Urey, Ringwood, and others have been under continual analysis and criticism by astronomers and geochemists under research stimulation provided by the explosive growth of the space sciences in the 1960s. It is not possible to cover these developments in a brief chapter. However, we take note of important contributions in the 1960s by A. G. W. Cameron, an astronomer, while conducting research in cooperation with Robert Jastrow at the NASA Goddard Institute for Space Studies in New York City.[*]

Cameron's concept of the collapsing interstellar cloud is quite different from that of the scientists mentioned above, in that his picture of a rotating nebular disk at first contains no central solar body. Instead, the sun is formed

[*] A. G. W. Cameron (1968), "Origin of the Solar System," pp. 611–642 of *Introduction to Space Science*, 2nd ed., W. N. Hess and G. D. Mead, eds., New York, Gordon and Breach, 1056 pp.

at a later stage by secondary processes. Planetary bodies first accumulated within the flattened rotating disk, which at this time consisted largely of hot ionized gases entrapping a magnetic field. As more and more energy was built up in the magnetic field, matter of the nebula was caused to flow inward toward the center of the nebula. This centripetal flow of nebular gas is described as a streaming motion.

Thus in Cameron's interpretation the planets were formed before the sun. Gases streamed past the planets to accumulate in the center of the nebula, forming the sun. At the same time, outward flow of gas was taking place at the outer edges of the nebula. Under Cameron's hypothesis, the inner planets captured substantial primordial atmospheres from gas which was streaming past them, but all subsequently lost these primordial atmospheres.

## EARLY HISTORY OF THE EARTH*

At a point in time about −4.7 b.y. aggregation of the planets was essentially complete, although infall of objects was to continue throughout all ensuing time, as the moon's surface shows. However, the completed earth was then very different in many respects from its present form. Its internal structure had yet to be reorganized. Lacking a fluid metallic core, the earth would have had no magnetic field and no magnetosphere to protect its surface from the sweeping action of the solar wind. Continents and ocean basins were probably not then differentiated. Furthermore, there probably existed no significant atmosphere and no oceans. We shall now attempt to reconstruct a schedule of events of profound change in various aspects of the earth's physical systems. These changes form an irreversible sequence leading to the relatively stable physical and chemical conditions that have prevailed in approximately the last 0.6 b.y.

The first eon† of the earth's history spans the time from the earth's accretion, about −4.5 to −4.7 b.y. before the present, up to the time recorded by the oldest known rocks, metamorphic in type, about −3.6 b.y. This first eon is a period of no tangible record, hence it is one of inference guided only by indirect lines of evidence. As we noted in Chapter 7 in discussing the early thermal history of the earth, the first eon was probably a time of vast internal earth changes. From a uniformly distributed original mixture composed largely of silicates and iron, the process of differentiation and gravity separation was carried out by episodes of melting under the accumulated heat of radioactivity. The layered structure of the earth —with its basaltic crust, mantle, and core— developed. The magnetic field and magnetosphere came into existence. Continental masses of less dense granitic rock began to appear, constituting the continental nuclei that today occupy central positions within the continental shields.

## ORIGIN OF ATMOSPHERE AND HYDROSPHERE

Let us look first into the question of the earth's early atmosphere and hydrosphere. The term *hydrosphere* is convenient to apply not only to the oceans, but to all surface and ground water readily available for circulation over the earth. When and how did the earth's atmosphere and hydrosphere originate? The history of scientific thought on this subject offers two quite different lines of hypotheses, one of which has been generally rejected. Consider the rejected possibility first. Could the earth's atmosphere and hydrosphere have been present continuously from the time of the earth's accretion, constituting a large primitive (primordial) reservoir of matter? We are referring now to a collection of substances that can be referred to as *volatiles,* because they are elements in a gaseous molecular state at fairly low temperatures, or easily attain that state in combination with oxygen or hydrogen. First and foremost is water ($H_2O$), which constitutes close to 93% by weight of the total quantity of excess volatiles within the atmosphere and hydrosphere, including water entrapped in sedimentary rocks (Table 12.5). Next in importance is carbon (C) in combination with oxygen as carbon dioxide ($CO_2$) making up about 5% of the total. Chlorine ($Cl_2$) is also important (1.7%), followed by molecular nitrogen ($N_2$, 0.24%) and sulfur ($S_2$, 0.13%). Molecular hydrogen ($H_2$) follows with 0.07%, and there are also traces of argon (Ar), fluorine ($F_2$), and many other elements.

The hypothesis of a dense primitive atmosphere is based on the supposition that the earth, at the time of its formation, was in a

---

* The remainder of this chapter and Table 12.6 are based in large part on data by Preston E. Cloud, Jr. (1968), "Atmospheric and Hydrospheric Evolution on the Primitive Earth," *Science,* vol. 160, pp. 729–736; and (1968), "Pre-Metazoan Evolution and the Origins of the Metazoa," pp. 1–72 in *Evolution and Environment,* E. T. Drake, ed., New Haven, Yale Univ. Press.
† The term *eon* is used here to denote 1 b.y.

Table 12.5. COMPOSITION OF GASES FROM INTERNAL EARTH SOURCES COMPARED WITH TOTAL EARTH VOLATILES

| | Excess Volatiles of Earth's Hydrosphere and Atmosphere | Gases in Hot Springs, Fumaroles, and Geysers | Volcanic Gases from Basaltic Lava of Mauna Loa and Kilauea |
|---|---|---|---|
| Water, $H_2O$ | 92.8 | 99.4 | 57.8 |
| Total carbon, as $CO_2$ | 5.1 | 0.33 | 23.5 |
| Sulfur, $S_2$ | 0.13 | 0.03 | 12.6 |
| Nitrogen, $N_2$ | 0.24 | 0.05 | 5.7 |
| Argon, Ar | trace | trace | 0.3 |
| Chlorine, $Cl_2$ | 1.7 | 0.12 | 0.1 |
| Fluorine, $F_2$ | trace | 0.03 | — |
| Hydrogen, $H_2$ | 0.07 | 0.05 | 0.04 |

Source: Data from W. W. Rubey (1952), *Geol. Soc. Amer. Bull.*, vol. 62, p. 1137, Table 6. Figures in table represent percentages by weight.

molten condition or, if not originally molten, at least passed through a molten phase. The hypothesis states that the volatile constituents, largely water and carbon dioxide, were entirely in a vapor state and surrounded the hot earth as a dense atmosphere. As the earth cooled and became solid, temperatures ultimately dropped to a sufficiently low level that most of the water condensed to form the primitive oceans.

The hypothesis of a primitive dense atmosphere surrounding a molten earth has been disqualified by various lines of evidence. If the earth had been molten, most of the water (perhaps as much as 99%) known to be present today would have been contained in solution in the melt, rather than being free in the gaseous envelope. Condensation of atmospheric water vapor upon cooling could have furnished only a fraction of the quantity of water existing in the present atmosphere and hydrosphere. A second line of reasoning concerns the chemical nature of the supposed primitive atmosphere and ocean water. It is reasonable to conclude that the water formed by condensation would have been highly acid because of the presence of dissolved chlorine, bromine, fluorine, and other volatiles now found in sedimentary rocks. Such a highly acid ocean would have reacted vigorously with the rock-forming minerals, eventually neutralizing the solution by combination of the acid radicals with the common bases—namely, calcium, magnesium, sodium, and potassium. It has been estimated that the total quantity of rock

required to be weathered to accomplish this neutralization would be considerably greater than the total quantity of igneous rock known to have been altered by weathering in all of geologic time.

We therefore conclude that the earth, early in the first eon of its life, had a very small and relatively unimportant original atmosphere. The present atmosphere and hydrosphere are now generally thought to have evolved slowly by emanation from sources deep within the solid earth, a process referred to as *outgassing*. This hypothesis holds that practically all of the excess volatile constituents came from within the earth. The new atmosphere would have consisted largely of carbon dioxide ($CO_2$), nitrogen ($N_2$), hydrogen ($H_2$), and water ($H_2O$).

It has been suggested that the dense atmosphere of Venus has developed largely by outgassing. Note that the Venus atmosphere, composed largely of carbon dioxide and almost entirely lacking in oxygen and water, is quite unlike that of the earth. Water in quantities comparable to the earth's hydrosphere may have been produced by outgassing from Venus, but the hydrogen may have largely escaped into space and the oxygen may have combined with mineral matter exposed at the planetary surface.

As we shall see in the remainder of this chapter, the abundant oxygen of the earth's atmosphere has developed and is maintained through biological activity. That neither Venus nor Mars have significant amounts of oxygen can be explained by the absence of life on those planets, and as yet there have been found no signs of life.

The extremely rarefied atmosphere of Mars may be due to a combination of factors unfavorable to outgassing and to holding of an atmosphere. First, Mars is a small planet, only one-tenth of the mass of Earth, and has an escape velocity of one-third that of Earth. A liquid iron core probably does not exist in Mars, and the planet seems to have no magnetic field. Consequently, Mars would easily lose its atmospheric gases under force of the solar wind. The cratered surface of Mars suggests that little igneous activity has occurred on that planet, hence outgassing would not have been aided by rise of magma and volcanic extrusion such as that which has characterized the earth's history.

That the process of outgassing is going on

today is evident from chemical analysis of gases emitted from hot springs, fumaroles, geysers, and lavas. A *fumarole* is a hole which emits superheated steam and a *geyser* is a type of hot spring which intermittently discharges steam and water under high pressure. Hot springs, fumaroles, and geysers are associated with volcanic activity. Their heat is derived from recently intruded igneous rocks at depth. Much of the water that is emitted is recirculated ground water, but part of the water may be *juvenile water*—i.e., water which is derived from the earth's interior and which has not previously existed above the earth's surface.

Table 12.5 shows the results of chemical analysis of samples of volatiles from hot springs, fumaroles, and geysers. Averaged together, these analyses show over 99% water by weight, about 0.3% carbon dioxide, and lesser amounts of chlorine, sulfur, hydrogen, fluorine, and argon. Compare these percentages with those of the excess volatiles of the earth's atmosphere and hydrosphere. The degree of agreement is quite high. The higher proportion of water in the hot springs can be explained through the addition of atmospheric water that has entered the ground-water reservoir and is being recirculated. Geologists have calculated that if only 0.8% of the water emerging from hot springs and related phenomena is truly juvenile water, the total quantity of juvenile water produced by the world's hot springs would be fully adequate to account for the entire volume of the world ocean, assuming this production to have gone on at the same rate for 3 b.y.

Another source of volatiles is lava of erupting volcanoes. Analyses of gases contained in fluid basalt from craters of the Hawaiian volcanoes Kilauea and Mauna Loa show a general correspondence in proportions with those of the earth's volatiles, as shown in Table 12.5. The proportions are not, however, as closely matched as for hot springs. Gases trapped in solid igneous rocks have also been analyzed. For granite samples, particularly, the percentages are quite closely matched with those of the earth's volatiles. On the basis of these observed proportions of gases derived from igneous rocks, some geologists have concluded that the excess volatiles of the hydrosphere and atmosphere are essentially of internal earth origin.

While outgassing was probably a continued

activity throughout the first eon of earth history, there is a possibility that the rate of outgassing was substantially speeded up about at −3.6 b.y. Preston E. Cloud has proposed as a hypothesis that the moon was captured by the earth at this point in time. He argues that the intense tidal flexing set up by close proximity of the moon would have generated additional heat within the earth and would have promoted both rapid outgassing and the rise of igneous magmas to form intrusive bodies in the crust. This *thermal episode,* if it occurred, might well have increased the rate of production of the atmosphere and hydrosphere, raising greatly the total quantity of excess volatiles.

During the first eon the salts of the sea were accumulating in a growing ocean from weathering products of rocks at the surface in island arcs and continental nuclei. To attempt to reconstruct the changes in composition of sea water as the oceans developed is highly speculative. It is reasonable to suppose that initially, and perhaps through some part of the first eon, ocean salinity was low and the water was highly acid because of the predominance of the volatile constituents. The total volume of the oceans was probably increasing rapidly. As acids in rainwater reacted with igneous rocks (which may have at first been mostly basaltic types), the proportions of bases in sea water perhaps increased rapidly and the acidity was greatly reduced.

## THE SECOND EON

Pausing for a review of conditions at about −3.5 b.y., it is inferred that both atmosphere and oceans then existed in substantial proportions but that the atmosphere contained almost no free oxygen.

Very small quantities of free oxygen were continually produced by photochemical action, in which the water molecule ($H_2O$) is dissociated into hydrogen and free oxygen by action of ultraviolet light. It is estimated that before −3.0 b.y. the free-oxygen content of the atmosphere was less than 0.01% of its present atmospheric concentration, because the oxygen produced by this process was immediately withdrawn by oxidation of minerals.

Ocean water may have reached a salinity comparable to that which exists today. Continents were well developed, though smaller than they are today. Substantial quantities of sedimentary rock were being produced by the accumulation of detrital materials released by weathering and transported by running water and currents to seas. Essentially, then, the processes of vulcanism, erosion, geosynclinal sedimentation, orogeny, and intrusion were well established by this time. Sedimentary rocks probably as old as −3.2 b.y. have been identified, along with what seem to be fossil remains of the most primitive life forms. We therefore turn to the consideration of the conditions surrounding the origin and development of that earliest life.

### BEGINNINGS OF LIFE ON EARTH

In the almost complete absence of free oxygen in the atmosphere, there would have been no ozone layer to absorb the ultraviolet rays of the sun's spectrum. As noted in Chapter 1, the existing ozone layer protects most forms of life on earth from extinction by ultraviolet radiation. The earliest forms of life must therefore have been without dependence upon oxygen (i.e., *anaerobic*) and either capable of surviving under ultraviolet radiation or able to develop in places protected from such radiation. It is beyond the scope of this treatment of earth history to attempt to explain the biochemical processes that may have bridged the gap from nonliving to living matter. The event of life origin, or simply *biogenesis,* probably occurred in shallow ocean water exposed to solar radiation some time in the period between −3.8 and −3.5 b.y. There is, of course, no record of this event.

The oldest known materials that can be speculatively interpreted as remains of life forms come from sedimentary rocks whose age is in the range from −3.2 to −3.0 b.y. These rocks are exposed in the Swaziland region of South Africa and are the oldest known sedimentary rocks that are largely unaltered by metamorphism. The life forms are found embedded in layers of chert, a rock composed largely of silica. As shown in the photographs in Figure 12.4, the objects in question are spheroidal in form and range in diameter from 0.0002 to 0.001 in. (5 to 25 microns). Also found are filamentlike wisps of carbonaceous matter. If truly organic in origin, these earliest life forms were organisms that manufacture their own substance.

What are generally accepted as the oldest undoubted fossils occur in sedimentary rocks dated as at least −2.7 b.y. and perhaps as old as the Swaziland rocks. Spheroidal objects 0.0002 to 0.0004 in. (4 to 10 microns) in

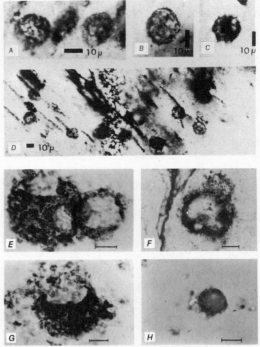

Figure 12.4. Contenders for distinction as the oldest fossils on earth. Forms seen through a microscope in thin rock slices. Length of the bar is 10 microns (0.0004 in.; 0.01 mm). (*A–D*) Microstructures possibly representing primitive algalike life forms, from the Onerwacht series, Eastern Transvaal, South Africa. Rock age is greater than 3.2 b.y. [Photograph by B. Nagy and L. A. Nagy (1969), *Nature,* vol. 223, p. 1227, Figure 1.] (*E–H*) Spheroidal microstructures considered to be possible algalike fossils, found in black chert of the Fig Tree series, near Barberton, South Africa. Rock age is greater than 3.1 b.y. [Photograph by courtesy of E. S. Barghoorn; see J. W. Schopf and E. S. Barghoorn (1967), *Science,* vol. 156, p. 509, Figure 1–4.]

diameter have been found in Minnesota in the Soudan iron formation, older than −2.7 b.y. and possibly exceeding −3.0 b.y. These structures may be remnants of bacteria or blue-green algae (see Figure 12.7). In carbonate strata of the Bulayawan series in southern Rhodesia there have been found spheroidal bodies, 0.0004 to 0.0008 in. (10 to 20 microns) in diameter, interpreted as primitive algae of a type that precipitate and bind mineral matter in layers, building up laminated structures (Figure 12.5). Such algal structures, well preserved in the late Precambrian and younger geologic record, are referred to as *stromatolites* and take the form of layers, crusts, and domes. Stromatolites are known to

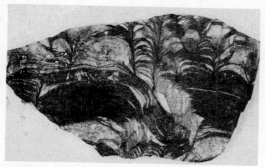

Figure 12.5. Polished limestone surface showing laminated structure of a stromatolite of the Bulawayan series, Rhodesia. The specimen is 6 in. (13 cm) long. (Photograph by courtesy of Preston Cloud.)

form in the intertidal and subtidal range of the marine environment (Figure 12.6). The intertidal forms are built up from tidal mud flats and attain heights approximating the level of high tide. The structures in the ancient South African rocks are a primitive form of algal stromatolite; thus they are built as a result of the life processes of a class of life form known as *procaryotes,* which are organisms having no nuclear wall within the cell and no well-defined chromosome structure. These organisms therefore do not undergo cell division by mitosis or display sexual reproduction in the usual sense.

The next important step in life history seems to have been the development of a type of photosynthesis in which oxygen is released in the chemical reaction, as in green plants of today. Development of the first oxygen-releasing organisms, a form of blue-green algae, was the first step in a major change in composition of the earth's atmosphere and evidently occurred in the period $-3.0$ to $-2.0$ b.y. But unless the atmospheric oxygen thus produced was also simultaneously removed from the atmosphere, it would have been a hazard to the organisms themselves. A likely acceptor of free oxygen is the ferrous form of iron oxide (FeO)

derived from rock weathering taking place on the land surfaces. Brought to the oceans by stream transport, this ferrous iron oxide would combine with additional oxygen, producing ferric iron oxide ($Fe_2O_3$), which could be deposited on the sea floor in accumulating layers of sedimentary rocks.

In fact, there exist banded iron formations whose age ranges from more than $-3.0$ to about $-2.0$ or $-1.8$ b.y. These rocks consist of thin layers of silica in which alternating bands are rich in ferric iron oxide in the mineral forms of hematite and magnetite. The banding suggests that there existed a fluctuating rhythm of precipitation and nonprecipitation of iron related to oxygen production. While the primitive procaryotes were the dominant life form, oxygen produced by photosynthesis was locked up in the sedimentary iron formations as fast as it was produced; thus oxygen could not accumulate in appreciable quantities in the atmosphere.

What seem to be the oldest fossils accepted without reservation as true remains of organisms are known as the *Gunflint microflora* and occur in cherty layers in banded iron formations in Ontario and Minnesota (Figure 12.7). These rocks are dated at more than $-1.7$ b.y. and possibly as old as $-1.9$ b.y. These forms are undoubted blue-green algae that have formed stromatolite mounds or reeflike masses (Figure 12.8).

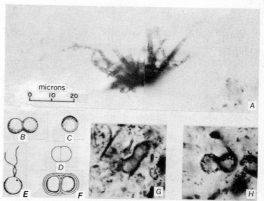

Figure 12.7. Fossils of the Gunflint microflora, north shore of Lake Superior, Ontario. (*A*) Filaments interpreted as a radiating algal colony. (*B, C,* and *D*) Sketches of modern one-celled blue-green alga, showing cell division and single cell. (*E* and *F*) Living form of dinoflagellate showing single cell and cell division. (*G* and *H*) Microfossils interpreted as algal cells undergoing division. (Photographs by courtesy of Preston Cloud.)

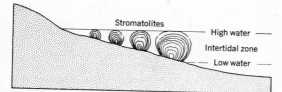

Figure 12.6. Schematic drawing of domelike stromatolites growing in the intertidal zone. [After Preston Cloud (1970), *Adventures in Earth History,* San Francisco, Freeman, p. 449, Figure 42.1.]

Figure 12.8. Stromatolites of the late Precambrian. (*Above*) Stromatolite dome, about 10 ft (3 m) in amplitude, from Paradise Creek limestone formation, northwest Queensland. Age about −1.6 b.y. (*Below*) Cross sections of small stromatolite domes from Dolomite series, Boetsap, South Africa, age about −2.0 b.y. (Photographs by courtesy of Preston Cloud.)

During the period from −3.0 to −2.0 b.y. changes were slowly taking place in the oceans and ocean basins. Outgassing continued to supply volatiles, largely water, which steadily increased the volume of ocean water. Unless the capacity of the ocean basins increased concomitantly to accommodate the larger water volume, the oceans would have inundated the continents and created a world ocean. To explain why this ultimate drowning did not occur, we can draw upon the principle of isostasy in conjunction with the program of continental evolution explained in Chapter 10. As granite magmas continued to rise and invade the continental crust, and as more igneous rock was converted by weathering, transportation, and deposition into less dense sedimentary rock, the continental crust was thickened as well as expanded in area. It has been estimated that the continental crust has increased in volume at an average rate of 0.3 mi³/yr (1.3 km³/yr) throughout geologic time.

In response to the requirements of isostasy, the thickened continents would have risen higher with respect to the basaltic oceanic floors, thereby deepening the ocean basins and increasing their total capacity. Obviously, it is not to be expected that the increase of seawater volume would at all times exactly balance the increase of basin volume, so that episodes of greater emergence and partial inundation of continents would be an expected part of the geologic record.

## DEVELOPMENT OF ATMOSPHERIC OXYGEN

A significant turning point in atmospheric composition may have come about at −2.0 to −1.8 b.y., as increased plant activity raised the atmospheric oxygen level to approximately 0.1% of the present-day value. The change is attributed to the development of more advanced oxygen-producing enzymes. One consequence of increased oxygen would have been the accumulation on land of much ferric iron oxide, which would form thin coatings upon sediment grains. Sedimentary strata produced by accumulation of such stained particles have a red color and are known as *red beds*. Extensive deposition of red beds did occur following −1.8 b.y., for these beds are an important part of the Precambrian sedimentary record.

## CARBON DIOXIDE AND CARBONATE ROCKS

During the time following −2.0 or −1.8 b.y., the carbon-dioxide content of the atmosphere is thought to have decreased greatly. Whereas earlier carbon dioxide may have constituted a substantial percentage of the atmosphere (as contrasted with the present value of 0.03% by volume), it was subsequently withdrawn from the atmosphere to be stored in carbonate rocks. Enormous quantities of carbon and oxygen exist in combination with the bases calcium and magnesium derived from rock weathering and converted into limestone and dolomites. It is estimated that at present some $73 \times 10^{15}$ tons ($67 \times 10^{21}$ gm) of carbon dioxide is stored in sedimentary rocks, a quantity about 600 times as great as the present quantity of carbon dioxide in circulation in the atmosphere, hydrosphere, and biosphere. Great amounts of organic carbon were also entrapped in sedimentary rocks and have added to the total amount of carbon removed from circulation.

Table 12.6.   A TIMETABLE FOR EARLY EARTH HISTORY

| Billions of Years Before the Present | Events (largely inferred or hypothetical) |
|---|---|
| −7.0 | Formation of our galaxy. |
| −5.0 | Nebular contraction in process. |
| −4.8 to −4.5 | Accretion of planets completed. No primordial atmosphere remaining on earth. No magnetic field or magnetosphere. Solar wind sweeps earth. |
| −4.5 to −3.5 (first eon) | Internal differentiation of earth in progress. Possible melting on large scale. Core and mantle segregated; magnetic field and magnetosphere formed. Outgassing in progress. Volatiles forming atmosphere and hydrosphere. No free oxygen (concentration 0.01% of present level); U-V (ultraviolet) radiation intense. No ozone layer. Continents begin to develop. Sedimentation begins. Ocean basins deepen. Ocean volume and salinity increasing. |
| −3.7 to −3.6 | Possible lunar capture. Possible episode of accelerated outgassing and magma rise. |
| −3.6 to −3.5 | Oldest known rocks (igneous and metamorphic) formed in continental crust. |
| −3.5 | Evolution of preliving compounds (amino acids) under U-V radiation. Biogenesis occurs (anaerobic forms). |
| −3.4 to −3.2 | Possibly oldest living forms (autotrophs) preserved in Swaziland system, South Africa; algal forms and carbonaceous filaments in chert. (Ocean volume increasing. Continents growing. Ocean basins deepening.) |
| −2.7 | Possibly oldest fossils: spheroidal objects in Soudan iron formation, Minnesota; algal stromatolites in Bulawayan series, southern Rhodesia. |
| −2.7 to −2.0 | Procaryotes develop. Rise of oxygen-releasing photosynthesizers in blue-green algae. Release of biological oxygen increases. Ferric iron compounds formed; banded iron formations deposited. Oxygen in atmosphere remains very low. $CO_2$ level high. |
| −2.0 to −1.8 | Advanced oxygen-mediating enzymes developed. Rate of free-oxygen production rises. Oxygen approaches 0.1% of present value. Gunflint microflora, blue-green algae, forming stromatolite mounds. |
| −1.8 to −1.0 | Red beds formed in thick accumulations. $CO_2$ content of atmosphere decreasing. Carbonate rocks deposited in abundance. Eucaryotic cell develops. |
| −1.0 to −0.7 | Oxygen level rises rapidly; approaches 1% of present value. Ozone layer begins to form, shielding earth surface from part of U-V radiation. |
| −0.7 to −0.6 | Precambrian-Paleozoic transition. Ocean salinity and pH at present level. |
| −0.57 | Start of the Paleozoic Era. Metazoa evolve. Rapid diversification of multicelled animal life in seas. Oxygen above 1% of present level. $CO_2$ at present level. |
| −0.57 to 0.0 | Paleozoic, Mesozoic, and Cenozoic eras of abundant life. Uniformity of atmospheric and oceanic environments prevails (except oxygen value). Rate of production of $CO_2$ by outgassing balanced by storage in carbonate rock and buried organic matter. |

Source: See footnote p. 281.

## THE LATE PRECAMBRIAN

At some point in time, which may have been earlier than −1.0 b.y., the carbon-dioxide content of the atmosphere and hydrosphere appears to have been established at a value close to that existing today, namely, 0.03% by volume. Once established, this low value has been maintained by a withdrawal of carbon dioxide at a rate equal to the rate at which it has been added by outgassing. It can be deduced that if significant releases of the stored carbon dioxide were to occur, raising the amount of carbon dioxide available for circulation, profound changes would occur in the life environment of the oceans. Many forms of marine life cannot tolerate marked changes in the acidity (pH) of the ocean water. That these same life forms have been maintained continuously throughout the entire geologic record since the time of their first appearance

suggests that the oceanic environment has held to remarkably uniform properties of temperature and acidity since at least late Precambrian time, commencing about one eon before present.

Atmospheric free oxygen in late Precambrian time has been estimated as about 1% of its present-day value. This is sufficient oxygen to screen much of the lethal ultraviolet radiation from the ocean surface. Below a depth of a few centimeters of sea water, which would have absorbed the remaining incoming ultraviolet radiation, complex life could evolve.

One consequence of this environmental change was the development of a more advanced form of marine life, the *eucaryotic cell*. This cell possesses a nuclear wall and well-developed chromosomes, and it is capable of mitotic cell division and sexual reproduction. Development of the eucaryotic cell in the late

Precambrian made possible the development of all advanced forms of life to follow.

In the time span −0.7 to −0.6 b.y., which represents the end of Precambrian time and the beginning of the Paleozoic Era, there evolved the *Metazoa*—the multicelled animal life forms that make up most of the animal world with which we are familiar. A metazoan organism can be described as one having a mouth and a digestive system, a circulatory system for oxygen distribution, and a nervous system for control. These animal forms diversified rapidly and became extremely complex in a relatively short period. Consequently, early in the Paleozoic Era animal life was represented by a highly diverse fauna, including most of the invertebrates.

### EARLY EARTH HISTORY IN REVIEW

Approximately four eons of earth history span the interval from the completion of earth accumulation to the end of the Precambrian time. Many profound and irreversible changes occurred during this early period, including internal reorganization of the earth, development of continents and ocean basins, and production of the atmosphere and hydrosphere by outgassing. Composition of the atmosphere reached its present proportions only near the very end of this four-eon time span. Consequently, the attainment of an oxygen-rich atmosphere, needed for development of advanced forms of life, represents only a terminal episode. Table 12.6 recapitulates the major events of early earth history in outline form.

The first four eons of earth history were dominated by physical and chemical systems in transient states—i.e., in rapidly changing states. However, the changes must have declined greatly in rate, tending finally to reach the steady state that has characterized the earth's surface environment ever since. So now we turn to the final stage in earth history, consisting of the three great geologic eras of abundant life under essentially uniform physical and chemical conditions.

### References for further study

Mehlin, T. G. (1959), *Astronomy,* New York, Wiley, 392 pp., chap. 14.

Bates, D. R. (1964), *The Planet Earth,* 2nd ed., Oxford, Pergamon, 370 pp., chaps. 2, 18.

Brancazio, P. J., and A. G. W. Cameron, eds. (1964), *The Origin and Evolution of the Atmospheres and Oceans,* New York, Wiley, 314 pp., chaps. 1, 6.

Mason, B. (1966), *Principles of Geochemistry,* 3rd ed., New York, Wiley, 329 pp., chaps. 2, 3, 7, 8.

Jastrow, R. (1971), *Red Giants and White Dwarfs: The Evolution of Stars, Planets and Life,* 2nd ed., New York, Harper & Row, 190 pp.

Blum, H. F. (1968), *Time's Arrow and Evolution,* Princeton, N.J., Princeton Univ. Press, 232 pp.

Lyttleton, R. A. (1968), *Mysteries of the Solar System,* Oxford, Clarendon, 261 pp., chap. 1.

Whipple, F. L. (1968), *Earth, Moon, and Planets,* 3rd ed., Cambridge, Mass., Harvard Univ. Press, 297 pp., chap. 14.

### Review questions

1. What basic conditions must be satisfied by a hypothesis of solar-system origin? Compare chemical composition of the sun with that of the solar system as a whole and with the earth. How can chemical composition of the sun be determined? What is the most striking difference in composition of the earth as compared with that of the sun? In what way is this difference significant in hypotheses of solar-system origin?

2. Compare chemical compositions of the inner and outer planets as two groups. Which group is most like the sun in composition? What elements and compounds are found in abundance in Jupiter and Saturn? What is the probable internal structure and composition of Jupiter? What is the significance of the group differences in terms of solar-system origin?

3. Review the early history of thought and speculation on the origin of the solar system. What is a nebula? Describe the nebular hypothesis of Laplace. For what reason was this hypothesis discarded? What kinds of hypotheses were put forward in the period 1900–1940? What objections do they face? In what way does deuterium figure in this body of evidence?

4. Describe in general terms the modern condensation hypotheses of solar-system origin. What details of planetary formation did von Weizsäcker postulate? How did he account for transfer of angular momentum from sun to planets? for loss of volatiles in the group of inner planets?

5. How did Kuiper modify von Weizsäcker's hypothesis? What did he mean by *protoplanets?* How did he account for loss of volatiles from the inner planets?

6. Review Urey's contributions to the condensation hypothesis of solar-system origin. What mechanism was proposed for transfer of angular momentum from sun to planetary masses? Describe steps in contraction of the

solar nebula and its condensation into lunar-size bodies. In what sense did Urey use the term *protoplanet?* Describe the accretion of the earth. How has the solar wind been invoked as a mechanism of slowing of the sun's rotation and of outward transfer of angular momentum?

7. Discuss the problem of loss of volatiles from the earth and other terrestrial planets. Could the solar wind have played a part in this process? How may a high-temperature episode have played a part in reduction of planetary iron and the dispersal of volatiles? What mechanisms can be invoked to produce a high-temperature episode?

8. How has Ringwood handled the problem of planetary melting and depletion of volatiles? Compare compositions of chondrite meteorites with average earth composition. What may be the significance of this comparison? In what principal respect does Cameron's hypothesis of solar-system origin differ from those already described?

9. What age, in billions of years before present, is assigned to the completion of earth as a planet? Would the earth have had a metallic core at that time? a magnetosphere? an atmosphere? oceans? Review the formation of the core and mantle (Chapter 7).

10. What events may be postulated in the first eon of the earth's history (−4.7 to −3.6 b.y.)? How did the atmosphere and hydrosphere come into existence? List the volatiles of the atmosphere and hydrosphere. Is it likely that the earth possessed a dense primitive atmosphere consisting of these same volatiles? Cite arguments in support of your answer.

11. Describe the process of outgassing. What constituents of the atmosphere and hydrosphere were contributed by outgassing? How is your list substantiated by the compositions of emanations from hot springs, fumaroles, and geysers? What is juvenile water? What proportion of water of hot springs is juvenile?

12. In what way does composition of volatiles in magmas and in igneous rocks support the hypothesis of origin of the atmosphere by outgassing? In what way might a thermal episode have increased the rate of outgassing? What might have caused such an episode?

13. Discuss the origins of the atmospheres of Venus and Mars. Why do these planets lack free oxygen in their atmospheres? Why has Mars such a rarefied atmosphere?

14. Discuss the question of accumulation of salts in ocean water. What are the principal salts? What is the origin of the bases in sea water?

15. Describe postulated events of the second eon of earth history (−3.5 to −2.5 b.y.). How could free atmospheric oxygen have been produced prior to −3.0 b.y.? In what concentration may it have existed? Is it possible that ocean salinity comparable to that at present was reached at an early date? If so, why has it not increased since? What would have been the role of continental denudation and sedimentation at this time? What is the age of the oldest known sedimentary rocks?

16. Review speculations as to the beginnings of life and the environmental circumstances surrounding that development. Where did biogenesis probably occur and at about what point in time? Would this earliest life have been dependent upon oxygen? Why would solar radiation have been an obstacle to development of life?

17. Describe what may perhaps be the oldest fossil forms of life. Where are they found, and what is their age? What are stromatolites? What is their significance in the earliest forms of life? What are the procaryotes?

18. Describe the development of life forms capable of releasing oxygen through photosynthesis. What role would ferrous iron oxide have played in this development? In what way do banded iron ores support this inference?

19. Describe the oldest known fossil forms of life of accepted authenticity. In what forms do they occur? What is their age?

20. Describe the growth of ocean basins and continents in the eon −3.0 to −2.0 b.y. How could increasing volume of sea water be accommodated? What is the significance of occurrence of red beds following −1.8 b.y.? To what process can the postulated rise in level of atmospheric oxygen be attributed?

21. How might the atmospheric content of carbon dioxide have been decreased throughout the eon following −2.0 b.y.? Compare the estimated quantity of carbon, as $CO_2$, stored in sedimentary rocks with the amount presently held in the atmosphere, hydrosphere, and biosphere. How is the $CO_2$ content of the atmosphere maintained?

22. What would have been the significance of attainment of an atmospheric oxygen concentration at about 1% of the present level?

How could this event have influenced the development of marine life? What is the eucaryotic cell? When did it evolve? What are the Metazoa, and when did they first appear? Describe the structure and function of the metazoan animal.

23. List in order of occurrence the most highly significant events in the early history of the earth so far as origin and evolution of life are concerned. What unique features of the earth's environment have contributed to evolution of primitive life? How do the other planets compare with ours in terms of equivalent environmental properties?

# chapter 13
# geologic systems through time:
# ii. eras of abundant life—the paleozoic era

Over the past 0.5 billion years (b.y.) life on earth has diversified greatly and has occupied the interface of lithosphere with hydrosphere and atmosphere, defining the *life-layer,* or *biosphere.* Complex life forms spread from the shallow seas to the surfaces of the lands, ultimately utilizing all favorable environments of our planet. While the evolution of plants and animals has been a succession of adaptations to environmental factors of water, heat, electromagnetic radiation, and the chemistry of atmospheric gases and aqueous solutions, the activity of those same plants and animals has in turn altered and controlled the chemistry of the atmosphere and oceans as well as the content of sediments and sedimentary rocks of the earth's crust. In brief, the theme of this chapter is that physical environment has controlled organic evolution, while at the same time organic processes have controlled evolution of important aspects of the physical environment. Here we see a remarkable linkage between

organic and physical systems, each receiving an input of matter and energy from the other.

This chapter and the next sketch broad outlines of geologic history in the eras of abundant life on planet Earth. We will emphasize the physical evolution of continents and ocean basins and the physical changes that the evolving biosphere has caused.

## THE ERAS OF ABUNDANT LIFE —THE PHANEROZOIC EON

The previous chapter brought us to the close of Precambrian time about 600 million years before the present (−600 m.y.), setting the stage for the start of three geologic eras of abundant life. In terms of life forms, Precambrian time constitutes the *Cryptozoic Eon. Cryptozoic,* derived from the Greek words *kryptos,* "hidden," and *zoo,* "life," signifies the obscurity and simplicity of life of Precambrian time. The eras of abundant life constitute the *Phanerozoic Eon,* derived from the Greek word *phaneros,* "visible." Phanerozoic time includes the *Paleozoic Era,* the *Mesozoic Era,* and the *Cenozoic Era,* listed in order from earliest to latest. Translating from the Greek roots of these three titles, they can be paraphrased as the eras of *ancient* (*paleos*), *middle* (*mesos*), and *recent* (*kainos*) life, respectively.

The inference of these names is clearly that while geologic processes operated in repetitive cycles, each one about the same as the next, life was changing through time in a one-way irreversible stream, making each era distinct from the next in terms of organic composition. Putting the point more sharply, the geologist cannot assign a given stratum of limestone or shale to a given era on the basis of lithology alone, for like rocks were formed in all eras.

Instead, it is the distinctiveness of the remains of life forms enclosed in that stratum that permit it to be assigned its place in geologic time.

The table of geologic time gives ages and durations of the three eras, together with their subdivisions into *periods* (Table 13.1). Notice that the Paleozoic Era with six periods had a duration of 345 m.y.; the Mesozoic Era with three periods lasted only 160 m.y.; while the Cenozoic Era has been too short (65 m.y.) to warrant subdivision by periods; it is only about as long as one average period of the preceding eras. There is no intrinsic significance in the diminishing of time spans of the three eras in terms of geologic processes or organic evolution; it is simply a reflection of the degree of

Table 13.1.  TABLE OF GEOLOGIC TIME

| Era | Period | Duration (m.y.) | Age (m.y.) | Orogenies |
|---|---|---|---|---|
| CENOZOIC (65) | | | | Cascadian |
| | | | — 65 — | |
| MESOZOIC (160) | Cretaceous | 71 | | Laramian |
| | | | —136— | |
| | Jurassic | 54 | | Nevadian |
| | | | —190— | |
| | Triassic | 35 | | |
| | | | —225— | |
| PALEOZOIC (345) | Permian | 55 | | Appalachian (Hercynian) |
| | | | —280— | |
| | Carboniferous | 65 | | |
| | | | —345— | |
| | Devonian | 50 | | Acadian (Caledonian) |
| | | | —395— | |
| | Silurian | 35 | | |
| | | | —430— | |
| | Ordovician | 70 | | Taconian |
| | | | —500— | |
| | Cambrian | 70 | | |
| | | | —570— | |
| PRECAMBRIAN | | (b.y.) | (b.y.) | |
| | Upper Precambrian | 0.3–0.4 | | |
| | | | 0.9–1.0 | Grenville |
| | | 0.6–0.8 | | |
| | Middle Precambrian | | 1.6–1.7 | Hudsonian |
| | | 0.7–0.9 | | |
| | | | 2.4–2.5 | Kenoran |
| | Lower Precambrian | 0.9–1.0 | | |
| | Oldest dated rocks | | 3.4 ± 0.1 | |
| | Earth accretion completed | | 4.6–4.7 | |
| | Age of universe | | 7–9? | |

(Left margin labels: PHANEROZOIC EON, CRYPTOZOIC EON)

Source: D. Eicher (1968), *Geologic Time,* Englewood Cliffs, N.J., Prentice-Hall, end paper; M. Kay and E. H. Colbert (1965), *Stratigraphy and Earth History,* New York, Wiley, p. 74.

completeness and availability of record, which improves as geologic time approaches the present. Each episode of crustal uplift followed by extensive denudation has wiped out a part of the previous geologic record as it was written in sedimentary strata. Thus the probability of finding information becomes poorer the farther back we look, just as in the case of the historical records of civilization. Where information is less abundant larger blocks of time suffice as subdivisions.

## METHODS OF HISTORICAL GEOLOGY

Because all of our knowledge of organic evolution and the sequence of events through geologic time has been built upon painstaking study of sedimentary strata and their enclosed remains and evidences of life, it will be necessary to look into some basic principles of *stratigraphy*, the study of strata as historical records. A geologic principle so simple as to seem self-evident is that among a series of sedimentary strata whose attitude is approximately horizontal, each bed is younger than the bed beneath, but older then the bed above it. This age relationship could not be otherwise in the case of sediment layers deposited from suspension in water or air. Thus the first inference to be made concerning the strata exposed in quarry walls or a cliff is that they are arranged in order of decreasing age of deposit from bottom to top.

Despite the simplicity of the *principle of superposition,* as this age-layering principle is termed, there are two possible causes for concern. First, it might be objected that the strata have been bodily overturned during orogeny, as may happen in close folding of strata, and that the uppermost beds are therefore actually the oldest. The geologist routinely checks against this possibility of error by examining closely certain details of the sedimentary rock. Features such as ripple-marking, curvature of fine layers (cross-bedding) in certain sandstones, and orientation of fossil shells give evidence of whether the strata are overturned from their original attitude. A second objection could be that the principle of superposition does not tell whether the successive strata differ greatly in age or only by very small intervals of time.

Looking at the upper walls of Grand Canyon in Figure 13.1, the eye spans about 3000 ft (900 m) of thickness of strata in almost perfectly horizontal, parallel arrangement. The entire sequence of strata consists of several major layers, each with a distinctive appearance and composition. Each of these layers is referred to as a geologic *formation* and has been given a name. At the base, forming the edge of the Tonto Platform, is the *Tapeats* formation, a sandstone layer about 200 ft (60 m) thick. Above this is a soft, gray, sandy shale layer, about 500 ft (150 m) thick, named the *Bright Angel* formation, which forms smooth, gentle slopes. Above this, forming a great sheer wall 500 ft (150 m) high, are three formations of limestone: the *Muav, Temple Butte,* and *Redwall* formations. Still higher are layers of red sandstone and shale, totaling about 1000 ft (300 m) in thickness, making up the *Supai* and *Hermit* formations. These are overlain by a pure creamy-white sandstone layer, the *Coconino* formation, whose sheer 300-ft (90-m) cliff is easily seen in the upper canyon walls. Forming the canyon rim are the *Toroweap* and *Kaibab* formations of limestone, together about 500 ft (150 m) thick.

The type of question not answered by the principle of superposition is this: Were all the sandstone, shale, and limestone strata of the Grand Canyon walls deposited in quick succession, so that in terms of available geologic time since the start of the Mesozoic Era (570 m.y.) we may consider them all as being of approximately the same age? Or do they represent widely different periods of geologic time, so that the lowest formation, the Tapeats sandstone, is extremely ancient, but the rim formation, the Kaibab limestone, is very recent? In this case there might conceivably be a difference in age of as much as 570 m.y. in the two formations. Assuming such an age difference to exist, we are faced with the further possibility that the entire sequence of rocks, 3000 ft (900 m) thick, represents slow, continuous deposition of sediment without interruption of any consequence throughout the entire span of time.

A quite different possibility is that each formation was deposited in a short period but that the records of periods of deposition are themselves separated by long intervals of time when no deposition took place. It is likely that for long periods of time, each tens of millions of years long, there would be no deposition or erosion of sediment.

We must therefore complicate the interpretation still further, as illustrated in Figure 13.2. Perhaps the bottommost three formations— Tapeats sandstone, Bright Angel shale, and

SOUTH

Vertical scale ft

Red Butte

Kaibab Plateau

Kaibab fm (ls.)
Toroweap fm (ls.)

Coconino fm. (ss.)

Hermit fm. (sh.)

Supai fm.  (sandstone and shale)

Redwall Cliffs

Redwall fm.  (Temple Butte fm.)  MISSISSIPPIAN
Muav fm.

Tonto Platform

Bright Angel fm. (sh.)  CAMBRIAN

Tapeats fm. (ss.)

Granite Gorge

Colorado R.

Shinumo Quartzite  Algonkian Wedge  Grand Canyon Group

Vishnu schist

Granite and pegmatite

PRECAMBRIAN

C

D

KAIBAB   KAIBAB

TOROWEAP   COCONINO

HERMIT

SUPAI

COCONINO

TAPEATS

VISHNU SCHIST

A

Figure 13.1. The geologic record of rock strata from Grand Canyon, Arizona, through progressively younger formations of Zion Canyon and Bryce Canyon, Utah. (*A*) Archean schists of the Inner Gorge at the foot of the Bright Angel Trail. These metamorphic rocks, of Precambrian age, are the oldest rocks of the entire sequence. (Photograph by Douglas Johnson.) (*B*) Precambrian sedimentary strata constituting the Algonkian wedge, in the eastern part of Grand Canyon. (Photograph by Carkhuff, U.S. Geological Survey.) (*C*) General view of sedimentary sequence of Grand Canyon from Point Sublime. (Photograph by A. N. Strahler.) (*D*) Uppermost strata of the rim of Grand Canyon. (Photograph by Douglas Johnson.) (*E*) The walls of Zion Canyon, Utah. These great cliffs are of Jurassic sandstone. (Photograph by A. N. Strahler.) (*F*) Bryce Canyon, Utah. Erosional forms in the Wasatch formation of Eocene age. (Photograph by D. L. Babenroth.)

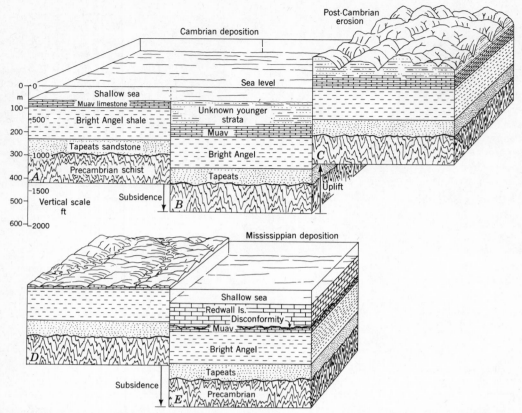

Figure 13.2. Sequence of events leading to the development of a disconformity in the walls of Grand Canyon.

Muav limestone—were deposited in rather rapid succession in a shallow sea, as shown in diagram *A*. Additional formations of which we have no record were possibly added to these three (diagram *B*). Then a broad rise of the earth's crust brought these formations above sea level, where fluvial erosion removed great quantities of rock (diagrams *C* and *D*). With only the Tapeats, Bright Angel, and Muav formations remaining, a down-sinking of the crust occurred, depressing them below sea level and producing a shallow sea in which a new period of deposition began (diagram *E*). This submergence would have allowed deposition of the Redwall limestone formation directly upon the older Muav formation.

Thus the thin line that we now see between the Muav and Redwall formations is the sole indicator of a vast period of lost record, i.e., of a time period for which no rock has been retained here. A surface of separation between two formations, representing a great gap of time, is termed a *disconformity*. The history of

events just described above for the Grand Canyon formations of lower Paleozoic ages is the actual history as worked out by stratigraphers. The strata of the walls of Zion Canyon do not resemble most of those in Grand Canyon. In Zion the most striking feature is the sheer sandstone wall, 1000 to 2000 ft (300 to 600 m) high, with scarcely a foothold. Steplike forms such as those in Grand Canyon occur only in the lower part of the walls. It seems certain that the strata of the two canyons were deposited under different conditions. Although it is possible that both series were deposited at the same time in unlike environments, this situation is not likely because the two regions are only a few tens of miles apart. It is more likely that the strata of Zion Canyon differ in age from those in Grand Canyon. Which sequence is the younger?

One means of ascertaining whether strata in two localities are of the same age or different ages is to travel the ground from one locality to the other, observing the strata continuously along the line of march. If one can actually walk upon the same rock layer throughout the entire distance, the similarity of age is proved by the *principle of continuity*. A simple case is shown in Figure 13.3, where the same layer can be followed for miles in the rim of a series of canyons and cliffs. Where strata have been partly removed from a region by erosion, a combination of continuity and superposition can be used, in traveling across country, to determine relative ages of rock strata in widely separated places. It is this combination method that is required to prove that the rocks of Grand Canyon are all of older age than those of Zion Canyon.

## FOSSILS

Of all sources of information, perhaps the most helpful to the stratigrapher are *fossils,* those ancient plant and animal remains or impressions preserved by burial in sedimentary strata. The science of fossils is *paleontology;* it is closely linked with stratigraphy.

About 1800 an English civil engineer and geologist, William Smith, observed that the fossils in strata exposed in canal excavations were of like species in all parts of a formation that could be proved to be one and the same bed by direct continuity. Fossil species in strata above or below were found to be distinctively different but to occur consistently in the same order in widely separate localities. Once the order was established by direct observation, the fossils themselves became the evidence for age of strata elsewhere in the world. For example, the fossils in certain strata in Wales were studied early in the nineteenth century, and these rocks became established as the original standard for the *Cambrian Period* (*Cambria* is the Latin name for Wales). One distinctive fossil animal, the *trilobite,* was abundant in the Cambrian seas, and, consequently, some of its various

species serve as guide fossils for the Cambrian Period throughout the world.

In the Bright Angel formation of Grand Canyon many fossil trilobites have been found (Figure 13.4). Because these trilobites belong to particular varieties resembling those found in the original Cambrian strata of Wales, the geologist can state that the two sets of strata are of almost the same age. Thus a jump of thousands of miles with no direct connection between the strata was bridged through the use of fossils.

Examples of distinctive fossils of Grand Canyon strata include ancient representatives of the *gastropods* (snails) and *pelecypods* (clams) from the Kaibab limestone formation, comprising the canyon rim rocks (Figures 13.5 and 13.6). These fossils are now composed of silica, which replaced the original shells of carbonate matter. They were released from the enclosing rock by use of an acid bath, which dissolved the carbonate matrix and left the silica intact. Extremely minute shell details are preserved in these fossils, even though no original shell matter remains.

Figure 13.7 illustrates a Grand Canyon fossil of a different kind. This object is easily recognizable as a plant leaf, resembling that of a modern fern. What we see here is merely an impression of the leaf on the bedding plane of a fine-grained red shale, the *Hermit* formation,

Figure 13.4. This fossil trilobite from the Bright Angel shale of Grand Canyon establishes the formation as being of Cambrian age. The head is to the left. About 1½ times natural size. (Photograph by courtesy of the Department of the Interior, Grand Canyon National Park.)

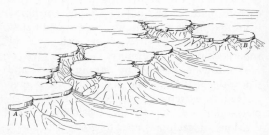

Figure 13.3. Principle of correlation of strata by direct continuity. The bed at *A* can be traced without interruption to a distant location, *B*.

Figure 13.5. A fossil gastropod from the Kaibab strata of Grand Canyon. The coiled shell somewhat resembles that of a modern snail. (Photograph by courtesy of N. D. Newell, American Museum of Natural History.)

Figure 13.7. This impression of a fern leaf was found on a bedding plane of fine-grained red shale of the Hermit formation in the walls of Grand Canyon. About natural size. (Photograph by courtesy of the Dept. of the Interior, Grand Canyon National Park.)

in the upper walls of the canyon. Many plant fossils consist of a thin layer of carbon representing the altered plant tissue. Some fossils consist of only the cavity in which the shell formerly existed, but from which the shell has been removed by action of circulating ground water.

The value of fossils in telling us the age of rock strata arises from the fact that all forms of plant and animal life have continually and systematically undergone changes with passage of time, a process termed *organic evolution.* If we have before us a complete, or nearly complete, description of past life forms as determined from fossils, and if we know the geologic age to which each fossil form belongs, it is often a simple matter to give the age of any sedimentary layer merely by extracting a few fossils from the rock and comparing them

Figure 13.6. Fossil clam shell (pelecypod) from the Kaibab strata of Grand Canyon. (Photograph by courtesy of N. D. Newell, American Museum of Natural History.)

with the reference forms. A fossil species particularly well suited to determination of age of strata is known as an *index fossil.* Although this practice works well in many cases, there are frequent difficulties. For one thing, many strata contain no fossils, usually because the conditions under which the sediment was being deposited were unsuitable for maintenance or preservation of plant or animal life. A second problem is that some fossil organisms showed such slow changes that almost identical forms survived over a long span of geologic time.

The determination of relative age of strata is much more convincing when an entire natural assemblage of animal forms, or *fauna,* is studied, because a distinctive combination of animal types is far less likely to persist through time than a single type. Establishment of a working sequence of ages of index fossils and faunas had to be made in the first instance from observations of the positions of those fossils in the stratigraphic column. The principle of *succession of faunas*—which is simply that each formation has a different fauna (or flora) from that in the formations above it and below it—was proved by use of the principles of superposition and continuity.

World-wide studies by stratigraphers and paleontologists over the last 150 years have yielded an extremely detailed and nearly complete reference table of the divisions and subdivisions of geologic time, together with index fossils for all ages from the Cambrian to the present.

The nature of life forms found as fossils in

strata gives much information on ancient environments (see Chapter 8). Presence in limestone layers of abundant shellfish bearing gill-like structures indicates the marine environment; reeflike masses of coral skeletons or algal growths indicate the littoral environment; layers of coal containing remains of plants and winged insects indicate the terrestrial environment; and so forth. Traced continuously across country for many miles, a single group of strata may show transition from marine to terrestrial environments, revealing the position of an ancient shoreline, and thereby allowing the ancient geography of lands and seas (*paleogeography*) to be interpreted.

## UNCONFORMITIES

Groups of sedimentary strata may be separated from one another not only by disconformities as described in earlier paragraphs, but also by an angular discordance in which one group of parallel strata lies across the truncated edges of a group of inclined strata beneath. A somewhat different relationship is seen in the case of a group of parallel strata resting upon igneous or metamorphic rocks. Either relationship is termed an *unconformity*. Excellent examples can be seen in the lower walls of Grand Canyon (Figure 13.1).

Precambrian rocks in Grand Canyon lie beneath the Cambrian Tapeats sandstone, the rim rock of the Tonto Platform which forms the brink of the Inner Gorge (Figure 13.1). Looking down into the narrow Inner Gorge, one notices that the walls here are completely lacking in horizontal bedding planes but instead have an extremely rough surface with sets of nearly vertical partings giving a grooved appearance to the rock walls. This rock, the *Vishnu schist,* is a metamorphosed sedimentary rock. Here and there bands of granite cut through the schist. No fossils or indications of life have been found in the Vishnu schist, although this is not surprising for a highly metamorphosed rock of this type. The Vishnu schist is dated as of lower Precambrian age, older than 2.4 b.y. (Table 13.1). In the Grand Canyon region this lower Precambrian division is named *Archean*. The orogeny in which the Vishnu schist was altered and intruded is perhaps equivalent to the Kenoran orogeny.

If we follow along the rim of the Tonto Platform, continuing to study the walls of the Inner Gorge below us, a new geologic feature enters the picture (Figure 13.1). A sloping wedge of tilted sedimentary strata appears between the Tapeats sandstone and the Vishnu schist. The wedge continues to thicken until several thousand feet of strata are exposed. This tilted sedimentary series, consisting of shales and sandstones, belongs to the *Grand Canyon Group*. In this area the Grand Canyon Group is assigned to the *Algonkian* time division of the Precambrian and is correlated with the middle to upper Precambrian rocks of the Canadian Shield. The age would perhaps be 1.7 b.y. or younger.

From the principle of superposition it is evident that the Algonkian sedimentary strata are younger than the Archean Vishnu schist, upon which they rest, but they are older than the Cambrian Tapeats formation, beneath which they lie. Thus, even without knowing their exact position in geologic time, it is fairly certain that the Algonkian rocks belong to the middle to upper Precambrian.

An explanation of the Algonkian rock wedge in Grand Canyon is given in the series of block diagrams of Figure 13.8. Geosynclinal sedimentary strata of early Precambrian age were crumpled and metamorphosed into the Vishnu schist by one of the earliest orogenies of which we have any record (*A*). Next, these mountains were reduced by erosion to a peneplain (*B*). After slow, uniform crustal sinking, a great thickness of Algonkian sediments was deposited in horizontal layers (*C*), but these layers were later tilted in great fault blocks (*D*). Again prolonged erosion removed the mountains, creating a second peneplain, above which a few of the harder sandstone masses projected as ridges (*E*). This topography existed at the close of the Precambrian time. Again, crustal sinking took place, causing the region to become a shallow sea, which received the Cambrian sediments (*F*). Hence in places the Cambrian layers rest directly upon the Vishnu schist, but in other places they rest upon a thick wedge of Algonkian strata.

The line of separation seen between the Algonkian beds and the Vishnu schist in the canyon wall is an *angular unconformity,* since the layers of one group are at an angle to the layers of the other group. The line is evidence not only of a vast erosion period that intervened between the formation of the two rock groups, but also of an orogeny that followed the development of the older rock group. A second unconformity exists in the line of separation between the Cambrian Tapeats sand-

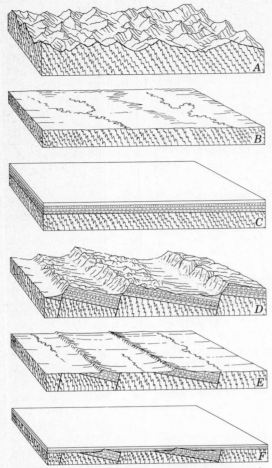

Figure 13.8. Block diagrams show the manner in which the great wedges of Algonkian strata came into existence in the lower Grand Canyon. [After C. O. Dunbar (1960), *Historical Geology,* New York, John Wiley & Sons, p. 96, Figure 53.]

stone and all of the Precambrian. This unconformity is shown in detail in Figure 13.1. Notice that a highly resistant formation, the Shinumo quartzite, stood as a residual mass above the general level of the late Precambrian peneplain. It protrudes through the Tapeats sandstone, which was deposited around the high mass but did not cover it.

## THE GEOLOGIC TIME SCALE

The methods of stratigraphy and paleontology establish relative ages of groups of strata in a generally satisfactory manner. As explained in Chapter 10, in reviewing the history of early estimates of the earth's age prior to discovery of radioactivity, establishment of the absolute age of rocks in terms of years before present

was successful only after the introduction of radiometric methods.

Table 13.1 gives radiometric ages for the beginning and end of each era and period. Because the principal radiometric dating systems described in Chapter 10 (uranium to lead, potassium to argon, and strontium to rubidium) are largely limited to use on igneous and metamorphic rocks, the assignment of absolute ages to sequences of sedimentary strata requires indirect inferences based upon physical relationships between contiguous sedimentary and igneous rocks. Figure 13.9 shows a hypothetical example as it might be applied to a case resembling that of rocks of the Inner Grand Canyon.

Suppose that radiometric ages are found for each of the three different igneous rock bodies, labeled 1, 2, and 3 in the diagram. If the igneous rock 1 has an age of 2.4 b.y., we can say that the adjacent schist, into which the igneous rock was intruded, is more than 2.4 b.y. old. We can also say that the tilted strata on the right are younger than 2.4 b.y. because they were deposited after igneous body 1 was leveled off by erosion.

Igneous body 2 is a *sill* which was intruded into the tilted strata, but whether before or after they were tilted can only be pure conjecture from the evidence shown. If the age of igneous rock 2 turned out to be 1.8 b.y., it would mean that the tilted strata are at least that old, perhaps much more, but not exceeding the 2.4-b.y. limit set by igneous rock 1.

If igneous rock 3, a thin vertical dike, yielded an age of 400 m.y., we would know that the Cambrian Period is older than 400 m.y. but that the Carboniferous Period is younger than 400 m.y.

The radiometric ages given in Table 13.1

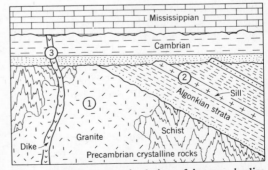

Figure 13.9. Radiometric dating of igneous bodies allows limiting ages to be established for the enclosing and overlying sedimentary strata.

will not agree completely with ages given in tables set up by other authorities, since some degree of interpolation is involved. However, these discrepancies are quite small and need not cause concern for the reliability of the geologic time scale as a whole.

Table 13.1 lists a number of orogenies of major significance in the geologic record. The nature of orogeny and its relationship to geosynclines has been described in Chapter 10. For many decades a popular doctrine among geologists was that orogenies should occur simultaneously along a number of belts variously distributed widely over the continents. Ideally, such world-synchronous orogenies would have brought to a close long periods of crustal quiescence in which geosynclinal deposition had occurred. The mountain belts produced by one orogeny would provide the sources of detrital sediments for geosynclinal deposition to follow. Each era and many of the periods would thus terminate with an orogeny. It is known that orogenies are not synchronous in any such simple pattern. While an orogeny was taking place in one part of a continent, geosynclinal deposition was occurring in another. Evidently the colliding of lithospheric plates to which orogeny is now attributed have followed a schedule that is not well correlated with the major blocks of geologic time defined on the basis of important evolutionary changes in major groups of plants and animals.

## CLASSIFICATION OF LIFE FORMS

To discuss organic evolution it is necessary to have some knowledge of the system of classification of plants and animals into a hierarchy of levels of grouping. The first basis of subdivision is into two groups: the *plant kingdom* and the *animal kingdom*. Plants more advanced than single-celled forms are organisms characterized by growth through the process of *photosynthesis,* in which atmospheric carbon dioxide and water are combined with solar energy in the presence of chlorophyll to produce carbohydrate, at the same time liberating free oxygen (see Figure E.1). Plants lack mechanisms of locomotion and either remain stationary and anchored in place or are transported by other mechanisms. There are, of course, exceptions to the last two statements—some plants (fungi, bacteria) lack chlorophyll and do not carry on photosynthesis, and some microscopic plants, particularly certain algae, can swim freely.

Animals are characterized by the need to ingest food manufactured by other animals or plants and to digest this food in order to provide growth materials and energy. Animals engage in respiration, in which oxygen is taken into the cell to burn food and release energy (see Figure E.2). Oxidation is accompanied by the release of carbon dioxide. Many forms of animals are capable of locomotion, but others are fixed in place and require that food be brought to them.

The first level of subdivision of both plants and animals is into *phyla*. Our interest here is primarily in organisms that are abundant as fossils or have played important roles in forming sediments.

For our purposes it will suffice to know that several plant phyla make up the aquatic plants. These include *bacteria* and *algae*. Another plant phylum includes the *fungi* (yeasts, molds, mushrooms). The green land plants are encompassed by two phyla, the *bryophytes* (mosses and liverworts) and the *vascular plants*. The term *vascular* refers to the presence of a *vascular system* of roots and conducting tubes by means of which water and nutrients are carried from one part of the plant to another. The vascular plants include all terrestrial herbs, shrubs, and trees and will be the main objects of our study of plant evolution in this chapter.

Ten animal phyla important in the fossil record are named in Table 13.2. The common name is given, along with some names of important animal groups within the phylum. Phyla which have few fossil representatives are not included.

The *Protoz*oa, or one-celled animals, are set apart from all remaining phyla, which are *Metazoa*. We have already referred to the Metazoa in Chapter 12 as animals with many cells differentiated into various tissues and organs for the purposes of carrying out such functions as ingestion, digestion, respiration, control, and so forth. All animals except the vertebrates are referred to as *invertebrates*. Whereas the vertebrates have an internal bony skeleton, the invertebrates have no internal skeleton but can have shells of mineral matter or external skeletons of hardened organic matter.

## MECHANISMS OF ORGANIC EVOLUTION

With the passage of time, as generation upon generation of individuals of a species of plant

Table 13.2.  PRINCIPAL ANIMAL PHYLA
IMPORTANT AS FOSSILS

| | Common Name of Phylum | Representative Groups |
|---|---|---|
| Invertebrates | Protozoa | Foraminifera, radiolaria |
| | [Metazoa] Sponges | |
| | Coelenterates | Corals, jellyfish, sea anemone |
| | Bryozoans | "Moss animals," "sea mats" |
| | Brachiopods | |
| | Molluscs | Pelecypods or bivalves (clam, mussel, oyster, scallop) |
| | | Gastropods (snail, slug, conch) |
| | | Cephalopods (squid, octopus, nautilus, ammonite) |
| | Annelids | Segmented worms, earth-worms, leeches |
| | Arthropods | Crustaceans (crab, lobster, shrimp) |
| | | Trilobites |
| | | Ostracodes |
| | | Insects |
| | | Arachinids (spiders) |
| | Echinoderms | Crinoids (sea lilies) |
| | | Sea cucumbers, sea urchins, starfishes |
| | Vertebrates (a subphylum) | Fishes |
| | | Amphibians |
| | | Reptiles |
| | | Birds |
| | | Mammals |

or animal are reproduced, the average set of physical characteristics of the population of individuals undergoes change. This change is termed *organic evolution*. While any one individual of a species can, by reaction with his environment, develop some physical attributes different from those of other individuals, such *acquired characteristics* cannot be passed on to another generation.

Evolution can proceed only through changes which can be inherited—i.e., transmitted from one generation to the next through genetic materials contained in the reproductive cells of the organism. The *gene* is the unit of genetic material, and each gene is responsible for the replication of a particular characteristic of the organism. No adult individual of a species is identical in all respects to either parent, to any sibling (except in the case of identical twins), or to any offspring. The reason that such differences exist is that genes of two individuals are exchanged in the process of sexual repro-

duction. In this way each new individual receives a unique combination of thousands of characteristics. This process of production of individual differences is known as *recombination*.

A second mechanism of inherited change occurs through a sudden change in a gene, or groups of genes, and is known as a *mutation*. This form of change is permanent in the sense that it will be transmitted to succeeding generations. Mutations occur in only a very small fraction of genes. Causes of mutations are not well understood, but it is thought that some mutations are caused by exposure to radiation or to certain chemical substances, or by temperature changes. In the broad sense, then, mutations are brought about by environmental forces over which the organism exerts no control.

Individuals of one species, differing from one another because of recombination of genetic materials or by mutations that are inherited, constitute a *population*. Since the processes of inheritance operate in a random fashion within the population, all physical variations due to recombination within the populations would be retained and there would be no net change from generation to generation. Mutations, while capable of causing population change, are not only rare events but offer no consistent direction of change. The fact that evolutionary changes are in one direction—for example, a progressive increase in size of a particular organ—points to a guiding mechanism of forced change of population characteristics.

Charles Darwin is credited with formulating and demonstrating the principle of *natural selection* as the control of change in populations of species. He reasoned from intensive studies of populations of various living animals that the struggle for survival against the unfavorable pressures of the physical environment and the competition of other animals tends to eliminate those lines of inheritance that produce the least fit individuals. On the other hand, individuals better equipped to survive tend to propagate a disproportionately larger number of the individuals of succeeding populations. For example, a predatory animal possessing better legs would be more successful in catching his prey. In times of scarcity of victims, the better-endowed animal would be more likely to survive and propagate a new generation than an animal with weak legs. The characteristics of populations would on the average trend in the direction of improvements of function. Hereditary changes introduced by recombination and mutations would eventually be eliminated if they contributed to failure to survive but would be retained if they contributed to success in survival.

We have used the word *species* without definition. Most persons have a good empirical concept of species based upon obvious physical differences and similarities among individuals in the animal world. We unhesitatingly assign a domestic cat to a different species from a bobcat, but we may not be so sure if the domestic dog is of a different species from the wolf. In the latter case, the dog (*Canis familiaris*) is of a different species from the wolf (*Canis lupus*), but the two species can interbreed, as witness certain dog varieties that resemble wolves in many features.

Assuming that the biologist has a satisfactory definition of species, let us go on to consider how a species evolves, or, more to the point, how a single species can give rise to two species. It is supposed that the change occurs because of geographical isolation of a segment of the species population. For example, a rising mountain chain might form a physical barrier between two regions, or the breakup and drifting of continents might place an impassable oceanic barrier between two landmasses formerly united. Isolation permits the progressive changes in the two populations to drift independently to the point that they can no longer be considered alike. Eventually the changes proceed to the point that interbreeding can no longer take place, and if brought together again the two populations would not have the genetic capability of reuniting. Various other kinds of barriers exist that effectively prevent interbreeding of similar species. When interbreeding does occur, leading to hybridization, a new species may result, although the survival of hybrids is generally an event of low probability.

Although this brief account of the evolutionary process is both incomplete and inadequate, it permits us to try to make some order out of the development of life in response to the changing environments throughout geological history.

## START OF THE PALEOZOIC ERA

Evidence was presented in Chapter 10 for crustal spreading now in progress on a vast scale. Under the theory of plate tectonics entire continents are undergoing separation in many parts of the world and collision in others. A widely supported hypothesis, for which several independent lines of favoring evidence can be mustered, is that late in Precambrian time there existed only two major continental shields: *Gondwana* and *Laurasia*. These were shields which had been built gradually about several nuclei of very ancient rock. Figure 13.10 shows a reconstruction of the nested continents and their nuclei. Gondwana and Laurasia were very close together and their combined landmass has been called *Pangaea*.

Acceptance of the hypothesis of a single world-continent at the opening of the Paleozoic Era has profound significance for organic evolution, because life developing in shallow seas could spread freely along all continental margins and throughout shallow continental seas. In contrast, if the continents had grown from widely separated nuclei the dispersions and interminglings of new populations of organisms would have been made extremely difficult, and

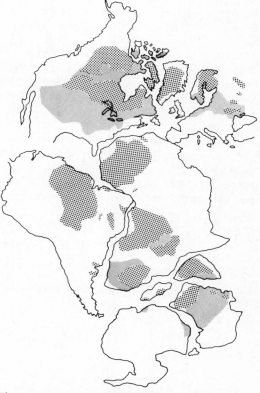

Figure 13.10. Reassembled continents, prior to start of continental drift. Dark pattern: areas of oldest shield rocks (older than −1.7 b.y.). Light pattern: rocks in the age range −0.8 to −1.7 b.y. [Map redrawn from P. M. Hurley and J. R. Rand (1969), *Science*, vol. 164, p. 1237, Figure 8.]

perhaps impossible, across deep intervening ocean basins. Later, as life spread to the lands, existence of a world-continent would have allowed plants and animals to migrate freely, subject only to limitations of favorable climatic environments. As we shall see, unity of the world-continent was probably maintained until after the close of the Paleozoic Era, so that the evolution and diversification of all phyla of plants and animals proceeded for more than 300 m.y. without being subjected to the effects of extreme isolation of one continental fragment from another.

Although we do not know the actual level of atmospheric oxygen at the start of the Paleozoic Era, it has been postulated to have stood at about 1% of the present level. Figure 13.11 is a graph of atmospheric oxygen levels throughout geologic time; it represents inferences of two scientists: L. V. Berkner and L. C. Marshall. This curve should be regarded as a carefully designed hypothetical model based upon inference, rather than as a plot of measured values. The level of atmospheric carbon dioxide is thought to have been stabilized then at about its present level, for reasons given in Chapter 12.

Judging from widespread occurrences of strata of lower Cambrian age, that first period of the Paleozoic Era was a time of widespread shallow seas favorable to the evolution of complex life forms. The lands, of course, must have been totally devoid of life, being still under the exposure to lethal amounts of ultraviolet radiation. Erosion by running water would have acted intensively upon barren expanses of weathered rock surface and the supply of detrital sediments would have been abundant wherever rising mountain arcs bordered subsiding geosynclines.

## LIFE OF EARLY CAMBRIAN TIME

Chapter 12 closed the review of earth history through the Precambrian time with the sudden appearance upon the scene of the Metazoa, a surprisingly diverse and complex animal assemblage. Somehow, in what seems to have been a very short interval of geologic time, the simple plant forms—bacteria and blue-green algae—had given rise to highly advanced animal forms.

Fossilized remains of invertebrate animals with hard shells or external skeletal parts are found in wide variety and great abundance in the lowest strata of the Cambrian Period. Evidently, most of the animal phyla present today were in existence then, yet there is no earlier fossil record by which we can trace the organic evolution of these forms.

One hypothesis, generally favored today, is that the evolutionary process operated so rapidly as the Paleozoic Era began that no earlier succession would have existed in Precambrian rocks. Others have argued that invertebrates gradually evolving in the later Precambrian time had no hard parts that could be preserved, hence that the fossil record begins only with the development of shells or skeletons. This second hypothesis seems difficult to accept because there are abundant Precambrian shales in which the impressions of soft-bodied animals could be preserved. It is also suggested that the Metazoa may have evolved over a long span of the late Precambrian but were physically limited to small isolated pockets in the sea where algae were concentrated and provided an

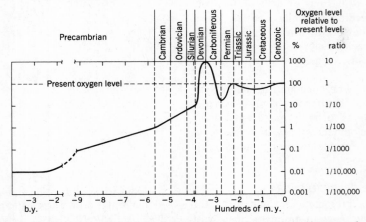

Figure 13.11. Postulated changes in the level of atmospheric oxygen throughout geologic time. [After L. V. Berkner and L. C. Marshall (1964), in *The Origin and Evolution of the Atmosphere and Oceans,* P. J. Brancazio and A. G. W. Cameron, eds., New York, John Wiley & Sons, p. 120, Figure 6.15.]

oxygen supply. Only in Cambrian time, when adequate supplies of atmospheric oxygen became available, were these animals able to spread widely and increase to large populations.

Among the invertebrate groups present in early Cambrian time were sponges, corals, jellyfish, segmented worms (annelids), and primitive crustaceans. (Figure 13.18, at the end of this chapter, shows organic evolution of major groups of plants and animals starting with the Cambrian Period.) Figure 13.12 shows how some of these animals may have looked on a sea floor of Cambrian time. Two other invertebrate forms, common then but either unknown or very few today, were the trilobites (Figure 13.4) and the brachiopods. Now extinct, the trilobites were exceptionally abundant in the Cambrian Period. They were bottom-feeding animals having a segmented outer skeleton of chitin and outwardly resembled the "horseshoe crab" of today. The brachiopods were shellfish, perhaps best described as outwardly resembling clams. They

lived with one shell attached to a rock surface or embedded in the mud of the sea floor.

The invertebrate fauna of Cambrian time is considered strikingly different in composition from that of ensuing periods because of the abundance of trilobites and brachiopods and the absence of a number of other invertebrate groups that were to arise and dominate the life of later periods. In this respect it has been said that Cambrian invertebrate evolution "got off to a false start." To understand what happened, we need to consider some additional principles of organic evolution.

## EVOLUTIONARY RADIATIONS AND EXTINCTIONS

The fossil record shows that numbers of new groups* of animals increase rapidly in abundance in certain limited spans of time, rather than showing a steady increase. This rapid diversification of groups constitutes *evolution-*

* As used here, the word *groups* may apply to any one of several levels in the hierarchy of taxonomy within a phylum: namely, *classes, orders, families,* and *genera.*

Figure 13.12. Restoration of the middle Cambrian sea floor of eastern British Columbia, showing conditions at the time of deposition of the Burgess shale formation. Sponges are shown at far left and right, trilobites and arthropods in the center and at left, segmented worms on the bottom, and a jellyfish at upper left. (Photograph by courtesy of the Smithsonian Institution.)

*ary radiation.* A period of radiation is followed by a much longer span of time in which the new groups persist with little change. The causes of evolutionary radiation are complex and not well understood, but it can be reasoned that the onset of a particularly favorable set of environmental conditions is partly responsible.

In the case of the almost explosive radiation of the earliest Cambrian faunas, the rapid increase in free atmospheric oxygen was perhaps a major factor, along with the crustal stability and presence of large expanses of shallow inland seas on a world-continent. Whatever the reasons, early Cambrian time was especially favorable to the diversification of trilobites and brachiopods.

Evolution tends to proceed on a series of one-way branching tracks. New groups form readily and proceed on parallel or diverging tracks, but the reverse trend, to have those tracks rejoin and unite with other groups into a common line, is forbidden by the impossibility of interbreeding and exchange of genetic materials. For many groups the evolutionary track simply ends by failure to propagate, and the result is *extinction.*

Extinctions of large numbers of animal groups seem to have occurred rapidly at certain points in the geologic column. Again, environmental changes of one sort or another are assumed to have been responsible for large-scale extinctions. Widespread volcanic and orogenic activity, accompanied by changes in atmospheric and oceanic temperatures, may be expected to place severe stresses upon faunas. Widespread emergence of continental shields and mountain belts has at times sharply reduced the areas of shallow seas, isolating one sea from another. Major extinctions of some groups have coincided with such conditions.

Rapid extinctions of large groups of organisms lead to vacant environments, and these are rapidly filled by adaptive radiation of other groups of organisms. We shall see that major episodes of extinction and subsequent rapid evolutionary radiation mark the transitions from one geologic era to the next.

## TRENDS OF MARINE LIFE IN THE LOWER PALEOZOIC

By the end of the Cambrian Period trilobites had been reduced greatly by extinctions. On the other hand, brachiopods, sponges, and crustaceans held their own and increased gradually in abundance (see Figure 13.18). With the coming of the Ordovician Period,

about −500 m.y., a rapid evolutionary radiation took place among several phyla. Corals, gastropods, pelecypods (bivalves), and cephalopods showed rapid divergence, as did crinoids (sea lilies), starfish, and echinoids (sea urchins). Thus during the Ordovician Period the important lines of invertebrate evolution were reestablished in a way that was to persist with only moderate changes through the remainder of the Paleozoic.

By the Silurian Period corals had become increasingly important and grew in such abundance as to produce important reef deposits of limestone.

## SPREAD OF LIFE TO THE LANDS

Until late Silurian time the lands were totally devoid of plant and animal life, so that the landscape would have presented everywhere a barren appearance. Lack of sufficient atmospheric oxygen was probably the major single deterrent to occupation of the terrestrial environment by plants and animals. For all organisms, the lethal effect of ultraviolet radiation was a barrier to life that could only be removed when sufficient oxygen was present to absorb this radiation and generate an ozone layer (see Chapter 2). For animals adequate oxygen was also a requirement for sustaining life processes. According to the model shown in Figure 13.11, the oxygen level rose quite steadily throughout the Cambrian, Ordovician, and Silurian periods. By late Silurian time the level had reached 10% of the present level, effectively shielding the ground from lethal ultraviolet radiation. Land plants appear in the fossil record at this time.

Transition from the water environment to the land environment posed serious difficulties to both plants and animals, requiring profound changes in structure and function. One difficulty for animals was to emerge from a salt solution to which the body fluids were matched and enter fresh water, which could rapidly dilute those fluids. A second difficulty for animals was posed by leaving the aqueous environment, from which oxygen in solution is absorbed by specialized tissues, to enter the atmospheric environment in which oxygen must be absorbed directly from a gaseous medium.

For all organisms, exposure to air would result in fatal desiccation (drying out) and required development of a protective coating to retain vital fluids or the means to replace them as fast as they were lost. Desiccation also constituted a barrier to sexual reproduction, for water-dwelling organisms release their reproductive cells (gametes) into fluid surroundings where fertilization takes place. New means of protecting these cells had to develop.

The transition from salt water to land seems logically to have been a two-stage process: salt water to fresh water, then fresh water to atmosphere. Difficult as the transition was, an environment with abundant oxygen for animals and intense sunlight for plant photosynthesis was awaiting occupation. An almost explosive evolutionary radiation took place, first among the plants.

## EVOLUTION OF THE LAND PLANTS

The vascular land plants are believed to have evolved from the green algae, which carry on photosynthesis in the same way as do the higher plants. The green algae were successful in making a transition to fresh water, as witness the familiar green "scum" seen on small fresh-water ponds. There is no fossil record of the supposed evolution from green algae to the vascular plants, but some measure of support for this relationship is found in the bryophytes, a plant phylum that includes the mosses and liverworts. These plants now live in wet, well-shaded environments on land but are limited to small size because they lack structures for transferring fluids from one part to another within the individual and, moreover, have no means of protecting the reproductive cells from drying out after they are separated from the parent plant. It seems possible that the vascular plants evolved through plants related to the bryophytes, but there is no fossil record of such an evolutionary chain.

The vascular plants met the needs of the land environment by developing roots for intake of soil moisture, leaves for photosynthesis, and stems containing a *vascular system* of specialized conductive tissue for transporting fluids between roots and leaves. In addition, plants have developed on their leaves a specialized outer cell layer covered by a protective layer, the *cuticle,* capable of preventing evaporative water loss, but also containing openings (*stomata*) through which the release of transpired water can be regulated.

The vascular plants are subdivided into two groups: those which are *seedless* and those which are *seed-bearing.* The former are ferns or fernlike plants and include the modern club mosses and horsetails. The reproductive process of the seedless plants is quite elaborate and

cannot be detailed here. It must suffice to know that the adult seedless plant releases *spores.* The spore produces a small specialized plant that usually releases both eggs and sperm, and these unite to produce the embryonic spore-producing plant.

The evolution of the vascular plants is shown in Figure 13.18. First to evolve were the seedless plants. One group appears first in the rocks of upper Silurian age; these were simple plants (psilopsids) lacking in roots or leaves. They diversified rapidly in the Devonian Period, but then rapidly subsided to minor importance. In Devonian time the remaining three groups evolved with great rapidity. These are represented today by the *club mosses,* the *horsetails,* and the *ferns.* All three plant groups included species of tall trees, although today only the ferns attain tree size.

By the middle of Devonian time, about −420 m.y., rich forests of seedless vascular plants covered the lands. You will notice that in Figure 13.11 the oxygen level shows a sharp increase in the Devonian Period, rising to a postulated level on the order of 10 times the present level. This rise is inferred from the great expansion of plant growth, resulting in the liberation of great amounts of oxygen that could not be used by animals or in mineral oxidation.

The Carboniferous Period started about −345 m.y. and ended about −280 m.y. (It includes two subperiods, the Mississippian and Pennsylvanian, often treated as separate periods.) The upper Carboniferous saw a world-wide trend toward extensive areas of low-lying fresh-water swamps repeatedly inundated by shallow seas. The terrestrial environment, with its great swamp forest and rich insect life, is an outstanding feature of late Paleozoic time.

In addition to the three groups of seedless vascular plants which had arisen in Devonian time, there evolved in the Carboniferous Period the first of the seed-bearing plants. These were the *seed ferns,* one of four classes of seed-bearing plants making up the *gymnosperms.* As Figure 13.18 shows, the seed ferns later gave rise to two of the four gymnosperm classes, the *cycads* and *ginkgoes,* but these became prominent only in the Mesozoic Era. The fourth class consisted of the *conifers,* or cone-bearing, needle-leaf gymnosperms. These also arose in lower Carboniferous time and had many representatives throughout the period, but they were primitive forms now largely extinct.

Figure 13.13 is a restoration of a Carboniferous forest showing seedless trees as well as seed ferns. Forests such as this must have grown in great luxuriance over long periods of time, judging from the thickness of coal seams derived from compaction of the partially decayed vegetative mass that was produced. The conversion of peat to coal has been discussed in Chapter 8.

The climate of the Carboniferous Period has been interpreted as exceptionally mild and equable over large areas of North America and Europe. The structure and succulent foliage of forest plants suggest a moist frost-free climate, while the existence of swamps is in itself proof of ample rainfall. Although coals are found in a wide range of ages in the geologic record, those of the upper Carboniferous Period are particularly remarkable. Vast expanses of the continents were then featureless plains close to sea level and were covered alternately by swamps bearing forest vegetation and by shallow seas in which sedimentary strata were laid down.

It has been estimated that some 30 ft (9 m) of peat was required to produce 1 ft (0.3 m) of coal. The rate of production of coal has been estimated at 1 ft (0.3 m) per 300 yr. On this basis the 50-ft (15-m) Mammoth coal seam of Pennsylvania would have required an initial production of 1500 ft (460 m) of peat in a continuous period of plant growth lasting over 450,000 yr. These figures are to a large degree purely speculative, but they give some idea of the extraordinary uniformity of environmental conditions that must have prevailed during the upper Carboniferous Period.

A decline in atmospheric oxygen to near-present levels in Carboniferous time is postulated on the supposition that the decay of great quantities of plant matter would have used substantial amounts of oxygen. The oxygen curve in Figure 13.10 is therefore shown as dropping sharply in Carboniferous time.

Among the invertebrates, two phyla invaded the terrestrial environment to become abundant in Carboniferous time. One of these is the gastropod, which was able to develop air-

Figure 13.13. Restoration of a Carboniferous forest. Seedless trees and seed ferns dominate. *F*, Seed fern. *L*, Lycopsid. *S*, Sphenopsid. (Photograph courtesy of Illinois State Museum, Springfield.)

breathing apparatus and to emerge from the water as a land snail. These animals were not abundant, however, until much later in the geologic column. By far the more striking evolutionary development was that of the insects and arachnids (spiders and scorpions), which became very abundant in the Carboniferous Period.

Insects are included within the same phylum (arthropods) as the crustaceans (Table 13.2). Like the crustaceans, the insects have a tough waterproof outer covering of organic matter. This covering was very likely an important factor in successful emergence from a water environment into the air. The development of wings for flight was an enormous advantage to the insects both in obtaining food and in evading predators. As a result the evolutionary radiation of the insects was spectacular. Some 400 kinds of insects are known from the Pennsylvanian Period. Although most were unlike modern insects, an exception was the cockroach, some species of which attained a length of several inches (Figure 13.14). A dragonflylike insect was perhaps the largest—a fossil specimen with wingspread of 29 in. (74 cm) has been found. Evolutionary radiation of insects continued throughout geologic time, and there are today about 500,000 insect species known.

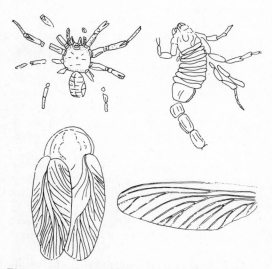

Figure 13.14. Sketches of fossil arachnids (*above*) and insects (*below*) from Carboniferous strata of Illinois and Germany. (*Upper left*) A spiderlike arachnid. (*Upper right*) *Eoscorpius*, a primitive scorpion. (*Lower left*) A cockroach. (*Lower right*) Wing of a dragonflylike insect of order Orthoptera. All about natural size. [Redrawn from K. A. von Zittel (1900), *Text-Book of Paleontology*, vol. 1, London, Macmillan and Co., pp. 679–684.]

## RISE OF THE VERTEBRATES

Origin of the vertebrates is obscure—there is no fossil record preceding the occurrence of fishes in the late Ordovician time. From that point on, the record is clear for the evolutionary succession from fishes to amphibians, then to reptiles and birds, and finally mammals. By Silurian time fishes with thick bony armor were well developed and included both bottom-scavengers and carnivorous types. Both the sharks and the bony fishes evolved from these early armored fishes before the close of the Devonian Period (see Figure 13.18).

Transition from fishes to land animals began with fishes having lobelike fins containing muscles and articulated bones outside the body. These fishes must have entered the freshwater environment and developed the capacity to breathe air by means of lungs. The modern lungfish retains this capacity and by resorting to air breathing survives the drying up of streams and lakes in the tropical climates having alternate wet and dry seasons. The fossil record shows that a group of lobe-finned fishes developed the capacity to move about on land through the modification of fins into stubby legs (Figure 13.15). Thus there emerged in late Devonian time an amphibian which became the dominant land vertebrate in the ensuing Carboniferous Period. These animals, which resembled a modern alligator, had representatives up to several feet in length. They probably spent much of their time in or near water and were inhabitants of the great swamp forests. The early amphibians declined rapidly in the Permian Period and became extinct early in the Mesozoic Era.

The first reptiles had evolved from amphibians during the Carboniferous Period and by late in that period were competing strongly with the amphibians for the terrestrial environment. Reptiles had developed the capacity to lay eggs with protective shells which could be hatched on dry land. Thus freed from dependence upon water bodies, the reptiles enjoyed an expanded environment.

An almost explosive evolutionary radiation of reptiles is a particularly outstanding feature of the Permian Period. These earliest reptiles have been called the *stem reptiles* because all other reptiles evolved from them. They were heavy-limbed alligatorlike creatures and attained lengths of several feet (Figure 13.16). Early in their history the stem reptiles gave rise to half a dozen reptile groups. Of these only one group, the *mammal-like reptiles*, achieved

Figure 13.15. Transition to the land. (*Left*) Lobe-finned fish, crossoptygerians of Devonian time, try the terrestrial environment. (*Right*) Labyrinthodont amphibians have made the transition. (Painted by F. L. Jaques under direction of William K. Gregory. Photographs by courtesy of American Museum of Natural History.)

dominance in the Permian. They made the transition into the Mesozoic Era, although with serious depletions, and declined rapidly in the Triassic Period. We shall have more to say about these reptiles in the chapter to follow.

A mammal-like reptile from southern Africa has also been found in the Permian strata of northern Russia, showing that routes of land migration existed between Africa and Eurasia. Under the hypothesis of united continents of Laurasia and Gondwana, this migration would be expected, and a free interchange of reptile faunas could continue well into the Mesozoic Era.

## POLAR WANDERING AND A GREAT GLACIATION

Some highly important independent evidence bearing on environmental changes of late Paleozoic time is based upon paleomagnetism, making use of principles of rock magnetism

Figure 13.16. Reconstruction of the skeleton of *Diadectes,* a representative cotylosaur from the Permian of Texas. Length about 6 ft (2 m). [From E. H. Colbert (1955), *Evolution of the Verte-brates,* New York, John Wiley & Sons, p. 113, Figure 36D.]

already explained in Chapter 9 in connection with the subject of reversals of magnetic polarity.

Recall that lavas, upon cooling, retain permanent residual magnetism with respect to the lines of force of the earth's magnetic field prevailing at the time of cooling. If undisturbed rocks are subject to analysis of magnetic declination and inclination, the position of the earth's magnetic pole at the time of rock formation can be ascertained within a small radius of error (on the order of a circle with radius 5° of latitude arc). The method can also be used on sedimentary rocks, such as sandstones and shales. Pole positions have now been determined at many places and for all major divisions of geologic time from Precambrian through Cenozoic.

For a given continent, the successive pole positions throughout geologic time form a curved line, or *pole path,* that travels over the scope of an entire hemisphere. Figure 13.17 shows the pole path inferred for the Gondwana continental cluster from Devonian through Permian time.

Now, it is generally agreed that the earth's dipolar magnetic field has always been closely related to the earth's axis of rotation, hence that the magnetic north pole throughout the geologic past has been approximately equivalent to a geographic pole of rotation. We can assume that the earth's axis of rotation has remained fixed in space (subject, of course, to

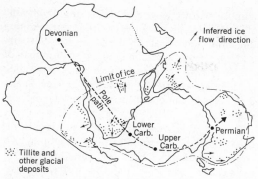

Figure 13.17. Hypothetical restoration of the nested continents of Gondwanaland. Location of tillites and other glacial deposits of upper Carboniferous time, together with inferred directions of ice motion and limit of a single great ice sheet, are as postulated by A. L. Du Toit in 1937. [Outlines of continents from A. G. Smith and A. Hallam (1970), *Nature*, vol. 224; path of pole wandering from M. W. McElhinny and G. R. Luck (1970), *Science*, vol. 168, p. 831, Figure 1.]

its processional motion). Therefore we should not consider the pole as wandering, but rather that the continent moves over the rotating globe, changing its latitude and longitude with respect to the axis of earth rotation.

One interpretation of a pole path such as that shown in Figure 13.17 is that the entire rigid lithosphere of the earth has slowly rotated over the weak asthenosphere beneath. This motion, known as *polar wandering,* must affect all surface points over the globe in exactly the same manner. Polar wandering can be attributed to changes in distribution of mass over the earth's surface. For example, the formation of a large icecap upon a continent would upset the equilibrium of rotation and might set off polar wandering to a new position of equilibrium.

Figure 13.17 shows the pole path as passing across Antarctica in upper Carboniferous time. A large, pole-centered landmass is, of course, ideally situated for the development of an ice sheet, as exemplified in modern Antarctica. There are unmistakable evidences of glaciation in late Carboniferous time in South America, southern Africa, India, and Australia. Grooved and scored rock surfaces underlie thick *tillites,* which are lithified glacial deposits of unsorted bouldery debris. Other sediments associated with glaciation are also found in conjunction with the tillites. Part of the geological evidence for a single continent rests upon the need for a much larger landmass than presently exists in the widely separated continental shield fragments. The glacial deposits range in age from

late Carboniferous into early Permian time. Overlying the tillites are terrestrial sedimentary strata, including coal-bearing formations. Distinctive and specialized plants of genus *Glossopteris* and genus *Gangamopteris* are found as fossils in these sedimentary strata. According to those who support the hypothesis of a single continent, the simultaneous development of these plants on widely separated continents would have been an impossibility.

Returning to the question of atmospheric evolution, Figure 13.11 shows the oxygen level as falling to a low point in late Carboniferous and early Permian time. This drop is postulated on the assumption that during the glaciation of that time the cold temperatures would have inhibited plant growth, at least in large areas of the continents, and would have resulted in reduced oxygen production by photosynthesis. After glaciation, the oxygen level is considered to have returned to a value close to that of the present.

## CHANGING ENVIRONMENTS AT THE CLOSE OF AN ERA

It was noted earlier in this chapter that a favorite theory held by geologists was that orogeny should be synchronous, occurring at the end of each era. Thus the *Appalachian orogeny* (*Hercynian orogeny*) which deformed Paleozoic strata of the Appalachian region has usually been assigned the position of a terminal event in the Paleozoic Era (Table 13.1).

Because the strata involved in that deformation are no older than of lower Permian age, orogeny may well have begun in the Appalachian belt by the middle of that period. In unconformities elsewhere in North America there is indisputable evidence that orogeny occurred in late Carboniferous time. Intense folding and overthrusting of geosynclinal strata occurred in the western and south-central United States and there was block faulting in the Maritime Provinces of Canada. Thus we find that crustal unrest in one place or another extended over all of the closing 70 to 80 m.y. of the Paleozoic Era.

Environments of sediment deposition in the Permian Period reflect this crustal unrest, for the continents stood comparatively high and terrestrial sediments are widespread. Permian strata are widespread over North America, Europe, and Asia. Two distinctly different environments are represented by these strata. Red strata with thick layers of evaporite minerals (such as gypsum and halite) in the Central

United States, Russia, and other localities suggest that there were large areas of arid climate. Occurrence of coal beds in the Appalachians, Siberia, and Manchuria indicate that other regions had warm moist climates. On the whole, however, there was an abundance of terrestrial environments in the Permian Period. Red strata containing fossils of land animals and plants were probably deposited on deltaic plains and flood plains. While these land environments fostered an almost explosive evolutionary radiation of the reptiles, the restriction of seas must have been highly unfavorable for many forms of marine life, for one of the great animal extinctions of geologic time occurred during the Permian.

Among the invertebrates a decline in abundances of many groups is striking. Approximately half of the invertebrate families present in the Permian Period became extinct and failed to make the transition into the Triassic Period which followed. The trilobites underwent total extinction along with several orders of corals, crinoids, bryozoans, and brachiopods. New groups which expanded in the early Mesozoic make up most of the modern invertebrates.

Permian time saw the extinction of the armored fishes and a sharp decline in the sharks. In contrast, the bony fishes underwent an expansion as Permian time gave way to Triassic time.

The evolutionary trends of the land plants do not seem to reflect the crisis that was so strongly felt by the marine invertebrates for their transition into the Triassic Period is not marked by sharp changes.

## AN ERA IN REVIEW

The word *Paleozoic* comes from the Greek words for "ancient" and "animal life." Ancient as this life may seem, it is significant that most of the animal phyla of the modern world had developed at or near the start of the Paleozoic Era. In that sense, ancient and modern life are one. However, within those phyla most of the early groups became extinct and were replaced with new ones at one time or another in the geologic record. In that sense, Paleozoic life is truly ancient. The evolutionary process led to many mistakes in terms of long-term survival, yet an environment vacated by extinction of one group seems never to have remained vacant for long, and evolutionary radiation has never lagged far behind.

This chapter has attempted to provide only a glimpse of the processes and forms of organic evolution in a changing environment. Among the many details of historical geology left untold are the ever-changing distributions of lands and seas, geosynclines, and mountain belts. Nor have the orogenies within the Paleozoic been documented in sequence in time and place.

The next chapter will take us through the Mesozoic Era, the middle time of animal life, and the Cenozoic Era, the time of new or recent life. Although the life forms changed significantly throughout these eras, the basic evolutionary mechanisms acted as they did throughout the Paleozoic Era. However, the study of new life forms will give opportunity to look into further details of the evolutionary process.

## References for further study

Dunbar, C., and J. Rodgers (1957), *Principles of Stratigraphy,* New York, Wiley, 356 pp.

Kay, M., and E. H. Colbert (1965), *Stratigraphy and Life History,* New York, Wiley, 736 pp.

Blum, H. F. (1968), *Time's Arrow and Evolution,* Princeton, N.J., Princeton Univ. Press, 232 pp.

Laporte, L. F. (1968), *Ancient Environments,* Englewood Cliffs, N.J., Prentice-Hall, 115 pp.

McAlester, A. L. (1968), *The History of Life,* Englewood Cliffs, N.J., Prentice-Hall, 151 pp.

Dunbar, C. O., and K. M. Waage (1969), *Historical Geology,* 3rd ed., New York, Wiley, 556 pp.

Strahler, A. N. (1971), *The Earth Sciences,* 2nd ed., New York, Harper & Row, 826 pp., chaps. 28, 29.

## Review questions

1. Name the eras of abundant life. What does each name signify? How long did each era last? Distinguish between the Cryptozoic Eon and the Phanerozoic Eon. What are periods of geologic time? What is the average length of a period? How many periods fall within each era?

2. What is stratigraphy? What scientific approach is used in the study of stratigraphy? Describe the principle of superposition and explain how it is used. Discuss the question of rates of deposition and durations of periods of non-deposition as interpreted from strata. Use Grand Canyon strata as examples. How are changes of crustal level and sea level factors in determining the stratigraphic sequence? What is a disconformity? What is the principle of continuity?

3. What is a fossil? How were fossils first used in the study of stratigraphy? How do fossils serve as guides to ages of strata and to correla-

tion of strata? What forms do fossils take and how are they preserved? Give examples.

4. What is the principle of organic evolution as applied to fossils? What is an index fossil? Why is a fossil fauna more useful than a single fossil in stratigraphic research? What is the principle of succession of faunas? How do fossils provide information on paleogeography?

5. What is an unconformity? How does it differ from a disconformity? Describe an unconformity exposed in Grand Canyon and give the geologic history leading to its development.

6. How can radiometric age determinations be used to establish absolute ages for geologic periods and events? Show by means of a simple diagram. How can an orogeny be dated? Did orogenies occur at the close of each era and period in the geologic record?

7. How are life forms classified? Distinguish between plants and animals on the basis of structure and function. Distinguish between photosynthesis and animal respiration.

8. What are phyla? Describe a number of important phyla of the plant kingdom. What two phyla include the land plants? What is a vascular system, and what function does it perform?

9. Distinguish between Protozoa and Metazoa. What are the invertebrates? Compare them with the vertebrates. Name several of the important animal phyla and list representative groups, using common names.

10. Review the important concepts in the process of organic evolution. What is the role of acquired characteristics? What roles do recombination and mutation play in the evolution process? How can the characteristics of a population change? Explain how natural selection guides the course of evolution of a species. Can two species reunite to form a single species? Explain.

11. Describe the continental masses of the earth at the start of the Paleozoic Era. What was Gondwana? Laurasia? Pangaea? What significance would a single world-continent have in terms of organic evolution?

12. Describe environmental conditions at the start of the Paleozoic Era. What was the level of atmospheric oxygen at this time? Describe the appearance of land surfaces. Where were environments favorable to existence of life forms?

13. Discuss the problem of the apparent sudden appearance of the Metazoa in lower Cambrian time. What explanations are proposed? What kinds of invertebrates were present at the start of Cambrian time? From the evolutionary standpoint, what is the significant feature of the composition of invertebrate faunas of lower Cambrian time?

14. What is meant by evolutionary radiation? Illustrate with a description of invertebrate evolution in the lower Paleozoic. What is evolutionary extinction? Illustrate with an example from the Paleozoic Era. What may have been some of the causes of extinctions?

15. Describe the spread of life to the lands. When did it occur? What environmental problems were involved and how were they met? What role may atmospheric oxygen have played in transition of life to the lands?

16. Describe the evolution of the land plants. How did vascular plants meet the needs of a land environment? Into what two groups are the vascular plants divided? Describe forests of the Devonian and Carboniferous periods. Of what classes of seed-bearing plants were they composed?

17. What climate prevailed in Carboniferous time? Describe the conditions of formation of peat and coal of this period. What invertebrate phyla became air-breathing animals at this time?

18. Review the steps in evolution of the vertebrates during Paleozoic time. How was the transition to the land made by vertebrates? What advantage did the reptiles have over the amphibians? Describe the stem reptiles. How does the distribution of mammal-like reptiles relate to the hypothesis of continental drift?

19. What is the pole path, and how does it change throughout geologic time? What is polar wandering? Distinguish polar wandering from continental separation. What is the evidence of glaciation of late Carboniferous time? Discuss the possible variations in atmospheric oxygen levels in the latter half of the Paleozoic Era.

20. Describe the Appalachian orogeny. When did it begin? What geologic environments were widespread in Permian time? What kinds of sedimentary deposits are related to these environments? What was the impact of Permian environments upon various animal and plant groups? What were the important extinctions of this time?

21. Summarize the major evolutionary trends and events of the Paleozoic Era. What major concepts of organic evolution are illustrated? What were the major steps in evolution of the physical environment during Paleozoic time? Link these changes with organic evolution.

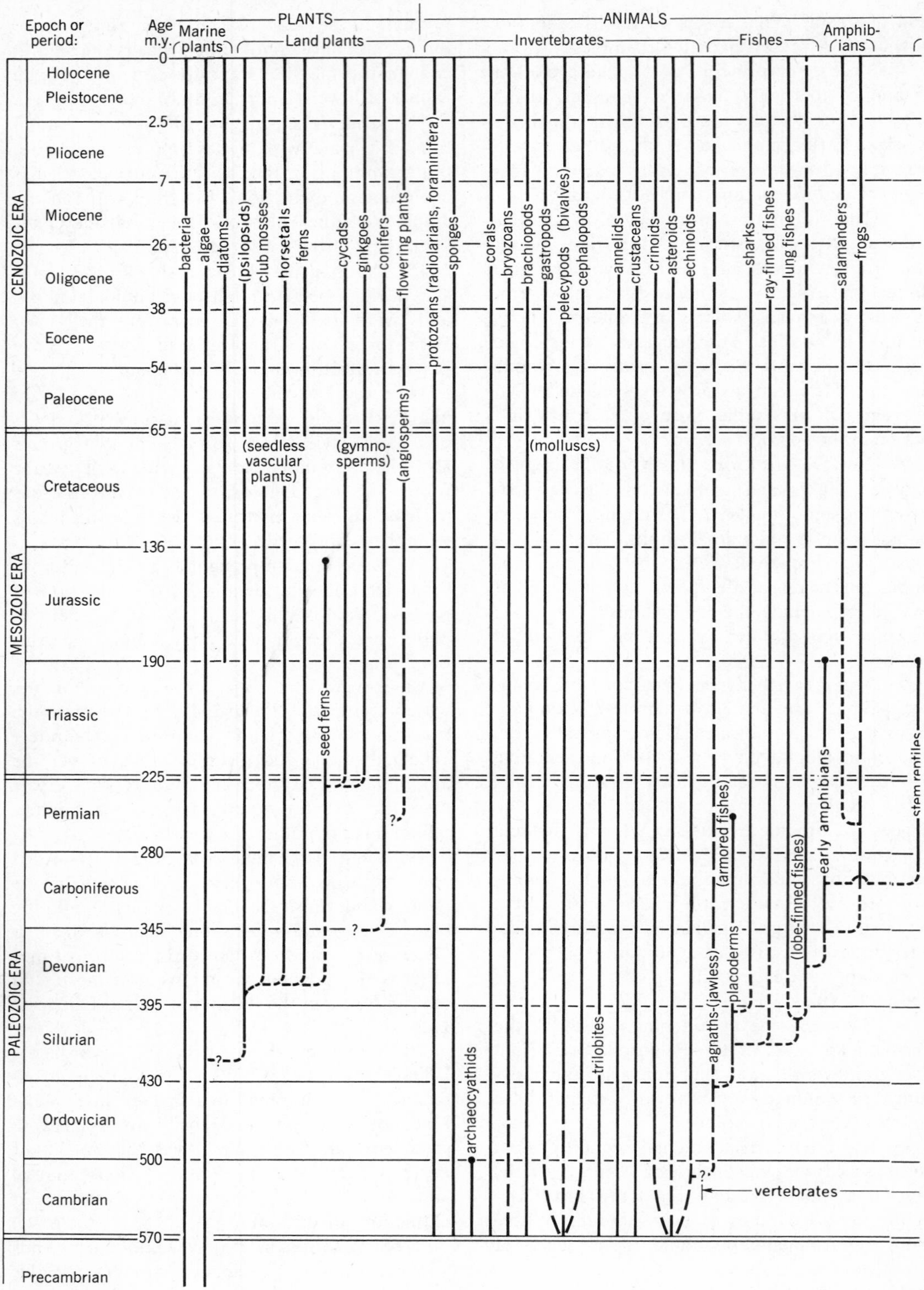
PLANTS
ANIMALS
Epoch or period:
Age m.y.
Marine plants
Land plants
Invertebrates
Fishes
Amphibians
CENOZOIC ERA
MESOZOIC ERA
PALEOZOIC ERA
Holocene
Pleistocene
Pliocene
Miocene
Oligocene
Eocene
Paleocene
Cretaceous
Jurassic
Triassic
Permian
Carboniferous
Devonian
Silurian
Ordovician
Cambrian
Precambrian
0
2.5
7
26
38
54
65
136
190
225
280
345
395
430
500
570
bacteria
algae
diatoms
(psilopsids)
club mosses
horsetails
ferns
cycads
ginkgoes
conifers
flowering plants
(angiosperms)
(seedless vascular plants)
(gymnosperms)
seed ferns
protozoans (radiolarians, foraminifera)
sponges
corals
bryozoans
brachiopods
gastropods
pelecypods (bivalves)
cephalopods
(molluscs)
annelids
crustaceans
crinoids
asteroids
echinoids
archaeocyathids
trilobites
agnaths-(jawless)
(armored fishes)
placoderms
sharks
ray-finned fishes
lung fishes
(lobe-finned fishes)
early amphibians
salamanders
frogs
stem reptiles
vertebrates
?

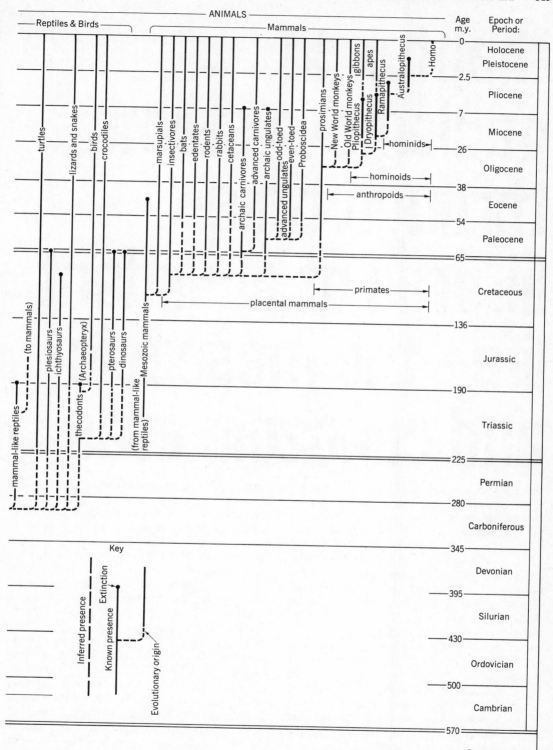

Figure 13.18. Summary chart of the evolution of major plant and animal groups from Cambrian time to present. [Based on data of A. L. McAlester (1968), *The History of Life,* Englewood Cliffs, N.J., Prentice-Hall, 151 pp.]

# chapter 14
# geologic systems through time:
# iii. eras of abundant life—the mesozoic and cenozoic eras

The era of middle life, the Mesozoic Era, offers many lessons of life adaptation to environmental opportunities as well as of survival failures. Because the Mesozoic Era saw both the rise and fall of several reptilian groups, including species of enormous individuals with almost unbelievable conformations, this era has been aptly subtitled the *Age of Reptiles*. Yet, almost equally dramatic evolutionary radiations and extinctions are to be found among the land plants and the marine invertebrates. If we are to accept the hypothesis of continental drift, the Mesozoic Era represents the time of fragmentation of the continents. We must look for effects of that event upon organisms incapable of crossing deep ocean basins.

The Mesozoic Era spans 160 million years (m.y.) and includes the Triassic, Jurassic, and Cretaceous periods (see Figure 13.18).

## EVOLUTION IN THE TRIASSIC PERIOD

As stated in the preceding chapter, the important mammal-like reptiles that dominated reptilian life of Permian time sustained heavy losses by extinctions at the close of that period. Nevertheless, many of these reptile forms persisted into the Triassic. Among the most interesting of the mammal-like reptiles was the genus *Lystrosaurus,* a small animal, somewhat resembling a hippopotamus, with massive wide-set legs (Figure 14.1). Fossil remains of *Lystrosaurus* are abundant in Triassic strata of southern Africa and are also found in India, Russia, and China. Search for *Lystrosaurus* fossils in Triassic rocks of Antarctica was intensified in view of increasing support for continental drift, since it is considered almost an impossibility for this animal to have migrated to Antarctica across the broad and deep ocean basin that now separates Antarctica from all other continents. The search met with success in 1969 when remains of *Lystrosaurus* were found in the Transantarctic Mountains, about 400 mi (640 km) from the south pole. The fossil find was hailed as one of the most significant in modern times, for it throws paleonto-

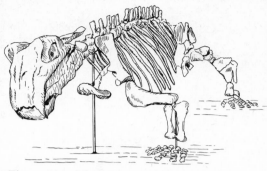

Figure 14.1. Mounted partial skeleton of *Lystrosaurus,* a mammal-like reptile of Triassic age, about 3 ft (1 m) long. (Sketched from a photograph by A. W. Crompton.)

logic evidence strongly in favor of the existence of a unified single continent of Gondwana as late as the Triassic Period.

More important from the standpoint of evolutionary radiation was the emergence in Triassic time of several important reptile groups that were to dominate the Mesozoic Era. Evolving from the stem reptiles of the Permian Period (see Chapter 13) were turtles, lizards and snakes, and two groups of marine reptiles now extinct, the *plesiosaurs* and the *ichthyosaurs* (see Figure 13.18). Turtles, quite similar to those of today, entered the scene in the Triassic Period and persisted steadily through all succeeding time. Their success is attributed to an effective protective shell, to aquatic habits, and to being omnivorous. Lizards do not appear until the upper Triassic, and they are rarely preserved as fossils. The snakes are believed to have evolved from the lizards but are not found as fossils until late in Mesozoic time.

The large carnivorous marine reptiles are particularly interesting, since they bear some superficial resemblance to whales (which are mammals) and can be thought of as having occupied an equivalent evolutionary niche. Like the whales of much later time, the plesiosaurs and ichthyosaurs returned from the land to the sea. Both were predatory animals that lived mostly on fish. The plesiosaurs were long-necked creatures with bulbous bodies and paddlelike fins (Figure 14.2). These animals reached lengths up to 50 ft (15 m). The ichthyosaurs outwardly resembled whales or dolphins but had narrow, sharply pointed jaws (Figure 14.2).

Lastly, of the reptile groups that arose from the stem reptiles, we come to the *thecodonts,* which had evolved as small animals in the Triassic Period. The thecodonts had achieved a major evolutionary advantage by acquiring good running legs. Their limbs, instead of spreading outward, projected down, directly beneath the body. In some thecodonts the hind legs took over the running function, becoming greatly enlarged. Simultaneously the forelegs became smaller and could easily be held off the ground, developing new functions such as grasping, clawing, and holding (Figure 14.3). These bipeds were to become the ancestors of the *ruling reptiles* (dinosaurs, flying reptiles, crocodiles) and birds. By late Triassic time there had evolved small predatory bipedal dinosaurs, whose agility enabled them to prey upon more sluggish reptiles and other animals.

Almost everyone is familiar with the appearance of several varieties of the great dinosaurs of Jurassic and Cretaceous times. The word *dinosaur,* a popular term, means "terrible lizard." Dinosaurs evolved in Triassic time

Figure 14.2. Reconstruction of plesiosaurs and ichthyosaurs. (From a painting by C. R. Knight; photograph by courtesy of American Museum of Natural History.)

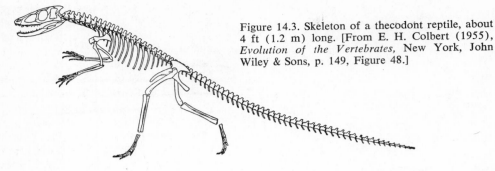

Figure 14.3. Skeleton of a thecodont reptile, about 4 ft (1.2 m) long. [From E. H. Colbert (1955), *Evolution of the Vertebrates,* New York, John Wiley & Sons, p. 149, Figure 48.]

from the thecodont reptiles (see Figure 13.18) and include both carnivores and herbivores. An example of the carnivorous dinosaurs is *Tyrannosaurus,* the largest terrestrial predator of any time. Possessing a huge head and fiercely armed jaws, this three-toed dinosaur reached a length of 50 ft (15 m) and stood 18 ft (5.5 m) high (Figure 14.4). Other dinosaurs reverted to the quadripedal stance and a herbivorous diet. They became huge animals like *Brontosaurus* (Figure 14.5). Perhaps sluggish in moving about, they may have had to seek safety in rivers and lakes. Other herbivorous forms developed a bony armor for protection. *Triceratops,* the example shown in Figure 14.4, had two long, vicious horns.

While the dinosaurs have drawn first attention among the reptiles of the Mesozoic, other groups are equally interesting. The marine reptiles have been discussed in earlier paragraphs. Another reptile group of much interest is the *pterosaurs,* winged batlike animals of the Jurassic and Cretaceous periods. The example shown in Figure 14.6 had a wingspread of 20 ft (6 m) and was probably a gliding and soaring animal. The wings were formed of a thin membrane of skin supported by bones of a single elongated finger.

Probably the most celebrated of all fossil finds is the remarkably preserved skeleton and feathers of the first known bird, *Archaeopteryx* (Figure 14.7). This animal was found in Bavaria enclosed in fine-grained lithographic limestone of Jurassic age. Predecessors of this highly developed animal are unknown, since the preservation of a bird as a fossil is an unlikely event. These first birds are thought to have evolved from the thecodonts and retain many of the characteristics of those reptiles. The Jurassic birds have teeth and their skeletal structure is like that of the small reptiles. Unlike reptiles, however, birds today are warm-blooded animals. When the transition to the warm-blooded state was made is not known, but it must have been a great advantage in adapting to life in cold climates.

## APPEARANCE OF THE MAMMALS

An evolutionary event of great significance is the appearance in the Jurassic Period of the primitive mammals. These had arisen from the mammal-like reptiles, which were abundant in

Figure 14.4. *Tyrannosaurus* (*right*) confronting *Triceratops* (*left*). (Restoration of a late Cretaceous landscape by C. R. Knight; courtesy of Field Museum of Natural History.)

Figure 14.5. Reconstruction of *Brontosaurus,* a herbivorous dinosaur of Jurassic age. Its overall length reached about 65 ft (20 m). (From a painting by C. R. Knight; courtesy of Field Museum of Natural History.)

Figure 14.6. Pterosaurs, gliding and soaring from marine cliffs, are shown in this restoration of a scene from the Cretaceous period. (Mural painting by Constantin Astori; courtesy of American Museum of Natural History.)

the Triassic Period (see Figure 13.18). Mammals are distinct from reptiles in several respects. First, the young of mammals are born live—the mammalian egg is fertilized within the female body and there attains an advanced state of development before entering a hostile environment. Along with this form of reproduction, the mammal possesses milk glands to provide food for the young after birth. Second, the mammals are warm-blooded. They not only can generate heat but can also reduce body temperatures below that of the surrounding air by means of evaporation. When provided with an insulating coat of hair, mammals can adapt to life under extremely cold conditions, as can the birds. Reptiles are cold-blooded animals, which is to say that they lack a body-heating mechanism and take on the temperatures of the surrounding air or water. Consequently, reptiles require warm climates, or climates with a warm season. Reptile growth continues throughout the life of the individual, whereas a mammal quickly matures to a fixed size, which it maintains.

Paleontologists distinguish the early mammals from the mammal-like reptiles on the basis of jaw and tooth structures. Mammal teeth developed specialized functions, including sharp incisors at the front and massive molars for grinding at the back (Figure 14.8). By late Cretaceous time two new orders of mammals had arisen: the marsupials and the insectivores. *Marsupials* are pouch-bearing mammals, of which the kangaroo and opossum are modern survivors. *Insectivores,* represented today by the moles and shrews, were later to give rise to

Figure 14.7. Drawing of a fossil of the earliest known bird, *Archaeopteryx*. A skeleton and impressions of the feathers were preserved in this rare specimen from the Solenhofen limestone of Jurassic age in Bavaria. The drawing is somewhat less than one-third natural size. Figure 14.9*A* shows reconstructions of this bird in its natural habitat. [From E. H. Colbert (1955), *Evolution of the Vertebrates,* New York, John Wiley & Sons, p. 177, Figure 57.]

the *placental mammals,* which underwent a phenomenal evolutionary radiation in the Cenozoic Era. The Mesozoic Era was, however, the initial period of evolutionary experimentation for the mammals, just as the Cambrian was the period of experimentation for the marine invertebrates.

## PLANT EVOLUTION THROUGH THE MESOZOIC ERA

Plant life underwent major evolutionary changes in the Triassic Period, setting the pattern for all of the remaining Mesozoic Era (see

Figure 13.18). Among the gymnosperms, the *cycads* and *ginkgoes* had arisen from the seed ferns and showed rapid evolutionary radiation in Triassic time. The cycads were palmlike in appearance, although they are not related to true palms. The ginkgoes were straight-trunked trees with fanlike leaves (Figure 14.9). Representatives of both cycads and ginkgoes survived through to the present, although most became extinct at the close of the Mesozoic Era. Silicified logs found in Triassic strata of the Petrified Forest of Arizona have been identified as *conifers* (Figure 14.10). Specimens up to 100 ft (30 m) long and 10 ft (3 m) in basal diameter have been found, attesting to the noble stature of these conifers of Triassic forests.

Equally significant to the development of early mammals in the late Cretaceous time was the sudden and explosive evolutionary radiation of the *angiosperms,* those flowering plants with covered seeds (see Figure 13.18). They succeeded the gymnosperms, or plants with naked seeds, which were the dominant vascular plants of the Mesozoic Era. The reproduction of the gymnosperms takes place through the dispersion by wind of embryonic seeds and pollen grains carrying the sperm. Union of a pollen grain with an embryonic seed allows fertilization to take place at some point on the ground far removed from the parent plant. Obviously, this mechanism has the disadvantage that the fertilization process takes place in unprotected surroundings, while the dispersal and union of spores and embryonic seeds depends upon the random actions of the wind.

In the angiosperms, pollen fertilizes an embryonic seed held within the base of the flower, producing a mature seed attached to the parent plant until it is ready to be dropped to the ground. Birds or insects, attracted to the flower, carry out the pollination process, which thus has a higher degree of reliability than in the case of the wind-transport of pollen. Enclosure of the angiosperm seed in a fleshy fruit attractive to birds as food further aids in the dispersal of the seeds over long distances.

Perhaps as a result of these advances in seed fertilization and dispersal, the angiosperms underwent a phenomenal evolutionary radiation at the very end of the Mesozoic Era, so that when the Cenozoic Era began the angiosperms had already replaced the gymnosperms as the dominant vascular land plants. As the Cretaceous Period drew to a close, the cycads

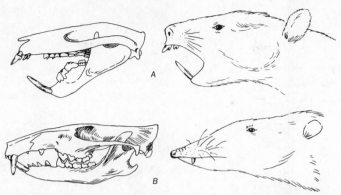

Figure 14.8. Mesozoic mammals—skulls and restoration of heads, about natural size. (*A*) A multituberculate mammal of the Jurassic Period. (*B*) A shrewlike insectivore of Cretaceous age. [After C. O. Dunbar and K. M. Waage (1969), *Historical Geology,* 3rd ed., New York, John Wiley & Sons, p. 365, Figure 15-20, and p. 395, Figure 16-24.]

and ginkgoes suffered a great decline. Of the gymnosperms, only the conifers persisted into the Cenozoic Era in abundance. The ferns also made this transition in abundance.

## RIFTING OF CONTINENTS IN THE MESOZOIC ERA

Under the hypothesis of continental drift the breakup of Pangaea, the world-continent including both Gondwana and Eurasia, began in Triassic time. Figure 14.11 shows a modern interpretation of the progress of continental fragmentation. A rift grew in Triassic time between Laurasia and Gondwana, while Gondwana itself began to break apart on rifts between Africa and India, and between India and Antarctica. Africa and South America remained in close contact through the Jurassic Period, but by the end of Cretaceous time these continents had separated widely to produce the South Atlantic Ocean basin. Notice that Africa and Eurasia retained contact at least at some points, through the entire Mesozoic as did North America and Eurasia with Greenland wedged between. The free migration of land animals and plants through three large continents was thus assured until Cenozoic time.

## EXTINCTIONS AT THE CLOSE OF THE CRETACEOUS PERIOD

Cretaceous time saw the culmination of the dinosaurs, along with marine reptiles, crocodiles, turtles, lizards, snakes, and flying reptiles. The close of the Cretaceous Period is marked by great extinctions, of which the total disappearance of all dinosaurs is the most cele-

brated (Figure 13.18). The large marine reptiles (not including the turtles) and flying reptiles also suffered total extinction. One important group of invertebrates, the *ammonites* (represented by today's *chambered nautilus*), became almost totally extinct at this point in time. Extinctions also affected certain groups of pelecypods and cephalopods other than the ammonites. Yet other animal groups successfully made the transition into the Cenozoic Era and some reflect no special evolutionary crisis at this time.

Cause or causes of the great extinctions continue to be a matter of scientific speculation. Onset of unfavorable heat and moisture environments on land through orogeny and the reduction in areas of shallow seas offer no specific causes that might act selectively upon one animal group but not upon another. Bursts of high-energy radiation from the sun or a passing star, disease epidemics, and disruption of the food chain by destruction of one-celled planktonic organisms are mechanisms of extinction that have been suggested for consideration. The fossil record itself has yielded no direct evidence bearing on the cause of extinction of a given species or genus. Perhaps new findings of geochemistry and geophysics will shed some light on this problem.

## THE CENOZOIC ERA

The Cenozoic Era, or era of "recent life," consists of only 65 m.y. of geologic time, whereas the Cretaceous Period which preceded it had a duration of 70 m.y. (see Table 13.1). The combined nine periods of Mesozoic and

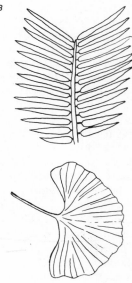

Figure 14.9. Gymnosperms of the Mesozoic Era. (*A*) Reconstruction of cycads of the Jurassic Period. Scene includes bipedal reptiles (*lower left*), primitive birds (*center*), and flying reptiles (*upper part*). (Painting by C. R. Knight; courtesy of the Field Museum of Natural History.) (*B*) Sketch of a fossil leaf of a Mesozoic cycad (*above*), and of a modern ginkgo leaf (*below*).

Paleozoic eras average about 62 m.y. each, which is close to the duration of the entire Cenozoic Era. Yet, because the geologic record is present in more completeness of detail as time approaches the present, the Cenozoic Era does not lack for a rich history. Much of the record of life of the Cenozoic Era is a familiar one, dominated as it is by mammals, seed-bearing plants, and invertebrate animals similar to those living today. At the same time, there were many animals, Cenozoic mammals in particular, that would seem quite bizarre if we were to encounter them on the modern landscape.

As shown in Table 14.1, the Cenozoic Era is divided directly into seven *epochs* of geologic time, omitting the designation of any period.* The syllable *cene* found in all epoch names and also in the first syllable of Cenozoic, comes from the Greek *kainos,* meaning "recent."

* Classical terminology considers the first five epochs to constitute the *Tertiary Period;* the final two to constitute the *Quaternary Period.*

The history of the Cenozoic Era was first deciphered from fossil assemblages within a series of superimposed strata in the regions surrounding London and Paris. (The English Channel cuts through what would otherwise be a single geological province.) It was soon recognized that among the invertebrate faunas of this stratigraphic column the percentages of species living today increased from low values near the base to a high proportion near the top.

Table 14.1.   EPOCHS OF THE CENOZOIC
ERA

| Epoch | Duration (m.y.) | Age (m.y.) |
|---|---|---|
| | | 0 |
| Holocene (recent) | | |
| | | (11,000 yr) |
| Pleistocene | 2 | |
| | | 2 |
| Pliocene | 11 | |
| | | 13 |
| Miocene | 12 | |
| | | 25 |
| Oligocene | 11 | |
| | | 36 |
| Eocene | 22 | |
| | | 58 |
| Paleocene | 7 | |
| | | 65 |
| (Cretaceous Period) | | |

Source: Ages from C. O. Dunbar and K. M. Waage
(1969), *Historical Geology*, New York, Wiley, Figure
17–2.

A French paleontologist had made detailed
studies of the faunas and had identified about
5000 species in the column, of which about
3000 species are now extinct. Based upon this
information, the English geologist Sir Charles
Lyell proposed in 1839 the following names
and definitions for three epochs:

| Epoch | Percentage of Species Now Living |
|---|---|
| Pliocene ("more recent") | 30–50 |
| Miocene ("less recent") | about 16 |
| Eocene ("dawn of recent") | about 3.5 |

Figure 14.10. Fragments of fossil (silicified) tree
trunks from the Chinle formation of Triassic age,
Petrified Forest National Monument, Arizona.
These logs are about 2 ft (0.6 m) in diameter.
(Photograph by U.S. Geological Survey.)

Subsequent study led to the insertion of the
Oligocene Epoch into this sequence and the
addition of a Paleocene Epoch at the base to
replace a part of the original Eocene. The
Pleistocene Epoch, replacing what was originally the upper part of the Pliocene, is essentially equivalent to the time of widespread
glaciations, the last of which ended about
−10,000 to −12,000 yr. Considerable difference of opinion exists as to the placing of a date
upon the Pliocene-Pleistocene time boundary;
figures range from 1 m.y. to 2.5 m.y. for this
boundary. The Holocene Epoch is, by definition, the brief interval from the end of the
Pleistocene Epoch to the present.

As the Cenozoic Era began, most of the
present continent of North America was land
and was to remain so throughout the entire era.
Two zones of marine sedimentation were, however, of major importance from the beginning
of the era. Largest of these was the continental
margin from Yucatan to Florida, almost surrounding the Gulf of Mexico. Here a geosyncline persisted and deepened. Today the
uplifted Cenozoic and Cretaceous strata of the
Gulf Coast and Atlantic Coast constitute the
Coastal Plain geologic province.

A second zone of important marine deposition lay along the western coast of the continent. Deep but narrow basins in California
received great thicknesses of detrital sediment
throughout the Cenozoic Era. For example, in
what is now the Great Valley of California a
thickness of over 16,000 ft (5 km) of shales
and sandstones was deposited in a narrow
geosyncline.

Over much of the Rocky Mountain region
and Great Plains mountains had been raised in
the *Laramian orogeny* at the close of he
Cretaceous Period (Table 13.1). The highlands
were furnishing detritus to streams that flowed
into intermontane basins and also eastward
over the Great Plains, depositing continental
sediments during much of Cenozoic time.
These strata are of particular interest because
they contain the fossil remains of land animals
and plants of the era.

In what is now the Alps region of southern
Europe, thick accumulations of detrital sediment were being laid down close to mountain
arcs raised in early Cenozoic time. Similar
developments were taking place in the sites of
the present Himalayan and Andean ranges and
elsewhere along the zone of primary mountain
arcs (see Chapter 10).

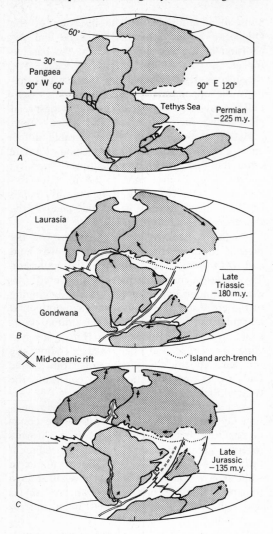

Mid-oceanic rift          Island arch-trench

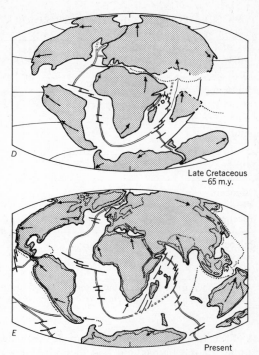

Figure 14.11. Five stages in the breakup of Pangaea to form the modern continents. Arrows indicate the directions of motion of lithospheric plates. The continents are delimited by the 1000-fathom (6000-ft; 1800-m) submarine contour in order to show the true extent of continental crust. [Redrawn and simplified from maps by R. S. Dietz and J. C. Holden (1970), *Jour. Geophys. Research,* vol. 75, pp. 4943–4951, Figures 2–6.]

pression between the Eurasia plate on the north and the Africa and India plates on the south.

## THE AGE OF MAMMALS

While the marine invertebrates have provided us with the means of subdividing the Cenozoic Era into epochs, it is the phenomenal rise of the mammals on land that makes the era unique.

The mammals which began this spectacular evolutionary radiation were not particularly prepossessing in any sense. They were small, long-tailed creatures with short legs and five-toed feet on which they walked flat-footed. The modern hedgehog has been cited as giving us a good example of the body shape and walking gait of these early mammals. Their brains were correspondingly small. Like the primitive mammals of the Jurassic and Cretaceous periods, from which they evolved, the early Cenozoic mammals had long pointed jaws.

Evolution among the groups of mammals

Under the hypothesis of continental drift, the Cenozoic zones of orogenic and volcanic activity, with associated basins of thick detrital sedimentation, represent the margins of lithospheric plates being crumpled against down-moving plates of oceanic crust (Figure 14.11E). The plate hypothesis explains why the eastern continental margins of the Americas were relatively stable throughout the Cenozoic Era, whereas the western margins, making up arcs of the circum-Pacific belt, were zones of almost continuous volcanic and orogenic activity during the same era. Here the America plate was being crumpled against the under-sliding Pacific plate.

The Eurasian-Melanesian orogenic belt, of which the Alps and Himalayas form segments, are interpreted as resulting from crustal com-

showed certain trends in common. Increase of size is very marked, along with a disproportionately large increase in brain size and hence in intelligence of several of the groups. Teeth have shown a high degree of specialization, the changes depending upon function. The principal divergence in tooth development has been into the high-crowned, deeply involuted teeth of the grazing herbivores, as contrasted with the sharply pointed or sharpened teeth of the carnivores, adapted to tearing and cutting of flesh. One of the most striking changes setting apart one mammal group from another has been in the feet and limbs. Grazing animals of the plains regions developed the capacity to rise up on one or two toes, which became elongated and strengthened, while the remaining digits disappeared. Thus equipped, these animals would run swiftly to escape from predators. Carnivores developed powerful sharp claws for slashing and holding their prey, while another mammal group developed long digits suited to tree climbing.

In this very limited review of the evolution of life forms we cannot begin to give a full picture of the Cenozoic history of mammals. Even the classification of mammals poses a formidable problem in itself. But by focusing attention upon a few evolutionary principles and trends we can at least gain some perspective about Man's place among his fellow mammals.

First, it is important to make a distinction between two groups of mammals, the *marsupials* and the *placental mammals*. Marsupials, or pouch-bearing mammals, give birth to very small immature young which must enter a pouch on the mother's abdomen. Here the offspring are suckled and grow to sufficient size to survive in the outside environment. Placental mammals retain the embryonic young in a fluid-filled membrane within the uterus where it can be nourished, until it attains an advanced state of development, through an umbilical tube receiving nutrients from a highly developed part, the *placenta,* of the membrane. This mechanism would seem to offer advantages in better protection of the young, although the marsupials have managed very well, as witness the kangaroo and opossum. Under competition, the placental mammals were the more successful in terms of evolutionary radiation and came to dominate the mammal world in all continents except Australia.

The placental mammals show an extreme diversification in terms of anatomical structure and adaptation to varied environments. Altogether 28 orders evolved during the Cenozoic Era, but 12 are now extinct. Table 14.2 gives common names of 11 of the living orders and representative animals. The remaining 5 orders, not listed, included rather rare and bizarre creatures, such as the sea cows, aardvarks, pangolins, and conies. Several extinct orders are grouped together under the title of the *archaic ungulates.* (Ungulates are hoofed animals.) The carnivores have been broken into two groups, the *advanced carnivores,* which include all living groups, and the *archaic carnivores,* all of which are extinct.

As the Paleocene Epoch opened, the marsupials and insectivores, both of which were important in the Cretaceous Period, were the two most important orders on the scene (see Figure 13.18). Their predecessors, the Mesozoic mammals, survived through the Paleocene Epoch but became extinct shortly thereafter.

Table 14.2.  PRINCIPAL ORDERS OF PLACENTAL MAMMALS

| Common Name of Order | Representatives |
| --- | --- |
| Insectivores | Shrews, moles, hedgehogs |
| Bats | |
| Edentates | Anteaters, sloths, armadillos |
| Primates | Lemurs, tarsiers, monkeys, apes, Man |
| Rodents | Squirrels, beavers, mice and rats, porcupines, chinchillas |
| Lagomorphs | Rabbits, hares |
| Cetaceans | Whales, porpoises, dolphins |
| Archaic carnivores (extinct) | Credodonts |
| Advanced carnivores | Dogs, wolves and foxes, bears, pandas, raccoons, weasels, mink, otters, wolverines, badgers, skunks, civets, cats, sea lions, seals, walruses |
| Archaic ungulates | Mostly hoof-bearing herbivores (extinct) |
| Odd-toed hoofed ungulates | Horses, tapirs, rhinoceroses |
| Even-toed hoofed ungulates | Pigs, peccaries, hippopotamuses, camels, deer, giraffes, pronghorns, antelopes, goats, sheep, musk-oxen, cattle |
| Proboscideans | Mastodons, mammoths, elephants |

Source: Based on data of E. H. Colbert (1955), *Evolution of the Vertebrates,* New York, Wiley, pp. 254–255.

The insectivores, which were the original order of placental mammals, gave rise to all other placental mammals. Among the first to appear were the two now-extinct groups, the archaic carnivores and the archaic ungulates. By the start of the Eocene Epoch these archaic groups had given rise to advanced carnivores and advanced ungulates, respectively.

Australia was populated largely by marsupials in the early Cenozoic time, when a land connection existed with Eurasia. Placental mammals, on the other hand, with the exception of bats and rodents, did not establish a foothold on Australia. The connecting bridge was then broken, and Australia remained isolated thereafter. In isolation free of competition from the placental mammals, the marsupials of Australia evolved into a bizarre mammalian fauna seen today in the kangaroo, wallaby, wombat, koala "bear," and Tasmanian wolf.

Evolution in isolation, seen in the example of Australia, illustrates the principle of *parallelism* in evolution. Under parallelism of evolution, unlike animal groups perform like functions, adapting to similar environments and developing analogous structures of quite similar forms.

## EVOLUTION OF THE ADVANCED UNGULATES

The advanced ungulates consist of two orders, one of which we can simply designate as *odd-toed,* the other as *even-toed* (see Figure 13.18). These herbivores were browsing or grazing animals, and many groups were forced to develop unusual leg and foot structures to secure the speed needed to escape from the carnivores. The ability to stand on the toes favored strengthening of the middle digits at the expense of those on the sides. Thus the five toes of the ancestral ungulates were reduced to three, two, or one. The odd-toed ungulates may have three toes, with the center line of the foot running down the center toe, or a single toe equipped with a solid hoof. The three-toed foot is seen in the tapir and rhinoceros, and the single-toed foot in the modern horse.

Evolution of the horse throughout Cenozoic time is a particularly fine example of adaptation to the need to run swiftly (Figure 14.12). As the animal increased in size, the legs and feet were lengthened and the lateral toes were lost. Ultimately there remained only a single toe equipped with a solid hoof. At the same

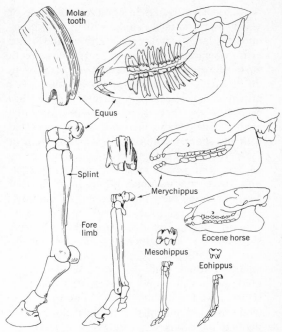

Figure 14.12. Evolution of the horse forelimb, skull, and molar teeth, beginning with *Eohippus* in the Eocene Epoch and ending with modern *Equus*. Skull of *Equus* is shown as cut away to expose the molars. [Forelimbs redrawn from W. D. Matthew; courtesy of American Museum of Natural History; teeth sketched from photographs prepared by Carl O. Dunbar from collections of the Yale Peabody Museum; skulls redrawn from E. H. Colbert (1955), *Evolution of the Vertebrates,* New York, John Wiley & Sons, p. 362, Figure 103.]

time important changes took place in the skull. The sharp incisor teeth were moved forward and separated from the molars, which moved to the sides and developed higher and flatter crowns. The jaws became heavier and deeper to accommodate the larger teeth, causing the face to project farther forward beyond the eyes.

In the even-toed ungulates three digits were lost, while the remaining two developed hooves. These cloven-hoofed animals are exemplified today by the camel, giraffe, goat, sheep, and cattle.

While some ungulates were developing improved facilities for running to escape predators, others were developing enormous bulk and tough hides. An example is seen in the formidable African rhinoceros, which has a sharp horn and an armorlike hide.

The elephants, constituting a separate order of mammals, arose early in the Cenozoic Era from the primitive ungulates. Evolution of the

Figure 14.13. Restoration of a landscape in Nebraska during late Miocene time. (*Left*) Short-legged rhinoceros. (*Right*) Four-tusked mastodon. (Painting by C. R. Knight; courtesy of Field Museum of Natural History.)

long trunk and tusks seen in the modern elephant and in the extinct mastodons and mammoths of the Pleistocene Epoch was slow in coming. A four-tusked mastodon with comparatively short trunk is shown in a reconstructed landscape of late Miocene time, together with rhinoceroses, in Figure 14.13. Notice the grasses and deciduous trees, lending a modern look to the scene.

### EVOLUTION OF THE PRIMATES

Leaving aside the evolutionary development of other important orders, such as the modern carnivores and the cetaceans (whales and porpoises), we turn finally to the evolution of the primates, which give rise to Man very late in the Cenozoic Era.

The order of primates consists of two suborders. The older of these, and the stem from which the remaining primates evolved, consists of the *prosimians* (*prosimian* means simply "premonkey"). The second suborder consists of the *anthropoids*, which includes monkeys, apes, and Man (see Figure 13.18).

Like all other orders of placental mammals, the prosimians arose early in the Cenozoic Era from the insectivores, small animals resembling the tree shrews of today. Prosimians are represented today by the lemurs, lorises, and tarsiers, which are small tree-dwelling mammals of Africa and Asia. Lemurlike prosimians entered in Paleocene time and were most abundant in the Eocene Epoch, after which they declined to minor importance. It is important to take note of this early evolution of the prosimians, because it means that the evolutionary line of Man and the other anthropoids

is as old as that of most of the other mammals, following a parallel course of evolution. However, important evolutionary radiation of the higher primates was long delayed and occurred only after that of the other mammals had been largely completed.

In Oligocene time there evolved from the prosimians three primate groups—the New World monkeys, the Old World monkeys, and primitive apelike *hominoids* (see Figure 13.18). This evolution is not adequately documented by fossil evidence, but seems to have occurred rather rapidly. The hominoids are considered more closely related to the Old World monkeys than to the New World monkeys, since the former are more advanced in development.

The hominoids can be subdivided into two classes: (1) gibbons and apes; (2) *hominids*, or simply *men*. The common ancestor to living apes (except gibbons) and men seems to have been an early hominoid known as *Dryopithecus* (formerly known as *Proconsul*). Fossil remains of Dryopithecus are found in Miocene and Pliocene strata and consist largely of skull fragments and jaws (Figure 14.14). It is not known whether these early apes were tree-dwellers or ground-dwellers. In any case, they gave rise to the chimpanzees, gorillas, and orangutangs, as well as to the oldest-known of fossil men, *Ramapithecus*. Distinction between a man and an ape in these fossils of Miocene and Pliocene age is based on dentition. Jaw fragments of *Ramapithecus* collected in India have well-preserved teeth, and these are distinctly manlike in contrast to teeth of apes (Figure 14.15). We shall continue the story of

Figure 14.14. *Dryopithecus,* a fossil ape from South Africa, living during the Miocene and Pliocene epochs. (*A*) Fossil skull found in 1948. (*B*) Restoration of *Dryopithecus* by Wilson. [Both illustrations reproduced by permission of the Trustees of the British Museum (Natural History).]

the evolution of Man in our review of the Pleistocene Epoch.

The primates showed a number of important specializations that led to their rapid evolutionary radiation late in the Cenozoic Era. In adapting to forest-living, the ability to judge distances accurately at close range was a necessity and led to development of binocular vision, in which the eyes came forward on the head to lie in the same plane and hence to secure maximum overlap of vision. The senses of smell and hearing were secondary in importance, so that the olfactory equipment underwent some decline. The need to grasp tree limbs firmly led to an evolution of the hands

Figure 14.15. Teeth and jaw fragment of *Ramapithecus,* the oldest fossil man, living in the Miocene and Pliocene epochs. This specimen was found in 1932 in India. (Courtesy of Peabody Museum of Natural History, Yale University.)

and feet in which a thumb and first toe became opposed to the remaining four digits. Most important of all was the large increase in brain size and the consequent increase in intelligence and in ability to control the limbs. Good binocular vision enabled the hands and feet to be put to use in manipulating food and various objects, ultimately leading to the use of tools by men.

## FINISHING TOUCHES TO THE PRESENT CONTINENTAL ARCHITECTURE

By late in the Cenozoic Era, in Miocene and Pliocene times, orogeny, vulcanism, broad-scale crustal warpings, and continental denudation brought the continents into essentially the configurations in which we find them today. The complex arrangement of exposed shields, marginal geosynclines, basin-and-range faulted structure, alpine mountain arcs, island arcs, and trenches has been described in Chapter 10. The motion of lithospheric plates is a continuing process, while seismic and volcanic activity leave no doubt that we are still in the midst of major crustal activity.

The most important changes in continental architecture during the middle and late Cenozoic took place along what are now the primary mountain and island arcs. In the western United States Pliocene and Pleistocene time saw the elevation of the Sierra Nevada and various coastal ranges by faulting on a grand scale. The

Cascade range was built of lavas and volcanic cones, and this activity has not yet ceased. Outpourings of basaltic lavas in the Columbia Plateau occurred throughout Miocene and Pliocene time, with some activity lingering through to recent time.

Elsewhere in the world, orogeny in middle and late Cenozoic time continued in the Andes, the Alps, and the Himalayas, raising enormous rock masses high in elevation and culminating in folding and overthrusting of strata as young as Pliocene age and even of Pleistocene age.

## THE PLEISTOCENE EPOCH

In these concluding paragraphs of our brief review of geologic history we turn to the events and problems of the most recent units of geologic time—the Pleistocene and Holocene epochs. Compressed into a time span of only 2 m.y., an almost trivial instant in planet Earth's long history, is a highly complex sequence of environmental changes affecting the atmosphere, the oceans, and the surfaces of the continents. It is perhaps due to the swiftness and intensity of environmental changes within the Pleistocene that the rapid evolution of Man occurred as it did, to the accompaniment of forced geographical displacements and redistributions of faunas and floras.

The Pleistocene inherited from the Pliocene a set of conditions likely to place severe environmental stresses upon plants and animals: The continents stood high, tectonism and vulcanism were active in narrow belts over the globe, and climatic contrasts were intensified from equator to poles. Yet the most potent environmental force, continental glaciation, withheld its action until the Pleistocene. The spread and recession of the great ice sheets described in Chapter 9 dominate the history of the Pleistocene and provide the events upon which the epoch is subdivided into time units.

## GLACIATION AND INTERGLACIATION

Study of glacial deposits and landforms shows us that the glacial history of the Pleistocene Epoch consisted not of a single cycle of growth and disappearance of ice sheets, but rather of at least four such cycles, each referred to as a *glaciation.* The oldest deposits, those of the first known glaciation, show most strongly the effects of time through the degree of chemical and physical weathering of the component mineral and rock fragments. The degree to which the silicate minerals in subglacial deposits have been altered to clay minerals and the degree to which calcium carbonate has been leached from masses of glacial sands and gravels provide evidence that deposits are of different ages.

As with strata of other kinds of sedimentary rock, glacial deposits of each glaciation are commonly found superimposed in order of age. Moreover, the discovery of an ancient soil layer, or *paleosol,* between two layers of glacial material not only serves to separate them into two glaciations but also provides proof of the long time that elapsed between those glaciations. Yet another type of evidence consists of the degree to which landforms of glacial deposition are modified by mass wasting and fluvial erosion. In general, glacial landforms become more subdued with passage of time as their scarps lose sharpness, their depressions are filled, and gullies and new valleys score their poorly consolidated clays and sands.

Another form of evidence of multiple glaciations comes from sediment deposits—usually types formed in bogs, lakes, or estuaries—in which are contained remains of plants and animals known to thrive only in relatively mild climates. Where such deposits separate layers of ice-deposited material they provide evidence of a period of warm climate, or *interglaciation,* which separated glaciations.

For several decades four glaciations have been recognized in North America, while a similar and possible equivalent four-glaciation history has been established for Europe on the basis of studies in the Alps. Recently, evidence has been found of two earlier glaciations in the Alps. Evidence of six cold-climate episodes is found in northwestern Europe and in Great Britain. Thus the total number of glaciations of the Pleistocene Epoch remains to be established and may even exceed six. Names of the four established glaciations of North America are given in Table 14.3. Maps of North America and Europe show maximum extent of Pleistocene ice sheets (see Figures 6.24 and 6.25).

Maximum southern extent of ice in each glaciation in the north-central United States is shown in Figure 14.16. The ice limit of each glaciation is usually marked by a terminal moraine which is a broad, low ridge of irregular surface configuration built of bouldery rock debris carried forward by the ice and left behind after the ice has melted away. Moraines usually include much sand and gravel deposited from streams of meltwater issuing from the ice margin.

Table 14.3. NORTH AMERICAN GLACIATIONS AND INTERGLACIATIONS

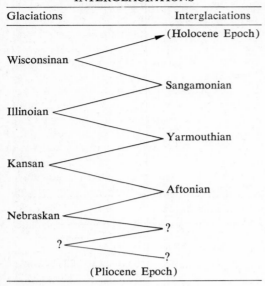

| Glaciations | Interglaciations |
|---|---|
| | (Holocene Epoch) |
| Wisconsinan | |
| | Sangamonian |
| Illinoian | |
| | Yarmouthian |
| Kansan | |
| | Aftonian |
| Nebraskan | |
| | ? |
| ? | |
| | ? |
| | (Pliocene Epoch) |

The ice front advances in great lobes, whose limits varied both with location and stage of glaciation. For example, the Kansan ice limit extended beyond those of other ice sheets in northeastern Kansas and northern Missouri, but it was generally surpassed by the younger ice sheets east of the Mississippi River.

The Wisconsinan Glaciation ended rather rapidly about −10,000 to −12,000 yr. Transition from the Sangamonian Interglaciation to the Wisconsinan Glaciation took place at about −75,000 yr, so that the last glaciation had a duration of about 65,000 yr. Actually, evidence shows that the Wisconsinan Glaciation consisted of a number of alternate ice advances and recessions, and this complexity was undoubtedly matched in older glaciations for which the record is obscure. Absolute ages of older glaciations and interglaciations is extremely difficult to ascertain, because the methods of radiocarbon dating are limited to about the last 40,000 yr.

The age of the time boundary between Pleistocene and Pliocene epochs is by no means settled. The figure of −2.0 m.y. given in Table 14.1 has been proposed on grounds of changes in fossil content of deep-sea sediments, which can be dated by means of the scale of paleomagnetic polarity reversals (see Chapter 10). An ice sheet has probably existed on Antarctica for at least the past 4 m.y. because of its pole-centered position.

## ORIGIN OF THE GREAT LAKES

A major phenomenon of late Pleistocene time was the formation of the Great Lakes, five interconnected inland water bodies. The existence of this assemblage of great natural freshwater bodies in the heart of a continent is a

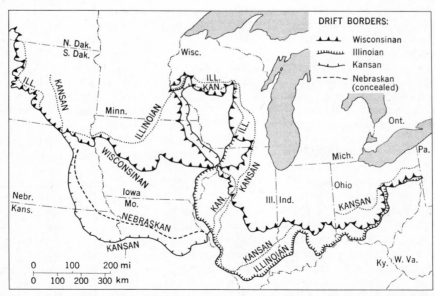

Figure 14.16. Ice limits in the north-central United States for the four glaciations. (© 1965, John Wiley & Sons, New York. Data of R. F. Flint.)

hydrologic phenomenon unmatched elsewhere on our planet and is highly significant in the environment of Man in North America.

In preglacial time, the area of the present Great Lakes was occupied by broad stream-eroded lowlands. Except for the basin of Lake Superior, which is entirely within the Canadian Shield, these lowlands were excavated in weak strata of Paleozoic age separated by hill belts of more resistant rocks. The preglacial lowlands were strongly scoured and considerably deepened by erosive action of successive Pleistocene ice sheets. Debris from the basins provided much of the material for moraine belts situated south of the Great Lakes (see Figure 14.16).

The Great Lakes came into existence during recessional substages of the Wisconsinan Stage, as ice evacuated basins lying between the wasting ice front and higher ground elevations to the south. Evidence of the existence of these early lakes is found in abandoned shorelines with beach ridges above present lake levels. Developmental history of the Great Lakes during recessional phases of the ice sheet is extremely complex, because the crust was rising and being tilted southward as the lakes were forming.

## EFFECTS OF SHIFTING PLEISTOCENE CLIMATIC ZONES

As the Pleistocene ice sheets spread into lower latitudes and average atmospheric temperatures fell to lower levels, climatic zones were pushed equatorward and crowded more closely together. We can infer that the upper-air westerlies extended their influence into lower latitudes and that the subtropical belts of high pressure were also displaced into lower latitudes. As a result, the desert belts migrated to latitudes as low as perhaps 10° to 15°, compressing the wet equatorial climate into a narrow zone. It seems reasonable to conclude that lowered atmospheric temperature would have greatly reduced atmospheric moisture and precipitation generally in low latitudes. As evidence, we find relict landforms of aridity, such as sand dunes in what are today areas of tropical forests.

Of particular interest to students of the Pleistocene Epoch are relict forms of arctic climates in unglaciated middle-latitude zones that bordered the southern limits of the ice sheets. Such features are described as *periglacial*, the prefix *peri* meaning "near" and implying that a cold environment existed near the ice sheets. Periglacial features consist of inactive structures or landforms of the kinds now found in the process of formation in tundra regions of the arctic and adjacent to the Greenland Ice Sheet.

Onset of the Holocene Epoch is rather clearly marked by a rapid rise in ocean temperatures starting at about −10,000 yr. As would be expected, climate zones on the continents shifted rapidly poleward as the periglacial tundra climates of North America and Europe gave way successively to subarctic climates and ultimately to present-day middle-latitude climates. Soil-forming processes began the development of soil profiles; forests and grasslands became reestablished.

One of the nonglacial phenomena correlated with glacial and interglacial stages of the Pleistocene Epoch is the rise and fall of water levels in inland lakes of arid and semiarid regions. Such lakes occupied intermontane basins of the western United States and, with one exception, had no outlets to the sea. They have been named *pluvial lakes,* the adjective *pluvial* suggesting the increase in depth and extent of the lakes as a result of increased precipitation and reduced evaporation. Today these basins contain greatly shrunken lakes or are completely dry. Altogether, about 120 pluvial lakes were in existence in optimum periods of the Illinoian and Wisconsinan glaciations. Many of these overflowed into neighboring lakes of lower elevation.

Largest of the western pluvial lakes was *Lake Bonneville,* of which the present-day shrunken remnant is Great Salt Lake. At its maximum extent Lake Bonneville was almost as large in area, 20,000 mi$^2$ (52,000 km$^2$), as present Lake Michigan and attained a maximum depth of 1000 ft (330 m).

## PLEISTOCENE CHANGES OF SEA LEVEL

One of the most important phenomena of the Pleistocene and Holocene epochs has been the changing of sea level with respect to the continents. Not only have sea-level changes caused the alternate exposure and inundation of continental margins, but also they have had many secondary effects relating to denudation of the continents and sedimentation upon the ocean floors.

It is well to keep in mind that changes of sea level relative to the land have a variety of causes, some of which act on a world-wide basis and others of which act locally. World-wide changes of sea level are related either to changes in the volume of ocean water or in the volume of the ocean basins. These changes are described as *eustatic*.

By far the most important single cause of ocean-volume change in the Pleistocene Epoch has been the alternate accumulation and melting of glacial ice. Amounts of sea-level change from this cause can be calculated from known volumes of existing ice masses and from estimates of volumes of former ice sheets. The Antarctic Ice Sheet alone holds sufficient water volume to provide a sea-level rise of about 200 ft (60 m), should all of that ice be melted. Assuming that the added load of this water upon the oceanic crust caused an isostatic down-warping of 65 ft (20 m), the net sea-level rise would still be about 135 ft (40 m). Estimates of the total sea-level rise that would accompany the melting of all existing glacial ice run to 200 ft (60 m), or somewhat higher. The effects of a 200-ft rise of sea level upon the heavily populated lowlands of the Atlantic and Gulf coastal plain have been a favorite theme of journalists and writers, thus they can hardly have escaped the attention of the majority of laymen. Of more interest, scientifically, is the very real lowering of sea level that accompanied each glaciation as enormous ice sheets spread over the continents in middle latitudes.

Assuming that the order of magnitude of sea-level lowering in the last major glacial advance is at least 325 ft (100 m), we find that the Atlantic continental shelf was exposed out to a distance of 60 to 125 mi (100 to 200 km) beyond the present shoreline off the northeastern United States. To this figure we may add perhaps an additional 100 ft (30 m) of emergence due to isostatic rise in response to removal of water load. It is interesting to note that analysis of pollen in fresh-water peat samples far out upon the shelf indicates presence of a forest vegetation consisting of such trees as fir, spruce, pine, and oak. Teeth of Pleistocene elephants (mastodons and mammoths) have been dredged up from points far out upon the shelf. All of these indications point to the last glacial substage as providing here a vegetated landscape populated with animal life.

## CRUSTAL RISE AND PLEISTOCENE MARINE SHORELINES

Many coastal zones the world over exhibit elevated marine shorelines in the form of wave-cut beaches, coral reefs, and beach ridges. In fact, one might perhaps say that coasts with a history of crustal rise during the Pleistocene and Holocene epochs are the rule rather than the exception. Crustal sinking, producing shorelines of submergence, seems largely to be associated with areas of heavy ice loading.

As explained in Chapter 10, fluvial denudation of the continents must be accompanied by isostatic uplift to compensate for the removal of load. This isostatic uplift may account in part for the progressive rise of continental margins of stable crust. Tectonic processes would be expected to produce uplift of extensive marginal zones of rigid crustal plates, such as those surrounding the Pacific basin.

Whatever the causes of crustal uplift, there is abundant evidence that the eustatic rise and fall of sea level throughout the Pleistocene has been superimposed in many places on a persistent rise of the crust. Successive elevated shorelines, such as those pictured in Figure 14.17, are one manifestation of crustal rise. Along the United States coastal plain are found many less spectacular indications of former higher sea levels. These evidences take the form of low terrace scarps, broad beach ridges, and long narrow swamps occupying what were formerly lagoons behind barrier beaches.

## MAMMALS OF THE PLEISTOCENE

Mammalian development progressed from Pliocene into Pleistocene time with no evidence of evolutionary crisis as world temperatures fell and the first ice sheets began their spread. Shifting of climate zones into lower latitudes seems to have been met by migrations of floras and faunas, although extinctions occurred locally in special geographical traps, such as islands and peninsulas from which migration could not take place.

Throughout the Old World landmasses—Eurasia and Africa—migrations were continuously possible during the entire Cenozoic Era. Animals of Africa were able to migrate into Europe during warm interglaciations of the Pleistocene. Moreover, Man evolved in the Old World and developed in continuous contact with the other mammals. In the New World, evolution was complicated by the separation of North and South America until the late Pliocene. As a result, mixing of grossly unlike faunas took place early in the Pleistocene in North America, yielding a mammalian assemblage somewhat different from that of the Old World.

Figure 14.17. Air view of a series of marine terraces representing elevated shorelines. Western side of San Clemente Island, California. (Photograph by courtesy of Robert S. Dietz.)

In the Pleistocene of North America there lived a number of now-extinct mammals whose bones, teeth, and tusks are abundantly preserved in interglacial and postglacial silts and peats. Undoubtedly the most spectacular were members of the elephant group, which were of two types. The *mastodons* were forest-dwellers. Their remains have been found widely distributed over the eastern United States and far out upon the now-submerged continental shelf. The true elephants, which arose from early mastodons, are represented by the *mammoths* of the Pleistocene and the modern elephants. The mammoths came to North America in the Pleistocene by way of the land bridge connecting Siberia with Alaska. Well known to all is the woolly mammoth, which—along with the musk-ox and, in Europe, the woolly rhinoceros —was adapted to cold periglacial climates (Figure 14.18).

Other grazing mammals of the Pleistocene Epoch in North America included the horse, bison, camel, and peccary (wild pig). From South America there had emigrated the ground sloths, some of which were huge animals.

Pleistocene carnivores included a number of now-extinct species, among them the *saber-tooth tiger,* with teeth adapted to stabbing its prey (Figure 14.19). The list includes, of course, all of the living carnivores—wolf, fox, lynx, puma, badger, otter, skunk, and weasel.

It is particularly interesting to find that few mammalian extinctions occurred in North America until after the close of the Wiscon-

Figure 14.18. Restoration of the woolly mammoth (*left* and *center*) and woolly rhinoceros (*far right*) in a European landscape of Pleistocene time. (From a painting by C. R. Knight; courtesy of the Field Museum of Natural History.)

Figure 14.19. Reconstruction of the saber-toothed tiger (*Smilodon*) from remains found in the La Brea, California, asphalt pits. Specimen about 3 ft (1 m) in height. The lower jaw could open much wider than shown to permit the upper teeth to be used for stabbing. (Sketched from a photograph prepared by Carl O. Dunbar from a model by R. S. Lull in the Yale Peabody Museum.)

sinan, about −10,000 yr, at which time Man spread widely over the continent. The inference has been made that extinction of species, particularly the mastodons and mammoths, was through having been hunted by Man. If so, this event serves as an ominous presage to greater Man-caused extinctions of the present and the total extinction of planetary life which he seems destined ultimately to achieve as his supreme contribution to the evolutionary process.

## THE EVOLUTION OF MAN

Recall from earlier paragraphs that through the Pliocene Epoch the apes had evolved independently from primitive hominoid stocks going back into Miocene time (see Figure 13.18). From *Dryopithecus,* the common ancestor of hominids and apes, there had evolved in late Miocene time *Ramapithecus,* the hominid ancestor of fossil men. Although evidence from limb or pelvic bones is lacking, it is supposed that *Ramapithecus* was bipedal and lived on the ground. Because only jaw fragments are known, we do not know the size of the *Ramapithecus* brain, but it was probably small, comparable to that of the modern apes.

A second genus of hominids, *Australopithecus,* seems to have evolved from *Ramapithecus* in Pliocene time. *Australopithecus* was named for a well-preserved skull found in South Africa in 1924. Subsequently, in the Olduvai Gorge of Tanzania, the skull of another species of *Australopithecus* was found. From associated volcanic rocks, dated by the potassium-argon method, this specimen is assigned an age of not less than −1.75 m.y., which is close to

the beginning of the Pleistocene Epoch. More recently, a jaw fragment of *Australopithecus* found near Lake Rudolph in Kenya has been dated at −5.5 m.y.

From a large number of bones, including jaws, skulls, and limbs, it is known that *Australopithecus* walked upright, although in a slouched attitude. His size ranged from that of a chimpanzee in the smaller species to that of a gorilla in the larger. Although his limb bones closely resemble those of modern Man, the *Australopithecus* skull had only half the brain capacity of modern Man (Figure 14.20). With his erect stance, *Australopithecus* developed the ability to use bones, sticks, and stones as tools and weapons, although he had not learned to shape tools (Figure 14.21). Advanced arm and hand functions tended to place a premium upon intelligence and promoted an evolutionary increase in brain size, the most important distinguishing characteristic setting Man apart from the apes.

*Australopithecus* spread widely over the Old World, for his remains have been found in Java. He became extinct some time in the middle Pleistocene, after giving rise to *Homo,* the third and final genus of hominids. Specimens of *Homo* found associated with those of *Australopithecus* in South Africa suggest that both hominids were in existence for a considerable span of time in the age range of −700,000 to −500,000 yr.

*Homo erectus,* the earliest known species of *Homo,* was discovered in 1891 in Java, where he was named "Java Man." Since then many jaws, skulls, and limbs of *Homo erectus* have been found in the Old World, including localities in China, Europe, and Africa (Figure 14.20). *Homo erectus* possessed a brain volume of about 900 to 1100 cm³, which is intermediate between that of *Australopithecus,* 600 to 700 cm³, and modern Man, 1400 to 1600 cm³ (Figure 14.20). The head of *Homo erectus,* with its protruding mouth and slanted forehead, jutted forward from a sloping neck with powerful muscles, giving him a distinctly apelike appearance. *Homo erectus* became extinct some time in the late middle Pleistocene, but he had already given rise to *Homo sapiens,* the single species that includes all present-day races of the human family.

*Homo sapiens* appeared on the scene early in the middle Pleistocene, at about −500,000 yr, and was for a long period a contemporary of *Homo erectus.* As with the latter species,

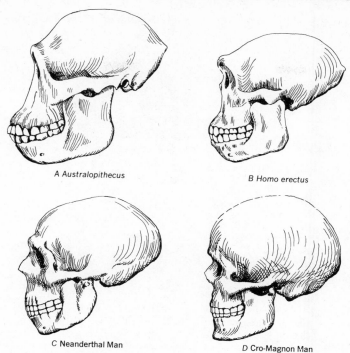

A Australopithecus

B Homo erectus

C Neanderthal Man

D Cro-Magnon Man

Figure 14.20. Reconstructed skulls of hominids of the Pleistocene Epoch. (Sketched from photographs by the American Museum of Natural History.)

*Homo sapiens* includes a number of men formerly designated as separate species but now regarded as races within the species. One of these was *Neanderthal Man,* who inhabited Europe from about −100,000 until −40,000 yr—late Sangamonian and early Wisconsinan time (Figure 14.20). Because Neanderthal Man was short, stocky, and heavy-boned, he was formerly designated as a separate species. It is true that his skull seems to resemble that of *Homo erectus* more than it does modern Man. However, his brain capacity was at least equal to that of modern Man and he made good stone tools, including stone axes, scrapers, and points. In terms of culture, Neanderthal Man is said to belong to the *Middle Paleolithic* culture, or "Old Stone Age."

In Europe at about −35,000 yr Neanderthal Man was replaced by a more advanced race of *Homo sapiens.* This newcomer was represented by *Cro-Magnon Man,* among others. He was tall, straight, and long-legged. His skull was centered directly over the top of the spine and showed a high forehead and prominent chin (Figure 14.20). In these respects he strongly resembled modern Man. Cro-Magnon Man belonged to the final phases of the Paleolithic culture, but the quality of his stone implements

was high, showing finely chipped forms. In addition, Cro-Magnon Man shaped bone and ivory into tools, weapons, and ornaments. He had developed the use of the bow and arrow and dressed himself in furs. Cro-Magnon Man was succeeded in the Near East at about −10,000 yr (start of the Holocene) by peoples of the Neolithic culture. These peoples learned to make pottery and to domesticate animals, then later turned to agriculture. At about −5000 yr the introduction of use of metals brought on the Age of Metals, and shortly thereafter came the dawn of recorded human history.

It is well established that *Homo sapiens* originated in the Old World. It is supposed that he migrated to the New World by way of the Bering Strait very late in the Pleistocene. He may not have spread south to the contiguous United States from Alaska until ice recession of the late Wisconsinan opened up migration routes. Radiocarbon dates establish the presence of Man in a number of widely separate places in North America (Texas, Alabama, Mexico City) at around −9000 to −10,000 yr. Association of human bones and weapon points with bones of the mastodon, mammoth, and saber-tooth tiger suggest that those animals

Figure 14.21. Reconstruction of a group of individuals of *Australopithecus* in their African habitat in early Pleistocene time. (Reproduced by permission from Z. Burian and Artia Publishers, Prague, from the original book *Prehistoric Man.*)

were living at the time Man occupied North America and, as already noted, their extinction was due in part to having been hunted by Man.

## GEOLOGIC SYSTEMS AND ORGANIC EVOLUTION

This chapter and the previous one have traced the course of organic evolution in broad strokes from the first appearance of complex marine animal forms at the start of the Paleozoic Era to the evolution of Man in the very last instant of a 600-m.y. span. During the eras of abundant life geologic, hydrospheric, and atmospheric processes have exerted a dominant control over the evolution of life. On the other hand, as life forms have spread to occupy all favorable environments, they have in turn modified the physical environment of the life layer.

The abundant free oxygen of our atmosphere we owe to photosynthesis of plants. That same oxygen layer shields all life forms from deadly ultraviolet radiation. Spread of plants to the lands profoundly altered the processes of rock weathering and soil formation and must have greatly reduced rates of continental denudation. Enormous quantities of

carbon have been put into storage as carbonate sediments secreted by plants and animals. Plants have put into storage huge quantities of hydrocarbons, now extracted as fossil fuels.

Interactions between life forms and their environments constitute the science of *ecology*. Ecology looms large in our thinking today as Man's activities press with ominous rapidity the deterioration of physical environments of the biosphere. What we have tried to accomplish in these chapters is to show that there is a *paleoecology* encompassing an enormously greater span of time than that in which Man has played his part. The massive slowness of organic evolution stands in impressive contrast to the instantaneous extinction which Man can now impose at will on great segments of the living world.

### References for further study

Flint, R. F. (1971), *Glacial and Quaternary Geology,* New York, Wiley, 892 pp.

Colbert, E. H. (1965), *The Age of Reptiles,* New York, Norton, 228 pp.

Kay, M., and E. H. Colbert (1965), *Stratigraphy and Life History,* New York, Wiley, 736 pp.

McAlester, A. L. (1968), *The History of Life,* Englewood Cliffs, N.J., Prentice-Hall, 151 pp.

Dunbar, C. O., and K. M. Waage (1969), *Historical Geology*, 3rd ed., New York, Wiley, 556 pp.

Strahler, A. N. (1971), *The Earth Sciences*, 2nd ed., New York, Harper & Row, 826 pp., chaps. 30, 41.

## Review questions

1. What position in time does the Mesozoic Era occupy? What reptile forms persisted into the Triassic Period? What is the significance of *Lystrosaurus* in terms of continental unity? Describe the evolutionary radiation of the reptiles in the early part of the Mesozoic Era. Describe the marine reptiles and their adaptation to the sea.

2. What were the thecodonts? What was their place in reptile evolution? What functional advantage did they develop? What animal groups are included within the ruling reptiles? Describe three different forms of dinosaurs and explain their environmental adaptation in terms of diet, habits, and protective structures.

3. What form of reptile took to the air? How was this adaptation achieved? Name the first fossil bird. To what period does it belong? From what animal group did the birds evolve?

4. List the principal differences between mammals and reptiles. What advantages do mammals possess in adaptation to varied environments? Describe the earliest mammals. What two orders of mammals had arisen by late Cretaceous time?

5. Describe plant evolution through the Mesozoic Era. Describe the appearance of cycads and ginkgoes. Where can fossil conifers of Triassic age be seen today? What are the angiosperms? How does the reproductive mechanism of the angiosperms represent an advantage in adaptation over that of the gymnosperms?

6. Describe the rifting apart of the continents in Mesozoic time, according to the hypothesis of continental drift. When and where did the rifting start? How did continental separation influence the course of organic evolution in Mesozoic time?

7. Describe the great extinctions that occurred at the close of the Cretaceous Period. Were the land plants similarly affected? Discuss the problem of causes of extinctions. What does the fossil record reveal as to causes of extinction?

8. Compare the Cenozoic Era with the two preceding eras in terms of duration. Into how many epochs is the Cenozoic Era divided? Name the epochs. Explain how the epochs were originally defined.

9. Describe North America at the beginning of the Cenozoic Era. What effect did the Laramian orogeny have upon sediment deposition of the Cenozoic Era? What events were taking place in Cenozoic time along the primary mountain arcs? How does the concept of plate tectonics explain orogenic belts of the Cenozoic Era?

10. Describe the appearance of the mammals of early Cenozoic time. Discuss trends in mammalian evolution through the Cenozoic Era and illustrate by examples of adaptations of both herbivores and carnivores.

11. Distinguish between marsupials and placental mammals. Which group is the better adapted to survival? Name several orders of placental mammals and give examples, using common names. Describe and explain the unique case of mammalian evolution in Australia. How does this example illustrate the principle of parallelism in evolution?

12. What are the ungulates? What are the two orders of ungulates? Give examples from modern forms. Describe the evolution of the horse in the Cenozoic Era, emphasizing the environmental adaptation shown by changes in head and limbs.

13. What are the primates? What two suborders are included within the primates? What primate forms are included within the anthropoids? Describe the evolution of the primates, starting in early Cenozoic time. What are the hominoids, and how are they related in evolutionary sequence to the monkeys?

14. Distinguish between hominids and hominoids. Explain the position of *Dryopithecus* in the evolutionary sequence of apes and men. Describe *Ramapithecus*. From what ancestor did *Ramapithecus* evolve? Describe the evolutionary adaptation of primates to their environment.

15. What geologic events took place late in the Cenozoic Era? Where were the belts of vulcanism and orogenic activity? What mountain ranges were elevated at this time?

16. How are the Pleistocene and Holocene epochs defined? What is the age and duration of the Pleistocene Epoch? At what point in time did the Holocene Epoch begin? When did it end?

17. What is a glaciation? an interglaciation?

What evidence is used to recognize the occurrences of glaciations and interglaciations? Name in order the glaciations and interglaciations recognized in North America. Are there European equivalents of these events?

18. Describe the southernmost extent of the ice sheets in North America during the four glaciations. How is the limit of a glaciation recognized? When did the Wisconsinan Glaciation begin and when did it end?

19. Explain the evolution of the Great Lakes. How did crustal movements influence the changing configuration of the lakes?

20. What global climatic changes accompanied each glaciation? What are periglacial features? Where can they be found today? In what way did inland lakes (pluvial lakes) respond to glaciation and interglaciation? Describe Lake Bonneville.

21. Describe the eustatic changes of sea level that accompanied glaciations and interglaciations. How does isostasy enter into the picture? What evidence is found of lowered sea levels during the last glaciation?

22. Why is persistent crustal rise to be expected through the Pleistocene? What is the physical evidence of such crustal rise? Where did crustal depression occur and what caused it?

23. Describe the mammals of the Pleistocene Epoch. Discuss their intercontinental migration. When did the most important mammalian extinctions occur and what may have been the cause?

24. Describe the evolution of Man, starting with *Ramapithecus*. What position in time and evolutionary sequence is occupied by *Australopithecus*? Describe the changes in brain size, stance, and arm and hand functions shown by *Australopithecus*. When did genus *Homo* first appear? Describe *Homo erectus*.

25. Review the evolution of *Homo sapiens*. When did this evolution take place, and where? Compare the appearance annd cultural development of Neanderthal Man with that of Cro-Magnon Man. When and how did Man first reach the New World?

26. Discuss in broad terms the linkage between organic evolution and the physical evolution of the atmosphere, hydrosphere, and lithosphere. Suppose that no life had existed throughout geologic time; in what respects would the atmosphere, hydrosphere, and lithosphere now be different in composition?

# chapter 15
# stellar systems and galactic evolution: a cosmology beyond the realm of man

Is any further understanding of planet Earth to be gained by inquiring into what lies in outer space beyond the limits of the solar system? Is it not enough to know how the sun produces electromagnetic radiation and a solar wind? Because our sun is the hub and mainstay of the planets and their life environments, influences from beyond the solar system seem almost inconsequential. Yet the earth receives from all points in space a barrage of energy in the form of light, radio waves, X-ray emissions, and highly energetic nuclear particles. This energy input requires that we know something of the stars beyond the sun and of their aggregations—along with diffuse matter in the form of gas and dust—that constitute the galaxies.

Astronomy on even the largest scale contributes knowledge of fundamental importance to an understanding of planet Earth. Astronomers and geologists have often worked as partners in

Parts of this chapter were prepared with the assistance of Professor Theodore G. Mehlin, Department of Astronomy, Williams College.

developing scientific hypotheses. This cooperation comes about because evidence obtained from matter on earth can in some instances be applied outward to problems in astronomy. A case in point, discussed in this chapter, concerns the establishment of ages of rocks on earth. An early calculation of the age of the universe proved incompatible with known ages of rocks, and the astronomical theory was accordingly revised.

The brief and incomplete treatment of so many highly complex and important subjects of astronomy in a single chapter can be justified only if the end result is to place our earth in its proper perspective in the total framework of mass, length, and time of the universe. It is with such an objective in mind that we venture out into interstellar space.

## UNITS OF INTERSTELLAR DISTANCE

The vastness of interstellar space requires units of length quite different from those applicable to the solar system. Consider that the nearest star to our sun, *Alpha Centauri*, is about 300,000 times more distant from the sun than the sun is from earth. A convenient unit of interstellar distance is the *light-year*, the distance traveled by light in one-year's time. Multiplying the speed of light, 186,000 mi/sec, by the number of seconds in the year gives a value of approximately 6 million million mi. A more nearly exact value is $5.880 \times 10^{12}$ mi ($8.898 \times 10^{12}$ km). Alpha Centauri is about 4.3 light-years distant from the sun. Distances to the 15 brightest stars are given in light-years in Table 15.1.

Astronomers also make use of another measure of distance based on the principle of *stellar parallax*. As the earth moves across its great orbital distance each year the nearer stars should seem to change their apparent positions in relation to the more distant ones. *Parallax*, a word used in optics, means a difference in the apparent relative positions of objects when viewed from different points. This principle is illustrated in Figure 15.1 (the angles are greatly exaggerated). A near star, *A*, may appear very close to a distant star, *B*, when viewed in the spring. But as the earth moves in its orbit star *A* will seem to shift its location in the sky, so that in the autumn star *A* may be separated from star *B* by a very small angle. The closer the star is to us, the greater the parallax effect.

The parallax of the stars was first measured in 1838 by the Prussian astronomer Bessel, who discovered that a faint star in the constellation of Cygnus was displaced annually by 0.4 sec of arc. Since then the trigonometric parallaxes of about 10,000 stars have been measured. The parallax of the nearest known star to the sun, Alpha Centauri, is only 0.75 sec of arc, a very small angle, indeed. A star having a parallax of exactly 1 sec of arc would lie at a distance of about 20 million million ($2 \times 10^{13}$) mi ($3.2 \times 10^{13}$ km) from the sun. This distance is one *parsec*, a term coined from the words *parallax* and *second*. Alpha Centauri lies at a distance of 1.3 parsecs from the sun. One parsec is equal to 3.26 light-years.

## THE SUN IN OUR GALAXY

In its larger setting, the sun is but one star among some 100 billion stars grouped into an assemblage termed a *galaxy*, which in turn is but one of a vast number of widely separated galaxies constituting the *universe*.

Our galaxy has the form of a great disk, or wheel, with a marked central thickening at the hub (Figure 15.2). If it could be seen from an outside vantage point, our galaxy would probably be quite similar to the *Whirlpool nebula* (galaxy M 51) and to the *Great Spiral galaxy* (M 31), located in the constellation of *Andromeda* (Figure 15.3).

The sun occupies a position more than halfway out from the center toward the rim of the galaxy (Figure 15.2). As we look out into the plane of the disk, we see the stars of the galaxy massed in a great band, the *Milky Way*, which completely encircles the sky. For this reason our galaxy is usually designated by the name *Milky Way galaxy*.

The Milky Way galaxy rotates about its hub, the center part turning more rapidly than the

Table 15.1. THE FIFTEEN BRIGHTEST STARS

| Name | Constellation | Apparent Visual Magnitude | Actual Luminosity (Sun = 1) | Distance (light-years) |
|------|---------------|---------------------------|------------------------------|------------------------|
| Sirius | Canis Major | −1.44 | 23 | 8.7 |
| Canopus | Carina | −0.72 | 1,500 | 180 |
| Alpha Centauri | Centaur | −0.27 | 1.5 | 4.3 |
| Arcturus | Boötes | −0.05 | 110 | 36 |
| Vega | Lyra | 0.03 | 55 | 26.5 |
| Capella | Auriga | 0.09 | 170 | 47 |
| Rigel | Orion | 0.11 | 40,000 | 800 |
| Procyon | Canis Minor | 0.36 | 7.3 | 11.3 |
| Betelgeuse | Orion | 0.40 | 17,000 | 500 |
| Achernar | Eridanus | 0.49 | 200 | 65 |
| Beta Centauri | Centaur | 0.63 | 5,000 | 300 |
| Altair | Aquila | 0.77 | 11 | 16.5 |
| Aldebaran | Taurus | 0.80 | 100 | 53 |
| Alpha Crucis | Southern Cross | 0.83 | 4,000 | 400 |
| Antares | Scorpius | 0.94 | 5,000 | 400 |

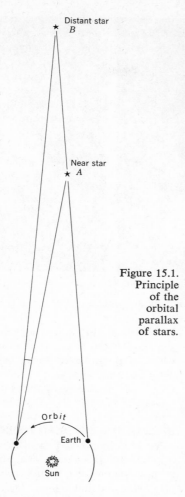

Distant star
B

Near star
A

Orbit

Earth

Sun

Figure 15.1.
Principle
of the
orbital
parallax
of stars.

Sun

10,000 Parsecs

Figure 15.2. Schematic diagram of the Milky Way galaxy as viewed from a point in the plane of the spiral. Large spots represent star clusters; small spots represent stars. [From O. Struve, *The Universe,* p. 76, Figure 44. © 1962 by the Massachusetts Institute of Technology.]

scattered stars and *globular star clusters* (Figure 15.4).

## PROPERTIES OF STARS

To understand our sun we must compare it with other stars. In this case the word *star* refers to discrete gravitationally bound concentrations of matter in our galaxy, as distinct from highly dispersed matter in the form of gas clouds and dust clouds. Measurable properties that distinguish one star from another and enable classification to be made are *mass, size* (volume, radius, or surface area), *density, luminosity,* and *temperature.* Temperature in turn determines the type of radiation emitted by the star and governs the type of spectrum observed.

Mass of a star, which refers to the quantity of matter present, varies over a wide range. Taking the mass of our sun as unity (1.0), the masses of stars range from as small as about one-tenth that of the sun to about 20 times greater than the sun. Stars also have a great range in diameter. For example, a small companion star to *Sirius* has a diameter only one-thirtieth that of the sun, whereas the diameter of *Antares* is almost 500 times greater than that of the sun.

Density of a star refers to the degree of concentration of mass within a given volume of space. Taking as a standard the density of water to be unity ($1 \text{ gm/cm}^3$), the average density of the sun is about 1.4 or only slightly more than the value for water at the earth's surface. Stars show a truly enormous range in density, from less than one-millionth that of the sun to more than a hundred million times as great. The companion star to Sirius, referred to above as a very small star, has a mass

more distant outer regions. At the position occupied by our sun, a full cycle of rotation requires about 200 ($2 \times 10^8$) million years (m.y.). The linear velocity of the solar system in this circuit is about half a million ($0.5 \times 10^6$) mph ($0.8 \times 10^6$ km/hr).

Thickness of the Milky Way galaxy is from 5000 to 15,000 light-years, its diameter about 100,000 light-years (Figure 15.2). The galaxy has a system of *spiral arms,* comparable to those in the Andromeda spiral, M 31. Each arm consists of individual aggregations of stars, known as *star clouds,* each having dimensions of 5000 to 20,000 light-years. Altogether, about 100 billion ($10^{11}$) stars are contained in the galaxy.

The Milky Way galaxy also contains gas clouds and clouds of cosmic dust. Concentration of these clouds is particularly heavy in the plane of the galactic disk (Figure 15.2). Surrounding the disk is a vast *halo* of widely

Figure 15.3. Three spiral galaxies photographed with the 200-in. (500-cm) telescope. (*Left*) The Great Spiral galaxy, M 31, in the constellation Andromeda. (*Center*) Whirlpool nebula, spiral galaxy M 51. (*Right*) Spiral galaxy NGC 4565, seen edge on. (The Hale Observatories.)

almost equal to that of the sun and, consequently, a density 35,000 times that of water.

Luminosity of a star is the measure of its total radiant energy output as if measured at the star itself and can be stated in reference to the luminosity of the sun taken as unity (1.0). The range of luminosity among stars is from as low as one-millionth that of the sun to as high as half a million times as great. However, for most stars the luminosity ranges between one ten-thousandth $(10^{-4})$ and 10,000 $(10^4)$ times that of the sun.

Star temperature, always given in degrees Kelvin, refers to the surface temperature as calculated in terms of the star's luminosity and diameter. Temperatures range from below 3500° K to 80,000° K. A star's color is closely related to its surface temperature: The hottest stars are blue; those only a little cooler are white; at progressively lower temperatures star color ranges from yellow through orange to red. Table 15.2 gives star color in relation to temperature.

## STELLAR DISTANCES AND BRIGHTNESS

To the observer on earth the great range in brightness of the stars has long been recognized by designations of star *magnitude* for purposes of navigation and general descriptive astronomy. Most persons are familiar with a system used on star charts in which the brightest stars are classed as of the *first magnitude,* those of lesser brightness as *second magnitude,* and so on, down to the sixth magnitude.

When placed on an exact basis, the *apparent visual magnitude* of celestial objects resolves itself into a scale of numbers in which each integer value represents an increase in light intensity by a factor of 2.5 over the next larger integer. Thus a star of magnitude 1.0 is 2.5 times as bright as one of magnitude 2.0, but 6.25 (2.5 × 2.5) times as bright as one of magnitude 3.0. The magnitude scale, which is a logarithmic (constant ratio) scale, extends through zero into negative numbers. According to this scale, the sun's apparent visual magnitude is −26.7, the full moon, −12.7, and Venus in brightest phase, −4.5.

Table 15.1 gives the apparent visual magnitudes of the 15 brightest stars, together with information on luminosity and distance. Ap-

Figure 15.4. Globular star cluster, M 13, in the constellation of Hercules. (The Hale Observatories.)

Table 15.2.   CHARACTERISTICS OF THE SPECTRAL CLASSES

| Spectral Class | Typical Stars | Color | Temperature (°K) | Characteristics of Lines in Spectrum |
|---|---|---|---|---|
| B | Rigel Spica | Blue-white | 11,000° to 25,000° | Helium and hydrogen strong |
| A | Sirius Vega | White | 7,500° to 11,000° | Lines of hydrogen reach greatest intensity |
| F | Canopus Procyon | Yellow-white | 6,000° to 7,500° | Hydrogen weakening, metals strengthening |
| G | Capella The Sun | Yellow | 5,000° to 6,000° | Metals, particularly calcium, very strong |
| K | Arcturus Aldebaran | Reddish | 3,500° to 5,000° | Maximum metallic lines, molecular bands appear |
| M | Betelgeuse Antares | Red | 2,000° to 3,500° | Many molecular bands, violet spectrum weak |

Source: From T. G. Mehlin (1959), *Astronomy*, New York, Wiley. See p. 50.

parent visual magnitude is measured by sensitive photoelectric meters attached to telescopes. Magnitudes as faint as +24 can be measured. It should be obvious that apparent visual magnitude depends upon two factors—luminosity of the star and its distance from earth. Light emitted from a point source diminishes in intensity inversely as the square of the distance. For two stars of equal distance from earth, the one with the greater luminosity will appear to be the brighter. There is also the factor that the apparent brightness of a star may be diminished by the presence of a dust cloud in the intervening space (a *nebulosity*).

Table 15.1 lists the luminosities of the 15 brightest stars. Note the very great range in values. Alpha Centauri is a star of low luminosity, about equal to the sun, but appears as an extremely bright star because it is very close to us. *Rigel*, of somewhat fainter apparent magnitude, has a luminosity about 27,000 times greater than that of Alpha Centauri but is at a comparatively great distance.

To reduce the actual stellar luminosities to a scale that correlates with the scale of apparent magnitudes a system of absolute visual magnitudes is used. The *absolute visual magnitude* of a star is the apparent visual magnitude it would have if it were located at a distance of 10 parsecs from the sun. In Figure 15.5, absolute visual magnitude is scaled on the left-hand side of the graph in numbers ranging from under −4 to over +16. By reading across to the right-hand side of the graph, a corresponding value of luminosity can be found.

## STAR MASS AND LUMINOSITY

It might be reasoned that the larger a star, the greater will be its luminosity, since the area of radiating spherical surface increases as the

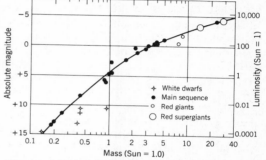

Figure 15.5. Mass-luminosity diagram. [From T. G. Mehlin (1959), *Astronomy*, New York, John Wiley & Sons, p. 45, Figure 2–3.]

square of the diameter, but this reasoning ignores the fact that a hot star may be radiating 10,000 times more strongly per square centimeter of its surface than a cool star. There is a sound scientific reason to associate increased mass with increased luminosity. The more massive the star, the greater will be the gravitational pressure tending to cause contraction and, consequently, the higher will be the internal temperature. As internal temperature increases, the rate of production of energy by the nuclear fusion processes also increases. Thus the larger the mass of a star, the greater will be its output of radiant energy.

Figure 15.5 is a graph in which luminosity (also absolute visual magnitude) is plotted against mass for a number of stars whose mass and luminosity have both been independently measured. For the most part, the stars fall on or close to a broadly curved line. At the upper right are enormous stars known as *red supergiants*, below them and to the left are *red giants*. In the middle of the graph are stars of the *main sequence*, ranging from 100 times to about one five-hundredth the sun's mass. There is, however, a group of stars known as the *white dwarfs,* whose plotted positions lie far off the typical curve. These are very small stars of extremely high density which produce far less heat from thermonuclear processes than do stars of the main sequence having equivalent masses. Apparently, the white dwarfs have largely exhausted their supplies of hydrogen and have contracted into an abnormally dense state.

The mass-luminosity curve is useful to the astronomer because it enables him to estimate the mass of a star when its luminosity is known, or to estimate the luminosity if only the mass is known.

## SPECTRAL CLASSES OF STARS

The radiation spectrum produced on the photosphere of a star consists of the full sequence of wavelengths appropriate to the temperature of the radiating surface (see Chapter 1). However, as this radiation passes through the star's atmosphere (chromosphere) the various elements that make up the atmospheric gas absorb certain wavelengths. Where absorption occurs, black lines show on the color spectrum. Such lines, first observed in the sun's spectrum, were known as *Frauenhofer lines.* Each element has its particular set of absorption lines and can be identified with certainty. Moreover, it is possible to determine the physical state of the absorbing element, whether it exists as neutral atoms or in the ionized state. From these observations the temperature of the star's atmosphere can be quite accurately determined. The proportions in which each element is present can also be determined.

The slit spectroscope is used to break up a light beam into its component colors (Figure 15.6). Attached to a telescope it can be focused upon a star and its spectrum photographed and analyzed (Figure 15.7). This procedure has been carried out upon a very large number of stars of our galaxy, with the result that they can be classified according to the *spectral class* to which each belongs. Arranged according to temperature, from hottest to coolest, the six major classes are designated *B, A, F, G, K,* and *M.* Table 15.2 summarizes the characteristics of the six major spectral classes. Figure 15.7 reproduces the actual spectra of six representative stars as photographed by telescope.

In addition to the six main classes, five spectral classes are added to accommodate a few stars which do not fit into the main tem-

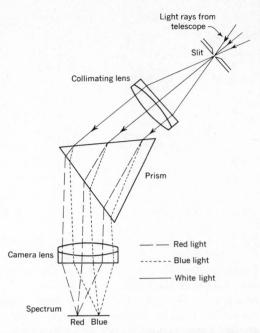

Figure 15.6. A slit spectograph focuses the image of a narrow spectrum upon a photographic plate. [After T. G. Mehlin (1959), *Astronomy,* New York, John Wiley & Sons.]

perature sequence. At the blue end of the sequence are added classes *W* and *O,* at the red end classes *N, R,* and *S.* Because the spectral classes grade from one to the next, intermediate positions on the scale are designated by numbered subdivisions, of which there are 10 within each letter class.

## SPECTRUM-LUMINOSITY RELATIONSHIPS

About 1910 two astronomers, Hertzsprung and Russell, working independently, plotted star luminosity against position in the main spectral-temperature sequence and found that a distinct and meaningful relationship exists. Figure 15.8 is the *Hertzsprung-Russell diagram* (or simply *H-R diagram*), in which each point represents a star. Luminosity is scaled on the vertical axis (ordinate), and corresponding scales in terms of star mass and absolute visual magnitude are given as well. On the horizontal axis (abscissa) spectral classes are arranged in sequence from highest temperature, on the left, to lowest temperature, on the right.

It is obvious that most of the stars plotted on the H-R diagram lie in a diagonal band commencing with high temperature and great luminosity at the upper left and ending with low temperature and small luminosity at the lower right. This band may be designated as the *main*

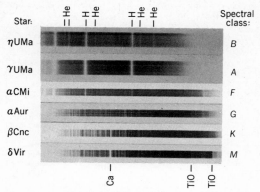

Figure 15.7. Representative spectra of stars of the major spectral classes. Symbols at left designate star and constellation. (Yerkes Observatory photograph, University of Chicago.)

*sequence*. Our sun lies about two-thirds of the way down this main sequence. A large isolated cluster of points above and to the right of the main sequence consists of the *supergiants* and *giants*. These are stars of enormous size which have great luminosity despite their cool temperatures. They fall into the spectral classes *K* and *M*. In the lower part of the diagram are a

very few stars, the *white dwarfs,* which we have already noted to be very small but of extremely great density. They are relatively hot stars.

## STELLAR EVOLUTION

Information about stars that we have reviewed thus far can be organized into a time-sequence pattern describing the life history of a star. Deferring for the moment a consideration of how the universe itself may have originated, we will start with a galaxy already in existence.

Within our Milky Way galaxy there are clouds of cold gas and dust whose temperature is close to absolute zero. Certain of these clouds appear as dark globules on astronomical photographs because the gas effectively absorbs most or all of the starlight that would otherwise pass through from distant stars on the far side. Diameters of the dark globules are on the order of 10,000 to 100,000 astronomical units. (The solar system has a diameter of about 80 astronomical units at the orbit of Pluto.)

As a working hypothesis, the cloud of cold gas that makes up a dark globule will be taken to represent the initial stage in the life history

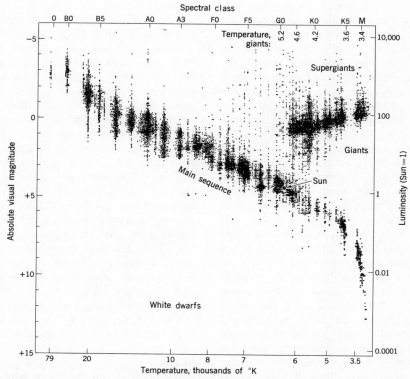

Figure 15.8. The Hertzsprung-Russell spectrum-luminosity diagram. Each dot represents a star. Altogether a sample of 6700 stars is recorded on the diagram. (Yerkes Observatory photograph, University of Chicago.)

of a star. Through the gravitational attraction which all particles of the gas cloud exert upon all other particles, the cloud would begin to contract, occupying a smaller volume. Through the Helmholtz principle, already explained, the temperature of the contracting body of gas would increase, and particularly so near the center of the mass, where pressures would be greatest. Eventually, a star would be formed and its interior temperature would attain a value exceeding 1 million ($10^6$) °K. At this point the first of a series of nuclear reactions would begin to take place, converting matter into energy and causing the star to begin emitting large amounts of electromagnetic radiation. As contraction continued and interior temperatures rose, other forms of nuclear reactions, which we have previously noted (Chapter 1), would develop and sustain a high level of energy production. A fully developed star such as our sun would then exist.

As the Hertzsprung-Russell diagram shows, stars of the main sequence span a very great range in both temperature and mass. Those of small mass can reach only comparatively low temperatures and pressures and therefore produce energy at a relatively slow rate, resulting in stars of faint luminosity. Such small stars will have an extremely long life because the utilization of the hydrogen supply takes place so very slowly. On the other hand, stars at the high-temperature and large-mass end of the sequence are converting their hydrogen supply into energy at an extremely fast rate. Their life expectancies will be short. For example, a star of mass 10 times that of the sun will radiate energy about 10,000 times as rapidly as the sun. The life of such a large star must therefore be on the order of 1% of the life of our sun, or as short as 100 m.y. The small stars will correspondingly have lives vastly longer than the sun, i.e., a duration of as great as thousands of billions of years.

Figure 15.9 is a graph with essentially the same field as the H-R diagram, but it does not show the plots of the individual stars. The diagonal band shows the position of the main sequence. The chain of arrows represents the evolution of a single star of about the size of the sun. The path enters from the right and moves horizontally toward the line of the main sequence. This horizontal path is covered comparatively rapidly and represents the stage of contraction of the gas cloud and its rise in temperature. When the star begins to consume

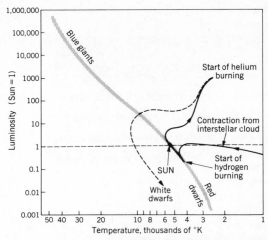

Figure 15.9. Simplified H-R diagram showing inferred evolution of an average star. [From O. Struve, *The Universe*, p. 55, Figure 36. © 1962 by the Massachusetts Institute of Technology.]

its hydrogen by thermonuclear processes it is located on the line of the main sequence. As appreciable amounts of the star's hydrogen are transformed into helium, the star may brighten slightly, probably by less than a magnitude, moving slowly to a position slightly above its original main sequence location.

The next stage in the life history of a star comes when its hydrogen supply is seriously depleted. Nuclear activity ceases first in the central region of the star, which then contracts. Nuclear activity continues in a surrounding zone that gradually moves outward from the center toward the surface. As this happens, the star may expand greatly. Although the luminosity remains high, the surface temperature falls and the star spectrum changes toward the red region. On the H-R diagram (Figure 15.8) this change requires that the plotted position of the star depart from the main sequence and move toward the upper right, occupying a position among the red giants and perhaps reaching the position of the supergiants (Figure 15.8). The final hypothetical stage in the life of the star is suggested in Figure 15.9 by a line that moves downward and to the left, then sharply downward to the region of the white dwarfs. These changes may be quite rapid. The star is now "burned out" and has only a faint luminosity despite its high temperature.

## NOVAE

On occasion, an extremely faint star bursts into intense brightness, then fades back to its original level. Such stars are known as *novae,* meaning "new," because they had not been observed to exist prior to the episode of brightness. A typical nova increases in brightness by 10 to 12 magnitudes in a time span of a few hours to a few days. Immediately after the outburst the brightness falls off rapidly for a time and then tends to level off and to diminish gradually over many weeks. Within years the brightness has returned to the original level.

Increase in brightness of the nova is associated with an explosive increase in its size, which may be a diameter increase of from 100 to 200 times. This expansion takes place in the photosphere of the star and is not an explosive enlargement of the entire star interior. The expanded layer of gases gradually dissipates and is lost into space, revealing the main body of the star intact. Novae are interpreted as being stars in the white-dwarf stage, near the end of the stellar life cycle. The explosion represents a short period of instability during the final stages of contraction into an extremely dense small star.

## STAR MOTIONS

For navigational purposes the stars are described as "fixed" in position in the celestial sphere, which is the frame of reference for all celestial bodies and corresponds to the terrestrial system of parallels and meridians. It is true that the stars appear to be absolutely fixed in celestial position as compared with the sun, moon, and planets, whose motions from day to day and month to month are easily seen with respect to the stars. Nevertheless, the stars are in motion in space, traveling in various directions and speeds relative to one another. Because of the great distances of the stars, their apparent motions can be observed only with modern telescopes capable of accurately measuring extremely small angles. The yearly amount of change of position of a star, stated as an arc (angular measure), is termed the *proper motion.* Obviously, the proper motion cannot be converted into absolute units of kilometers per second unless the star's distance is known.

Let us analyze in more detail the geometry of stellar motion. Figure 15.10 shows a particular star, *61 Cygni,* in relation to the earth's orbit (angles are enormously exaggerated). Using rounded figures, the parallax of this star is about ³⁄₁₀ of 1 sec of arc while the proper motion is about 5⅕ sec/yr. Using a simple

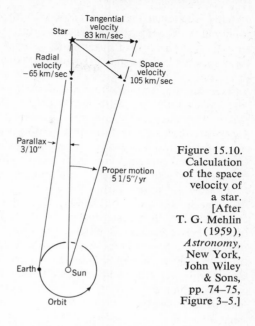

Figure 15.10. Calculation of the space velocity of a star. [After T. G. Mehlin (1959), *Astronomy,* New York, John Wiley & Sons, pp. 74–75, Figure 3–5.]

formula,* the *tangential velocity* can be calculated and proves to be 83 km/sec. Tangential velocity is the speed of motion at right angles to the line of sight, whereas the true motion, or *space velocity,* is at some angle with respect to this line (Figure 15.10). There is also a vector component of the true motion in the line of sight, either toward or away from the observer. The speed in this line is the *radial velocity.*

Radial velocity can be measured by means of the amount by which the color spectrum of light is shifted by motions that increase or decrease the distances between light-emitting sources and the observer. The principle involved is familiar in the *Doppler effect* on sound waves, in which the pitch of a sound of fixed vibration period sounds higher as the emitting source is brought rapidly toward us and lower as it recedes from us. A very simple analogy may help to illustrate the principle. Suppose that we stand beside a long horizontal conveyer belt and place small objects, such as pebbles, on the belt at uniform intervals of time. If the belt speed is constant, the pebbles will be uniformly spaced. Now, if as we place the pebbles we also walk slowly in the direction in which the belt is moving, the pebbles will be spaced closer together; whereas if we walk in a direction opposite to the belt motion, again

---

* Tangential velocity (km/sec) equals 4.74 times the proper motion (sec/yr), divided by the star's parallax (sec).

placing pebbles at the same intervals of time, they will be spaced farther apart on the belt.

Take now the case of a star emitting a given light spectrum. If the star is moving earthward, it appears to us that the frequencies of vibration constituting the light rays are all increased slightly, resulting in a slight change in the color, since the color we observe is determined by the frequencies of light and these have been increased by the motion. If the star is moving away from the earth a reverse effect occurs: the frequencies of vibration are reduced.

In practice, displacement of a given absorption line in the spectrum is measured in terms of wavelength. In the case of the star 61 Cygni, the *H* line of calcium is displaced toward the blue end of the spectrum in an amount equal to 0.86 Angstrom unit. (Refer to Chapter 1 and Figure 1.3 for explanation of units.) By use of a simple formula* the radial velocity can be calculated and proves to be −65 km/sec. The negative sign means that motion is toward the observer. As shown in Figure 15.10, the space velocity of about 105 km/sec is calculated as the length of hypotenuse of a triangle whose sides are the radial velocity and the tangential velocity: $65^2 + 83^2 = 105^2$, approximately.

From measurements of proper motions and radial velocities of many stars in all directions from the sun, so that their individual space velocities can be averaged out, it has been determined that with respect to the other stars in our region of the Milky Way galaxy, our sun is moving with a speed of about 12 mi/sec (20 km/sec) toward the position of the star *Vega*. Similar measurements on stars in various positions around the Milky Way and on other galaxies outside our own have shown, as was noted in an earlier paragraph, that our entire galaxy is rotating.

**BINARY STARS AND VARIABLE STARS**

Two stars sufficiently close together may be held within each other's gravitational fields to form a two-body system revolving about a common center of gravity. The mechanics of such a system are essentially similar to that of the Earth-Moon pair and are discussed in Chapter 3. Such star pairs are known as *binary stars* and are quite numerous in our galaxy. In some instances, both stars of the pair can be

observed as separate individuals. In other instances, they cannot be optically separated and appear as a single light source that varies regularly in intensity, for if the plane of their orbits is edgewise to the earth, there is a sharp drop in brightness as one star of the pair passes behind the other. Still other binary star systems can be detected only through variations in their spectra.

Quite a different class of stars are those in which the variations in brightness result from actual changes in the intensity of surface radiation of the star and represent changes in the star itself. One class of such stars are the *pulsating variable stars,* which undergo regular pulsations of brightness in cycles that range in length from as short as 1 hr to as long as several years. Pulsations are known to be associated with rhythmic expansions and contractions of these stars (Figure 15.11) since the Doppler shift reveals that the star surface moves first toward, then away from the observer.

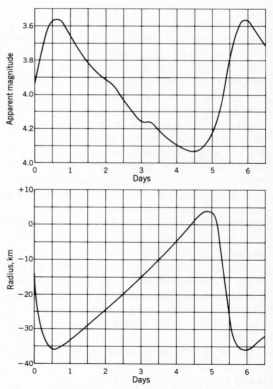

Figure 15.11. Curves of apparent magnitude and radius for Delta Cephei for 6½ days. [From T. G. Mehlin (1959), *Astronomy*, New York, John Wiley & Sons, p. 140, Figure 6–2; based on data of Lick Observatory.]

* Ratio of radial velocity to velocity of light is equal to ratio of change of wavelength to normal wavelength.

In some of the pulsating variables, particularly the Cepheids described below, it is now believed that the variation occurs mostly in the outer part of the star. Changes in the amount of ionization of hydrogen and helium not far below the star's surface make the star more or less transparent to radiation coming from the star's interior. When the flow of energy is blocked the temperature and pressure slightly below the surface increase; the star becomes brighter and expands. The changing degree of ionization then permits a freer flow of energy and the star cools, contracts, and becomes fainter. Pulsating stars that are very large red giants and supergiants show very long periods of pulsation; those that are relatively hot stars of blue color (*blue giants*) pulsate more rapidly.

The stability of our sun, with its remarkable constancy of energy output over hundreds of millions of years of time, stands in strong contrast to the behavior of the pulsating variable stars. Life on planet Earth has depended upon the sun's constancy of energy emission. We might infer that planetary systems belonging to variable stars would not provide stable environments for the evolution of life.

## CEPHEID VARIABLES AND DISTANCE MEASUREMENT

A particular class of variable stars, the *Classical Cepheids,* deserve special attention because of their role in making possible measurements of distances to stars far beyond the limits of direct measurement by parallax, and even of distances to galaxies other than our own. The curves of apparent magnitude and radial velocity shown in Figure 15.11 are those of a Classical Cepheid. Stars of this group have light-variation periods of from 1 to 45 days, but most are not far from a 5-day period.

An important discovery made in 1908 arose from observations of a particular group of Classical Cepheids located in the Magellanic clouds. Henrietta Leavitt of Harvard Observatory found that when the average brightness (apparent visual magnitude) of each Cepheid was plotted against its light period on a logarithmic scale, the points fell approximately along a straight line, as shown in Figure 15.12. Because all of these stars lie at about the same distance, their apparent magnitudes must be in direct proportion to their absolute visual magnitudes.

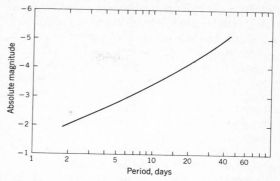

Figure 15.12. Period-luminosity curve of Classical Cepheids. [Data from W. M. Smart (1968), *The Riddle of the Universe,* New York, John Wiley & Sons, p. 95, Figure 5.3.]

Though Henrietta Leavitt's work clearly indicated a close correlation between the absolute magnitudes and the periods of the Cepheid variables, it did not establish the zero point of the absolute magnitude scale, and this proved to be a difficult task. The Magellanic clouds are a thousand times too far away for direct trigonometric determinations of their distances. In fact, not a single Cepheid was known that was close enough for a direct trigonometric measurement of its parallax which could be combined with its apparent magnitude to give its absolute magnitude. But if the distances of even a few Cepheids within our galaxy could be determined relatively accurately by indirect methods, they would establish the zero point of the period-luminosity curve and provide a new and powerful tool for the astronomers.

The radial velocity of a star can be measured accurately by means of the Doppler effect without regard to its distance. Hertzsprung assumed that if the individual space velocities of the stars were completely random in their direction, then statistically their tangential velocities would equal their radial velocities. This would not necessarily be true for any individual, but if enough different stars were investigated, the individual variations should average out. Assuming that the tangential velocity for an individual star was equal to its radial velocity, then combining it with the star's proper motion would give the star's distance or parallax. By this method, Hertzsprung was able to derive a provisional zero point for Henrietta Leavitt's period-luminosity curve.

By using the proper motions of members of star clusters containing Cepheids in our own galaxy, and also by fitting the apparent magnitudes and spectral types of the cluster stars to the established spectrum-luminosity diagram, Harvard astronomer Harlow Shapley was able to sharpen still more the location of the zero point of the period-luminosity curve. Depending on their individual periods, the absolute magnitudes of the Cepheids were found to range from 0 to −5, indicating that the brightest are 10,000 times as luminous as our sun.

Because of their extreme luminosity, the brighter Cepheids can be used to determine the distances of other galaxies as far away as several million light-years. When its distance is known, the size and absolute magnitude of each individual galaxy can be determined, thus setting up scales which can be used for getting at least the approximate distances to galaxies that are too far away for even individual Cepheids to be observed. We shall see in later paragraphs that the spectra of these more distant galaxies show a shift to the red which appears to be directly proportional to the distance of the galaxy. This red shift-distance relationship provides a method for measuring intergalactic distances out to several billion light-years.

## PULSARS AND SUPERNOVAE

Most recently discovered of stars whose brightness varies are the *pulsars*. These stars flash "on" and "off" rapidly, emitting both light waves and radio waves in the same rhythm. Light pulses range in frequency from about 1 pulse per 4 sec in the slowest rhythm to as high as 30 pulses per 1 sec. In the case of the high rate of pulsation, the star appears to the eye and on photographs to be continuously bright, but special techniques can reveal the flashing on and off (Figure 15.13). To explain the periodic emission of pulsars it has been suggested that they are extremely small, dense *neutron stars* (dwarfs) rotating rapidly on an axis. The emitting source is situated at one spot on the star and thus gives forth a single turning ray of light or of radio waves, as does a lighthouse or rotating beacon light. The magnetic field of a pulsating neutron star is thought to be enormously strong—some thousand-billion times as strong as that of our sun. A measurable slowing of pulse rate in these stars suggests that energy is being dissipated at a rapid rate.

A very rare type of nova is one that attains sudden brightness now believed to be in the

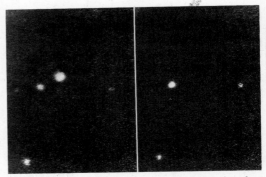

Figure 15.13. Comparison photographs of pulsar NP 0532 in "on" (*left*) and "off" (*right*) phases. (Lick Observatory photograph, University of California.)

range between ¼ billion and 1½ billion times the luminosity of the sun. If it is in our own galaxy its apparent magnitude may exceed that of the brightest planets. Such phenomena are known as *supernovae* and occur within our galaxy with a frequency of about one in several hundred years. Following the outburst, an expanding cloud of gas and dust (an expanding nebula) has been observed surrounding the site of the supernova (Figure 15.14).

The supernovae probably originate from extremely massive stars that have transformed so much of their hydrogen to heavier elements that they become explosively unstable. Unlike the typical nova, the outburst of a supernova blows off the major part of the material of the star, changing the nature of the star drastically. In 1969 the central star of the Crab Nebula was shown to be a pulsar, or rapidly rotating neutron star, only a few miles in diameter, but having a density on the order of 1 million billion ($10^{15}$) times the density of water. It emits extremely regular radio pulses at the rate of 30 per second. Thus, evidence seems to be accumulating that a neutron star is the dense mass remaining after the outburst of a supernova.

## GALAXIES AND THE UNIVERSE

To the most distant limits of telescopic penetration our universe consists of widely spaced galaxies, of which an estimated 10 billion ($10^{10}$) can now be observed, but no outer limit to the universe can be recognized. The total extent of possible observation of light from distant galaxies is estimated to be 10 billion ($10^{10}$) light-years. Within this theoretical maximum radius of observation there may be as many as 100 billion ($10^{11}$) galaxies.

Figure 15.14. The Crab nebula in the constellation of Taurus, photographed in red light. This nebula is the remains of a supernova of A.D. 1054. (The Hale Observatories.)

Galaxies fall into several classes, according to their shapes. *Spiral galaxies,* such as our Milky Way, are illustrated by the Andromeda spiral, which is the closest galaxy to our own (Figure 15.2). Its distance is about 1.8 billion ($1.8 \times 10^9$) light-years, and its diameter is a bit larger than our Milky Way galaxy. Another class of galaxies are the *barred spirals,* in which the two arms uncoil from a central bar (Figure 15.15). Equally important are galaxies of the *elliptical* group (Figure 15.16). These are ellipsoidal or spherical masses having a

Figure 15.15. Barred spiral galaxy NGC 7741 in the constellation of Pegasus. (The Hale Observatories.)

Figure 15.16. Elliptical galaxy NGC 205 in the constellation of Andromeda. (The Hale Observatories.)

high degree of symmetry, a form that suggests that they, like the spirals, are rotating. In addition, there are galaxies of highly irregular shape, but these are relatively few.

Within the nearer galaxies individual stars and star clusters can be recognized. Clouds of dust and gas that are typical of the spiral galaxies seem to be absent from the elliptical types. Attempts have been made to arrange the several forms of galaxies into an evolutionary series. Edwin P. Hubble, the astronomer who did much of the pioneering work in galactic investigation, suggested a classification which began with the almost spherical elliptical galaxies and then progressed to the more flattened systems, branched into two parallel arms for the spirals and barred spirals, and perhaps ended with the irregular galaxies (Figure 15.17).

When more was known about the galaxies and the ages of the stars in them, Harlow Shapley suggested that the evolutionary sequence might well begin with the irregular galaxies, developing into spiral systems in which the nucleus would move tightly into the arms with increasing age. Then, as the stars aged and the interstellar clouds of gas and dust were eliminated, the spirals might evolve into elliptical systems of varying degrees of flattening. It is still not understood why some spirals take the normal form and some become barred spirals.

## COSMOLOGY AND AN EXPANDING UNIVERSE

*Cosmology* as a science concerns itself with the nature and origin of the universe. Only in the past 40 years or so have observations of the galaxies been adequate to encompass the real

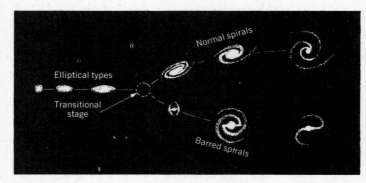

Figure 15.17. Diagram of sequence of nebular types as arranged by E. Hubble. No nebulae have been recognized in the transitional stage, which is hypothetical. [From E. Hubble (1936), *The Realm of the Nebulae*, New Haven, Yale Univ. Press, p. 45.]

order of magnitude of the universe. Modern cosmology is truly one of the young sciences. As new information comes in from increasingly distant parts of the universe cosmological theories continue in a state of flux.

One of the most remarkable phenomena related to the galaxies is that the red shift of their spectra increases in direct proportion to their radial distance from our point of observation in the solar system (Figure 15.18). Assuming that the red shift is a true Doppler effect, all galaxies must be in radial motion, receding from our galaxy. Moreover, the speed of recession increases proportionately with increasing distance. Figure 15.19 shows the radial velocities of galaxies of Figure 15.18 plotted against their distances. True proportionality would be represented by a straight line originating at the zero point on both scales and slanting upward to the right.

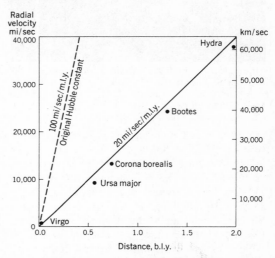

Figure 15.19. Plot of radial velocity versus distance for the five galaxies shown in Figure 15.18.

The relationship of radial velocity to distance has been called *Hubble's law*, and is given by the equation:

$$V = kD$$

where $V$ is radial velocity in miles per second,
   $D$ is distance in millions of light-years,
and $k$ is a numerical constant, or constant of proportionality.

(Units of kilometers per second and millions of parsecs may also be used.)

When first discovered by Hubble in the 1920s, the red shift was combined by him with other astronomical measurements to yield the conclusion that radial velocities of the galaxies increase by about 100 mi/sec (160 km/sec) for every increase of 1 million ($10^6$) light-years distance (Figure 15.19).

The geometry of such apparent radial outward motion can be visualized in terms of a universe that is expanding uniformly in vol-

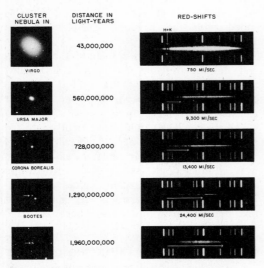

Figure 15.18. Spectra of five galaxies, showing the relationship of red shift to distance. Arrow on each spectrum shows the shift of calcium lines $H$ and $K$. (The Hale Observatories.)

ume. From any single vantage point in this system all other objects will appear to be moving radially outward. Hubble's discovery of a law of increase of radial velocity proportionate with distance quickly led to a new theory of origin of the universe. Among the first to propose such a cosmological theory was Canon Lemaître, a Belgian, who referred to the concept as a "fireworks theory." The theory requires an initial point in time at which all matter was concentrated into a small space. From this center it expanded explosively outward in all directions. The elements were created during this explosion and were later formed into the galaxies. Although now commonly referred to as the "big-bang" theory of the universe, the title of *evolutionary theory* is perhaps more fitting.

Using Hubble's first derived estimates of the rate of velocity increase with distance of separation, it could be calculated that all matter of the universe was concentrated into a small space about −2 billion years (−2 × 10⁹ b.y.). This point in time was designated the *age of the universe*. Figure 15.20 shows Hubble's law for various values of the constant, $k$. Age of the universe in years would be equal to distance in light-years of the most rapidly traveling galaxy. As explained in Chapter 12, age determination of meteorites and rocks based upon analysis of radioactive decay of certain elements gives ages much greater than −2 b.y. Ages of meteorites and certain lunar rock fragments are found to be −4.5 b.y. and are the oldest known objects whose ages have been measured directly. Theoretical investigations along a number of lines—such as the probable

ages of the stars and the stability of star clusters in our galaxy—suggest an age about twice this great for the universe.

In 1952, data obtained from the 200-in. reflector at the Mount Palomar Observatory required Hubble's calculations to be modified to revise the rate of increase in velocity to 40 mi/sec (65 km/sec) per million light years and, consequently, to increase the calculated age of the universe to nearly −5 b.y. (Figure 15.20). This modification placed the evolutionary theory in accord with the established ages of meteorites and rocks. More recently, the figures have been revised to reduce the rate of increase of velocity to 20 mi/sec (32 km/sec) and thus to increase the age of the universe to as great as −10 b.y. (10¹⁰) (Figures 15.19 and 15.20).

The evolutionary theory conforms to the principle that the distribution of galaxies is uniform in all directions throughout space. Under this concept, to an observer from any galaxy the average composition of the universe would appear the same. It is interesting to consider that under Hubble's principle the radial velocity of extremely distant galaxies, with respect to our observation point in the solar system, must reach and finally equal the speed of light (Figure 15.20). This distance would constitute the observable limit of the universe, beyond which we could receive no light or radio waves from the emitting sources.

The hypothesis of a *pulsating universe* has also been suggested as a modification of the "big-bang" hypothesis. Immediately after the initial explosion all of the matter would be moving outward with high velocities, but the mutual gravitational attraction between all of the parts would tend to slow the outward motion, perhaps finally stopping it and causing the entire system to contract. All of the material would eventually come back to a central point in an implosion that would annihilate all forms of matter—stars, galaxies, and even individual atoms. The result would be another "cosmic bomb," which would explode and start the whole process over again. The interval for one complete cycle has been estimated to be something less than 100 b.y.

A major rival theory of the universe holds that there was no single point in time at which matter was concentrated in one place. Instead, the production of matter has gone on throughout intergalactic space at a constant rate during all time. Rate of production of matter in the

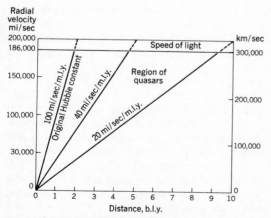

Figure 15.20. Relation of radial velocity to distance for different values of Hubble's constant.

form of hydrogen atoms has been equaled by the rate at which matter is dispersed by the expansion of the universe. This *steady-state theory* of cosmology, proposed in 1948 by the astronomers H. Bondi, T. Gold, and F. Hoyle, has attracted great interest but is currently enjoying fewer supporters than it had a decade ago.

The most recent evaluations of information concerning galaxies and other distant objects, based upon such methods as radio astronomy (discussed in the succeeding section), seem to place the evolutionary theory of the universe in a stronger scientific position than the steady-state theory. However, we can anticipate modified and new cosmological theories of the universe to be brought forward from time to time as new information is gained from the development and use of newer tools of astronomy.

## RADIO ASTRONOMY AND QUASARS

Part of the electromagnetic radiation spectrum, that in the longwave region, consists of *radio waves* (see Figure 1.3). In the range of wavelengths between about 1 cm and about 20 m, radio waves can pass through our atmosphere and be received by *radio telescopes*. These instruments use a huge concave bowl-shaped (parabolic) antenna that can be aimed at a distant emitting source.

Thousands of radio-emitting sources have been discovered and their positions plotted, but only a few can be identified with stellar objects that appear on photographs. Some sources of radio emission lie within our Milky Way galaxy; others are in distant galaxies, referred to as *radio galaxies*. These radio galaxies, of which about 150 have been identified, are the most powerful of all radio-emission sources. What appear to be two galaxies in collision are identified with radio-wave emission. Hydrogen gas clouds within our galaxy are also emitting sources. Our sun shows strong radio-wave emission at those times when a solar flare is in progress. A number of stars are known to have flares of similar nature; at such times their brilliance is greatly increased, thus radio emissions received from these stars are believed to be associated with flares.

Among the most important of astronomical discoveries in recent years (since about 1963) has been the finding of extremely small sources of intensely powerful radio emission not related to any surrounding galaxy. Named *quasi-stellar radio sources,* a term since reduced to *quasars,* these emission sources appear only as pinpoints of light. The distribution of the 100 or so quasars identified is quite uniform with respect to direction from the earth.

A particularly striking feature of quasars is that the lines in their spectra show a very great shift toward the red. Although its use here may be questioned, if the same red shift-distance relationship developed for galaxies is applied to quasars, the extremely large red shift would lead to the conclusion that they are on the order of 1 to 10 billion ($10^9$ to $10^{10}$) light-years away, and are thus the most distant known objects in the universe. If so, the luminosities and energy outputs of the quasars are truly enormous. One hypothesis explains the quasars as formed from gas clouds sent outward from the center of an exploding universe at a speed up to 80% that of light.

## COSMIC PARTICLES (COSMIC RAYS)

The earth's atmosphere is continually bombarded with elementary particles traveling at speeds approaching the speed of light and having enormous energy and penetrating power. This form of radiation from outer space, the *cosmic particle* (*cosmic ray*), is an entirely independent phenomenon from the electromagnetic radiation spectrum of a star.

Cosmic particles are *protons,* i.e., parts of the atomic nucleus. Approximately 90% are hydrogen nuclei, 9% are helium nuclei, and 1% are heavier nuclei. The energy of cosmic particles is enormous. Measured in units of *electron volts,* the energy of single cosmic particles ranges from 1 billion electron volts (Bev) to 100,000 Bev, but some have energies up to 100 million Bev.

Cosmic particles approach our earth from all directions. Their space paths seem to be quite at random and they can be visualized as constituting a kind of cosmic "gas" in which particles undergo random collisions and can thus take an infinite variety of paths and a wide range of speeds. Sources of cosmic particles are considered to be varied. They are produced in solar flares, but most come from other sources, believed to be the explosions of supernova and other forms of explosive activity in the central parts of our own and other galaxies. It has been suggested that galaxies which emit radio waves are also sources of important amounts of cosmic radiation.

Cosmic particles are important in the environment of life on the earth's surface. Certain harmful parts of the solar radiation spectrum—the X ray and gamma rays—are largely stopped by our atmosphere (Chapter 1), but the extremely high energy of cosmic particles enables them to penetrate deep into the lower atmosphere and to reach the earth's surface. This penetration is accompanied by an elaborate series of secondary nuclear reactions making up a *shower* of particles and secondary forms of radiation (Figure 15.21). When a high-speed cosmic particle impacts the nucleus of an atom within the atmosphere, there are produced neutrons and protons, mesons, and gamma radiation. The effect of such radiation upon life forms is to induce genetic changes (mutations in genes) which are important in the process of organic evolution.

## MAN'S PLACE IN THE UNIVERSE

Seen in its relative position among the other stars of the Milky Way galaxy, our sun is a fairly typical star in most respects. It lies somewhat below the midpoint of the main sequence of stars, belonging to the spectral class, *G,* which has moderate surface temperatures in terms of the total temperature range. Luminosity and mass are about midway on the constant-ratio (logarithmic) scale of those values. Extreme constancy of energy output over vast spans of geologic time characterizes the sun, a behavior in strong contrast to the changing energy fluxes of the variable stars and novae.

Our sun represents one of the basic forms of energy systems, that of conversion of matter to energy in nuclear reactions occurring within a gaseous medium under enormously high pressures and temperatures. The life span of our sun is neither very short nor very long in comparison with the range found among stars, but it is long enough to assure that our terrestrial environment can continue with little change for a span of time vastly longer than that which has already transpired as geologic time.

In reference to the total size of our Milky Way galaxy, the sun is no more than an insignificant particle of matter, while in the context of the universe of galaxies, it comes infinitesimally close to being nothing at all. Within the universe there must be a very large number of stars quite similar to our sun, and many of these must have planets resembling our own. Reason leads us to suppose that spontaneous development of organic life and its evolution to highly complex states must have been replicated a great number of times on unknown planets. But we also realize that the vastness of interstellar and intergalactic space reduces

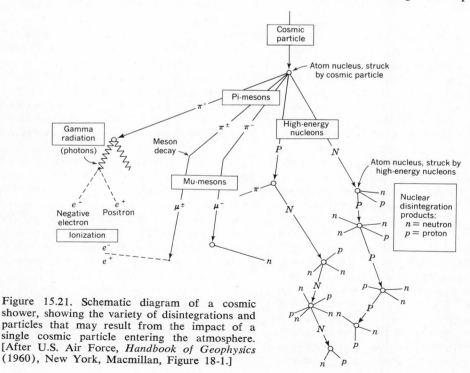

Figure 15.21. Schematic diagram of a cosmic shower, showing the variety of disintegrations and particles that may result from the impact of a single cosmic particle entering the atmosphere. [After U.S. Air Force, *Handbook of Geophysics* (1960), New York, Macmillan, Figure 18-1.]

almost to zero the possibilities of identifying and communicating with even the closest of such organic complexes. Despite such odds, the possibility of a discovery that Man on planet Earth is not alone in the universe continues to fire the popular imagination.

## References for further study

Lyttleton, R. A. (1956), *The Modern Universe,* New York, Harper & Row, 207 pp., chaps. 4–6.

Mehlin, T. G. (1959), *Astronomy,* New York, Wiley, 392 pp., chaps. 1–8.

Bondi, H. (1960), *The Universe at Large,* New York, Doubleday, 154 pp.

Struve, O. (1962), *The Universe,* Cambridge, Mass., M.I.T. Press, 159 pp.

Smart, W. M. (1968), *The Riddle of the Universe,* New York, Wiley, 228 pp.

Alfvén, H. (1969), *Atom, Man, and the Universe,* San Francisco, Freeman, 110 pp.

## Review questions

1. What units are used in the measurement of interstellar distances? How far away is the nearest star? Describe the phenomenon of stellar parallax and show how it is used to measure distance to a star. What is the parsec?

2. Describe the Milky Way galaxy and its motions. What are spiral arms, star clouds, the halo, and globular star clusters? Where in our galaxy is the sun located?

3. What important physical properties of stars are subject to measurement? Compare our sun with other stars in terms of mass, density, luminosity, and surface temperature.

4. Define apparent visual magnitude. What range of apparent visual magnitudes is found among celestial objects? What relation does luminosity bear to apparent visual magnitude? What is the absolute visual magnitude of a star, and why is it used?

5. Relate star mass to luminosity. Explain the process responsible for luminosity. Describe the mass-luminosity curve. Where on this curve are the red supergiants? the red giants? the main sequence? Where are the white dwarfs located with respect to the mass-luminosity curve? Explain their position.

6. Describe the radiation spectrum of a star. How is the spectrum observed and recorded? What are the Frauenhofer lines? Describe a slit spectroscope. What are the main spectral classes? List them in order from hottest to coolest. What additional classes are needed?

7. What spectrum-luminosity relationships emerge from the Hertzsprung-Russell diagram? Describe this diagram. How do the major groups of stars fit into the diagram?

8. Discuss stellar evolution, beginning with a cloud of cold dust and gas. What causes interior heating of a star? At what point do nuclear reactions begin to occur? Plot the stages of development of a star on the H-R diagram. In what way is the life expectancy of a star related to its mass? What is the end stage in the life of a star?

9. What are novae? Describe the occurrence of a nova and explain what happens to the star. What is a supernova? What event does it represent in the life history of a star?

10. What is the proper motion of a star? How can the space velocity of a star be measured? Explain the Doppler effect upon the spectrum of a star. How is the Doppler effect used to measure radial velocity of a star? In what direction and at what speed is our solar system moving in our galaxy?

11. What are binary stars? How do they differ from pulsating variable stars? How are the periods of pulsation of these variable stars related to their temperatures?

12. What are the Cepheid variables? Explain how apparent visual magnitude of these stars is related to their periods of light variation. How was this information used to determine distance to a single group of Cepheid variables?

13. What is a pulsar? Describe the periodic emission of these stars. What hypothesis is put forward to explain the pulsation? To what class of stars do the pulsars belong?

14. About how many galaxies can be observed with existing telescopes? How far away are the most distant of the galaxies from which light might be received? Within that maximum range how many galaxies are estimated to exist?

15. Classify galaxies according to their forms. What sequence of development of galaxies was proposed by E. P. Hubble? by Harlow Shapley?

16. What is cosmology? Describe the red shift of spectra of the galaxies and relate it to their radial velocities. What is Hubble's law? Describe the geometry of a universe conforming to Hubble's law.

17. Describe the evolutionary ("big-bang") theory of the universe. How, according to this theory, can the age of the universe be estimated? Compare earlier and recent estimates of age of the universe. Do these estimates agree with radiometric ages of meteorites?

18. Describe the hypothesis of a pulsating universe. In what way does the steady-state theory differ from the evolutionary theory?

19. Describe the radio-emitting sources in space beyond the earth. How are radio emissions received? Does the sun emit radio waves? What are radio galaxies? What are quasistellar radio sources (quasars), and what is remarkable about their emission spectra? How are quasars interpreted?

20. What are cosmic particles (cosmic rays)? Of what forms of matter are they composed? What energy levels do they represent? What happens when a cosmic particle enters the earth's atmosphere? Where do cosmic particles come from?

21. Summarize the characteristics of our sun as compared with other stars, and comment upon the importance of those characteristics in determining our planetary environment through geologic time. What do you estimate to be the probability of existence of planets with life systems similar to those of planet Earth in other solar systems in our own and other galaxies? Would communication with advanced life forms on such distant planets be possible?

# epilogue
# man as an
# agent of change
# on planet earth

An epilogue is that final part of a literary work needed to place the body of the work in its proper perspective. While the 15 chapers of this book could scarcely qualify as a literary work, there is need for an epilogue—or at least the analogue of an epilogue. Chapter 14 ended with an account of the meteoric rise of men (hominids) late in the Cenozoic Era, culminating with the evolution of *Homo sapiens* in the final instant of geologic time. The history of Man's civilization is itself only a brief instant within the evolution of the species, yet that history has seen an explosive rise in the world population of human beings and has witnessed an equally rapid increase in the rate at which Man can release stored energy. With vast supplies of energy at his disposal, Man can disturb the action of natural systems and their energy and mass balances, alter the face of the land, and disperse huge quantities of materials and energy accumulated through geologic time. It is to these events that the Epilogue addresses itself.

This Epilogue has two parts, although their subject matter is not entirely independent under this division. First, we look into man-induced changes in the operations of natural systems. These changes are for the most part reversible, or we at least hope that they are. Second, we look into Man's use of earth resources. These uses represent irreversible changes, the consequences of which form a major order of business among the agenda of human problems.

# part i. man's impact on the atmosphere, the hydrosphere, and the lithosphere

## A. MAN'S IMPACT ON THE RADIATION AND HEAT BALANCES

The balances of radiation, heat, and atmospheric water analyzed in Chapters 1, 4, and 5 are subject to alteration by Man's activities that change the parameters of the respective equations. Briefly, changes fall into these categories: (a) changes in proportions of the component gases of the lower atmosphere; (b) changes in water-vapor content of the atmosphere; (c) introduction of finely divided solids into suspension in the lower atmosphere, along with gaseous compounds that are not normally measurable constituents of the atmosphere; and (d) alteration of the characteristics of the ground surface and its cover.

## ATMOSPHERIC CARBON-DIOXIDE AND OXYGEN LEVELS

Consider first the changes in proportions of the so-called nonvarying component gases of the troposphere, listed in Figure 1.10. Most critical from the environmental standpoint are carbon dioxide ($CO_2$) and free molecular oxygen ($O_2$), since both are chemically active and play essential roles in the life processes of plants and animals. Both of these gases also play important roles in the absorption of electromagnetic radiation in the atmosphere. Recall that carbon dioxide is an important absorber (along with water vapor) of longwave radiation, converting it into sensible heat, while molecular oxygen absorbs incoming shortwave radiation to form the protective ozone layer, at

the same time yielding heat in the region of the stratopause. Recall also, from Chapter 12, that atmospheric $CO_2$ was originally acquired by outgassing through geologic time but that the great bulk of the carbon thus produced is now in storage as carbonate rock and hydrocarbons (fossil fuels). By photosynthesis, plants liberated molecular oxygen from carbon dioxide and gradually through geologic time built up the free-oxygen level to its present value of 21% by volume (Figure 13.11). As things now stand, the atmospheric proportions of both $CO_2$ and $O_2$ are held approximately constant by the interaction of two cycles: the *carbon cycle* and the *oxygen cycle*. These cycles are diagrammed and briefly described in Figures E.1 and E.2.

Increase in atmospheric carbon dioxide during the past 120 years is reasonably well documented. The $CO_2$ percentage has risen from about 0.028% or 0.029% to about 0.032% during this period; the rate of increase being much more rapid as the most recent decade is approached. Now, if a calculation is made of

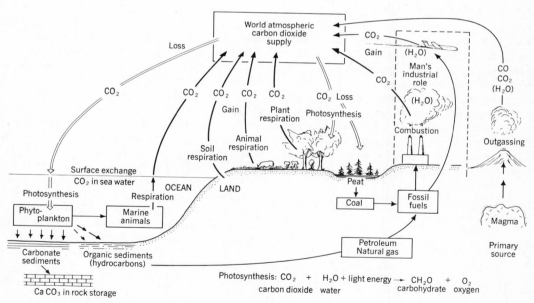

Figure E.1. The carbon cycle. Carbon is held as $CO_2$ both as free gas in the atmosphere and in solution in ocean waters. Through photosynthesis by land plants and marine plants (*phytoplankton*) $CO_2$ is withdrawn to produce carbohydrate compounds in plant tissues. Animals consume plant tissue, releasing the $CO_2$ during the process of biological oxidation (respiration). Decomposition of plant matter entering the soil also releases $CO_2$ to the atmosphere. Some partially decomposed plant matter enters long-term storage in marine and terrestrial sedments as hydrocarbons in petroleum and coal (fossil fuels). Carbon is also used in the production of carbonate sediment which accumulates on the ocean floor and may enter permanent storage in crustal rocks. Throughout geologic history this loss of atmospheric $CO_2$ has been balanced by new supplies emanating from deep within the earth by outgassing. Combustion of wood and fossil fuels releases $CO_2$ into the atmosphere, a process largely attributable to Man's activities.

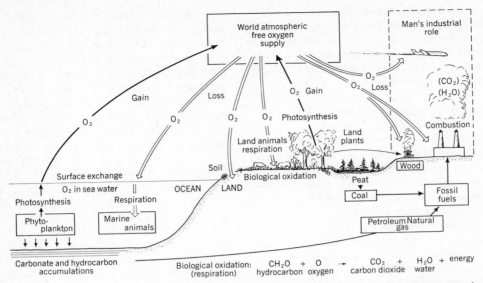

Figure E.2. The oxygen cycle. The world's supply of free molecular oxygen is derived and sustained by release of $O_2$ accompanying photosynthesis in plants. Losses of atmospheric $O_2$ occur through respiration in marine and terrestrial animals and in decay of organic matter, altogether described under the term *biological oxidation*. In combination with carbon, oxygen is accumulated in storage as hydrocarbon compounds in fossil fuels. Oxygen is also placed in storage along with carbon in accumulating carbonate sediments (not shown). These losses to long-term storage are essentially balanced by oxygen released as CO and $CO_2$ into the atmosphere by outgassing. Large-scale combustion of wood and fossil fuels by Man withdraws free oxygen from the world supply.

the $CO_2$ that was released by fossil fuels burned during the same period, it will be found that almost three times as much $CO_2$ has been discharged into the atmosphere as is represented by the measured increase in $CO_2$ content. Figure E.3 shows these facts by two curves. The lower curve represents observed amounts of $CO_2$ in the atmosphere; the upper curve shows the amounts that would be present, based upon estimated fuel consump-

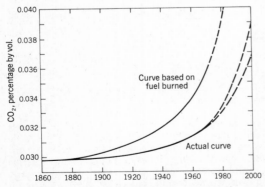

Figure E.3. Rise in percentage of atmospheric carbon dioxide since 1860, with projections into the future. [Data of Bert Bolin (1970), *Scientific American*, vol. 223, no. 3, p. 132.]

tion. Obviously, the difference represented by the two curves must be explained. The excess $CO_2$ gas has gone largely into solution in the oceans, while some has gone into an increased level of production of plant matter. There is a very large flux of $CO_2$ between the ocean surface and atmosphere. An estimated 100 billion tons of $CO_2$ per year passes in each direction but most of this exchange is within a shallow surface layer of the ocean. Figure E.3 shows the $CO_2$ curves of increase projected toward the year 2000. The rate of increase appears to be exponential; each decade brings about a twofold increase. Given very long periods of time (thousands of years) and a constant rate of annual input of $CO_2$ into the atmosphere, an equal amount of $CO_2$ withdrawal could be achieved through oceanic absorption and precipitation as carbonate sediment. Clearly, however, the response time of the oceans is enormously slow in comparison with the present rate of increase, so that we must anticipate the effects of rapidly increasing $CO_2$ content of the atmosphere for many decades to come, and perhaps for centuries. It is not yet known what fraction of the $CO_2$ produced by combustion will enter the oceans over the next century or so, but estimates range from 40% to 60%.* Using a projected rate of increase in consumption of burning of fossil fuels of 5% per year, the 60% value yields an atmospheric concentration of $CO_2$ of 0.040% by the year 1990; using the 40% value and a 4% per year increase in fuel-burning, the 0.040% level will be reached in the year 2010. The latter estimate is represented by the curve in Figure E.3.

What effects are to be anticipated from increase in the atmospheric $CO_2$ level? These effects follow logically from the role of $CO_2$ as an absorber of longwave radiation. A rise in average temperature of the lower atmosphere is indicated as net longwave flux upward is reduced and there is a gain in sensible heat of the air itself. Observations seem to lend some support to this predicted temperature rise; but there is also conflicting evidence, and the situation proves to be far more complex than merely a simple relationship between two variable quantities. Figure E.4 is a graph of change in average hemispherical temperature based upon observation for about the past century. From 1920 to 1940 the temperature had increased by about 0.6 F° (0.4 C°), but since then it has been falling. Evidently, other causes of temperature change working in the opposite direction have been more important than rising $CO_2$ in the past three decades; we shall return to the subject in later paragraphs.

* Based upon data in the *First Annual Report of the Council on Environmental Quality*, August, 1970, pp. 93–104.

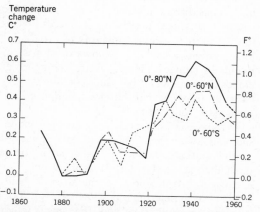

Figure E.4. Trends of global mean annual air temperatures for three ranges of latitude. [Data of J. M. Mitchell, Jr., NOAA (1970), in *Global Effects of Environmental Pollution*, S. F. Singer, ed., New York, Springer-Verlag, p. 142, Figure 1.]

Calculating on the basis of complete combustion of all estimated available world supplies of fossil fuels (coal, petroleum, natural gas) and the assumption that 50% of the $CO_2$ thus produced will be added to the atmosphere, the rise of world average air temperature from this cause alone is judged to be between 2 and 4 F° (1.1 and 2.2 C°).* Potential environmental effects of such a temperature rise, if it actually followed from the $CO_2$ increase, include melting of some parts of the great ice sheets of Antarctica and Greenland, with a concomitant small rise in sea level. Even this result is open to question, since the small rise in global air temperature might not be uniformly distributed from pole to pole and might even increase the rate of nourishment of the ice sheets.

The combustion of fossil fuels withdraws atmospheric oxygen, as shown in Figure E.2. Fears have been expressed that the consumption of all fossil-fuel reserves would lead to a substantial lowering of the level of atmospheric free oxygen, but geochemical considerations indicate that no serious threat of oxygen depletion exists. Concern has also been expressed that a substantial reduction of phytoplankton activity, brought on by pollution of the oceans, could bring on severe reduction in oxygen levels and constitute a real threat to terrestrial animal life. Again, recent investigation has shown that no serious threat of insufficient oxygen exists from this cause.

## ATMOSPHERIC WATER VAPOR, CLOUDS, AND PRECIPITATION

Like carbon dioxide, water vapor plays a vital role in absorption of longwave radiation. As pointed out in Chapter 5, the proportion of water vapor present in the air is a highly variable quantity, both from place to place and from time to time. The total quantity of the earth's available water held at any one time in the atmosphere is very small indeed (about 0.001% in terms of the earth's total supply; see Table 6.1). It would be next to impossible to measure changes in the yearly average of world total water vapor, but some inferences might be drawn from principles. Since the capacity of air to hold water vapor increases with increasing temperature, there should be a tie-in with world atmospheric temperatures. If an increase in $CO_2$ brings on atmospheric warming, that

* *Ibid.*

warming should also tend to increase the water vapor held in the atmosphere and might also result in an increase in annual global precipitation. As already noted in Chapter 14, the opposite change is documented in times of Pleistocene glaciations by equatorward expansion of the tropical deserts and a shrinkage of the equatorial belt of heavy rainfall.

Recently, the effects of jet-aircraft emissions upon the stratosphere have come under close scrutiny, and the questioning is intensified by general debate over the merits of the supersonic transport aircraft (SST) and its possible environmental influences. Some recent estimates* indicate that large fleets of these jet aircraft might contribute enough water vapor to raise the stratospheric content by some 20%. There would also be an increase in the proportion of $CO_2$, released by the same combustion. The changes would tend to increase the degree to which that atmospheric layer absorbs incoming solar radiation, and there would be corresponding increases in the temperature of the layer. As yet there is no way to evaluate such changes. Concomitant decreases in concentration of ozone in the overlying atmospheric region have been also inferred, and these would tend to offset a temperature rise, perhaps leaving lower stratospheric temperatures essentially unchanged.

Another possible environmental role of jet aircraft is through the effects of contrails (condensation trails) upon the earth's albedo. Along belts of heavy jet traffic contrails are frequently seen to broaden into cirruslike clouds, and these can at certain times and places produce an appreciable cloud layer capable of reflecting more shortwave radiation back into space. However, such belts cover only a small fraction of the global surface. If an increase in albedo from this cause has, or will in the future have, any appreciable effect upon surface temperatures, it should be in the direction of lower mean values.

Man's agricultural activities must have resulted in various changes in the water balance of the soil and lowermost air layer where crop farming replaced forests, but whether significant changes in air-mass water vapor and precipitation on a large scale can be attributed to these activities is difficult to determine. Recently, interest has centered on the possibility that large-scale crop irrigation is responsible

for a rise in precipitation over the same region. For example, increases in precipitation have been recorded over the Texas Panhandle region in the same period that extensive irrigation has been introduced. Water-vapor content of the lower atmosphere in this region seems also to have been increased. In any case, the influence of an increased input of water vapor from the ground would probably act through the triggering of more frequent convective storms, and this relationship is suggested by the fact that the recorded increases in precipitation are for the months of June and July, which is generally within the season of most convectional activity in the western Great Plains and Rocky Mountain region.

Yet another possibility of man-made changes upon atmospheric moisture and precipitation is through attempted rain-making by artificial cloud-seeding. Experiments conducted in the 1940s by Irving Langmuir and Vincent Schaefer showed that the release of dry-ice pellets into a stratus cloud set off rapid growth of frozen particles at the expense of liquid droplets in a layer of supercooled cloud particles. Subsequent experimentation by Bernard Vonnegut led to the use of silver iodide smoke to provide freezing nuclei. These have since proved capable, under favorable basic conditions, of intensifying sublimation within dense cumulus cloud masses and transforming them through release of latent heat of fusion into cumulonimbus clouds with heavy rainfall. Potentiality for substantial increases in average precipitation in favorable regions through cloud-seeding methods remains unevaluated, but it has been the basis of much scientific discussion. A real possibility of success seems to exist in increasing the quantity of orographic precipitation over the windward slopes of mountain ranges. Here, water content of clouds is normally high and conditions very close to those of natural precipitation persist for long periods of time.

A four-year pilot project to increase winter snowfall over the San Juan Mountains of southwestern Colorado by the silver-iodide method began early in 1971. Concurrently, an ecological investigation of the area is being carried out to determine possible effects of both increased precipitation and the silver iodide itself upon plants and animals.

Other possible man-made changes in condensation processes include suppression of hail formation in cumulonimbus clouds by cloud-

* Halstead Harrison (1970), *Science,* vol. 170, p. 734.

seeding and the reduction in intensity of hurricanes by seeding of clouds surrounding the central eye. As yet, it is too soon to attempt an evaluation of these techniques and their consequences.

## ATMOSPHERIC PARTICULATES AND POLLUTANTS

If the speculations of the preceding paragraphs seem not to lead to definite environmental predictions, the case is quite different for man-made changes in the quality of the lower atmosphere over densely populated areas where industrial activity is intense. This activity injects into the overlying air layer two classes of contaminants. First, there are solid and liquid particles designated as a group by the term *particulates.* Most of the particles comprising smoke from fuel combustion are in this category, as are droplets of clouds and fog. Figure E.5 is a grade scale of sizes of various kinds of particulates to be found in the atmosphere. Second, there are compounds in the gaseous state that can be covered under the heading of *chemical pollutants,* since they are not normally found in appreciable quantities in clean air over uninhabited regions. Excess of $CO_2$ over the normal values would by this definition constitute a pollutant, but for the most part industrial and urban pollutants consist of *carbon monoxide* (CO), *sulfur dioxide* ($SO_2$), hydrocarbon compounds, and oxides of nitrogen. Actually, the chemical pollutants cannot be treated independently of particulates of solid dusts and droplets, since they may be combined within a single suspended particle. Many of the dust particles are hygroscopic and readily absorb a film of water.

Sulfur dioxide may combine with oxygen to produce sulfur trioxide ($SO_3$), which in turn reacts with water of suspended droplets to produce *sulfuric acid* ($H_2SO_4$), a particularly irritating and corrosive ingredient of polluted air over industrial areas. Yet another undesirable product of pollution is ozone, formed in the presence of sunlight during reactions between nitrogen oxides and organic compounds. These reactions are described as *photochemical.* Another class of pollutants are the hydrocarbons, among them *ethylene,* a compound highly toxic to plants.

The entire contaminant mixture in its dense state is well known by the name of *smog* and is so familiar to all that its appearance and effects upon the eyes and respiratory system scarcely need to be mentioned. Lesser concentrations of particulates and pollutants produce *haze,* and it is well to remember that atmospheric haze can develop through the natural processes of lifting of mineral dusts, crystals of sea salts, and hydrocarbon compounds exuded by plant foliage in slow-moving air masses of the troposphere.

Major sources of air contaminants in the United States are given in Table E.1, in units of millions of tons per year. Although these figures will undergo some modification, several relationships are obviously independent of such errors or changes as may affect the data. First, practically all of the carbon monoxide, two-thirds of the hydrocarbons, and one-half of the nitrogen oxides are contributed by exhausts of gasoline and diesel-powered vehicles. Industrial processes and the generation of electricity furnish most of the sulfur oxides through the combustion of coal and lower-grade fuel oil,

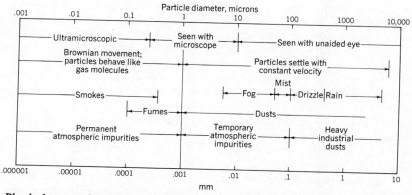

Figure E.5. Physical properties of atmospheric particulates. The scale is logarithmic. [Data of W. G. Frank, American Air Filter Company, Inc., Louisville, Ky. Reference: *Air Conservation* (1965), Washington, D.C., Amer. Assoc. for the Advancement of Sci., Publ. 80, p. 110, Figure 5.]

Table  E.1.  COMPONENTS OF AIR POLLUTION AND THEIR SOURCES IN THE UNITED STATES

| Sources | Contaminants (millions of tons per year) | | | | | | |
|---|---|---|---|---|---|---|---|
| | Carbon Monoxide | Sulfur Oxides | Hydro-carbons | Nitrogen Oxides | Particu-lates | Others | Totals |
| Transportation | 66 | 1 | 12 | 6 | 1 | <1 | 86 |
| Industry | 2 | 9 | 4 | 2 | 6 | 2 | 25 |
| Generation of electricity | 1 | 12 | <1 | 3 | 3 | <1 | 20 |
| Heating | 2 | 3 | 1 | 1 | 1 | <1 | 8 |
| Refuse disposal | 1 | <1 | 1 | <1 | 1 | <1 | 4 |
| Totals | 72 | 25 | 18 | 12 | 12 | 4 | 143 |

Source: From H. E. Landsberg, *Metropolitan Air Layers and Pollution*, in *Challenge for Survival*, P. Dansereau, ed., p. 133. © 1970 by the Columbia University Press. Reproduced by permission.

comparatively rich in sulfur. These sources also supply most of the particulates. Heating is a relatively small producer of contaminants, because the fuel is largely oil of higher grade and is efficiently burned. Refuse disposal appears as a minor contributor in all categories.

Particulates in the smog of cities, in addition to the compositions mentioned above, contain special contributions from automobile and truck engines and exhausts. These include solid particles in the size range 0.02 to 0.06 micron, containing lead, chlorine, bromine, and carbon. Lead-bearing particles make up about one-half of the particles in automobile exhaust. Not surprisingly, another contribution by the automobile is finely divided rubber worn from tires.

If the lifting of particulates and chemical pollutants into the lower troposphere by rising air currents is a normal atmospheric process, the reverse process of settling out under gravity, or *fallout*, is also a normal process. Only the larger solid particles engage in fallout. No city dweller needs to be told what fallout his cleanly washed automobile exterior will acquire when left parked for a few hours. To gravity fallout must be added *washout* by precipitation, which sweeps down particles too small to fall readily by gravity. Fallout and washout tend to rid the atmosphere of its contaminants, so that there is achieved in the long run a balance between recharge and elimination of contaminants.

Contaminants can also be partly eliminated from the atmosphere over the source or reduced in concentration by dispersion through advective transport in persistent and turbulent winds. Such elimination normally follows the passage of a cold front in middle latitudes, but the effect diminishes to zero in the center of a cell of high pressure where calm air prevails.

In connection with this discussion of man-made air pollution it might be well to point out that major natural sources of excessive particulate concentrations have always existed. Forest fires, set by lightning and by primitive Man, on many occasions introduced vast smoke palls into the troposphere. But even more significant are the large-scale discharges of volcanic dusts into the atmosphere that must surely have occurred spasmodically throughout all of geologic time. Particularly interesting was the effect of a great explosion of the Indonesian volcano Krakatoa in 1883. The enormous quantities of dust from this explosion were given global distribution at high levels by the planetary wind systems. At Montpellier, France, an observatory recorded short periods of decreased intensity of solar radiation ranging from 10% to 20% below average for 3 yr as a result of the increased reflection loss to space caused by the suspended dust particles. Eruptions of three other volcanoes within the 10-yr period following Krakatoa continued the supply of volcanic dusts and caused additional periods of reduced solar radiation. Now, it might be inferred that reduced solar radiation would be reflected in reduced atmospheric temperatures, but the records do not show this effect. Notice in Figure E.4 that a period of no significant temperature change covers the decade 1883–1893, during which reduced radiation was observed.

Returning again to Figure E.4, the marked decline in atmospheric temperature since 1940, despite the rapid rise in carbon dioxide, has aroused much interest among environmental climatologists. If this trend were to continue, the accumulated temperature decrease might constitute a significant environmental change. The cause of temperature decline may lie in a sharp increase in the quantity of volcanic dust present in the stratosphere, starting about 1947 with the eruption of the volcano Hekla and followed by eruptions of five other volcanoes in the 1950s and 1960s. In contrast, the previous three decades had seen very low volcanic activity. Evidently, the cooling effect of this dust through reduced incoming solar radiation, as referred to in the previous paragraph, has been sufficient to reverse the warming trend attributed to increase of carbon dioxide. We should not lose sight of the fact that climatologists consider that both the observed rise and decline in air temperatures may have had other natural causes.

Are man-made dusts also involved in the recent decline of air temperature? Dust content of snow layers in the Caucasus Mountains (elevations over 12,000 ft; 3.6 km) showed a dramatic increase (about 19-fold) from 1930 to 1963, and this dust is attributed to industrial activity in eastern Europe. There is in progress a very slow rise in the total quantity of man-made dust in the atmosphere. Scientists seem agreed, however, that man-made dust stays largely within the lower atmosphere and is removed by fallout and washout almost as fast as it is produced. While this dust may not be significant in the stratosphere (as compared to volcanic dust), it has important effects at low levels, particularly so in urban areas of intensive dust production. These effects are taken up in later paragraphs.

Returning again momentarily to the subject of clouds, it can be noted that the man-made dust contribution to the lower atmosphere is capable of increasing the production of low clouds, since the particles can serve as nuclei of condensation. The present average world value for cover by low clouds is about 31%. As noted in Chapter 1, this cover is the primary determinant of the earth's albedo. It has been estimated that if the average cloud cover should increase to 36%, the increased albedo would result in a drop of world average annual air temperature of 7 F° (4 C°), an amount sufficient to bring on significant advances of glaciers and ice sheets.*

## INVERSION AND SMOG

The heaviest concentrations of contaminants over a source area occur when vertical mixing

\* Based on data in the *First Annual Report of the Council on Environmental Quality,* August, 1970, pp. 93–104.

(convection) is inhibited by a stable temperature structure of the air mass. For basic principles we look to temperature lapse rates and their relation to atmospheric stability (Figure E.6). (Refer to Chapter 5 for explanation of stable and unstable air masses.) The normal lapse rate of 3.5° F per 1000 ft (0.6° C per 100 m) represents a condition under which vertical movements do not spontaneously occur, for there will be resistance to mixing. Suppose, for example, that a parcel of air (say, a cubic foot of air) is taken from level $A$ to level $B$. Since the temperature of this rising parcel falls by the dry adiabatic rate more rapidly than the lapse rate, it will always be cooler than the surrounding air. If cooler, it is also denser and will tend to sink back to its starting point. Next on the left is a greater (steeper) lapse rate, assumed equal to the dry adiabatic rate. In this case, if the parcel is lifted from $C$ to $D$ its temperature and density remain the same as the surrounding air and it can be raised with practically no work. To the right is the lapse rate associated with an *inversion,* or reversal of the normal temperature gradient—i.e., air temperature becomes higher as we measure it upward. Now, if a parcel of air is carried up from $E$ to $F$, its temperature and density drop very rapidly in comparison with the surrounding air. It will offer strong resistance to being lifted. The inversion of temperature gradient is thus a condition of extreme stability. In contrast, the steep lapse rate shown at the far left is one of great instability and leads to spontaneous rise of air in convective columns, because the rising air parcel in going from $G$ to $H$ is continuously warmer than the surrounding air.

Two kinds of inversions are associated with air pollution. A *low-level inversion* can be

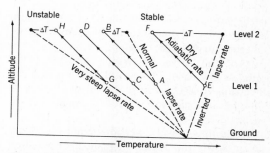

Figure E.6. Relation of air-mass stability to lapse rate. The label $\triangle T$ refers to the difference between temperature of the rising air and the surrounding air at level 2.

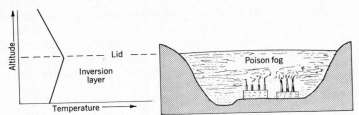

Figure E.7. Low-level temperature inversion as the predisposing condition for poison fog accumulated at Donora, Pennsylvania, in October, 1948.

developed by nocturnal cooling of the ground and lower air layer under conditions of a stagnant air mass (Figure E.7). The inversion of lapse rate is developed up to a height of perhaps 500 to 1000 ft above the ground and forms the layer of contamination. The inversion *cap*, or *lid*, coincides with the level at which a normal lapse rate sets in. A particularly good example of a low-level inversion is that which developed at Donora, Pennsylvania, in late October, 1948. As shown in the right side of Figure E.7, the city lies in a river valley hemmed in by rising valley walls several hundred feet high. Pollution of air trapped in the inversion layer increased for five days. The high concentration of trapped industrial smoke and gases, together with high humidity, resulted in a poisonous fog that caused illness to several thousands of people and death to 20.

Another type of inversion occurs in certain areas under favoring weather situations; it is called an *upper-level inversion*. The principle is illustrated in Figure E.8. Recall that in the center of an anticyclone, or cell of high pressure, air is subsiding and spreads laterally (divergence). Subsiding air is adiabatically warmed (dry adiabatic rate), and the entire column experiences a temperature rise as it descends. This warming is shown in Figure E.8 by the diagonal arrows in the upper part of the curve. In other words, the normal temperature-lapse-rate curve is displaced toward the right. Suppose, now, that the subsidence ends at a particular level, leaving the layer of air beneath it stagnant and unaffected. The temperature-altitude curve must develop a kink in which part of the curve follows an inverted lapse rate. As shown in Figure E.8, this upper-level inversion zone constitutes the lid of the inversion, because air strongly resists mixing across the zone.

While upper-level inversions readily develop under slowly moving or stagnant high-pressure centers over various parts of the United States, a very special set of circumstances surrounds its occurrence over the Los Angeles basin of southern California. This basin is a low-sloping plain rising gradually inland from the sea and terminating on the north and east in steeply rising mountain slopes. Weak winds from the south and southwest carry cool air from over the adjacent cold California current inland over the basin, but the inland spread of this air is blocked by the bordering mountains. Now, a second factor comes into play. This part of the western coast of the United States lies under the influence of the semi-permanent subtropical high-pressure cell centered over the Pacific Ocean. The eastern part of this cell is a region of general air-mass subsidence, along with its southerly flow around the eastern side of the cyclone (Figure E.9). This subsiding air, which is strongly warmed both adiabatically and (during the day) by solar radiation, cre-

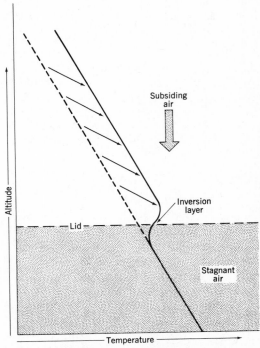

Figure E.8. Cause of an upper-level inversion of air temperature.

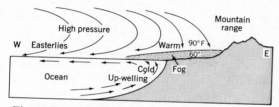

Figure E.9. Schematic diagram of descending air over a desert west coast and formation of a coastal temperature inversion.

ates and maintains an upper-level inversion, located at an elevation of about 2000 ft (600 m), as shown in Figure E.9. The cool-air layer below cannot be lifted through the inversion lid and accumulates pollutants. Smog of the Los Angeles basin tends to be more of a dense haze than a fog, as water content is generally low, but the ingredients are particularly irritating to the eyes. The upper limit of smog contrasts sharply with the clear air lying above it and is a familiar landmark to air travelers arriving from the east (Figure E.10).

An important atmospheric effect of man-made air pollution is upon visibility and illumination. Although the sun may be shining through a cloudless sky, the smog layer cuts illumination appreciably—by some 10% in summer and 20% in winter.* Ultraviolet radiation is at times almost completely prevented from reaching the ground, and this depletion may be important in allowing increased bacterial growth at ground levels.

Horizontal visibility can be reduced by city smog to only 10% to 20% of normal values for uncontaminated air. The hygroscopic suspended particles can readily acquire condensed water films to result in fogs, which are said to be from two to five times more frequent over cities than in the surrounding countryside.

## ATMOSPHERIC EFFECTS OF CHANGES IN GROUND-SURFACE CHARACTERISTICS

The study of climate near the ground—sometimes called *microclimatology* because it deals with differences across very small ranges of height and distance—shows clearly the impact of Man on the balances of radiation and heat. The effect of urbanization upon these balances is particularly strong, because as buildings and paved streets and parking lots replace a preexisting surface clothed in trees,

* H. E. Landsberg (1970), in *Challenge for Survival,* P. Dansereau, ed., Columbia Univ. Press, p. 137; see also *Science* (1970), vol. 170, pp. 1271–1272.

shrubs, and grass, a completely new set of surface properties is substituted. In addition, the construction of buildings produces a large number of vertical masonry surfaces, which affect the radiation balance as well as influence the structure of winds close to the ground. These changes, of course, must be viewed in conjunction with emission of heat and air pollutants through combustion.

Consider first the changes in thermal environment. A general decrease in albedo occurs in the urban area, a change permitting absorption of a larger fraction of incoming radiation.* The absorption of solar radiation produces higher ground-surface temperatures in urban areas for two additional reasons. First, there is no shading by foliage and no cooling effect of transpiration. As in a desert environment, ground-surface temperatures can rise to high levels under direct solar heating. This heat is conducted readily into the ground, and a very large quantity is stored there. Second, evaporation may be nil on pavement and masonry surfaces, and there can be no cooling such as that which occurs by evaporation from a moist soil surface. Vertical masonry surfaces also absorb direct and reflected radiation, and this is radiated back into the air between buildings.

Maximum daytime air temperature in summer may average several degrees higher in the center of a city than in the surrounding suburbs, as shown by the map of Washington, D.C., for a day in August (Figure E.11). The city is said to produce a *heat island.* Although one might reason that, conversely, the minimum values of nighttime temperatures would be lower in the city than in the suburbs because of more rapid radiational cooling of bare, exposed ground, the warmer regime persists, instead, through the night because of availability of a large quantity of heat stored in the ground during the day. In winter, buildings warmed by interior heating radiate an additional quantity of heat throughout the night, or in summer, cooled by air conditioning, inject heat into the outside air. In addition, the pres-

* This statement is based on H. E. Landsberg (*Science,* 1970, vol. 170, p. 1270), who states that "the albedo is usually lowered" in the change from rural to urban environment. To the contrary is the statement, "Densely built-up regions have a higher albedo than forests and cultivated soils" (*First Annual Report of the Council on Environmental Quality,* August, 1970, p. 100).

Figure E.10. Smog layer over downtown Los Angeles. The base of the temperature inversion lies immediately above the top of the smog layer, at a height about 300 ft (100 m) above ground level. (Photograph by Los Angeles County Air Pollution Control District.)

ence of suspended particulates allows the lower air layer to absorb and return to the ground longwave radiation during the night.

One side effect of the heat island is to increase atmospheric convection. At night, heated air tends to rise over the city. The warm air spreads radially outward from the city into the surrounding countryside and is replaced by cooler air moving into the city at low levels. This return flow is designated a *country breeze*.

The rise of water vapor, particulates, and other pollutants produced by burning of fuels above the heat island causes a marked increase in cloudiness and precipitation over a city. It is thought that certain of the pollutants rising above centers of intense industrial activity act as cloud-seeding agents, effective in increasing rapid condensation. Over the city of London thundershowers produce 30% more rainfall than over the surrounding country area.* The

* H. E. Landsberg (1970), *Science*, vol. 170, p. 1271.

general increase of precipitation over urban areas is estimated at about 10%.

Before leaving the subject of the urban heat island, consider more broadly the question of Man's ability to heat the entire world atmosphere through the various processes of energy release—largely through combustion of fossil fuels and use of nuclear energy. This energy is an added ingredient of the earth's radiation balance. At present, the man-made heat contribution is a very small and relatively insignificant part of the total radiation balance, but it could become very important if the world population rises to a large figure and the energy consumed by each individual is greatly increased. Along with other man-made changes trending in the direction of atmospheric warming (higher $CO_2$, more water vapor) the added heat contribution through energy consumption might well lead to substantial melting of glacial ice and rising of sea level.

Buildings of large cities contribute to the

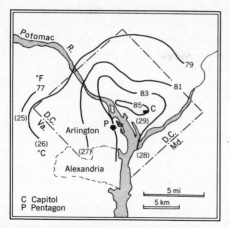

Figure E.11. Heat island over Washington, D.C. Isotherms of air temperature at 10 P.M. local time on a day in early August. [Data of H. E. Landsberg (1950), *Weatherwise,* vol. 3, no. 1.]

heat-island effect through a reduction of wind speeds by as much as 10% to 30%, reducing the rate at which cooler air is imported and warmer air exported. On the other hand, buildings induce greater vertical air mixing within the lower wind structure, and this may assist in diluting pollutants to higher levels. Records show that wind speeds at the weather-observation station in Central Park in New York City (actually well removed from high buildings) average from 2.6 to 3.3 mph (4.2 to 5.3 km/hr) less than at the LaGuardia Airport throughout each quarter of the year, with an average reduction of 23%.

## OIL FILMS ON THE OCEAN SURFACE

Everyone is familiar with the environmental problems caused locally along shorelines by oil spills in coastal waters. Some of these events arise from accidents to vessels transporting petroleum and from the deliberate pumping of waste from oil tanks while the vessel is at sea. Another class of oil spills is from blowouts during offshore petroleum drilling operations. There are also a few natural seepages of petroleum through fractures in the ocean floor. Leaving aside the damage of spilled oil to plant and animal life of the coastal zone and to shore recreational facilities, let us consider briefly the effect of an oil film upon the processes of energy and water-vapor transport across the interface of sea surface and atmosphere. One effect of an oil film is to reduce evaporation; a second is to reduce the wave-generating ability of wind. Both of these processes play a part in

the energy, heat, and water balances of atmosphere and oceans. As yet, possible effects of oil spills upon these global balances are not recognizable, but they should be kept in mind in the total picture of environmental change.

## B. MAN'S IMPACT ON THE WATER BALANCE OF THE LANDS

Man and all other life forms of the lands depend for survival upon availability of pure fresh water necessary to sustain physiological processes. The water balance by means of which this water is made available is the subject of Chapters 5 and 6. Fresh water occurs as surface water—in streams, lakes, and marshes—and as soil and ground water beneath the land surface.

Environmental problems related to fresh water fall into two major categories. The first category relates to physical systems and includes man-induced changes in water movements within the hydrologic cycle. It is with this aspect of water that we are concerned here, since the subject of this book is one of physical systems of our planet. The second category of problems includes chemical and biological processes and products. Foremost among these is pollution of water, as, for example, by introduction of viruses (from sewage), pesticides (such as DDT), nondegradable detergents, and mercury compounds into fresh-water supplies (and also into the oceans). Biological consequences of water pollution and other related changes in the water environment are the subject matter of ecology. Chemical and biological problems of the environment are only touched upon at a few points in this Epilogue, but it should be obvious that physical, chemical, and biological process are inseparable in environmental science—as witness the carbon-dioxide and oxygen cycles described in earlier pages.

### CHANGES IN INFILTRATION AND RUNOFF

Relationships between infiltration and runoff are sensitively balanced with respect to the physical and biological structure of the ground surface. In North America, as in Europe, Man's agricultural activities transformed vast areas of forest and grasslands into croplands and pastures, radically changing the balances of water and heat in the soil layer and inducing a host of unwanted environmental effects.

First to be affected by clearing and agricul-

tural use of the land is infiltration capacity
(Chapter 6). Figure E.12 shows how infiltration rate varies with time after the onset of a
prolonged and copious rainfall following a dry
period. The upper graph illustrates the fact that
soil texture is a natural variable factor, the
capacity being much greater for coarse-
textured soils than for fine. The middle graph
shows that intense grazing by cattle has resulted in greatly lowered infiltration capacity
because the destruction of vegetation and the
trampling of soil by hooves lead to closing of
soil openings. Carefully managed, however,
grazing can permit a high infiltration rate. The
lower graph shows that destruction of pine-
forested land and subsequent abandonment of
the land led to sharp reduction in infiltration

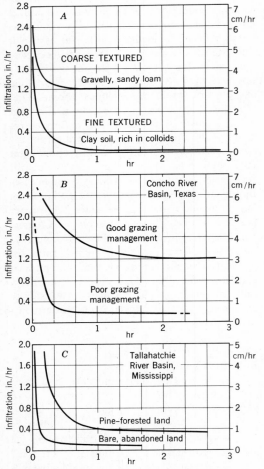

Figure E.12. Rate of infiltration of rainfall varies
with soil texture and land usage. (© 1960, John
Wiley & Sons, New York. Data by Sherman and
Musgrave; Foster.)

capacity in a region of silty (loess) soils not
naturally endowed with a high capacity.

What happens when Man's activity sharply
reduces infiltration capacity? Obviously, the
yield of overland flow is correspondingly increased, and with it an intensification of soil
erosion (discussed in later paragraphs). Peak
discharges of stream channels culminate in
high flood stages in downstream valley reaches.
Conversely, the reduced infiltration cuts down
on recharge of the water table, which in turn
reduces the contribution of ground water to
base flow of streams and to the water levels of
ponds and marshes. The total hydrological
effect is that of altering the runoff regime from
one of sustained water yield to one of intensified flows interspersed with periods of relative
dryness.

Man has radically altered the relationships
of infiltration to runoff in the processes of
highway construction and urbanization. Highway construction changes preexisting drainage
systems by blockage of channels and diversions
of flow, but for the most part these are localized effects. In the case of growth of large cities
and their suburbs the effects are on a large
scale. Pavements serve as a barrier to infiltration and the runoff of storms is channeled into
storm sewers, greatly increasing the ratio of
runoff to infiltration. Flood peaks are sharply
increased by urbanization of a watershed.
Studies have shown that when half of the surface has been made impervious by pavements
and roofs the flood height is increased by as
much as 75%, as compared to equivalent floods
under the preurban conditions in which surfaces were largely under cultivation.

In coastal cities, storm sewer runoff, with its
contaminants from atmospheric fallout and
washout, is allowed to empty into salt-water
bays and estuaries, resulting in dilution of
salinity as well as pollution. Together with
effluent sewage and wastes from industrial
processes, these contributions to the salt-water
environment may prove highly deleterious to
the complex assemblage of life forms found
there. Much the same can be said of large fresh-
water bodies, such as the Great Lakes, ringed
by urban development and heavy industry.

### CHANGES IN QUALITY OF FRESH-WATER LAKES

Fresh-water lakes result from a wide variety
of causes and, consequently, take a wide range
of sizes, shapes, and depths. In North America

and Europe, and generally throughout high mountain ranges the world over, glacial erosion and deposition account for vast numbers of fresh-water lakes, ranging in size from ponds a few yards across to huge water bodies, of which the Great Lakes are an outstanding group. Another common class of fresh-water lakes in humid climates the world over are those occupying cutoff meander bends on floodplains. A few large lakes, such as those of east Africa (Victoria, Tanganyika, Nyasa) occupy depressions created by geologically recent faulting and crustal warping. Another class of lakes is associated with volcanoes; these may occupy craters or calderas, or may be formed by a lava dam across a stream valley. Man-made fresh-water lakes are now perhaps second in importance only to glacial lakes in numbers and in total volume.

Water level of a fresh-water lake may be determined by the position of a surface outlet. Most large lakes in regions of a large water surplus discharge runoff through an outlet stream which is upheld by resistant bedrock, acting as a fixed sill. Many small lakes and ponds in glacial materials have no surface outlet, and in these types the lake level is determined by the level of the ground-water table in the surrounding overburden; these are called *water-table ponds*.

In the natural scheme of things, lakes are short-lived. Their physical evolution is one of destruction either by filling with sediment or by down-cutting of the outlet, or both. Man can greatly accelerate the rate of sedimentation in a lake by inducing rapid soil erosion, a process discussed in later pages.

Lakes also undergo changes in chemistry and biology with the passage of time, and it is with Man's influence upon these changes that we are concerned here. Since the subject of fresh-water lakes is not covered in earlier chapters of this book, a few background facts will be needed at this point.

The *limnologist* (scientist who studies lakes) recognizes two important classes of fresh-water lakes in humid climates of middle latitudes. First is the *oligotrophic lake*, poor in nutrients required by life processes. Second is the *eutrophic lake*, rich in those nutrients.

The typical oligotrophic lake is deep, has rocky or sandy shores and bottom, supports relatively sparse plant and animal life, and has clear, blue water. Oxygen, dissolved in the lake water, is present in abundance uniformly from surface to bottom. Dissolved solids, particularly nitrogen in ammonia form ($NH_4$), phosphate ($PO_4$), and compounds of iron and manganese are present in only very small quanties in the oligotrophic lake. Few animals live on the bottom and plankton are sparse or absent. Fish are present in only a few species, but these may be numerous and of excellent quality (e.g., trout, bass, landlocked salmon).

The typical eutrophic lake is comparatively shallow, has a layer of organic sediment on the bottom and shores, and sustains a large number and variety of aquatic plants in the shallow shore zone. During the summer months oxygen declines rapidly in concentration with depth and may be completely absent near the bottom, where anaerobic life forms thrive. Plankton are abundant and give the water a marked turbidity and yellowish green color. The deficiency of oxygen in the deep water results from intensive oxidation through bacterial action and respiration of organisms. The dissolved solids mentioned above (nitrate as ammonia, phosphates, iron, and manganese compounds) are concentrated in the deep water. The nitrogen and phosphorus compounds are nutrients for plant growth. Although the total production of organic matter in the eutrophic lake is large, fish of the eutrophic lake are of the less desirable kinds.

The important point from the standpoint of environmental science is that lakes which are originally oligotrophic undergo a gradual change toward the eutrophic type. This change is regarded as an aging process and is termed *eutrophication*. Man has in many instances greatly accelerated the rate of aging of lakes by supplying large quantities of the nutrients—nitrates and phosphates—from sewage, certain industrial processes, and in agriculture byproducts. These substances enter the lake as runoff in feeder streams or directly from points along the shore. Algae may increase to the extent that they form a heavy scum over the lake surface. The value of the lake as a source of edible fish and for recreation declines rapidly. In the case of Lake Erie, this large but comparatively shallow lake has undergone rapid and deleterious eutrophication, along with other forms of chemical and physical pollution. Eutrophication also affects freshwater streams through the addition of excessive nutrients.

## CHANGES IN GROUND-WATER HYDROLOGY

Large supplies of fresh water for Man's use come from two basic sources. First is direct use of surface water, i.e., withdrawal from stream channels and from fresh-water lakes and reservoirs. This renewable resource is self-limiting, since without recycling no more can be used in a given year than the hydrologic cycle provides. The second source is ground water, present in an enormous volume compared with surface water. Referring back to Table 6.1, we find that the world's available ground water constitutes about 34 times the volume contained in fresh-water lakes and stream channels. One can easily be misled into thinking that there is no limit to the amount of this ground water that can be withdrawn for Man's use, but unfortunately this conclusion is false. Quite apart from depletion of nonrenewable resources, a topic discussed in later pages, excessive withdrawal of ground water leads to changes in the hydraulic system of flow and has many environmental side effects, a few of which are mentioned here.

Most water wells are simply tubes or shafts drilled or dug to a depth below the water table and are supplied by gravity flow from the surrounding ground-water zone. If left undisturbed, the water level comes to rest at the level of the water table. Water must be drawn or pumped to the surface. For effective and prolonged use a well must be protected from collapse by means of a solid casing, which may be a masonry wall (in the case of a dug well) or a steel pipe (in the case of a drilled well). Perforations through the lower part of the casing permit water to enter.

Dug wells, excavated by hand labor, are usually less than 50 ft (15 m) deep and are effective where the water table lies close to the surface in a thick layer of overburden, such as alluvium. A dug well for domestic use may yield as little as a few gallons per day or as much as 500 gal/min (2000 liters/min) in a highly permeable deposit. Drilled wells, which may have diameters up to 18 in. (45 cm) can be driven to depths of over 1000 ft (300 m) and, with powerful pumps, will furnish as much as many millions of gallons per day if located in highly permeable material.

Pumping of water from a well commonly exceeds the rate at which water can enter the well, so that the water level drops progressively lower (Figure E.13), depressing the water table into a conical form, or *cone of depres-*

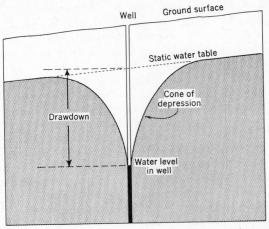

Figure E.13. Rapid pumping of a well causes drawdown and a cone of depression. (© 1960, John Wiley & Sons, New York.)

*sion,* surrounding the well. The *drawdown* is the difference in height between water table and water level in the well. Formation of the cone of depression actually increases the rate at which water flows into the well, thereby increasing the yield of the well, but this effect is limited. Beyond a critical limit of drawdown the yield no longer increases.

The cone of depression may extend several miles from a large well, and the combined effect of closely spaced wells is to depress the water table generally. Heavy pumping may thus exceed the rate of natural recharge, and the water table will continue to fall, eventually leading to a serious decline in water yield. In arid regions, particularly, the ground water stored in alluvial deposits can be withdrawn much faster than it is restored by influent seepage from surface streams. In humid regions careful regulation of pumping and the artificial recharge of the ground-water table by waste water pumped down into recharge wells can bring about a balance in the rates of withdrawal and recharge.

An example of the modification of ground-water flow by well pumping is illustrated in Figure E.14, in which a well has been placed close to a perennial stream of large discharge. Whereas normally (diagram *A*) this *effluent stream* receives ground water from the surrounding and subjacent zone, the effect of pumping and drawdown (diagram *B*) is to cause stream water to flow to the well within the ground-water zone. Actually, this well placement can be used effectively to augment

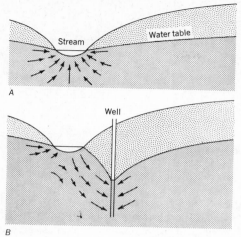

Figure E.14. Placement of a well close to a stream can cause a diversion of ground-water flow from stream to well. [After D. K. Todd (1959), *Ground Water Hydrology,* New York, John Wiley & Sons, p. 267, Figure 11.8.]

ground-water supplies under favorable conditions, since it uses fresh water that might normally be lost as runoff to the oceans. The stream water is filtered in the process and may actually improve the quality of the well water.

Ground-water supplies are subject to contamination by various kinds of man-made wastes that infiltrate the ground and become a part of ground-water recharge. Discharge of sewage and liquid industrial wastes into infiltrating basins constitute one potential pollution source, while landfill waste-disposal sites (dumps) are another. In both cases, because of the abnormally high rate of infiltration, a ground-water *mound* is produced and there ensues lateral movement of the infiltrating fluid outward to peripheral regions where it may emerge in streams or lakes, or may be drawn into nearby wells (Figure E.15).

Creation of large fresh-water lakes by construction of dams has introduced hydrologic changes over many parts of the South and Middle West. These areas had originally very few lakes of appreciable size, because Pleistocene glacial processes of erosion and deposition

that produced most natural North American lakes did not reach them. An effect to be anticipated from creation of a deep lake is the rise in water table in adjacent areas, and this change may be deleterious or beneficial to agriculture, depending upon position of the ground surface with respect to the raised water table. A deleterious effect would be the impediment to drainage of soils very close to the water table. In other instances, a water table brought closer to the surface can provide capillary water within range of plant roots, leading to increased production.

Of considerable interest in environmental science is the relation of fresh ground water to salt ground water in coastal areas and beneath islands. Figure E.16 is a highly diagrammatic cross section of the ground-water relations under an island or in a long, narrow peninsula. Fresh water, being less dense than salt, forms a ground-water body resembling a huge lens, with convex surfaces above and below. The fresh-water body actually floats upon the salt, much as the hull of a ship displaces water and floats at rest. Normally, the densities of fresh water to salt water are in the ratio of 40 to 41. Thus the elevation of the upper surface of the water table above sea level is one-fortieth as great as the depth of the base of the fresh-water body below sea level. For example, if the bottom of the fresh-water lens lies 400 ft below sea level, the ground-water table will stand 10 ft above sea level.

As the shoreline is approached, the contact between fresh and salt water rises in elevation and emerges on the sea floor along a line close to the land. As the arrows in Figure E.16 indicate, the fresh ground water follows deeply curving paths, and these paths turn upward and seaward to emerge under the ocean close to the coast. The salt ground water remains essentially stagnant beneath the fresh. Some mixing, or diffusion, of the salt and fresh water will occur through the effects of tidal changes in ocean level.

One problem of practical interest is that the rapid pumping of water from wells located

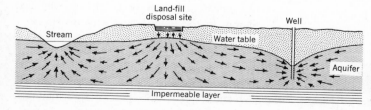

Figure E.15. Pollution from a solid-waste disposal site can move within the ground water beneath to reach a well or a stream.

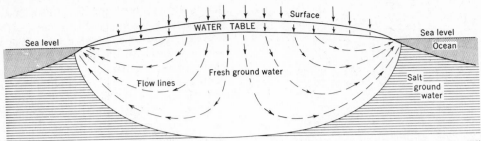

Figure E.16. Relation of fresh to salt ground water under an island or peninsula. (© 1960, John Wiley & Sons, New York. Based on data of G. Parker.)

close to a coastline will draw the salt-water–fresh-water contact landward until the salt water begins to be drawn into the well, contaminating the fresh water supply (Figure E.17). If pumping is stopped for a long period, the salt water will again be pushed seaward, a process that can be hastened by pumping fresh water down into the contaminated wells or into new wells in the vicinity so as to create a barrier of fresh water.

Along an embayed coast with large belts of salt marsh the intrusion of salt water into wells seems to have been accelerated by dredging for navigation. This action removes a relatively impermeable barrier between salt water and fresh ground water.

## C. MAN'S IMPACT ON EXOGENETIC PROCESSES AND FORMS

### INTENSIFICATION OF WEATHERING AND MASS WASTING

Weathering processes, particularly alteration of exposed rock surfaces, are accelerated by washout of atmospheric pollutants in urban

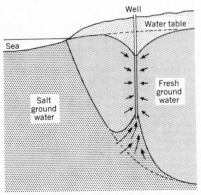

Figure E.17. Salt-water intrusion into a well situated near the ocean.

areas, a fact long recognized by studies of the decomposition of building stones and masonry. Sulfuric acid, in particular, promotes the etching and crumbling of rock surfaces. Another effect of the increase in compounds of sulfur in cities has been the damage to plants, and in particular to lichen growth, which has been eliminated from heavily polluted areas. Chemical weathering related to air pollution affects a wide range of man-made substances with a resulting heavy economic loss. Steel, rubber, and paints are susceptible, as are paper and fabrics.

Entirely different as a physical process is mass wasting, the spontaneous flowage or sliding of soil or bedrock under the influence of gravity (Chapter 9). Man is responsible for many occurrences of mass wasting through engineering of highways, canals, and construction sites. Indeed, an important branch of civil engineering, *soil mechanics,* is concerned with causes and prevention of expensive and sometimes lethal occurrences of mass movements. Instances of unwanted effects are numerous in the history of great engineering projects. For example, in construction of the Panama Canal the excavation of deep cuts into partially weathered rock rich in clay minerals led to flowage and slump of enormous rock masses, which filled the canal floor. In recent times, a great disaster occurred at Aberfan, Wales, when a great culm (waste) heap 600 ft (180 m) high, built during coal-mining operations, spontaneously lost strength and moved quickly downslope. The tongue of debris overwhelmed buildings in the town below with loss of over 150 lives (Figure E.18).

In southern California real-estate development has turned toward extremely steep mountain slopes carved in deeply weathered igneous and metamorphic rocks rich in clay minerals. Terraces and road grades are carved into these

Figure E.18. Debris flow at Aberfan, Wales. (Sketched from a photograph.)

slopes by earth-moving machines and the material excavated is pushed into adjacent embankments where its instability constitutes a threat. Saturated by heavy rains, this material can be set in motion to become an earth flow that moves rapidly down the steep slopes and into canyons below. There it may become further diluted by storm runoff to constitute mudflows capable of inundating inhabited alluvial fan slopes over which the flow spreads widely. Even under natural conditions these steep hill slopes are notorious producers of mudflows and debris floods, particularly after a fire has denuded a watershed of its protective plant cover (Figure E.19). The fires are, of course,

Figure E.19. Debris deposits at the mouth of Benedict Canyon, Ballona Creek basin, California, following a flood in January, 1952. (Photograph by U.S. Army Corps of Engineers.)

mostly set by Man through carelessness or by design.

## SOIL EROSION INDUCED BY MAN

College students of the 1930s and early 1940s will remember a battle then in progress to preserve a vital segment of the environment —the soil of farmlands upon which we depend for survival. Crusaders were active on campuses as well as among farm organizations, spreading the word of depredations upon our irreplaceable resources of food production. Scientists of the Soil Conservation Service studied the forms of soil erosion and its side effects. They devised remedial measures and tested them at experimental farms. Fortunately, sufficient resources were brought to bear to stabilize the situation with long-term practices capable of permitting sustained crop cultivation with a minimum of undesirable side effects. Much marginal land was removed from cultivation and is now reforested.

To the geologist, whose viewpoint spans vast periods of time and whose interest is in processes acting on a continental scale, erosion of the soil is a process of nature whereby the many landscape features of the earth's surface are slowly carved. Soil erosion is, to him, a normal geologic process associated with the hydrologic cycle. In humid climates, where vegetation is dense, soil erosion is normally very slow, and the characteristic soil profiles are maintained as erosion proceeds. In arid climates, especially where rock is of a weak and highly impermeable nature (as in the Badlands of South Dakota), normal erosion is rapid and furnishes vast quantities of sediment to streams. We conclude, therefore, that there is a *geologic norm* of soil erosion appropriate to the particular conditions of climate and bedrock prevailing in an area.

Where Man has cut the forests and converted the land to agricultural uses, or where a forest or prairie fire has destroyed the vegetation, there may be a sudden large increase in the erosion rate, producing a state known as *accelerated erosion*. Soil horizons are removed at a much faster rate than they can be formed, resulting in a rapid decline in fertility of the soil. Streams become burdened with quantities of sediment far in excess of the normal amounts to which their courses have been adjusted.

Applying our knowledge of the factors affecting the rate of soil erosion (Chapter 9), we see that accelerated erosion comes about because the resistance of the surface and the rate of infiltration have been sharply reduced by destruction of the vegetative cover. Not only is a greater proportion of overland flow then produced from a given rain, but also the ease with which the mineral grains are entrained is also increased.

Clearing of forest and cultivation of the ground create the opportunity for splash erosion to seal the soil openings and hasten sheet flow. Soil is removed by sheet flow in relatively thin uniform layers by a process termed *sheet erosion*, which may escape notice. Gradually, however, the fertile upper horizons of the soil are lost, and eventually only the infertile subsoil or bedrock remains.

Soil removed in sheet erosion is carried to the base of the slope. Here it may accumulate in thin layers to form a deposit known as *colluvium*, or *slope wash*. Some particles will, of course, be carried into stream channels, to be deposited as *alluvium* on the valley floor. The term *sedimentation*, which in general geologic usage simply means the accumulation of any sediment, is applied in agricultural engineering studies to the accumulation of both colluvial and alluvial deposits derived from accelerated soil erosion. Sedimentation can bury fertile agricultural land under a coarse permeable layer unfit for cultivation.

On steep slopes laid bare of vegetation, intense runoff forms long, narrow channels termed *shoestring rills* (Figure E.20). Al-

though resembling stream channels, such rills merely score the surface and do not have adjoining ground surfaces sloping toward them. Moreover, shoestring rills are often seasonal features, obliterated by freeze and thaw in winter or by plowing of the land.

Shoestring rills can coalesce and deepen to form gullies of awesome proportions (Figure E.21). Gully development is particularly striking in regions underlaid by a thick layer of weathered overburden (saprolite), in regions with a weak wind-transported silt (loess), or in regions with a soft shale bedrock.

Allowed to continue unchecked, severe gullying will produce a landscape resembling the Badlands of the West. Applying basic principles of slope erosion, engineers of the Soil Conservation Service have effectively halted accelerated soil erosion by construction of terraces (to reduce slope steepness and length), by cultivation in contour belts (to reduce length of slope exposed by tillage), by planting trees and vines (to reduce surface erodibility and increase infiltration), and by building check dams in gully floors (to induce gully

Figure E.20. Shoestring rills on a barren 55% slope, Ventura County, California. At the left, weeds are taking hold to form a protective cover. (Photograph by Soil Conservation Service, U.S. Department of Agriculture.)

Figure E.21. A great gully system in Stewart County, Georgia, in 1936. Such severe gullying has now been largely controlled. (Photograph by Soil Conservation Service, U.S. Department of Agriculture.)

sedimentation and filling). Much badly abused land has been removed permanently from cultivation and restored to forest cover. Since major soil-conservation efforts began in the 1930s vast strides have been made in soil-erosion and sediment control throughout the United States, but much remains to be done to reduce undesirable effects to the practical minimum.

## EFFECTS OF DAMS AND RIVER ENGINEERING WORKS

Dams are built across the courses of large trunk rivers for production of electric power and to divert water for major downstream irrigation systems. These big dams are among the great engineering achievements of Man, and he may well take pride in them; but what was conceived as a benevolent giant can turn into a monster, when long-term effects begin to spread upstream and downstream from the new structure and its great reservoir of water.

A large dam offers an interesting exercise in the principles of stream transportation and erosion, explained in Chapter 9. Consider, first, the upstream changes that such a dam initiates. The reservoir behind the dam constitutes a body of standing water of zero gradient. Bed load carried by the stream and much of the suspended load comes to rest in the reservoir as a delta and its extension into a layer of fine silt and clay over the lake floor. One can easily see, and in fact predict rather closely, that the days of the reservoir as a holder of water are numbered. Both for generating of electric power and for water supply, a substantial reservoir of water is needed to regulate the distribution of flow. Water must be stored in times of high stream flow and released at time of low stream flow. Thus, whatever its purpose, the dam has a limited future.

Next, as the delta is built out into the reservoir, the stream channel begins to aggrade. A wedge of coarse alluvium is spread over the valley floor and begins to spread up-valley (Figure E.22). Inundation of fertile floodplain soils, and along with it roads, railroads, and towns, can ensue. A case in point is the valley of the Rio Grande, upstream from the Elephant Butte Reservoir in New Mexico. Thirty years after completion of this dam aggradation had reached a depth of 10 ft (3 m) at the head of the reservoir, burying the village of San Marcial, while at Albuquerque, 100 mi (160 km) upstream, aggradation had reached a depth of 4 ft (1.2 m). So long as the delta deposition continues in the reservoir, aggradation will spread up-valley, for the stream must maintain a gradient for the transportation of its bed load.

Looking in the down-valley direction below a large dam, we must anticipate the effects of release of water practically free of load of any kind. Here it flows over a bed previously adjusted to transport of a large quantity of coarse bed load (Figure E.22). In the case of Hoover Dam on the Colorado River, the release of a large flow of clear water caused rapid scouring of the river bed, and this effect has spread far down-valley. In the first 25 mi (40 km) deepening ceased when a residual layer of boulders on the stream bed prevented further erosion. At Yuma, 350 mi (560 km) below the dam, permanent channel changes included a lowering of average position of the stream bed by about 10 ft (3 m). The load carried past this point is only about one-fifteenth of its original value, since all load must come from tributary surfaces and streams entering below the dam. Stream depth has about doubled, but because of down-cutting, gauge height of the river in high stages is not appreciably lower than formerly. One deleterious effect of the overall down-cutting has been to lower the

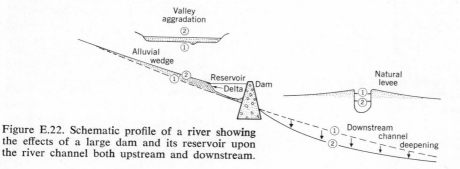

Figure E.22. Schematic profile of a river showing the effects of a large dam and its reservoir upon the river channel both upstream and downstream.

stream cross section several feet below its former position with respect to natural levees in floodplain reaches, thus rendering unworkable the system of gravity-flow irrigation previously in use. Pumping must now be used to lift the river water into the irrigation intakes.

Alluvial rivers, with their sinuous meanders, natural levees, and very low gradients, have long posed an environmental problem because of the overbank flooding that is normal on an annual basis and the much higher floods that occur a number of years apart. A conflict of interest arises over the fact that overbank flooding adds a layer of silt rich in dissolved solids (bases) that maintain fertility of the floodplain soils, particularly in regions having heavy rainfall that tends to leach out these bases. Opposed to this beneficial effect is that of destruction of life and property caused by inundation of low areas between the natural levees and the floodplain bluffs. Cities that have grown up on the floodplain can suffer damage to industrial and residential properties of high economic value. Flood-control engineering has long been practiced with a view to reducing to the minimum the occurrences of overbank flooding. The example of the lower Mississippi River is without doubt preeminent among all such projects on the North American continent.

At strategic points along major river systems of the United States are located 85 offices of NOAA, National Weather Service, from which the River and Flood Forecasting Service operates. River-stage and flood forecasts are issued by each office to the communities of the associated district. Flood warnings are widely publicized and close cooperation is maintained with the municipal authorities, the American Red Cross, the U.S. Army Corps of Engineers, and the U.S. Coast Guard. Thus evacuation of persons from threatened areas and the protection of property can be handled with maximum efficiency.

The study of long periods of record of river stages enables the National Weather Service to estimate the probability of a given stage being reached in any month of the year. An expectancy graph for the Mississippi River at Vicksburg, Mississippi (Figure E.23), illustrates the characteristic annual cycle of flood stages occurring in late winter and spring and of relatively small maximum stages in late summer and fall.

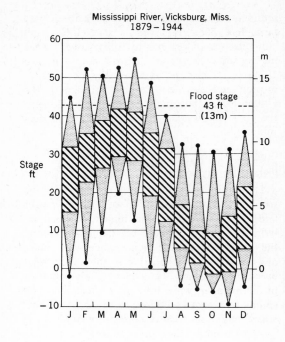

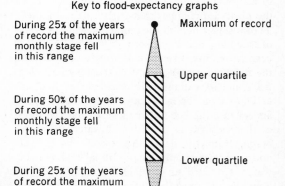

Figure E.23. Highest observed river stage in each month of the year for the entire period of record forms the basis for this stage-expectancy graph of the Mississippi River. (© 1965, John Wiley & Sons, New York. Data of NOAA, National Weather Service.)

In general, reduction of flood-peak discharges can be brought about by two forms of control. First, storm runoff on slopes of the smaller tributary basins can be detained and delayed, thus passing the flow to downstream parts of the system more gradually. Second, the lower reaches of larger streams can be improved in efficiency or can be provided with protective structures to confine peak discharges to the natural channel.

Under the first program, watershed slopes can be treated by reforestation and by crop planting in contour belts and terraces so as to increase the infiltration capacity of the surface and thereby reduce the rate of runoff. To these measures may be added the construction of many small dams, usually of compacted earth, to store floodwaters temporarily and distribute the downstream discharge over a long period of time. Watershed treatment also has the beneficial effects of reducing soil erosion, hence of reducing the undesirable effects of sedimentation upon the stream channels and of increasing recharge to the ground-water zone.

Control of inundation on floodplains may be based on one of two principles. First, a system of *levees,* or *dikes,* can be built adjacent to the channel to contain overbank flow in stages at which the water would otherwise overspread the floodplain (Figure E.24). Most levees are broad earth embankments, although flood walls of reinforced concrete can be used where a city lies close to the river channel. If overtopped by an unusual flood discharge, the levee may be broken at a low point to produce a great breach, known as a *crevasse,* through which the floodwater will quickly flow to inundate the floodplain (Figure E.25).

The lower Mississippi River, under the supervision of the Mississippi River Commis-

sion from 1897 to 1934, was controlled by a vast levee system designed to protect the floodplain from inundation. The system has been continuously improved and now includes over 2500 mi (4000 km) of levees, in places up to 30 ft (10 m) high.

A second principle of river control is that of channel modifications designed to shorten the length of the stream and hence to steepen the gradient. The resulting increase in velocity of flow reduces the area of cross section, hence lowering the height of water at flood crest. Shortening is accomplished by the artificial cutoff of meander bends.

Figure E.26 shows such engineering changes shortly after they were completed. The program was successful in reducing the river-surface height in flood, but considerable difficulty has been experienced in preventing the river from reforming its meanders and returning to the previous condition. Against the advantages of increased security from floods gained by such measures must be weighed the losses of natural landscapes offering scenic beauty, wildlife habitats, and recreational uses.

## WAVE EROSION AND SHORE PROTECTION

Postglacial rise of sea level, mentioned in Chapter 14, has brought the powerful erosive action of storm waves to bear upon great lengths of continental shorelines consisting of readily erodible materials, particularly glacial

Figure E.24. During the flood of March, 1903, this artificial levee along the Mississippi River at Greenville, Mississippi, proved barely high enough to contain the river. A break in the levee (distant point, marked $X$) is permitting river water to pour out and spread over the floodplain at the left. (Photograph by Mississippi River Commission.)

Figure E.25. Water flows through a crevasse in the Mississippi River levee at Poydras, 12 mi (19 km) below New Orleans, Louisiana, during the first day of the break, April, 1922. (Photograph by Elias Green.)

and alluvial sedimentary deposits. Once Man has occupied these coastlines with expensive habitations, he feels obliged to resist the wave action that cuts away his land foot by foot and yard by yard.

One example of the man-made disturbance of a natural flow system is seen in the use of *groins* to collect beach sand and thus to build a buffer zone that can absorb the short-lived but intense attacks of storm waves. A groin is simply a broad wall of huge rock masses built perpendicular to the shoreline (Figure E.27). A succession of closely spaced groins is normally built along a shore suffering from beach depletion and wave erosion. The groin interferes with the littoral drift of sand, causing a crescentic beach deposit to accumulate on the updrift side of the groin (Figure E.27). In the case of the single groin shown in the diagram, the trapping of sand results in a deficiency of sand along the downdrift side, with the result that the beach is depleted and the shoreline recedes. A similar effect is seen where a pair of jetties (sea walls) has been built in the mouth of an inlet through a barrier beach in order to confine the tidal flow and maintain a navigable inlet (Figure E.28). Sand accumulates on the updrift side of the inlet. Tidal currents move sediment arriving at the inlet mouth seaward to form a submarine deposit, while the downdrift section of shoreline is depleted of sediment and undergoes recession. These simple examples illustrate the principle of compensatory reaction, which is basic to many problems of the physical environment.

## WIND AS AN AGENT OF ENVIRONMENTAL CHANGE

Briefly mentioned in Chapter 9 is the work of wind as a transporter of sediment in suspension in dust storms and as a mover of sand close to the ground to form drifts and dunes. Just as overland flow is an agent of intense land erosion under natural environmental conditions prevailing in arid and semiarid lands, so wind is a natural process of the same climates. Where Man makes his impact upon natural processes related to wind action is in subhumid and humid regions, where under prevailing climate soil and dunes are fairly well stabilized by a natural cover of grasses, shrubs, or forests. Removal of this protective cover lays bare the soil and sediment mass to intensive wind action.

While the Great Plains region, including part or all of the states of New Mexico, Texas, Oklahoma, Kansas, Colorado, Nebraska, and the Dakotas, is normally the source of dust storms generated by turbulent winds blowing over a dry surface, the phenomenon rose to disastrous levels during the mid 1930s when the region achieved recognition as the *Dust Bowl*. A series of drought years followed agricultural expansion in which wheat cultivation had bared vast expanses of rich brown and chestnut soils formed on loess. A typical dust storm begins with the passage of a strong cold front. Enormous quantities of clay and silt-sized particles were lifted into the turbulent air structure, creating a formidable black wall of dust (see Figure 9.23). Within the dust cloud

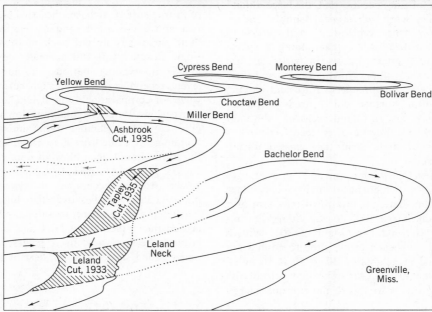

Figure E 26. Oblique air photograph, looking north, of the Mississippi River, showing three artificial meander cutoffs made by the Corps of Engineers to reduce river length. Taken in 1937, this photograph shows sediment plugs blocking the ends of Bachelor Bend, which formerly flowed past the city of Greenville, Mississippi. (Photograph by War Dept., Corps of Engineers.)

visibility might be reduced to nothing and total darkness would prevail at midday. The dust penetrated tightly closed buildings and interfered seriously with breathing. Estimates of the quantity of dust suspended in a single storm are given in Chapter 9.

A particularly damaging effect of the re-peated dust storms in the Dust Bowl was that of accumulation of coarser fractions of the soil as drifts over fence rows and buildings (Figure E.29). So long as large expanses of this region are in cultivation the dust storm and its attendant drifts can be anticipated as a recurrent problem of drought years. Alleviation of the

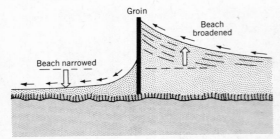

Figure E.27. Construction of a groin causes marked changes in configuration of the sand beach.

problem is obtained through improved farming practices. For example, deeply plowed furrows (listed furrows) can act as traps to drifting soil. Tree belts may be effective in reducing wind stress at ground level.

Perhaps one of the clearest illustrations of Man's role in setting off environmental disturbances in a delicately balanced system is seen in the case of *phytogenic dunes,* particularly those of coasts of the oceans and of large inland lakes. The word *phytogenic* simply means "originating with vegetation" and refers to dunes constructed while maintaining a sparse plant cover. Certain grasses, in particular, are capable of survival on growing dunes, and their presence serves as a baffle to trap sand moving over the dune surface. Large areas of phytogenic dunes exist in inland areas of subhumid climates, where they have replaced freely moving dunes of loose sand that existed during glaciations.

Of particular environmental interest are coastal dunes, which occur in irregular ridges located immediately landward of the berm of a sand beach. Generally, coastal dunes are referred to as *foredunes* (Figure E.30). With a good cover of beach grasses, the foredunes are constructed to heights of 20 to 50 ft (6 to 15 m) or even higher. An important role of the foredune ridge is to absorb the extreme energy

Figure E.29. An abandoned farm, Dallam County, Texas, 1937. This Dust Bowl scene shows a drift of sand and silt, too coarse to be carried in suspension, built up along a fence row during repeated dust storms. (Photograph by Soil Conservation Service, U.S. Dept. of Agriculture.)

of storm surf, which reaches to heights many feet above the usual limit of the swash. The dune ridge may be cut back many yards in a single storm, but it will normally be rebuilt in longer intervening periods of normal wave levels, receiving sand from high berms built by waves of comparatively low height during summer periods. Where Man breaks down the dune-grass cover by vehicular traffic and grading of building sites, the foredune ridge experiences the formation of deep blowout depressions (see Figure 9.36). At these low points, swash of severe storms, accompanied by abnormally high sea level, washes over the dune belt and reaches the lower zone of salt marsh or open lagoon that typically lies landward of a barrier beach. The overwash itself buries salt marsh under broad sheets of sand, destroying the life

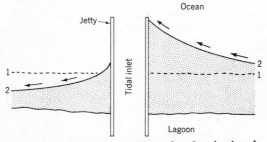

Figure E.28. An inlet cut through a barrier beach and protected by jetties leads to marked changes in width of the barrier.

Figure E.30. Beach grass on foredunes, Provincelands of Cape Cod, Massachusetts. (Photograph by A. N. Strahler.)

environment. Damage to man-made structures is also a consequence of such overwash. In other cases, where a large lagoon lies behind the barrier, storm overwash may create a breach through which hydraulic currents quickly scour an inlet (Figure E.31). Such inlets may persist, or they may be subsequently sealed over by littoral drift. Note, however, that the creation of inlets by storm breaching is a normal process of shoreline evolution and is not necessarily deleterious to the natural environment of the coast as a whole.

A particularly striking case of Man's interference with a dune environment is that of the Provincelands of Cape Cod. Here on the "fist" of the Cape, a broad belt of sand dunes, built upon a series of beach ridges, lies north of Provincetown, a town located on the sheltered southern shore of the dune area. Originally a forest cover stabilized these dunes, but early settlers cut away the forest for fuel, and overgrazed as well, allowing sand to drift freely to the southeast. Sand drifts invaded Provincetown and threatened to bury the streets and houses under a deep sand layer. Between 1810 and 1830 beach grass and pitch pine were planted and the dunes again stabilized. Under protection of law the surface has since been held essentially stable, although close to the northern shore active dunes are locally uncon-

trolled and their slip faces continually advance upon highways and trails.

## D. MAN'S IMPACT UPON THE ROCK ZONE

A fourth category of changes which Man makes upon his planet includes activities affecting the rock zone beneath the land surface. These changes are quite varied in process as well as in time and place of action; hence they are not necessarily related to one another.

### SCARS ON THE LAND

Man removes huge masses of bedrock and its overburden in the extraction of mineral resources. For the most part, the results are so obvious as to need little description. Open-pit mining of ore bodies and quarrying for building stone and construction materials leave huge gaping pits of bare rock. Waste rock accumulates in enormous dumps (*tailings*) in the vicinity of mines extracting both metallic ores and coal. Strip-mining of coal leaves deep trenches and adjoining embankments of rock waste in sinuous lines running for miles along the contour of hillsides. Hydraulic mining, in which a powerful jet of water is directed against a gravel deposit, not only creates deep scars in valley sides, but sweeps coarse debris into adjacent stream channels. The debris is then carried downstream, where the resulting aggradation causes flooding and damage to agricultural lands. Borrow pits for highway construction are yet another type of scar. All of these operations destroy the natural cover of soil and vegetation, disrupt the ecology of many life forms, and radically alter the configuration of the land surface. Runoff, infiltration, and ground-water movements may be adversely affected, and these influences can spread far into adjoining areas. Destruction of natural beauty of a landscape is an inevitable resource loss from large-scale scarring of the land.

### SUBSIDENCE OF THE LAND

One consequence of removal of fluids or solid mineral matter from bedrock or its overburden is the subsidence of the overlying land surface. The circumstances and effects are of greatly varied form and intensity.

One simple example is from tidal marshes that have been separated from tidal interchange with the sea by means of dikes. Salt water is excluded from the marsh and replaced by fresh

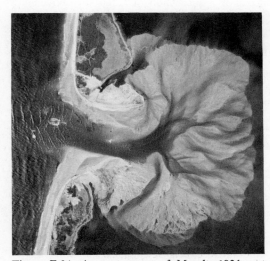

Figure E.31. A great storm of March, 1931, cut this breach through Fire Island, allowing tidal currents to carry sediment from the open Atlantic Ocean (*left*) into the lagoon (*right*) and construct a tidal delta. The entire area shown is about 1 mi (1.6 km) across. East Moriches Inlet, Long Island, New York. (U.S. Air Force photograph.)

water. Drainage works allow excess water to escape to the sea and the land becomes suitable for cultivation. Large areas of drained tidal marsh are found in England (*fenlands*) and in Holland (*polders*). As a result of drainage, the layers of peat are compacted and the ground surface subsides. Subsidence as much as 13 ft (4 m) has been documented in the English fenlands. The depressed surface constitutes a hazard zone subject to inundation by sea water, should the retaining dikes be breached by waves during a storm.

Another example of subsidence is that following withdrawal of petroleum and gas from beneath a producing oil field. A particularly good example is the Goose Creek oil field, near Houston on the Texas coast. In eight years following intensive withdrawal of oil, gas, and water an elliptical area 2 mi (3 km) across subsided to a maximum of 3 ft (1 m) near the center. Part of this land was submerged beneath sea water; structural damage occurred to derricks and buildings. This subsidence has been attributed to compaction of sedimentary strata taking place after withdrawal of gas and fluids, which were not replaced by ground water from the surrounding area. Similar instances of subsidence have been reported following extraction of salt and sulfur from sedimentary strata underlying the Gulf coast.

Closely related to the above cases is subsidence due to withdrawal of ground water, permitting compaction of sediment under the area of pumping. One example is from the San Joaquin Valley of California, where subsidence locally exceeding 10 ft (3 m) took place over a 35-yr period. Damage resulted to casings of wells in this area.

More localized, and more often resulting in damage to surface structures, is subsidence occurring over mines from which large volumes of rock have been removed. Particularly serious is subsidence over abandoned coal mines. One example is that of Scranton, Pennsylvania, where portions of the city were built over now-abandoned anthracite mine workings. Subsidence has produced gaping cracks and steps, tilting and damaging buildings close to the structures. Associated with abandoned coal mines are other environmental effects. One is the burning of coal and lignite beds beneath the ground, followed by subsidence. Another is the emission of highly polluted ground water from abandoned mine shafts and drifts.

## EARTHQUAKES—INDUCED AND CONTROLLED

Although earthquakes generally are driven by deep-seated crustal forces far beyond the power of Man to modify, there are instances in which Man's activities have set off earthquakes. Increase in numbers of earthquakes following underground nuclear test explosions has been documented. A particularly strange case of a different type is that of the Rocky Mountain Arsenal near Denver, Colorado. Since 1962 hundreds of earthquakes have been recorded in that area and seem to be correlated with the pumping of fluids under pressure into a disposal well 12,000 ft (3600 m) deep. One hypothesis is that the fluid pressure set off the quakes by releasing strains already present within the rock.

Although the causal relationship between fluid pumping and earthquakes has been questioned, some support of man-induced earthquakes is found in the occurrence of numerous quakes following the filling of a large reservoir behind a dam (example: Lake Kariba, behind a dam on the Zambezia River in Zambia). Apparently, the added water load was sufficient to trigger the earthquakes in rock already in a state of being strained. These occurrences have led to consideration of the possibility that large and destructive earthquakes can be controlled by man-made actions to induce steady movement or a succession of small slip movements along the fault structures and thus to prevent buildup of rock strain to dangerous levels.

## MAN'S ROLE AS AN ENVIRONMENTAL AGENT IN REVIEW

This brief review of a number of facets of the environmental scene spans a wide range of dimensions and structures of the atmosphere, hydrosphere, and lithosphere. It should certainly leave one with a realization that most environmental problems are complex, and it is the exception when an induced change in a single parameter does not lead to compensatory changes in one or more additional parameters. Most frustrating of all, perhaps, is the feeling that we cannot really evaluate the long-term cumulative effects of changes that Man's activities seem to be inducing. This frustration is particularly acute with respect to problems of the atmosphere and hydrosphere, in which fluxes of matter and energy occur readily on vast scales. Solutions to environmental problems call for an extraordinarily great breadth of inquiry into all sciences, and this is only one side of the coin. Man, as a social animal, is not always prepared to act in what seems to be the obvious way to alleviate or eliminate a given problem, for he cannot readily alter his long-established goals and sources of satisfaction.

Nevertheless, a study of the physical systems of planet Earth can provide the basic information on process and form that underlies all environmental problems. Without this information progress in environmental problem-solving cannot even begin.

## References for further study

### GENERAL

Wilson, C. L., ed. (1970), *Man's Impact on Global Environment: Assessment and Recommendations for Action,* Cambridge, Mass., M.I.T. Press, 319 pp.

Detwyler, T. R. (1971), *Man's Impact on Environment,* New York, McGraw-Hill, 731 pp. (Collected papers of more than 50 authors.)

Murdoch, W. W., ed. (1971), *Environment,* Stamford, Conn., Sinauer Associates, 448 pp.

### ATMOSPHERE

Landsberg, H. E. (1956), "The Climate of Towns," pp. 584–606 of *Man's Role in Changing the Face of the Earth,* W. L. Thomas, Jr., ed., Chicago, Univ. of Chicago Press, 1193 pp.

Schaeffer, Vincent J. (1956), "Artificially Induced Precipitation and Its Potentialities," pp. 607–618 of *Man's Role in Changing the Face of the Earth,* W. L. Thomas, Jr., ed., Chicago, Univ. of Chicago Press, 1193 pp.

Plass, Gilbert N. (1959), "Carbon Dioxide and Climate," reprint no. 823 from *Scientific American,* July, 1959; San Francisco, Freeman, 9 pp.

Air Conservation Commission (1965), *Air Conservation,* publ. no. 80, Washington, D.C., Amer. Assoc. Advancement of Science, 335 pp.

Shaw, R. H., ed. (1967), *Ground Level Climatology,* publ. no. 86, Washington, D.C., Amer. Assoc. Advancement of Science, 395 pp.

Bolin, B. (1970), "The Carbon Cycle," *Scientific American,* vol. 223, no. 3, pp. 124–132.

Cloud, P., and A. Gibor (1970), "The Oxygen Cycle," *Scientific American,* vol. 223, no. 3, pp. 110–123.

*First Annual Report of the Council on Environmental Quality,* transmitted to the Congress, August, 1970, Washington, D.C., U.S. Govt. Printing Office.

Gates, D. M. (1970), "Relationship Between Plants and Atmosphere," pp. 145–154 in *Challenge for Survival,* P. Dansereau, ed., New York, Columbia Univ. Press, 235 pp.

Landsberg, H. E. (1970), "Man-Made Climatic Changes," *Science,* vol. 170, pp. 1265–1274.

Landsberg, H. E. (1970), "Metropolitan Air Layers and Pollution," pp. 131–140 of *Challenge for Survival,* P. Dansereau, ed., New York, Columbia Univ. Press, 235 pp.

Newell, R. E. (1971), "The Global Circulation of Atmospheric Pollutants," *Scientific American,* vol. 224, no. 1, pp. 32–42.

### RUNOFF, FLOODS, LAKES, GROUND WATER

Ruttner, F. (1952), *Fundamentals of Limnology,* 3rd ed., D. G. Frey and F. E. J. Fry, trs., Toronto, Univ. of Toronto Press, 295 pp.

Colman, E. A. (1953), *Vegetation and Watershed Management,* New York, Ronald, 412 pp.

Leopold, L. B., and T. Maddock, Jr. (1954), *Big Dams, Little Dams, and Land Management,* New York, Ronald, 278 pp.

Leopold, L. B., and T. Maddock, Jr. (1954), *The Flood Control Controversy,* New York, Ronald, 255 pp.

Hoyt, W. G., and W. B. Langbein (1955), *Floods,* Princeton, N.J., Princeton Univ. Press, 469 pp.

U.S. Department of Agriculture (1955), *Water,* Yearbook of Agriculture, 1955, Washington, D.C., U.S. Govt. Printing Office, 751 pp.

Thomas, H. E. (1956), "Changes in Quantities and Qualities of Ground and Surface Waters," pp. 542–563 of *Man's Role in Changing the Face of the Earth,* W. L. Thomas, Jr., ed., Chicago, Univ. of Chicago Press, 1193 pp.

Vallentyne, J. R. (1957), "Principles of Modern Limnology," *American Scientist,* vol. 45, pp. 218–244.

Todd, D. K. (1959), *Ground Water Hydrology,* New York, Wiley, 336 pp.

Leopold, L. B. (1968), *Hydrology for Urban Land Planning,* U.S. Geological Survey, Circular 554, Washington, D.C., U.S. Govt. Printing Office.

### SOIL EROSION, SEDIMENTATION

U.S. Department of Agriculture (1938), *Soils and Men,* Yearbook of Agriculture, 1938, Washington, D.C., U.S. Govt. Printing Office, 1232 pp., Part II.

Bennett, H. H. (1955), *Elements of Soil Conservation,* 2nd ed., New York, McGraw-Hill, 358 pp.

Leopold, L. B. (1956), "Land Use and Sediment Yield," pp. 639–647 of *Man's Role in Changing the Face of the Earth,* W. L. Thomas, Jr., ed., Chicago, Univ. of Chicago Press, 1193 pp.

Strahler, A. N. (1956), "The Nature of Induced Erosion and Aggradation," pp. 621–638 of *Man's Role in Changing the Face of the Earth,* W. L. Thomas, Jr., ed., Chicago, Univ. of Chicago Press, 1193 pp.

Stallings, J. H. (1957), *Soil Conservation,* Englewood Cliffs, N.J., Prentice-Hall, 575 pp.

## RIVER AND SHORELINE ENGINEERING

Mackin, J. H. (1948), "Concept of the Graded River," *Geological Society of America Bulletin,* vol. 59, pp. 463–512.

Leopold, L. B., and E. Maddock, Jr. (1953), "The Hydraulic Geometry of Streams," *U.S. Geological Survey,* Professional Paper 252, Washington, D.C., U.S. Govt. Printing Office, 57 pp.

Davis, J. H. (1956), "Influences of Man upon Coast Lines," pp. 504–521 of *Man's Role in Changing the Face of the Earth,* W. L. Thomas, Jr., ed., Chicago, Univ. of Chicago Press, 1193 pp.

Bascom, W. (1964), *Waves and Beaches,* New York, Doubleday, 260 pp., chap. 11.

Burton, I., R. W. Kates, and R. E. Snead (1969), *The Human Ecology of Coastal Flood Hazard in Megalopolis,* Chicago, Dept. of Geography, Univ. of Chicago, 196 pp.

## MASS WASTING, LANDSLIDES, SUBSIDENCE, EARTHQUAKES

Sharpe, C. F. S. (1938), *Landslides and Related Phenomena,* New York, Columbia Univ. Press, 137 pp.

Terzaghi, K. (1950), "Mechanism of Landslides," pp. 83–123 in *Berkey Volume,* New York, Geological Society of America, 327 pp.

Highway Research Board (1958), *Landslides and Engineering Practice,* E. B. Eckel, ed., NAS–NRC publ. 544, Washington, D.C., National Academy of Sciences, 232 pp.

Pakiser, L. C., *et al.* (1969), "Earthquake Prediction and Control," *Science,* vol. 166, pp. 1467–1473.

Flawn, P. T. (1970), *Environmental Geology,* New York, Harper & Row, 313 pp. (see pp. 33–50).

## Review questions

1. Describe in detail the carbon cycle. How is carbon dioxide used by plants? Describe in detail the oxygen cycle. How is oxygen used in the process of biological oxidation? Relate the carbon and oxygen cycles to each other.

2. What increase in level of carbon dioxide has been observed in the past century or so? Compare the observed increase with that calculated from combustion of fuels in the same period. Explain the difference. What roles does the ocean play in regulation of atmospheric carbon dioxide?

3. What environmental effects can be anticipated from a rise in level of carbon dioxide? Does the record of world average air temperatures conform with predicted changes? Discuss this problem.

4. What effect can combustion of fuels have upon the world supply of atmospheric free oxygen? How do phytoplankton contribute to maintenance of the world's oxygen supply?

5. In what ways can man-made changes in content of atmospheric water vapor induce environmental changes? How, in general, is temperature related to water-vapor content of the atmosphere? In what ways might the products of fuel combustion by jet aircraft in the stratosphere influence the environment?

6. How might agricultural activities alter the water-vapor content of the lower atmosphere, and what other changes might be induced? Cite a possible example. Describe the effects of cloud seeding. To what extent have man-made efforts to alter precipitation patterns been successful?

7. What sorts of particulates and pollutants enter the atmosphere from combustion and other industrial activities? What are the photochemical reactions? What is smog? What is the principal source of carbon monoxide and hydrocarbons in polluted air? of sulfur oxides? of particulates?

8. How are contaminants eliminated from polluted air? Do man-made dusts enter the stratosphere in significant quantities? Describe the aftereffects upon the atmosphere of major periods of volcanic activity. How can the introduction of man-made dust into the atmosphere alter cloud coverage and planetary albedo? What might be the environmental effects of such changes?

9. Explain the development of a temperature inversion in the lower atmosphere. Refer to lapse rates in your explanation. How can a low-level inversion trap pollutants? Cite an example. What causes an upper-level inversion? Describe the factors contributing to persistent inversion and smog in the Los Angeles basin. How does smog affect visibility?

10. How does urbanization change the physical characteristics of the ground surface, and what local climatic effects follow? What is a heat island? Describe air circulation over a heat island. What effect does heat emission and air pollution have upon cloudiness, fog, and precipitation over an urban area? How are winds affected by buildings in a city?

11. How important is the total heat added to the atmosphere by Man's activities in terms of the earth's heat balance? How important may this contribution become in the future?

12. In what way can oil films upon the ocean surface modify the normal processes of

interchange of energy and matter between atmosphere and oceans?

13. How does Man's modification of the land surface through agriculture influence infiltration and runoff? What effects do these changes cause in stream flow and floods? What changes of a similar nature are brought about by urbanization? How can discharge of storm runoff and sewage into bays and estuaries cause environmental deterioration?

14. List a number of origins of fresh-water lakes. Compare the physical, chemical, and biological characteristics of oligotrophic lakes with those of eutrophic lakes. Which is the more productive of organic matter? What is eutrophication, and how is it accelerated by Man's activities?

15. Describe the kinds of wells used to extract ground water. What is the effect of pumping upon the water table? What is a cone of depression? How can surface-water flow be diverted into ground-water supplies by pumping of wells?

16. In what ways can ground-water supplies be contaminated by disposal of liquid and solid wastes into the ground? What changes in ground-water hydrology can result from manmade lakes? How does salt-water intrusion take place, and how can it be remedied?

17. How does atmospheric pollution in an urban area intensify chemical weathering processes? How does Man induce mass wasting of various forms by engineering activities? Cite a number of examples.

18. Compare accelerated soil erosion with the geologic norm. What forms of environmental deterioration and resource loss are brought about by soil erosion and related processes? What measures can be taken to control soil erosion?

19. Describe the effects upon a stream and its valley of the construction of a large dam and reservoir. What effects are transmitted upstream? What changes in stream-channel form can be anticipated downstream from a dam? Give an example.

20. What changes in the environment of an alluvial valley are brought about by engineering works designed to regulate floods? What basic forms of flood control are practiced? How effective is each?

21. How do engineering works designed to achieve shore protection from wave attack cause changes in the normal littoral drift of beach sand? Illustrate with examples.

22. What is Man's role in aggravating dust storms? What measures can be taken to cope with effects of wind upon agricultural lands? What are phytogenic dunes? Explain the role of coastal dunes in maintaining the stable environment of barrier beaches. Why is stabilization of coastal dunes a desirable achievement?

23. In what ways does the extraction of mineral resources scar the bedrock surface of the land? Give several examples. What forms of land subsidence can be attributed to Man's activities? Illustrate with examples.

24. Can Man's activities set off earthquakes? Explain and give an example. Evaluate the prospects for Man's control of earthquakes at some future time.

25. What recommendations would you make for a far-reaching and effective program to eliminate or minimize the undesirable effects of Man's activities upon the environment? How would your program be implemented, administered, financed, and enforced? In what ways might such a program run counter to existing economic, industrial, social, and governmental practices?

# part ii. man's consumption of earth resources

This second part of the Epilogue deals with time in an order of magnitude that is geological; it stands in contrast to the subject matter of the first part, which concerns itself largely with short-term disturbances of atmospheric, hydrologic, and geomorphic systems. Our theme here is that Man is rapidly consuming earth resources that required geologic spans of time to prepare. So slowly do the geological processes operate that rates of replenishment are infinitesimally small in comparison with the present rates of consumption. The geological resources are therefore finite, and once we know approximately the world extent of a particular resource, we can predict its expiration according to any number of use schedules.

A pervasive principle in an analysis of geologic resources is that of change from concentrated states to dispersed states, and this is exactly the opposite of geological processes that achieved the initial concentrated states. For example, coal represents an extremely dense concentration of hydrocarbons in large quantities. Combustion of coal disperses this matter into atmospheric constituents, and the stored energy is transformed and dissipated into outer space. We have no way to reverse this process without expending an equivalent amount of energy. In the case of one comparatively rare metal—lead—geologic processes have concentrated the element into rich ores. We disperse much of it into the atmosphere through combustion of leaded gasoline.

On the other hand, a great deal of used lead is recovered and used again—a process known as *recycling*. Aluminum provides an example of a metal of which only a small proportion (about one-twelfth) is recycled; the remainder is widely dispersed, as witness the ubiquitous aluminum beer can.

Actually, Man himself usually must carry out the final stages of mineral concentration, as in the case of nuclear fuels, copper ores, or most iron ores. In terms of percentages by weight in the earth's crust, these deposits as mined represent an extraordinary degree of concentration, but it is still not enough. So the principle of concentration and dispersion must be invoked with caution and with due regard for instances when it does not apply.

Two of the geologic resources falling into the nonrenewable category have been discussed in Part I of this Epilogue. These are soils and ground water. Their slow rates of accumulation are quasi-geologic in time, at least in comparison with other mineral resources. Nevertheless, the rates of expenditure of both soils and ground water can vastly exceed the rates of their accumulation, and in this sense they are truly nonrenewable resources.

Nonrenewable earth resources can be grouped about as follows:

Soils
Ground water
Metalliferous deposits (examples: ores of iron copper, tin)
Nonmetallic deposits, including
    Structural materials (examples: building stone, gravel, and sand)
    Materials used chemically (examples: sulfur, salts)

Fossil fuels (coal, petroleum, and natural gas)
Nuclear fuels (uranium, thorium)

Notice that the last two groups represent sources of energy, whereas the preceding two groups are sources of matter (materials). In this brief review, emphasis must be on concepts rather than upon data. Our aim will be to gain insight into the nature and distribution of these natural resources as a guide to broader issues related to planning for the future.

## SOILS

Little needs to be added to the basic principles of soil formation (pedogenesis) covered in Chapter 8, or to the process of accelerated erosion treated in its hydrologic context in Part I of the Epilogue. Soils of the podzolic type, the youngest on earth as a group, have evolved since recession of ice sheets and are for the most part less than 10,000 yr old. Over unglaciated uplands of the continental shields, surfaces have been exposed to soil-forming processes continuously for much and perhaps all of the Cenozoic Era. It is very difficult to establish rates of soil production, although many attempts have been made to do so. One guess is that soils reach a final stage when no further change of state occurs in a span of perhaps 0.5 million years (m.y.) to 1 m.y. One estimate of the rate of formation of tropical latosols is that the production of 3 ft (1 m) of soil from granitic rock may require between 20,000 and 100,000 yr. Even the fastest of the estimated rates of soil production require that most of the upland soils that yield the bulk of the world's agricultural production have required at least several thousands of years to attain their present depths and horizons. Perhaps an ideal goal would be to attempt to achieve a geologic norm of soil erosion, in which rate of removal is balanced by rate of soil production from the parent mass.

## GROUND WATER

Knowledge of the hydrologic cycle and the movements and recharge of ground water given in Chapter 6 and in Part I of the Epilogue shows clearly that the ground-water resource is limited in the long run to the rate of recharge. Utilization that exceeds recharge must ultimately lower the water table to the point that production rates decline to unsatisfactory levels, and there may be various undesirable side effects as well. In humid climates with large water surpluses in the annual water budget, various methods can be used to return water to the ground-water body. This is done by means of *recharge wells* or by design of surfaces into which infiltration can take place. Obviously, the method used depends upon the water source and its schedule of availability. One fairly simple example is the return of ground water used for cooling in air conditioning or industrial processes. The warmed but otherwise uncontaminated water is returned directly by recharge wells. Recharge from stream runoff has been previously explained (Figure E.14). Other sources of recharge include storm sewer discharge and treated effluents of sewage-disposal plants.

Semiarid and arid regions face particularly difficult problems in the utilization of groundwater supplies, for the obvious reason that the climate is one of a water deficit as an annual average. Evapotranspiration exceeds precipitation in areas of water use, a factor that not only places exceptional demands upon ground water as a source for irrigation, but at the same time reduces the possibilities of use of surface runoff for recharge. In such regions, natural recharge comes from sources at high elevation, often at considerable distance from the groundwater body. Two specialized ground-water structures are significant in these regions: One is the alluvial fan (Chapter 9); another is the artesian ground-water system.

Alluvial fans hold ground water confined in *aquifers*. An aquifer is a rock body capable of transmitting water freely and storing it in substantial quantities. In the case of the alluvial fan the aquifers are layers of sand and gravel deposited by streams which built the fan (Figure E.32). These water-bearing layers receive recharge near the head of the alluvial fan, where water enters the permeable layers by infiltration from the channels of streams originating in mountain watersheds. Water in the aquifers is retained under relatively impermeable layers of mud spread over the fan surface during its construction at times when mud-bearing floods issue from the canyon mouths. (A layer that resists the flow of ground water is referred to as an *aquiclude*.) Now, because the sediment layers of an alluvial fan slope downward to lower elevations in radial lines from the apex of the fan, water that enters the aquifers makes its way to lower levels and is confined under pressure beneath the impermeable layers; this water possesses a *hydraulic head*. When a well is driven into the periphery of the alluvial fan, water will spontaneously rise in the well, which is described as an *artesian well*.

Various other kinds of alluvial deposits in intermontane basins store ground water derived from runoff from mountainous areas where orographic precipitation is copious. All these supplies face the basic problem of depletion by pumping at rates far greater than those of natural recharge. In many of these areas the water table has declined alarmingly. Attempts to increase recharge in times of abundant channel flow consist of water-spreading structures, including various designs of basins and other traps.

What is usually meant by artesian ground water is a geologic system of strata arranged so that an extensive aquifer, usually a sandstone formation, is confined by an aquiclude, usually a shale formation, in such a way that the aquifer is exposed to infiltration in a zone of comparatively high elevation and dips gradually to lower elevations under cover of the aquiclude (Figure E.33). Water confined under pressure will rise toward the surface, either in natural artesian springs, where fractures in the rock permit, or in artesian wells. In some instances the water rises above the well head.

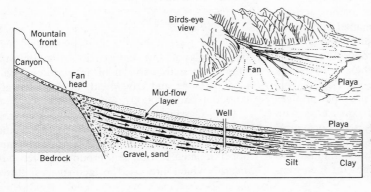

Figure E.32. Idealized cross section of an alluvial fan showing the relation of mud-flow layers (aquicludes) to sand layers (aquifers).

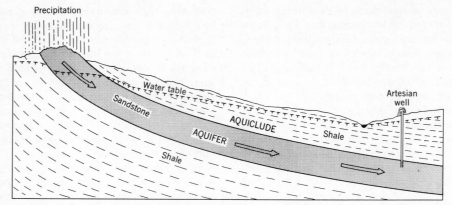

Figure E.33. Schematic structure section showing conditions favorable to the occurrence of artesian flow.

A particularly good example of an artesian system is found over wide areas of the Great Plains region. Here the aquifer is the Dakota sandstone of Cretaceous age, which crops out along the foothills of the Rocky Mountain ranges and around the Black Hills. From these intake zones the aquifer descends beneath impermeable shales. In the past, this aquifer, and others in similar sedimentary sequences, have provided substantial supplies of artesian water. Again, because recharge is very slow, these sources are easily depleted by overpumping.

This brief discussion of ground water as a resource—renewable within limits under favorable conditions, but nonrenewable under others—will serve its purpose if it gives some appreciation of the problems that require careful research and the need for water-resource planning far into the future.

## METALLIFEROUS DEPOSITS

Metals occur in economically adequate concentrations as *ores*. An ore is a mineral accumulation that can be extracted at a profit for refinement and industrial use. A number of important metallic elements are listed in Table E.2, together with *clarke of abundance,* or percentage by weight in the average crustal rock. The *clarke* is a unit named for F. W. Clarke, a geochemist who did extensive research on the chemical composition of the earth's crust. (The clarke is the same quantity given for abundance in Table 7.2.) An important point is that magmas are the primary sources of many metals. Our concern is with the natural geological processes of concentration of metallic elements and compounds into ores of various kinds. Whereas aluminum and iron are relatively abundant, most of the essen-

Table E.2.    SELECTED METALLIC ABUNDANCES IN AVERAGE CRUSTAL ROCK

| Symbol | Element Name | Clarke (percentage by weight) | Annual World Consumption (tons) |
|---|---|---|---|
| Al | Aluminum | 8.1 | 6,100,000 |
| Fe | Iron | 5.0 | 310,000,000 |
| Mg | Magnesium | 2.1 | 150,000 |
| Ti | Titanium | 0.44 | 10,000 |
| Mn | Manganese | 0.10 | 6,000,000 |
| V | Vanadium | 0.014 | 7,000 |
| Cr | Chromium | 0.010 | 1,400,000 |
| Ni | Nickel | 0.0075 | 400,000 |
| Zn | Zinc | 0.0070 | 3,800,000 |
| Cu | Copper | 0.0055 | 5,400,000 |
| Co | Cobalt | 0.0025 | 13,000 |
| Pb | Lead | 0.0013 | 2,800,000 |
| Sn | Tin | 0.00020 | 190,000 |
| U | Uranium | 0.00018 | 30,000[a] |
| Mo | Molybdenum | 0.00015 | 45,000 |
| W | Tungsten | 0.00015 | 30,000 |
| Sb | Antimony | 0.00002 | 60,000 |
| Hg | Mercury | 0.000008 | 9,000 |
| Ag | Silver | 0.000007 | 8,000 |
| Pt | Platinum | 0.000001 | 30 |
| Au | Gold | 0.0000004 | 1,600 |

Source: Data from B. Mason (1966), *Principles of Geochemistry*, 3rd ed., New York, Wiley, pp. 45–46, Table 3.3 and Appendix III.

[a] As $U_3O_8$.

tial metals of our industrial civilization are present in extremely small proportions—witness mercury and silver with clarkes of only 0.000008 and 0.000007, respectively.

In a classification of metals by uses, iron stands by itself in the production of iron and steel. (Table E.2 gives annual world consumption.) Related to iron is a group of *ferro-alloy metals,* which are used principally as alloys with iron to create steels with special properties. The ferro-alloys include titanium, manganese, vanadium, chromium, nickel, cobalt, molybdenum, and tungsten, listed in order of appearance in Table E.2. Other important metals (nonferrous metals), standing apart individually with respect to industrial uses, are aluminum, magnesium, zinc, copper, lead, and tin. A minor group listed in Table E.2 includes antimony, silver, platinum, and gold. Finally, there are metals which are radioactive, including uranium, listed in Table E.2, thorium, and radium.

From the standpoint of metallic abundances as ores, the clarke is an abstraction of no practical value. Instead, the economic geologist is interested in the proportion of a given metal present in the form of the ore of its usual occurrence, either as an element or a compound. While a few metals, among them gold, silver, platinum, and copper, occur as elements (i.e., as *native metals*), most occur as compounds. Oxides and sulfides are the most common forms, but more complex forms are present in many ores. The abundance of an element actually present in an ore is given as a multiplying factor known as the *clarke of concentration*. For example, manganese has a clarke of crustal abundance of 0.1 (Table E.2). A common ore of manganese is the mineral *pyrolusite*, composition manganese oxide ($MnO_2$), in which manganese is present in the proportion of 63.2% by weight. The clarke of concentration for pure pyrolusite is therefore 632 ($63.2\% \div 0.1 = 632$). A manganese ore containing pyrolusite as the principal mineral would be sufficiently rich for

extraction with a concentration clarke of 350, which in this case represents an ore consisting of 35% of the element manganese ($0.1 \times 350 = 35\%$). Table E.3 lists a number of metals with their clarkes of crustal abundance, concentration clarkes, and approximate percentages of the elements required to be present for profitable extraction.

A notable trend in mineral extraction has been a shift from ores of simple composition to ores of complex composition. Certain ores yield a principal commodity plus one or more by-products: for example, silver-bearing galena (lead is the principal metal). In certain complex ores each of the constituents is necessary to make the operation profitable.

Principles of magma crystallization, contact metamorphism, mineral alteration, the action of streams and waves, and deposition of hydrogenic sediments can be put to good use here in a brief sketch of the origin and classification of metalliferous mineral deposits.

One major class of ore deposits is formed within magmas by direct segregation in which mineral grains of greater specific gravity sink through the fluid magma while crystallization is still in progress. Masses or layers of a single mineral accumulate in this way. One example is chromite, the principal ore of chromium with a specific gravity of 4.4. Bands of chromite ore are thus sometimes found near the base of the igneous body. Another example is seen in the nickel ores of Sudbury, Ontario. These sulfides of nickel apparently became segregated from a saucer-shaped magma body and were concentrated in a basal layer (Figure E.34). Magnetite is another ore mineral that

Table E.3.  CONCENTRATION CLARKES OF ORE BODIES FOR SELECTED MINERALS

| Metal | Clarke (percentage by weight) | Concentration Clarke Required for Ore Body | Approx. Percentage of Metal in Ore Needed for Profitable Extraction |
|---|---|---|---|
| Aluminum | 8.13 | 4 | 30 |
| Iron | 5.00 | 6 | 30 (lower possible) |
| Manganese | 0.10 | 350 | 35–27 |
| Chromium | 0.02 | 1500 | 30 |
| Copper | 0.007 | 140 | 0.8 to 0.5 |
| Nickel | 0.008 | 175 | 1.5 |
| Zinc | 0.013 | 300 | 4[a] |
| Tin | 0.004 | 250 | 1 |
| Lead | 0.0016 | 2500 | 4 |
| Uranium | 0.0002 | 500 | 0.1 |

Source: Data from B. Mason (1966), *Principles of Geochemistry*, 3rd ed., New York, Wiley, p. 50, Table 3.5.
[a] Percentage in a multiple-element ore.

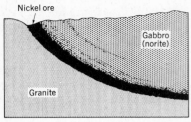

Figure E.34. Cross section of a sulfide nickel-ore deposit at Sudbury, Ontario. The ore layer lies at the base of a body of gabbro (norite), overlying an older granite basement. [After A. P. Coleman (1913), Canada Dept. of Mines, Monograph 170, p. 34.]

has been segregated from a magma to result in an ore body of major importance.

The process of contact-metamorphism, referred to in Chapter 10, is a second source of important ore deposits. High-temperature fluids from within the magma soak into the surrounding country rock, introducing ore minerals in exchange for components of the rock. For example, a limestone layer may have been replaced by iron ore consisting of hematite and magnetite (Figure E.35). Ores of copper, zinc, and lead have also been produced in this manner. Valuable deposits of nonmetallic minerals have also resulted from contact metamorphism.

A third type of ore deposit is produced by the effects of high-temperature solutions, known as *hydrothermal solutions*, that leave a magma during the final stages of its crystallization and are deposited in fractures to produce mineral *veins*. Some veins are sharply defined and evidently represent the filling of open cracks with layers of minerals. Other veins seem to be the result of replacement of the country rock by the hydrothermal solutions. Where veins occur in exceptional thicknesses and numbers, they may constitute a *lode*.

Hydrothermal solutions produce yet another

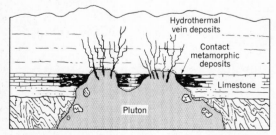

Figure E.35. Schematic cross section of vein deposits and contact metamorphic deposits adjacent to an intrusive igneous body.

important type of ore accumulation, the *disseminated deposit*, in which the ore is distributed throughout a very large mass of rock. Certain of the great copper deposits are referred to as *porphyry copper* deposits because the ore has entered a large body of igneous rock of a class known as a *porphyry*, which had in some manner been shattered into small joint blocks that permitted entry of the solutions. One of the most celebrated of these is at Bingham Canyon, Utah (Figure E.36).

Hydrothermal solutions rise toward the surface, making vein deposits in a shallow zone and even emerging as hot springs. Many valuable ores of gold and silver are deposits of the shallow type. Particularly interesting is the occurrence of mercury ore in the form of the mineral *cinnabar* as a shallow hydrothermal deposit. Most renowned are the deposits of the Almaden district in Spain, where mercury has been mined for centuries and has provided most of the world's supply of that metal.

A fourth category of ore deposits embodies the effects of downward-moving solutions in the zone of aeration and the ground-water zone (see Chapter 6). Enrichment of mineral deposits to produce ores in this manner is described as a *secondary* process. Consider first a vein containing primary minerals of magmatic origin (Figure E.37). These minerals, mostly sulfides of copper, lead, zinc, and silver, along with native gold, are originally disseminated through the vein rock and may not exist in concentrations sufficient to qualify as ores. Through long-continued denudation of the region, the ground surface truncates the vein, which was formerly deeply buried. Assuming a humid climate, there will exist a water table and a ground-water zone, above which is the zone of aeration. Water, arriving as rain or snow-melt, moves down through the zone of aeration. The geologist refers to this water as *meteoric*, which is perfectly acceptable from the standpoint of atmospheric science. The meteoric water becomes a weak acid, since it contains dissolved carbon dioxide (carbonic acid) and will also gain sulfuric acid by reactions involving iron sulfide (mineral: *pyrite*).

The result of downward percolation of meteoric water is to cause three forms of enrichment and thus to yield ore bodies. First, in the zone closest to the surface, as soluble waste minerals are removed, there may accumulate certain insoluble minerals, among them gold and compounds of silver or lead, in

Figure E.36. Open-pit copper mine at Bingham Canyon, Utah. (Photograph by courtesy of Kennecott Copper Corporation.)

sufficient concentration to form an ore. This type of ore deposit is known as a *gossan* (Figure E.37). Iron oxide and quartz will also accumulate in the gossan. In Colonial times, iron-rich gossans constituted minable iron ores, but they have been exhausted. Leaching of other minerals carries them down into a *zone of oxidation*. In this second zone there may accumulate a number of oxides of zinc, copper, iron, and lead, along with native silver, copper, and gold. A third zone is that of *sulfide enrichment* within the upper part of the ground-water zone, just beneath the water table (Figure E.37). Sulfides of iron, copper, lead, and zinc may be heavily concentrated in this zone. (Mineral examples are pyrite, chalcopyrite, chalcocite, galena, and sphalerite.) Sulfide enrichment may also affect large primary ore bodies of the disseminated type, such as the

porphyry copper of Bingham Canyon, Utah, referred to above. Here, the enriched layer has already been removed, and mining has progressed into low-grade primary ore beneath.

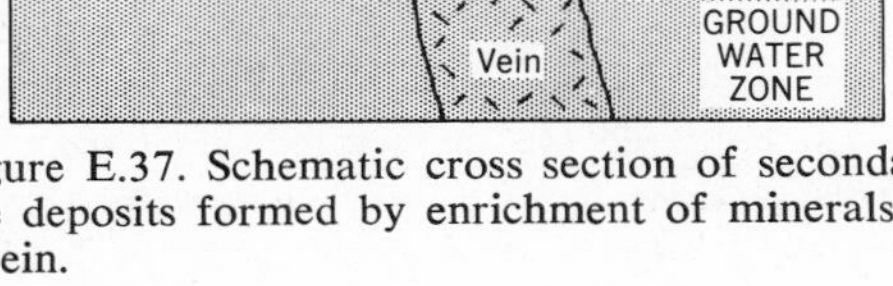

Also in the category of secondary ores is *bauxite*. This principal ore of aluminum accumulates as a near-surface deposit in tropical regions where the soil-forming regime of laterization prevails (see Chapter 8). Bauxite, a mixture of hydrous oxides of aluminum derived from the alteration of aluminosilicate minerals, is practically insoluble under the prevailing climatic conditions and can accumulate indefinitely as the denudation of the land surface progresses. Produced under similar environmental conditions are residual ores of manganese (mineral: *manganite*) and of iron (mineral: *limonite*). The term *laterite* is commonly applied to these residual deposits.

A fifth category of ore deposit is that in which concentration has occurred through fluid agents of transportation: streams and waves. Certain of the insoluble heavy minerals derived from weathering of rock are swept as small fragments into stream channels and carried down-valley with the sand and gravel as bed load (see Chapter 9). Because of their greater specific gravity, these minerals become concentrated in layers and lenses of gravel to become *placer deposits*. Native gold is one of the minerals extensively extracted from placer deposits; platinum is another. A third is an oxide of tin, the mineral *cassiterite,* which

Figure E.37. Schematic cross section of secondary ore deposits formed by enrichment of minerals in a vein.

forms important placer deposits. Diamonds, too, are concentrated in placer deposits, as are other gem stones. Transported by streams to the ocean, gravels bearing the heavy minerals are spread along the coast in beaches, forming a second type of placer deposit, the marine placer.

Finally, we can recognize a sixth group of ore deposits in the hydrogenic category of sediments, explained in Chapter 8. For the most part, sediment deposition is the principal source of nonmetallic mineral deposits, considered below, but some important metalliferous deposits are of this origin. Iron, particularly, occurs as sedimentary ores in enormous quantities. Sedimentary iron ores are oxides of iron—usually *hematite*. A particularly striking example is iron ore of the Clinton formation of Silurian age, widespread in the Appalachian region. For reasons not well understood, unusually large quantities of iron oxides, derived by weathering of mafic minerals in rocks exposed in bordering lands, were brought to the sea floor and were precipitated as hematite. Another metal, manganese, has been concentrated by depositional processes into important sedimentary ores.

Table E.4 will give some appreciation of the future demands for the same metals of Table E.2, as estimated by the U.S. Bureau of Mines for the year 2000. (Primary production is that derived from mining of ores.) The table also shows what part of the 1968 United States demand for primary metals came from domestic sources. This information is highly significant in demonstrating the dependence of a large, heavily industrialized nation upon foreign sources of metals. An approximate factor of increase in demand is given in the last column.

A particularly striking fact shown in Table E.4 is that a number of the metals for which the factor of increased demand is the largest are those derived largely or entirely from foreign sources. For example, metallic titanium demands are shown to increase by a factor of

Table E.4. COMPARISON OF UNITED STATES PRIMARY METAL DEMAND IN 1968 WITH PROJECTED DEMAND IN THE YEAR 2000

| Metal | Units | 1968 U.S. Primary Production | 1968 U.S. Primary Demand | Projected U.S. Primary Demand in Year 2000 | Approx. Factor of Increase |
|---|---|---|---|---|---|
| Aluminum | Thousand ST[a] | 420 | 3,900 | 28,000 | 7 |
| Iron | Million ST | 56 | 84 | 150 | 2 |
| Magnesium (metal) | Thousand ST | 98 | 91 | 390 | 4 |
| Magnesium (nonmetal) | Thousand ST | 1,000 | 1,100 | 1,800 | 1½ |
| Titanium (metal) | Thousand ST | 0 | 13 | 150 | 12 |
| Titanium (nonmetal) | Thousand ST | 300 | 440 | 1,600 | 4 |
| Manganese | Thousand ST | 48 | 1,100 | 2,100 | 2 |
| Vanadium | ST | 6,100 | 5,800 | 31,000 | 5 |
| Chromium | Thousand ST | 0 | 450 | 1,100 | 2½ |
| Nickel | Million pounds | 30 | 320 | 930 | 3 |
| Zinc | Thousand ST | 530 | 1,400 | 3,000 | 2 |
| Copper | Thousand ST | 1,200 | 1,500 | 6,400 | 4 |
| Cobalt | Thousand lb | 1,300 | 14,000 | 25,000 | 2 |
| Lead | Thousand ST | 360 | 900 | 2,000 | 2 |
| Tin | Thousand ST | Almost nil | 59 | 85 | 1½ |
| Uranium | ST | 10,000 | 2,700 | 64,000 | 20 |
| Molybdenum | Million pounds | 94 | 56 | 180 | 3 |
| Tungsten | Thousand pounds | 9,800 | 16,000 | 74,000 | 5 |
| Antimony | ST | 1,900 | 21,000 | 40,000 | 2 |
| Mercury | Thousand flasks | 29 | 62 | 130 | 2 |
| Silver | Million ounces | 33 | 90 | 210 | 2 |
| Platinum | Thousand ounces | 5 | 460 | 1,400 | 3 |
| Gold | Thousand ounces | 1,500 | 6,600 | 24,000 | 4 |

Source: Data of U.S. Bureau of Mines. Figures rounded to two places.

[a] Short tons.

about 12, but none is now produced in the United States. Aluminum demand will be up sevenfold but we produce only one-tenth of our primary aluminum. A similar situation holds for chromium, nickel, cobalt, and platinum. Our dependence is strong upon foreign supplies of iron, manganese, zinc, lead, tungsten, antimony, silver, and gold. Actually, the only metals which the United States produced in substantial surplus relative to demand in 1968 were uranium and molybdenum. It is predicted by the U.S. Bureau of Mines that in the year 2000 domestic production of primary minerals in all categories (including nonmetallic minerals) will supply substantially less of the demand for primary minerals than it does at present.

Of increasing importance in manufacturing today is the secondary production of metals through reprocessing of durable metal goods manufactured in the past 10 to 100 yr. We are not here referring to new scrap metal, derived as cuttings during initial manufacture, but to the old materials from discarded products. Metals can be reclaimed from old scrap by processes of distillation, electrometallurgy, mechanical separation, and chemical processes. As the total output of manufactured goods increases through time, the input of metals from secondary sources will also rise in volume.

Recycling of metals is rising in importance as national mineral resources are becoming depleted at increasing rates and as the grade of ores being mined is declining. Some idea of the importance of recycled nonferrous metals is given by data in Table E.5. Secondary consumption figures include both new and old scrap metal. Comparing secondary consumption with primary consumption for 1967, we find that the secondary quantity of copper is only a little smaller than the primary quantity. A similar ratio prevails for lead consumption.

In contrast, secondary consumption values of aluminum and zinc amount to only about one-quarter and one-fifth, respectively, of the primary consumption values.

Since the data of Table E.5 combine new and old scrap, they conceal marked differences in proportions actually derived from old scrap. Percentages of total recovered metal derived from old scrap in 1967 are as follows:

|          | Percentage |
|----------|-----------|
| Copper   | 42 |
| Aluminum | 18 |
| Lead     | 87 |
| Zinc     | 25 |

The recovery of lead from old scrap is almost 90%; three-quarters of this comes from plates of discarded batteries. Recovery of copper from old scrap is also of major importance, while that of zinc and aluminum is of comparatively minor importance. Recovered metals are largely in the form of alloys. For example, most of the recovered copper is in brass and bronze; most of the recovered lead is antimonial lead from battery plates; most of the recovered zinc is in brass and bronze; practically all of the recovered aluminum is in alloys. These facts indicate that secondary metal sources are not, in general, capable of furnishing substantial quantities of pure metals under prevailing conditions of recovery technology.

## NONMETALLIC MINERAL DEPOSITS

Nonmetallic mineral deposits (not including fossil and nuclear fuels) include such a large and diverse assemblage of substances and cover such a wide range of uses that it would be impossible to do the subject justice in a few paragraphs. In outline form we offer some examples of these mineral deposits classified by use categories:

### STRUCTURAL MATERIALS

**Clay:** For use in brick, tile, pipe, chinaware, stoneware, porcelain, paper filler, and cement.

Table E.5  COMPARISON OF PRIMARY AND SECONDARY UNITED STATES CONSUMPTION OF FOUR METALS IN 1967

|          | Primary Consumption | | Secondary Consumption | | Total Consumption | |
|----------|------|------------|------|------------|------|------------|
|          | MST[a] | Percentage | MST | Percentage | MST | Percentage |
| Copper   | 1.5  | 55 | 1.2  | 45 | 2.7  | 100 |
| Aluminum | 3.8  | 81 | 0.9  | 19 | 4.7  | 100 |
| Lead     | 0.75 | 58 | 0.55 | 42 | 1.30 | 100 |
| Zinc     | 1.33 | 84 | 0.26 | 16 | 1.59 | 100 |

Source: Data of U.S. Bureau of Mines.

[a] Millions of short tons.

Examples: kaolin (for china manufacture) from residual deposits produced by weathering of felsic rock; shales, marine and glaciolacustrine clays for brick and tile.

**Portland cement:** Made by fusion of limestone with clay or blast-furnace slag. Suitable limestone formations and clay sources are widely distributed and are of many geologic ages.

**Building stone:** Many rock varieties are used, including granite, marble, limestone, sandstone. Slate is used as a roofing material.

**Crushed stone:** Limestone and "trap rock" (gabbro, basalt) are crushed and graded for aggregate in concrete and in macadam pavements.

**Sand and gravel:** Used in building and paving materials such as mortar and concrete, asphaltic pavements, and base courses under pavements. Sources lie in fluvial and glaciofluvial deposits and in beaches and dunes. Specialized sand uses include molding sands for metal casting, glass sand for manufacture of glass, and filter sand for filtering water supplies.

**Gypsum:** Major use is in calcined form for wallboard and as plaster, and as a retarder in Portland cement. Source is largely in gypsum or anhydrite beds in sedimentary strata associated with red beds and evaporites.

**Lime:** Calcium oxide (CaO) obtained by heating of limestone, has uses in mortar and plaster, in smelting operations, in paper, and in many chemical processes.

**Pigments:** Compounds of lead, zinc, barium, titanium, and carbon, both manufactured and of natural mineral origin, are widely used in paints.

**Asphalt:** Asphalt occurs naturally, but most is derived from refining of petroleum. It is used in paving, and in roofing materials.

**Asbestos:** Fibrous forms of four silicate minerals, used in various fireproofing materials.

## MINERAL DEPOSITS USED CHEMICALLY AND IN OTHER INDUSTRIAL USES

**Sulfur:** Principal source is free sulfur ocurring as beds in sedimentary strata in association with evaporites. Chief use is for manufacture of sulfuric acid.

**Salt:** Naturally occurring rock salt, or *halite,* is largely sodium chloride (NaCl) but includes small amounts of calcium, magnesium, and sulfate. It occurs in salt beds in sedimentary strata and in salt domes. Major uses include manufacture of sodium salts, chlorine, and hydrochloric acid.

**Fertilizers:** Some natural mineral fertilizers are phosphate rock, of sedimentary origin, potash derived from rock salt deposits and by treatment of brines, and nitrates, occurring as sodium nitrate in deserts (Atacama Desert of Chile).

**Sodium salts:** Found in dry lake beds (playas) of the western United States are various salts of sodium, such as borax (sodium borate). These have a wide range of chemical uses. Also important are sodium carbonate and sodium sulfate, found in other dry lake accumulations.

**Fluorite:** The mineral fluorite is calcium fluoride (CaF$_2$). It is found in veins in both sedimentary and igneous rocks. Uses are metallurgical and chemical, e.g., to make hydrofluoric acid.

**Barite:** Barite is barium sulfate (BaSO$_4$) and occurs as a mineral in sedimentary and other rocks. It is used as a filler in many manufactured substances and as a source of barium salts required in chemical manufacture.

**Abrasives:** A wide variety of minerals and rocks have been used as abrasives and polishing agents. Examples are seen in garnet, used in abrasive paper or cloth, and diamond, for facing many kinds of drilling, cutting, and grinding tools.

The above list is by no means complete, and it can serve only to give an appreciation of the strong dependence of industry and agriculture upon mineral deposits and the substances manufactured from them.

The impact of Man upon all forms of mineral resources of the continents is admirably summarized in a statement written by a distinguished economic geologist, Thomas S. Lovering, in a report by the *Committee on Resources and Man* of the National Academy of Sciences –National Research Council:

The total volume of workable mineral deposits is an insignificant fraction of 1% of the earth's crust, and each deposit represents some geological accident in the remote past. Deposits must be mined where they occur—often far from centers of consumption. Each deposit also has its limits; if worked long enough it must sooner or later be exhausted. No second crop will materialize. Rich mineral deposits are a nation's most valuable but ephemeral material possession—its quick assets. Continued extraction of ore, moreover, leads, eventually, to increasing costs as the material mined comes from greater and greater depths or as grade decreases, although improved technology and economics of scale sometimes allow deposits to be worked, temporarily, at decreased costs. Yet industry requires increasing tonnage and variety of mineral raw materials; and although many substances now deemed essential have understudies that can play their parts adequately, technology has found no satisfactory substitutes for others.*

## MINERAL RESOURCES FROM THE SEA†

If the prospect of eventually running out of various mineral resources from the lands seems all too real, we may want to turn to consider possible substitutions of mineral resources from the sea. Sea water has always been available as a resource, and it has long provided the bulk of the world's supply of magnesium and bromium, as well as much of the sodium chloride. The list of elements present in sea water includes most of the known elements and, despite their small concentrations, these are potential supplies for future development. It is thought that sodium, sulfur, potassium, and iodine lie in the category of recoverable elements. It is, however, beyond reason to hope for extraction of ferrous metals (principally iron) and the ferro-alloy metals in significant quantities to provide substitutes for ore deposits of the continents.

The continental margins, with their shallow continental shelves and shallow inland seas, are already being exploited for mineral production, as witness the working of placer deposits of platinum, gold, and tin in shallow waters. The petroleum resources of the North American continental shelf are already under development along the Gulf coast; zones of potential development are believed to exist on the shelf off the Atlantic coast as well. Possibility exists of finding and using mineral deposits of continental crystalline rocks submerged to shallow depths, although this has not yet happened.

Exploration of the deep ocean floor as a source of minerals is still in an early stage, but already the layer of manganese nodules found in parts of all of the oceans is regarded by

some as a major future source of manganese, along with a number of metals in lesser quantities. Presence of substantial amounts of silica with the manganese oxide may render the nodules unfit for exploitation of manganese by present extraction methods, but this does not rule out the possibility of future use.

In reviewing the overall prospects of mineral resources from the oceans and ocean basins we are only being realistic in concluding that contributions from sea water itself are limited only to a few substances, that most of the contributions of the sea floor will be from shallow continental shelves where petroleum and natural gas are the major resources, and that prospects of substantial mineral contributions from the deep ocean floor are rather poor at this time. In the light of these conclusions, the need for conservation and careful planning for the use of mineral resources of the lands becomes all the more evident.

## SOURCES OF ENERGY*

Before looking into the sources of energy that are derived from the solid earth, let us review the full picture of world energy resources to gain a better perspective in terms of natural physical systems. Sources of energy are found in both sustained-yield and exhaustible categories. A sustained-yield source is one that undergoes no appreciable diminution of energy supply during the period of projected use. Consider first the sustained-yield sources.

Solar energy has been described in some detail in Chapter 1, dealing with the radiation balance. Stated in terms of power, solar radiation intercepted by one hemisphere (or rather, the area of a circle equal in diameter to the earth and presented at right angles to the sun's rays) is calculated to be about 100,000 times as great as the total existing electric power generating capacity. The problem is, of course, that solar radiation derived from a large receiving area must be concentrated into a very small distribution center. To produce power equivalent to that of a large generating plant (i.e., 1000 megawatts capacity) would require at an average location a collecting surface of about 16 mi$^2$ (42 km$^2$), represented by a square measuring 4 mi (6.5 km) on a side. While

* From T. S. Lovering, "Mineral Resources from the Land," p. 110 of *Resources and Man,* © 1969 by the National Academy of Sciences, W. H. Freeman and Co., Publishers. Reproduced by permission of the National Academy of Sciences.
† Based on data of Preston E. Cloud (1969), "Mineral Resources from the Sea," pp. 135–155 of *Resources and Man,* National Academy of Sciences. San Francisco, Freeman.

* Data in the remainder of the Epilogue have been drawn largely from M. K. Hubbert (1969), "Energy Resources," Chapter 8 of *Resources and Man,* National Academy of Sciences. San Francisco, Freeman.

there seems to be no technological barrier to building such a plant, the cost at present is far too high to make this energy source a practical one. However, the source will always be available for future use.

Water power under gravity flow is a second source of sustained energy and has been developed to a point just over one-quarter of its estimated ultimate maximum capacity in the United States. In 1965 water power supplied about 4% of the total energy production of the United States (see Figure E.38). Since we have a good knowledge of stream runoff and stream profiles, the estimate of maximum capacity is probably not much in error. For the world as a whole, present development is estimated to be about one-nineteenth of the ultimate maximum capacity. Potential power is particularly great in South America and Africa, where coal is in very short supply. A serious defect in such calculations is one referred to in earlier pages —the loss of capacity of artificial reservoirs through sedimentation. Most large reservoirs behind big dams have an estimated useful life of a century or two at most. Perhaps, after all, water power is not in reality to be categorized as a "sustained" source of energy.

Tidal power is a third sustained-yield energy source. The nature of tidal energy is discussed in Chapter 3. To utilize this power a bay is located along a coast subject to a large range of tide. Narrowing of the connection between bay and open ocean intensifies the differences of water level that are developed during the rise and fall of tide. A strong hydraulic current is produced and alternates in direction of flow every 12½ hr (for a semidiurnal tidal cycle). The flow is used to drive turbines and electrical generators, with a maximum efficiency of about 20% to 25%. Assessment of the world total of annual energy potentially available by exploitation of all suitable sites comes to only 1% of the energy potentially available through water-power development.

Yet another sustained-yield energy source is classified as *geothermal;* it uses heat within the earth at points of locally high concentration— e.g., hot springs, fumaroles, and active volcanoes. Wells drilled at such places yield superheated steam, which can be used to power an electric generating plant. Electric power is presently being generated from a number of geothermal fields. Estimates of the potential total of energy that can be developed from geothermal sources run to about on the same value as for potential tidal power development, both being very small fractions of existing energy requirements.

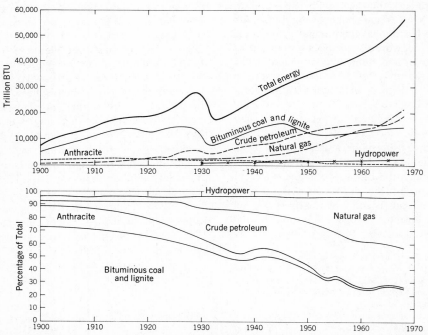

Figure E.38. Production of mineral energy resources and of electricity from hydropower from 1900 through 1968. The quantity of nuclear power is too small to be shown. (Data of U.S. Bureau of Mines, Minerals Yearbook.)

## ENERGY FROM FOSSIL FUELS

So we return to the principal sources of energy expended in the past century. These are the fossil fuels: coal and lignite, petroleum (oil), and natural gas. The nature, origin, and occurrence of these hydrocarbon compounds have been described in Chapter 8. Figure E.38 is a graph showing the production of energy (scaled in units of heat) from fossil fuels plus water power since 1900. Water power has, over the past 70 years, amounted to about 3% to 4% of the yearly production of energy, so that only a small allowance needs to be made for its inclusion. The actual contributions and relative contributions of the several sources of energy since 1900 are shown in Figure E.38. The two graphs tell us that while the total production of energy has increased over fivefold since 1900, the contributions of the several sources have changed markedly in ratio. Coal and lignite together have been reduced to less than half of the starting percentage, while anthracite has declined to almost nothing. Both petroleum and natural gas have increased in proportion in the same period, but of the two, natural gas has greatly expanded its ratio to become about equal with petroleum.

Since the quantity of stored hydrocarbons in the earth's crust is finite, and the rate of geologic production and accumulation of new hydrocarbons is immeasurably small in comparison with the rate of their consumption, the ultimate exhaustion of this energy souce is inescapable. When this event will happen is, however, a difficult thing to predict, since we have to project into the future two independent curves. First is the rate of production, which at present is increasing by about 6% per year for petroleum (crude oil). So far, discoveries of new oil reserves have more than kept pace with production, so there has been a moderate increase of known reserves. In terms of time, we are running about 12 years ahead on discoveries of new oil reserves in the United States. But in due time the rate of increase in new discoveries must slow down and then begin to decline. The reserves will then dwindle and eventually be entirely used, after which point production itself must begin a decline and will ultimately approach zero.

The complete cycle of petroleum production is envisaged as a symmetrical, bell-shaped curve (Figure E.39). Two estimates are shown, each based upon a different value for the ultimate amount of oil produced. Peak of production is shown as occurring in either 1990 or 2000, with decline to a rate equal to that of 1927 being arrived at in either 2050 or 2070.

Estimates of the world resource of natural gas are more difficult to arrive at, but a similar bell-shaped curve of production is anticipated on roughly the same time schedule. Are there other petroleum sources that can be developed? One possibility is the use of *heavy oil* enclosed in sands and not as yet exploited. Estimated reserves of these heavy-oil accumulations show that they are an important fraction as compared with petroleum reserves and development work is presently under way to begin production.

Another possibility is the use of *oil shales* as hydrocarbon sources. Although the hydrocarbon is in solid form, disseminated throughout the shale formation, treatment can ultimately yield petroleum in an amount estimated to range from 10 to 100 gal of oil per ton of

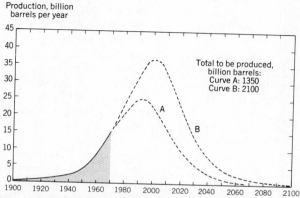

Figure E.39. Projected curves of world crude-oil production based upon two estimates of the total ultimate production. [After M. K. Hubbert (1969), in *Resources and Man,* San Francisco, Freeman, p. 196, Figure 8.23.]

shale. Known resources from oil shales are thought to be comparable to the ultimate world capacity of petroleum (about 2500 billion barrels of oil), although less than one-tenth of that amount is considered recoverable under present conditions.

What of the future of our coal resources? The picture is quite different from that of petroleum and natural gas. Estimates of coal resources are regarded as quite realistic, since the existence and thickness of coal seams can be directly sampled from borings. A careful estimate of total world coal that can be mined comes to about 17,000 billions of short tons, of which more than half lies in Asia and the European Soviet Union, and about one-third in North America. (The figure includes coal already mined, but this is only a small fraction of the total.) Projected curves of coal production indicate a peak around the year 2100 to 2200, which is a century or two beyond the peak for petroleum. Furthermore, the present rate of production (about equal to that of petroleum) is only a small fraction of the peak value. The conclusion must be that coal will become our main hydrocarbon energy source by the year 2050 or thereabouts and will continue in that role thereafter until it, too, is exhausted.

## NUCLEAR ENERGY AS A RESOURCE

The controlled release of energy from concentrated radioactive isotopes can be achieved through one of two processes: *fission* and *fusion.* Atomic fission makes use of uranium-235. The fission of 1 gm of this substance yields an amount of heat equivalent to the combustion of about 3 metric tons of coal or about 14 barrels of crude oil. While uranium-238 is the basic fissionable material, it is a rare isotope of a very rare element (see Table E.1) and the world supply would be rapidly exhausted if nothing else were used. It is, however, possible to induce fission in other isotopes, notably other isotopes of uranium and isotopes of plutonium and thorium. This induced fission, known as *conversion,* and in other cases as *breeding,* can greatly reduce the expenditure of uranium-235. Great concern has been expressed over the necessity to develop breeder reactors to conserve uranium. If such development is successful, low-grade deposits of uranium can be exploited, making available a source of energy judged to range

from hundreds to thousands of times greater than all reserves of fossil fuels.

Energy from fusion depends upon fusing isotopes of hydrogen into helium with a consequent large release of energy. As everyone knows, the explosive release of enormous quantities of energy has been achieved through the hydrogen (thermonuclear) bomb. As yet controlled release of energy through hydrogen fusion has not been achieved, although research is in progress. In theory, the quantities of energy available through fusion could exceed that of all fossil fuels by a factor ranging up into the hundreds of thousands.

Nuclear-energy development is accompanied by a host of difficulties and attendant environmental problems. One is the generation of unwanted heat that raises water temperatures of rivers or lakes into which it is discharged. This activity is known as *thermal pollution,* and its importance is the subject of debate. Of more far-reaching importance is the environmental problem of disposal of radioactive wastes from chemical plants with process nuclear fuels and the possibility of accidental release of radioactive substances from reactors in nuclear-power plants. Consideration of these problems brings into play all of the concepts of systems of water circulation within the hydrosphere, including runoff, ground-water movement, and oceanic circulation. In addition, atmospheric circulation systems may become involved, as in the case of fallout of radioactive particulates released into the atmosphere by nuclear explosions. These are problems we shall not discuss here, but their relation to the earth's physical systems of energy and mass exchange should be kept in mind.

## THE HUMAN PROSPECT

To bring to a close this brief discussion of Man's consumption of earth resources, it is appropriate to read the words of a distinguished geophysicist, M. King Hubbert, in closing his report on world energy resources as part of a study by the Committee on Resources and Man of the National Academy of Sciences–National Research Council:

To sustain a high-energy-dependent world culture for a period much longer than a few centuries requires, therefore, a reliable source of energy of appropriate magnitude. The largest and most obvious of such sources is solar radiation, the continuance of which at close to present rates may be relied upon for millions of years into the future. The energy from solar radiation, with the exception of that fraction manifested as water power, does not offer much promise as a means of large-scale power production, although future technology may circumvent this difficulty. This leaves us with nuclear energy as our only remaining energy source of requisite magnitude. Although the earth's resources of uranium and thorium, and of deuterium, are finite and therefore exhaustible, the magnitudes of these resources in terms of their potential energy contents are so large that with breeder and fusion reactors they should be able to supply the power requirements of an industrialized world society for some millennia. In this case, the limits to the growth of industrial activity would not be imposed by a scarcity of energy resources, but by the limitations of area and of the other natural resources of a finite earth. It now appears that the period of rapid population and industrial growth that has prevailed during the last few centuries, instead of being the normal order of things and capable of continuance into the indefinite future, is actually one of the most abnormal phases of human history. It represents only a brief transitional episode between two very much longer periods, each characterized by rates of change so slow as to be regarded essentially as a period of nongrowth. It is paradoxical that although the forthcoming period of nongrowth poses no insuperable physical or biological problems, it will entail a fundamental revision of those aspects of our current economic and social thinking which stem from the assumption that the growth rates which have characterized this temporary period can be permanent.*

Whether we share this scientist's views or not, his long look into the future of Man on earth must receive our serious attention as we ponder our best course in the light of our knowledge of the planetary energy systems through geologic time.

## References for further study

### MINERAL RESOURCES

Bateman, A. M. (1950), *Economic Mineral Deposits,* 2nd ed., New York, Wiley, 916 pp.

Landsberg, H. H. (1964), *Natural Resources for U.S. Growth,* Resources for the Future, Baltimore, Johns Hopkins Press, 268 pp.

* From M. K. Hubbert, "Energy Resources," pp. 238–239 of *Resources and Man,* © 1969 by the National Academy of Sciences, W. H. Freeman and Co., Publishers. Reproduced by permission of the National Academy of Sciences.

Emery, K. O. (1965), "Some Potential Mineral Resources of the Atlantic Continental Margin," U.S. Geological Survey, Professional Paper 525-C.

Mero, J. L. (1965), *The Mineral Resources of the Sea,* New York, Elsevier, 321 pp.

Flawn, P. T. (1966), *Mineral Resources,* Chicago, Rand McNally, 406 pp.

Mason, B. (1966), *Principles of Geochemistry,* 3rd ed., New York, Wiley, 328 pp. (see pp. 41–50).

Hibbard, W. R., Jr. (1968), "Mineral Resources: Challenge or Threat?" *Science,* vol. 160, pp. 143–150.

Cloud, P. (1969), "Mineral Resources from the Sea," pp. 135–155 of *Resources and Man,* National Academy of Sciences, Publ. No. 1703, San Francisco, Freeman.

Lovering, T. S. (1969), "Mineral Resources from the Land," pp. 109–134 of *Resources and Man,* National Academy of Sciences, Publ. No. 1703, San Francisco, Freeman.

Skinner, B. J. (1969), *Earth Resources,* Englewood Cliffs, N.J., Prentice-Hall, 149 pp.

Brown, H. (1970), "Human Materials Production as a Process in the Biosphere," *Scientific American,* vol. 223, no. 3, pp. 195–208.

### ENERGY RESOURCES

Weeks, L. G. (1958), "Fuel Reserves of the Future," Amer. Assoc. Petroleum Geologists, Bull. 42, pp. 431–438.

Weinberg, A. M. (1960), "Breeder Reactors," *Scientific American,* vol. 202, no. 1, pp. 82–94.

Daniels, F. (1964), *Direct Use of the Sun's Energy,* New Haven, Yale Univ. Press, 374 pp.

Glasstone, S. (1964), *Controlled Nuclear Fusion,* Understanding the Atom Series, Washington, D.C., U.S. Atomic Energy Commission, 50 pp.

Duncan, D. E., and V. E. Swanson (1965), "Organic-Rich Shales of the United States and World Land Areas," U.S. Geological Survey, Circular 523.

Hendricks, T. A. (1965), "Resources of Oil, Gas, and Natural-Gas Liquids in the United States and the World," U.S. Geological Survey, Circular 522.

White, D. E. (1965), "Geothermal Energy," U.S. Geological Survey, Circular 519.

Fox, C. H. (1967), *Radioactive Wastes,* Understanding the Atom Series, Washington, D.C., U.S. Atomic Energy Commission, 46 pp.

Averitt, P. (1969), "Coal Resources of the United States," U.S. Geological Survey, Bull. 1275.

Hubbert, M. K. (1969), "Energy Resources," pp. 157–242 of *Resources and Man,* National Academy of Sciences, Publ. No. 1703, San Francisco, Freeman.

Singer, S. F. (1970), "Human Energy Production as a Process in the Biosphere," *Scientific American,* vol. 223, no. 3, pp. 175–190.

## Review questions

1. What are the principal groups of nonrenewable earth resources? State briefly the importance of each group in an industrial society.

2. In what sense is the true soil (topsoil) a nonrenewable natural resource? How long does it take for soil to form? What rate of soil erosion can be sustained on a long-term basis without loss of agricultural productivity?

3. At what rate can ground water be consumed without depletion as a resource? What is the importance of recharge in maintaining the ground-water supply? What is a recharge well? Should treated sewage and storm runoff be returned to ground water?

4. What is an aquifer? Describe the structure and configuration of a large alluvial fan. How is ground water held in a fan, and how does it move? What is an artesian well? How is ground water recharged within an alluvial fan?

5. Describe an artesian water structure involving extensive sedimentary strata. Illustrate with an example. How do such artesian sources compare with other water resources in quantity and sustained yield?

6. What is an ore? Name in order of crustal abundance the 5 most abundant metals. Name at least 10 other metals of industrial importance. What is the clarke of abundance? What is the primary source of all metallic deposits? Name the ferro-alloy metals. For what purpose are they used?

7. What is the clarke of concentration? Explain the derivation and significance of this quantity. Cite two or three examples.

8. Review the principal classes or types of ore deposits in terms of origin. How can an ore be derived directly from a body of magma? Give examples.

9. How can contact metamorphism result in ore deposits? What are hydrothermal solutions? How and where are vein deposits formed? What is a lode? How are disseminated ore deposits formed? Give an example.

10. Describe the formation of ore deposits by secondary processes. What zones are recognized, from the surface downward? What is meteoric water? How is a gossan formed, and of what minerals is it composed? What minerals accumulate in the zone of oxidation? in the zone of sulfide enrichment?

11. What ore deposits accumulate close to the surface in tropical regions? What ore deposits are related to alluvial and beach deposits? Give examples. What are the sedimentary ores? Name an important occurrence.

12. List the important nonmetallic mineral deposits that are used as structural materials. Name several types of mineral deposits used chemically in industrial processes.

13. Comment upon scarcity of usable mineral deposits and the problems involved in meeting the needs of industry in future decades. What courses of action to conserve mineral resources would you recommend in view of the outlook for future needs?

14. Evaluate the prospects of meeting future industrial needs by extraction of mineral resources from the sea and the ocean basins. What elements can perhaps be extracted from sea water at a profitable level? What resources are being exploited from the continental shelves? What are manganese nodules? What future lies in their exploitation?

15. Name the major sources of energy for Man's industrial economy. Which are capable of sustained yield? which are not? Evaluate solar energy as a resource both at present and in the future.

16. What proportion of total energy consumption is derived from gravity flow of water? What is the future value of this resource, and how does it compare with other energy sources?

17. Explain how tidal power is developed. How does this energy source compare with water power from rivers? What is geothermal energy? How is it developed?

18. Describe the trend of production of energy from the fossil fuels since 1850. How have relative rates of energy production changed among the various forms of fossil fuels in the past 65 years? What is the significance of these changes?

19. Describe the present relationship between rate of production of petroleum and the rate of discovery of new petroleum reserves. What ultimately will be the relationship between these rates, and what will be the consequences? When is peak petroleum production anticipated? When will world supplies be exhausted? Make a similar evaluation of natural-gas resources.

20. What is the future of heavy oil (oil sands) and oil shales in terms of supplying future energy requirements? Describe the world reserves of coal and the projected curve of coal production. When is the peak anticipated? When will coal be exhausted?

21. Describe briefly the nature of the pro-

cess of energy release from processes of nuclear fission and fusion. What will be the roles of conversion and breeding processes in conserving uranium supplies? Compare potential nuclear-energy production with that of other sources. What are some of the environmental problems and hazards related to development of nuclear-energy sources?

# appendix
## cross-reference to supplementary publication

Available as a separate paperbound book is a text supplement by the author titled *Planet Earth Data Resources* (1972) Harper & Row. The supplement consists of 13 *data banks,* each relating to a text chapter of the same number in *Planet Earth: Its Physical Systems Through Geologic Time.* (There are no data banks for Chapters 11 and 12.)

The data banks contained in *Planet Earth Data Resources* can do much to fill in the framework of a dynamic system with information on the nature and classification of the structures and substances that are products of those systems, and they also explain much about the tools of scientific investigation and how they are used to measure the fluxes of energy and matter of the various planetary systems. Those students who want to make field and laboratory observations in various areas of the earth sciences—astronomy, meteorology, hydrology, mineralogy, petrology, stratigraphy, glacial geology, and others—will find the data banks particularly useful.

In the following table of contents of *Planet Earth Data Resources,* the numbers in the right-hand column designate those textbook pages for which the particular data bank will be useful as a supplement.

Contents of

PLANET EARTH DATA RESOURCES

| Data Banks | | Pages in PLANET EARTH to which data apply |
|---|---|---|
| *Bank 1* | Earth coordinates and earth-sun relationships | 12–14 |
| | A. The earth-grid; latitude and longitude | |
| | B. Projections of the earth-grid | |
| | C. Earth's orbit, revolution, and year | |
| | D. Seasons: solstice and equinox | |
| *Bank 2* | Earth magnetism | 36–39 |
| | A. Elements of the earth's magnetic field | |
| | B. Measurement of magnetic elements | |
| | C. Isogonic map of the United States | |
| *Bank 3* | Earth's figure and gravity | 58–59 |
| | A. Earth ellipsoids | |
| | B. Nautical mile, meter, statute mile | |
| | C. Gravity and gravity corrections | |
| | D. Earth's mass and density | |
| *Bank 4* | Atmospheric temperature, pressure, and winds; ocean currents | |
| | A. Measurement of radiation | 23–25 |
| | B. Measurement of atmospheric temperature | 28–30 |
| | C. Measurement of barometric pressure | 75–76 |
| | D. Measurement of winds | 75 |
| | E. World maps of sea surface temperatures | 29–30 |
| | F. World maps of air temperatures | 29–30 |
| | G. World maps of barometric pressures and winds | 90–91 |
| | H. World ocean currents | 94–95 |

# index

72 73 74   7 6 5 4 3 2 1